FUEL

SOLID, LIQUID AND GASEOUS

BY

J. S. S. BRAME, C.B.E., F.R.I.C.

AND

J. G. KING, O.B.E., D.Sc., Ph.D., A.R.T.C., F.R.I.C., F.Inst.F., Hon.M.Inst.GasE.

FIFTH EDITION

Rewritten by Dr. J. G. KING

LONDON

EDWARD ARNOLD (PUBLISHERS) LTD

Printed in Great Britain by
Butler & Tanner Ltd., Frome and London

PREFACE

"Fuel" was first written by J. S. S. Brame in 1914. In 1935, its coming-of-age year, he was joined by J. G. King, when a considerable revision was made. Further revision on the same scale was intended for about 1940, but the incidence of war prevented this. It was not until 1951 that it became possible to begin the preparation of the Fifth Edition.

Owing to this considerable lapse of time, and the important changes which had come about in fuel technology, the reconstruction of the book had become a major operation, involving much new material.

During the course of this reconstruction Professor Brame died (December 1952) at the age of 80. It is hoped that this 1955 edition will stand as a memorial to a man and a scientist, whose teaching and example will stand for many years.

Since the 1935 edition was published an important change has come about in the control of fuel in Great Britain, through the nationalization of the three main groups of coal, electricity, and gas, and no doubt this will develop into a unified fuel control in which the appropriate fuel will be used for most suitable purposes.

In the case of coal, pulverized fuel has made considerable advances, and all new large power stations are being constructed to work on this principle.

The conversion of coal to oil, by processes of hydrogenation or synthesis, has passed through the stage of high production in Germany during the war to a greatly-reduced effort in the chemical field, but remains an important field of research and, mainly in the United States, of development.

In the field of petroleum we have seen emerge the full-scale development of catalyst-cracking, which has revolutionized refining in the United States. Secondary catalytic processes have also widened the range of oil products, and raised the knock-rating of motor spirits without the addition of lead. The advances in aviation technique which have brought jet-propulsion to the forefront have added greatly to the science of combustion, and have also focused attention on the importance of the kerosine fraction as a fuel.

Methods of examination, control, and economy in fuel usage have all advanced, perhaps at first because of wartime necessity, but now because of the much higher price-levels of all fuels. This has meant a considerable increase in instrumentation in industrial processes.

It should be made clear that this volume is not written to include the details of processes of production or utilization of fuels. It is limited strictly to the properties of fuels and their methods of application. It is intended to serve as a broad introduction to fuel technology, and to give the necessary guidance for further study.

J. G. KING.

ACKNOWLEDGMENTS

With the greatly increased volume of work on fuel technology no book of this kind could be written without the advice and practical help of the experts in the different fields. The author wishes to express his gratitude to the many friends in the fuel world who have helped him in the preparation of this Fifth Edition.

In particular, owing to the loss of his co-author, he is specially indebted for new material in the field of oil technology to Mr. Gollin of the Fuel and Light Oils Technical Section of the Shell Petroleum Co., and his colleagues, particularly Mr. C. W. G. Martin, Mr. J. G. C. Pope, and Mr. A. D. Cooper.

He is grateful to the Director of Fuel Research, Dr. A. Parker, for permission to use the Intelligence Section and Library of the Fuel Research Station and for the valuable help given by the staff, Dr. S. R. Craxford, Mr. R. B. Clarke, Mr. B. H. Regan, and Mr. P. S. Harris ; also for similar help from Mr. L. G. M. Roberts of the British Gas Council and formerly of the Gas Research Board. He is particularly grateful to Dr. C. Forrester for valuable assistance in proof reading.

Information on Colonial coals and fuels has been kindly provided by Mr. G. E. Howling and Mr. E. H. Beard of the Colonial Geological Survey. Information on Dominion fuels has been kindly provided by the following :

Mr. L. J. Rogers, Australia ; Dr. H. Herman, Victoria ; Dr. J. G. Malloch and Dr. R. E. Gilmore, Canada ; Dr. R. S. Whitaker, Director of Fuel Research, India ; Dr. A. J. Petrick, Director of Fuel Research, South Africa ; Mr. R. A. MacMullen, Alberta.

To former colleagues at the Fuel Research Station he is grateful for technical data, Mr. D. MacDougal, Mr. H. Bardgett, Mr. A. Fitton, and particularly, Mr. T. F. Hurley and Mr. J. H. Carlile.

Three Research Associations have been most helpful through their Directors. Dr. D. T. A. Townend, British Coal Utilization R.A., has provided data on gas producers through Dr. G. W. C. Allan, and on domestic heating through Mr. J. S. Hales. Dr. C. A. Seyler has also contributed his latest coal classification chart. The Director, British Coke R.A., Mr. G. Lee, has given useful advice on coke problems, and Mr. J. P. Graham and Dr. R. A. Mott have provided technical information. The Director, British Internal Combustion Engine R.A., has provided valuable data on engine efficiency. The Institution of Gas Engineers, Mr. A. G. Higgins and Mr. Morgan have provided useful data.

Technical information on special subjects has been provided by a number of industrial specialists, to whom the author records his grateful thanks :

Motor Benzole : Dr. G. Claxton, Research Dept., National Benzole Association.

Alcohol Fuels : Mr. J. H. Randall, The Distillers Co., Ltd.

Liquid Fuel Gases : Mr. K. R. Garrett, Calor Gas (Distributing) Co., Ltd.

Gas Appliances : Mr. L. W. Andrew, Mr. E. A. Patrick and Mr. Wills, Watson House, North Thames Gas Board.

Shale Oil : Dr. G. H. Smith, Scottish Oils Ltd.

Coke Ovens : Mr. F. S. Townend, The Woodall-Duckham Co.

Atomic Energy : Sir John Cockcroft, Ministry of Supply.

Steam Engineering : Mr. B. Samuel, Mr. G. M. C. Peacock, Babcock and Wilcox, Ltd.

Fuel Efficiency : Dr. C. Forrester, Ministry of Fuel and Power, The B.E.A. Secretarial Dept.

Oil Statistics : Mr. G. Sell, The Institute of Petroleum.

Gas Producers : Mr. Beswick, Dr. G. Milner, The Power Gas Corporation.

Surface Combustion : Mr. H. E. Robinson, Radiant Heating Ltd.

Aero-engine Fuels : Joseph Lucas Ltd., Dr. A. E. Watson, and Mr. O. N. Lawrence.

C.A.B. Reactivity Test : Mr. H. E. Blayden.

A considerable number of commercial firms, and also the above specialists, have provided diagrams and illustrations which have been essential to the adequate presentation of the data. Acknowledgment of these is recorded with gratitude ; the name of the firm concerned is given under the title in each case. The firms were :

Babcock and Wilcox Ltd. (Boilers) ; Baird and Tatlock (London) Ltd. (Calorimeter) ; Humphreys and Glasgow Ltd. (Water-gas Plant) ; International Construction Co., Ltd. (Gas Producer) ; International Furnace Equipment (Gas Producer) ; Coalite and Chemical Products Ltd. (Carbonizing Plant) ; North Thames Gas Board (Gas-fired Equipment) ; Scientific and Projections Ltd. (Gas Calorimeter) ; Woodall Construction Co., Ltd. (Carbonizing Plant) ; Rippingilles Ltd. (Oil Burner) ; Radiant Heating Ltd. (Surface-combustion Burner) ; Thermic Equipment and Engineering Co., Ltd., and Wellman, Smith Owen Eng. Corp. (Industrial Gas Burners) ; Solex Ltd. (Carburettor) ; Joseph Lucas Ltd. (Jet Aero-engines) ; Wallsend Slipway and Engineering Co. (Oil Burners) ; Urquharts (1926) Ltd. (Oil Burner) ; Radiation Group Sales (Gas-fired Furnace).

The Institute of Fuel and the *Heating and Ventilating Engineer* are thanked for permission to reproduce illustrations from their Journals.

CONTENTS

ix

LIST OF TABLES

FUEL—SOLID, LIQUID AND GASEOUS

CHAPTER I

INTRODUCTION

The purpose of this book is to provide, at the level of the science graduate, a review of all the types of fuel now in common usage. The book has been limited in size in order that it may be widely available.

Although the uses of the different types of fuel are discussed in some detail it is not intended that descriptions shall be in detail of the processes and plant involved, nor was it considered necessary to do more than indicate the applications of fuels as raw materials, or to draw attention to the associated researches which do not bear directly on their uses as fuels.

In using the word "fuel" it is generally implied that the materials under review are the "stored" fuels available in the earth's crust, or derived from such material by an industrial process. It is important, there-fore, that the reader should have a clear picture of the relationship which this stored fuel bears to the broad picture of power and energy from all sources.

Prior to the industrial age the stored fuels were used for providing warmth for human comfort and the preparation of food. Since the advent of the industrial age this has entirely changed and, although a high propor-tion of the fuel consumed is still used for this purpose, the amount required for industrial use is increasing year by year.

Industrial usage implies the utilization of the fuel for the production of heat and power so that stored fuel is now part of the much wider pattern of total available heat, power, and energy in the universe. To-day, with the utilization of atomic energy on the threshold, it would seem wise, at the beginning of this book, to review the position briefly and place stored fuels in their right perspective.

To look backwards in time for a moment, we find that, while the first step beyond human power towards harnessing a greater power was probably the sailing vessel, and dates back to 3000 B.C., it was not until very much later that a real step forward was made by harnessing natural power through the watermill (A.D. 1000) and the windmill (A.D. 1300). In Great Britain, after the year 1600, when population was beginning to increase rapidly, the use of watermills was very common. Flour-mills alone reached 10,000 in number, equivalent to one for every village.

These were small changes, however, and it was not until the beginning of the industrial era of the eighteenth century, and the appearance of the steam engine, that power from coal began to change the picture. The following British figures show the immense advance made in 150 years from 1800, even excluding petroleum.

Year.	Population. Millions.	Coal. M. tons/year.	Coal. Tons/head/year.
1800	10·5	10·2	1·0
1950	49·0	220·0	4·0

Of this 4·0 tons consumed per head per annum, more than half is used for warmth, while the remainder eventually does useful work. This means that civilized man, in this industrial age, has working for him the equivalent of 2 tons of coal per year. If this standard is to be improved, or even maintained, in face of the one per cent. per annum increase of world population (3500 million by A.D. 2000), it is apparent that the fuel problem of the future is a very difficult one, particularly in view of the steadily decreasing reserves of stored fuel.

Power Resources.   On this Earth the original source of energy is the sun. In our present state of knowledge we can only assume the permanence of the solar system and the continuance of the flow of energy substantially for ever. We do know, however, that the sun's energy is formed by atomic change $(H \rightarrow He)$ which, so far as we can calculate now, will come to an end in some 10^{12} years.

The sun radiates energy at the high rate of 4×10^{23} h.p., but only a small fraction strikes the earth $\left(\dfrac{1}{2 \times 10^9}\right)$, and half of this is reflected, and much of the remainder is lost by radiation at night. It can be calculated that the power reaching the earth, if even one-hundredth of this were utilized, would be equivalent to $1·7 \times 10^{12}$ tons of coal per year or a thousand times the amount which is being used to-day.

The scientist has failed so far to trap solar energy in a practical way, except in utilizing the secondary effects of water, wind and tidal energy, and this is only a tiny fraction of the amount available. The evaporation of moisture and the promotion of plant growth are natural means of absorbing solar energy.

During past ages a small proportion of the sun's energy has been stored in the earth's crust, through the medium of plant decay, in the form of solid and liquid fuels, coal, shale, etc., and petroleum. This is the store with which we are concerned to-day and which we are consuming at an alarming rate that must be thousands of times greater than the rate of accumulation. Water power is reducing the load appreciably, and power from atomic energy is just around the corner, but only the immediate future is secure. The present industrial era has lasted only about 200 years, and already we have squandered the greater part of the store of organic energy accumulated through the ages. We have consumed 85,000 million tons of coal and 9000 million tons of petroleum, and half of this during the last thirty years. The only possible justification is that this shall also be the era of the finding of new scientific knowledge which will effectively replace the losses. The greater utilization of continuous sources of energy should be attempted more energetically, particularly that of the sun.

Coal. The distribution of coal is not uniform throughout the world. In Britain the reserves are probably 700 times the present annual rate of consumption, but it is unlikely that workable coal will last more than 200 years. In the United States and Russia the time is probably ten times as long as this. Reserves of peat are about one-sixtieth of those of coal.

Petroleum. The known reserves of petroleum are supposed to be about one-tenth of those of coal, but could be supplemented by the conversion of coal to oil. Information on petroleum is more uncertain than that on coal and this estimate may be badly at fault; however, the peak of production will probably be passed in some 25 years. Petroleum reserves are mainly in Asia 50 per cent., America 30 per cent., S. America 15 per cent., while Europe has only about 1 per cent.

When petroleum reserves become depleted they can be supplemented by the distillation of shales, the immense deposits of which have hardly been touched as yet. They are mainly in the United States and could yield about twice as much oil as the present reserves of petroleum.

Associated with petroleum is natural gas, the energy value of which corresponds to about 40 per cent. of petroleum. This is exploited at present mainly in the United States, but other oil-fields are ready to follow.

Other Resources. These include wood and vegetable wastes and in amount are quite negligible in comparison with coal; they can, however, have considerable importance. Atomic energy comes under this head since the uranium, etc., minerals are stored fuels and are also subject to limitation of quantity.

Continuous Sources of Power. In contradistinction to the stored resources of power, there are natural resources which are practicably inexhaustible, i.e. which come from the sun. These are the actual heat radiated, and the secondary effects of tidal, water and wind power, and the residual heat of the earth.

The use of wind power has gone out of fashion and only experimental work remains and small local applications. Water power has been exploited with considerable success and is on the increase. Practically nothing has been done, other than in the shape of experiment, on the utilization of radiation from the sun, or of the heat stored in the earth. In the former case the main reason is that a method of storage on a large scale, either of thermal or electrical energy, has not been discovered. Until one is discovered the difficulty of bridging the hours of darkness will prevent any large-scale development.

If radiant energy reaching the earth could be recovered with an efficiency of only one per cent., an area the size of Egypt could supply the whole of the world's requirements. Experiments so far are limited to accelerated photosynthesis (the mechanism of plants) and house-heating by thermal collectors in house-heating in temperate[1] zones. In the latter, the amount necessary for a medium-sized dwelling-house (0·5 therm per day) could be collected from a surface of about 250 sq. ft.

The recovery of terrestrial energy has not been seriously attempted, but it is true that the temperature of the earth at a depth of 3 miles (120° C.) is above the boiling point of water, and at 500 miles is 1400° C., i.e. in the range of metallurgical operations. The total heat reserve is as large as 100 million times the world's present reserves of stored organic fuels.

In the case of water power, considerable advances have been made during the last twenty years, but still only some 4 to 5 per cent. of the potential power at mean rates of flow are being utilized, which is equivalent to some 10 per cent. of the coal now mined. Obviously much of the remaining water power is not accessible to industry at present, but the proportion utilized in certain very suitable places is very high already. Switzerland has reached 67 per cent., Great Britain 30 per cent. and the United States 30 per cent. The present level of installed plant represents about 70 million kW.; in 1952 Britain developed about 1,600 million kWh., representing a saving of about one million tons of coal.

Tidal power is very unevenly distributed and only in certain places is the difference between high and low tide sufficient to justify harnessing this power. It could, therefore, never represent more than a very small fraction of total power requirements.

Wind power constitutes a large source of kinetic energy which is equivalent in magnitude to the rate of mining coal So far, large-scale utilization has not been attempted because of high capital cost and the variations and uncertainties of wind velocities; it seems unlikely that it will ever be.

Atomic or Nuclear Energy. The development of power from the nuclear energy of the atom has been hailed as the saving of civilization when the stored reserves of energy run out, but it must be realized that, so far as present knowledge goes, the elements uranium and thorium, which are the raw materials, are available only in strictly limited quantities. If we look far enough ahead, therefore, the use of atomic energy is as limited as that of coal. At the moment it would seem that the relative factors are 1 lb. uranium$_{235}$ to 1500 tons of coal.

Although uranium ores are not plentiful, and the cost of recovery may be high, the material is easily transportable and the practical advent of

[1] Latitude 20–40°.

power from atomic energy may have an important effect upon world economics and the distribution of population since industries may well develop in those areas where development is now retarded by the absence of native fuel but where minerals are available or living conditions could be particularly comfortable.

Development work is now finding methods of converting fissile material into energy in the form of heat which can be applied by existing technical methods to the raising of power in a conventional power station. A number of reactors have been built and plans are made for further building. The U.S.A. hope, by 1960, to build 15 million kilowatts of capacity, or seven times the normal annual increase of output of their electrical industry.

In view of the importance of this subject to the future of mankind some hundred years hence or earlier, it is desirable to deal with it in some detail in the introduction to a book such as this.

The proposal to harness " atomic " energy is based on the discovery, as recently as 1939, that the nucleus of the atom of one form of uranium, U_{235}, could be split and that the splitting (fission) could be controlled to liberate energy in high proportion to the mass of the element. Development work is now finding out methods of recovering this energy in the form of heat so that it can be utilized for the raising of power in a conventional power station.

Several types of reactor are possible for the liberation of the energy under control. The first, of which the B.E.P.O.[1] unit at Harwell is an example, consists in the spacing of uranium metal rods in a regular lattice in a moderating screen of graphite bricks as shown diagrammatically in Figure 2 (a). Reaction begins when a critical quantity (25 tons) is loaded and about 170,000 fissions take place spontaneously every second, liberating neutrons which continue the process of fission by collision with other atoms. Each fission liberates 2·55 neutrons, each of which has an energy of about one MeV. ($4·45 \times 10^{-20}$ kW.), corresponding to a speed of about 10^9 cm./sec. These fast neutrons lose energy by collision with U_{238} atoms and with carbon nuclei in the graphite and after about 200 collisions reach the energy of the carbon atoms (0·025 eV.). As the neutrons are slowed down, fission in U_{238} decreases to zero but continues in U_{235}. This type is therefore called a " slow " reactor; it has a critical size when each fission is succeeded by not less than one more fission.

The second type of reactor is the " fast " reactor in which the fission process proceeds without moderation. Since the chance of fission in U_{238} is small compared with the chance of capture of the neutron without fission, a high proportion of U_{235} is required. A fast reactor therefore contains a reacting core of U_{235} and only a small proportion of U_{238}, as shown in Figure 2 (b). The heat developed in the core is removed by a thermal fluid, and the fuel rods are in suitable sheaths.

[1] British Experimental Pile.

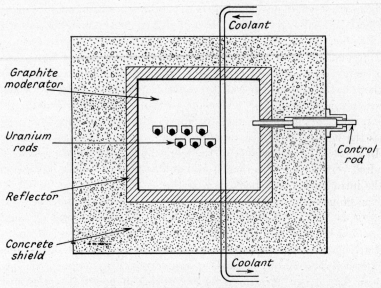

FIG. 2 (a).—Schematic of Graphite-modulated Thermal Reaction.
(Sir J. Cockcroft, *Proc.I.E.E.*, 1953, **123**, 99.)

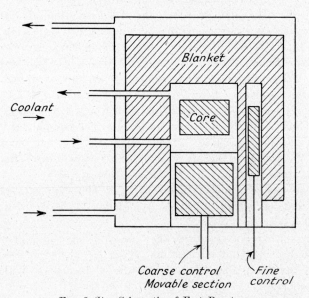

FIG. 2 (b).—Schematic of Fast Reactor.

Intermediate forms of these two types can be built and within each type there are possible variations, as for example the enrichment of the metal of the slow reactor to allow of its uniform distribution throughout the moderator.

A third type is " regenerative " in that excess neutrons from the fission of U_{235} which are captured in U_{238} convert part of this to plutonium, which can be split by slow neutrons in the same way as U_{235}. If it could be arranged that losses of energy were reduced until the secondary fuel formed exceeded the U_{235} consumed, reaction would continue until a high proportion of the U_{238} were consumed, a most important consideration in view of the low proportion of U_{235} in uranium minerals. This type is termed a " breeder " in view of the secondary production of fissile material.

The most important factor in constructing a reactor is its neutron balance. Of the 2·55 neutrons liberated by the fission of a U_{235} nucleus, 1·0 carries on the chain reaction, 0·9 is absorbed in U_{238} to form plutonium, 0·2 forms U_{236}, and the remainder is absorbed in the moderator, or the structure, or is lost. It is important that the excess be adequate and also controllable and the provision of control rods is necessary.

Technical Problems. It is apparent that there are difficult problems of control evolved in the adjustment of the liberation of energy from a reactor and in the transfer of this energy to a power unit without danger from harmful emanations. The transfer medium may be water or gas under pressure for the slow reactor or liquid metals (Na/K alloy) in the fast reactors. The fuel elements must be protected from corrosion, the protection must be a low absorber of neutrons, and very heavy dense protection must surround the reactor to prevent escape of radioactive material. Finally, the radioactive spent residue must be carefully disposed of.

Protection from harmful radiation would normally be done by shielding with heavy concrete walls. One foot of concrete reduces the radiation by one-tenth, so that a 7-ft. shield would reduce it by a factor of ten million. It is apparent that the necessity for adequate screening must introduce difficulties in the design of small or mobile units.

Cost of Power Production. Although uranium ores are quite plentiful, the cost of recovery of the metal is high and the proportion of U_{235} in it is of the order of only one per cent. A very tentative estimate of the world reserves of uranium is about 25 million tons, from which the metal could be recovered at a cost of about $50 per lb. At a higher cost of, say, $100 per ton the quantity could reach 75 million tons. In view, however, of the fact that it is only recently that survey work has started, it seems probable that the reserves are much higher than this. Even at the higher figure, however, the fuel cost in power production would only be about one-twentieth of that which obtains with coal (20 to 30 per cent. of the total cost).

The higher figure represents fifty times the energy equivalent of world coal reserves, assuming the use of a breeder reactor and the utilization of all the uranium.

At the present stage of progress the use of a slow or thermal reactor shows definite limitations. A power station to produce 50 MW. would, at 25 per cent. efficiency, have to generate the equivalent of 200 MW. of heat. If the initial charge were 50 tons of natural uranium, and this were operated to give 4 MW. per ton, the reactor would consume 200 g. U_{235} per day. Since one ton contains only about 7 kg. of U_{235}, the 350 kg. present would last theoretically about five years. The complete consumption of the U_{235} in this type of generator is not, however, possible for several reasons, including the slowly increasing absorption of neutrons in the accumulating fission fractions.

If it is assumed the one-third can be utilized, the life period would be reduced to 1·7 years. Further, since one ton of natural uranium is consumed per day, the U/coal ratio is only 1 lb./3 tons, which is much too high. It is true that plutonium is formed, however, and that the original charge could be reprocessed to concentrate the remaining quantity of U_{235} and an amount of Pu almost equal to the U_{235} split. In this way, most of the original uranium could be utilized, but at heavy cost for reprocessing.

The obvious type for power production is therefore the breeder reactor, and development is proceeding to this end. Should it prove possible to utilize all the uranium available in such a unit, the U/coal ratio would then become 1 lb. U/1500 tons coal as a minimum.

It is apparent that development work has still a long way to go, and that the production of electrical energy would seem to be the main objective. With this in view, it would seem that atomic energy power stations must begin in some twenty years' time to take the increasing load of this form of fuel. In Great Britain alone the increase in terms of coal is of the order of two million tons per annum.

World Resources of Fuel and Fuel Consumption. The data relating to the reserves of fuels stored in the earth's surface are understandably open to question if stated in too exact terms, but a consideration of the data now accepted is the only way of obtaining a numerical appreciation of the relationship between these reserves and ever-rising level of consumption in the world.

For this reason, Tables I to V are included in this chapter. These should be studied in relation to the wider use of the recurrent sources of energy which are represented by the utilization of wind and water power and the possibility of recovery of energy from solar radiation directly. The utilization of atomic energy is admittedly a long-term project in comparison with the prospective lifetime of our present fuels, but, in the present state of our knowledge, even this source comes under the heading of stored fuels and will be exhausted in due time.

It is interesting to observe that the present proportions of usage of energy in the world are :

Food 10 : Coal 47 : Petroleum 22 : Natural gas 6 :
Wood 7 : Water 6 : Misc. 2

Table I shows very approximately the world resources of coal, lignite and peat, and their approximate locations. In arriving at these figures

TABLE I

RESOURCES OF COAL, LIGNITE AND PEAT

(Hundred millions of tons)

	Coal and anthracite.	Lignites.	Peat.
Europe :			
U.S.S.R.	9,800	2000	700
Germany	2,750	560	100
U.K.	1,700	—	35
Poland	800	—	60
Finland	—	—	35
France	60	4	20
Sweden	—	—	90
Estonia	—	—	20
Latvia	—	—	16
Others	340	164	8
North America :			
Canada	560	320	—
U.S.	20,000	840	120
Alaska	240	60	—
South America :			
Argentina	—	—	1
Africa :			
S. Africa	2,000	2	—
Others	10	—	—
Asia :			
China	10,000	5	—
India	600	3	—
Japan	160	5	—
Australasia :			
Australia	140	400	—
N. Zealand	1	1	1
Total (approx.)	50,000	4400	1200

seams are excluded which are less than one foot in thickness or more than 4000 ft. deep ; it is possible that this exclusion is not rigid enough since it may never be an economic proposition to mine such thin seams or work to so great a depth. The effective reserves are therefore less, rather than more, than the amounts stated.

It would appear that there are some 5×10^{12} million tons of coal, 4×10^{11} million tons of lignite, and 12×10^{10} million tons of peat still in reserve as fuels stored in the earth's crust. The unequal distribution

of these reserves is an important factor when the future is under consideration.   The very large reserves of the U.S.S.R., the United States and China
are noteworthy.

Table II gives the petroleum reserves in the same way, indicating some
11×10^9 million tons, with a preponderance of reserves in the Middle

TABLE II

PETROLEUM RESOURCES AND CONSUMPTION (1947)

(Millions of tons)

	Reserves.	Consumed 1947.	Consumed 1952.
Europe :			
U.S.S.R.	1000	25	47
Roumania	60	4	4
Others	30	2	5
North America :			
United States	3500	237	314
Mexico	120	7	11
Canada	30	1	8
South America :			
Venezuela	1400	55	95
Colombia	70	3	5
Trinidad	35	3	3
Others	75	5	8
Africa (Egypt)	10	1	2
Asia, M.E. :			
Bahrein	1250	5	2
Iran	1200	19	1
Iraq	900	5	19
Kuwait	900	2	37
Qatar*	150	—	3
Saudi Arabia	—	—	40
Asia, F.E. :			
Indonesia	170	2	8
Sarawak	30	—	—
Others	40	2	1
Approx. totals	11,000	378	613

OIL SHALE RESOURCES

(Million tons)

	Oil % in shale.	Oil million tons.
U.S.S.R.	14	7700
Estonia	25	1250
Others Europe	·5 to 10	450
United States	3	13,000
Others	—	100
		22,500
Canada oil sands		5,000 (oil)

East.   Oil will also be obtainable from oil shales when these come to be

* 1954 estimate, 20,000 million tons.

seriously worked. In the meantime, only a small proportion is being worked and in only certain places. The oil available from this source is shown to be about 22×10^9 tons, or twice the reserves of petroleum.

Associated with petroleum is natural gas, which is being utilized so effectively in the United States. Until arrangements can be made to utilize the gas as effectively in other oilfields, there is bound to be considerable waste of this valuable fuel, and it is difficult to estimate the reserves fairly. The amount of gas associated with petroleum is about 15,000 cu. ft. per ton of petroleum, or 40 per cent. of its thermal value. If it could be utilized, the reserves would amount to 150×10^{12} cu. ft., having the thermal equivalent of 4×10^3 million tons of oil. In the United States at present some 4×10^{12} cu. ft. are being utilized annually, which is equivalent to 17,000 cu. ft. per ton of petroleum refined in the country.

A " natural " gas is also associated with coal measures and is mostly lost during mining. A pioneer experiment has shown that the amount of gas recoverable is about 350 cu. ft. per ton of coal mined. Since the gas consists mainly of methane, it is equivalent in thermal value to one per cent. of the coal, and the reserves could be increased by this amount by its recovery. It is unlikely that more than a small proportion will indeed be recovered, but see p. 369.

Other sources of energy are wood and water power, but these really come under the heading of replaceable, rather than stored, fuels since they are restored year by year.

If it is assumed that half of the wood grown for structural and other purposes were to be utilized as fuel, this would give as a recurrent source of energy some 100 million cu. ft., which is the equivalent of 700 thousand tons of coal. The disadvantages of wood, however, are such that it is not until coal supplies become more nearly exhausted that the use of any appreciable proportion of this considerable total will be attempted.

Other minor sources of energy are fermentation alcohol, sewage methane, refuse destruction, and waste vegetable products.

Alcohol is normally produced for the manufacture of whisky and as an industrial solvent, and only a small proportion is used for the production of fuel or power. The total world production of alcohol is of the order of 4 million tons, but only perhaps one-fifth of this is used for fuel, say 0·5 million tons. In Great Britain the amount consumed is small, about 20,000 tons per annum. Alcohol is never likely to make more than an insignificant contribution to the fuel problem.

Sewage methane is obtained by fermentation in sewage disposal systems and, if these are closed, the methane is recoverable in 75 per cent. concentration in association with carbon dioxide. The West Middlesex system recovers 1·5 million cu. ft. per day, which is more than sufficient for the power requirements of the works. If recovery could be extended to, say, 35 million of population, there could be recovered 30 million cu. ft. of gas

per day (1 cu. ft. per person per day).   At a calorific value of 700 B.Th.U.
(CO_2 25 per cent., CH_4 75 per cent.), this would be equivalent to 200,000 tons
of coal annually, a valuable contribution to national economy.

The collection of town refuse is a source of fuel which is applied only in
small proportion to the total amount available.   It has been estimated that
300,000 tons of fuel of this type could be available per annum per million
of city population, and that its conversion into electricity would save
100,000 tons of steam coal yearly.

Vegetable wastes are consumed as useful fuel mainly at the source of

TABLE III

PRODUCTION OF COAL, LIGNITE AND PEAT IN 1947

(Millions of tons)

	Coal and anthracite.	Lignites.	Peat.
Europe :			
United Kingdom . .	193	—	5·2
Germany . . .	64	147	0·5
France	42	2	0·1
Poland	45	—	2·0
U.S.S.R. . . .	112	—	—
Czechoslovakia . .	14	19	5·7 (Denmark)
Netherlands . . .	8	—	0·7
Others	34	22	2·3
	512	190	16·5
North America . . .	—	7	0·1
United States . . .	576	—	—
Canada	11	—	—
Others	1	—	—
	588	7	0·1
South America . . .	4		
Africa :			
S. Africa . . .	24		
Others	2		
	26		
Asia :			
China	12		
India	29		
Japan	23		
Others	5		
	69		
Australasia :			
Australia . . .	14	6	
N. Zealand . . .	1	2	
	15	8	
Total (World)	1214	205	16·6

production and the heat developed used for raising power or heat required in the preparation of the product for the market. Bagasse is used in sugar manufacture, rice husks in rice drying, sisal waste in the drying of the fibres, and so on. In some places over-produced vegetable products are used in quantity for power production, as, for example, the generation of electrical power from grain in the Argentine.

Fuel Consumption. In order to illustrate the magnitude of the above reserves in comparison with the present-day rate of consumption, Table III gives data for coal, lignite and peat in the year 1947. It may be assumed that these quantities are increasing yearly, probably by at least 5 per cent. The corresponding figures for petroleum are included with the reserves data in Table II. It will be seen that the world is consuming coal, lignite, and peat at the annual rates of 1214, 205, and 16·6 million tons. Admittedly, these represent small proportions of the reserves—coal 1/4000, lignite 1/2200 and peat 1/7000, but in certain places the rate is proportionately very high. In Great Britain, for example, the coal rate is only 1/800.

In the case of oil the position is not so bright, with the ratio less than 1/20. In other words, unless new sources of oil continue to be found, supplies will be exhausted in less than twenty years' time. Before then, something will have to be done to bring into use the considerable reserves of oil shale, comparatively little of which is now being mined.

In order to make the overall position clear, Table IV includes the reserves as shown in the other tables, in comparison with the present rates of consumption, showing against water power the coal equivalent, assuming it

TABLE IV

SUMMARY OF FUEL RESOURCES AND CONSUMPTION

(Thousands of million tons)

	Reserves.	Consumed yearly.
Coal and lignite . . .	6000	1·40
Peat (air-dry)	120	0·02
Petroleum	11	0·61
Natural gas (as oil) . .	5	0·11
Shale oil	22	—
Uranium, coal equivalent .	250×10^{12} tons	—
Water power, continuous	15×10^8 kW.	$0·3 \times 10^{12}$ kWh.
Solar energy, continuous	6×10^{12} kW.	—

is all utilized for the generation of electricity. Without this water power the consumption of coal or oil would be correspondingly greater. Water power can obviously be a greater saving factor in the consumption of stored fuel as can be the much larger untapped continuous source of solar energy. The possible contribution by uranium is shown as stored energy in accordance with our present state of knowledge of the utilization of the energy of the atomic nucleus.

Utilization of Coal in Great Britain. Table V is included in order to make clear the relative importance of the consuming agencies for coal in this country.

TABLE V

Coal and Fuel Utilization in Great Britain (1951)

(Millions of tons)

Production.	Deep-mined.	Open-cast.	Per man/year mined.	% Mechanization.
1913	287	—	260	8
1938	227	—	290	60
1951	212	11	303	80
	1950		1951	1951%
General industry	45		48	23
Merchants (household) . .	33		33	15·5
Electricity	32		36	17
Gas	26		27	13
Coke ovens	24		25	12
Railways	14		14	6·5
Collieries	11		11	5
Miners	5		5	2·5
Miscellaneous	10		12	5·5
	200		211	100

Industrial, etc., Separation, 1951 (million tons)

General industry	33	House coal	30
Iron and steel	8	,, anthracite	2
Engineering	4	Bunkers, coast	1
Non-industrial	4	,, overseas	13
Pulverized coal	13	N. Ireland	3

Gas Industry (1951)

Coal used	27·15 million tons
Oil used	0·47 ,, ,,
Gas made	496,582 ,, cu. ft.
Gas purchased	65·760 ,, ,,
Coke sold	10·40 ,, tons

Distribution of gas (%)

Domestic.	Industrial.	Offices.	Public Administration.	Lighting.
58	25	13	2	2

Coke Oven Industry (1951)

Coal used	25 million tons
Coke made	16 ,, ,,
Breeze made	1 ,, ,,
Gas made	254,214 million cu. ft.
,, used at ovens	42 per cent.
,, ,, for heating	2·7 ,,
,, sold	55 ,,

TABLE V—*continued*

Electricity (1951)

Coal burned	35 million tons
Water power	900 thousand tons equivalent coal

Distribution (%)

Domestic.	Industrial.	Railways.	Farms.	Commercial.	Streets.
32	50	2	1	14	1

Tar and Benzole

Tar made	2·7 million tons
Benzole made	97 million gallons
Motor benzole	50 ,, ,,
Coalite spirit	1·1 ,, ,,
Hydrogenation spirit	34·8 ,, ,,
Other oils	35·4 ,, ,,

Tar distillation (*thousand tons*)

Road tar.	Creosote- pitch.	Naphtha- lene.	Phenol.	Cresylic acid.	Anthraceen.
608	632	41	11	11	2·6

Creosote oil—103 million gallons.

The figures quoted are for the year 1951. The importance of the data in this table lies in the fact that it is not always clear what is the relative importance of coal type in relation to the exact needs of the consuming industry. For example, the carbonizing industries require the selection and sometimes careful preparation of their coals : surely the requirements have a more important bearing on the general plan of coal preparation for the market than those of the minor industries.

The greatest proportion of the coal is consumed in industry and therefore used largely for steam-raising. The next greatest is that of the domestic market, for which sized coal with clear burning properties is the ideal. The gas industry and coke take 13 per cent. each and make special demands on quality as regards caking power and size grading. For electricity the proportion is higher than that shown, since most of the water power is used for this purpose and in its absence the amount of coal necessary would be increased from 36 to 37 million tons. Theoretically, good burning quality is required, but in actual fact a high proportion of high-ash, small-sized coal is allocated and the proportion of pulverized coal is rapidly increasing for power stations.

In addition to the above figure for coal, the domestic market is supplied with 3 million tons of coke, and town gas equivalent in thermal value to 4·3 million tons of coal, and electricity equivalent to 11 million tons of coal. In addition it consumes briquettes amounting to 0·77 million ton.

Utilization of Oil in Great Britain. The total consumption of petroleum products in Great Britain during 1951 was 26·6 million tons. Of this quantity, 16·8 millions were imported as crude and process oil and 9·8 millions were refined products, such as motor and aviation spirit 3·4, kerosine 1·9, gas oil 1·5, fuel and diesel oil 2·4 million tons, with smaller quantities of other spirits, lubricating oil and paraffin wax.

The crude and process oils were refined into motor and aviation spirit 2·9 millions, kerosine 0·25 million, gas and diesel oil 3·1 millions, fuel oil 7·7 millions, lubricating oil 0·4 million, bitumen 0·7 million, wax 0·02 million, and gases 0·01 million tons.

Since 1952 the growth of the oil-refining programme in Great Britain towards the target of 25 million tons has altered the proportion of imported and refined products considerably, but the sum of the two has shown only the increases of consumption normal to the growth of the fuel industries. The total consumption in 1952 was (in millions of tons):

Aviation spirit⎱		Kerosine	1·44
Motor spirit⎰	5·44	Gas, diesel	2·82
Other spirit	0·21	Fuel oil	3·46
		Lubricating oil	0·75

All products 17·5

A proportion of the refinery gases is already being utilized, but only a small proportion, and the efficient use of all of it is a national problem.

These quantities are only of immediate interest since consumption is increasing year by year in the order of 5 to 10 per cent.

Total Fuel Consumption. It is interesting to compare the present-day consumptions of energy in the two areas in which the level of human comfort may be said to be highest. This is best done by conversion to an equivalent coal basis, when it emerges that the two quantities were 7·32 and 4·02 tons per head per annum for the United States and Great Britain respectively in 1951. This difference is quite remarkable and difficult to assess in terms of climatic differences.

	Coal.	Oil.	Natural gas.	Town gas.	Coke.	Electricity.	Total.
U.S.A. (tons)	1·64	2·95	1·07	0·17	0·42	1·07	7·32
G.B. (tons)	2·18	0·45	—	0·29	0·53	0·56	4·02

The higher consumption of coal in Great Britain is completely overshadowed by much higher consumption of oil and natural gas in the United States. Now, in 1953, the "equivalent coal" quantities have increased to 8·66 and 4·72 tons respectively.

REFERENCES

Ministry of Fuel and Power Statistical Digests (Annual).
World Power Conference Statistical Year-Books.
World Energy Resources and their Utilization. A. Parker. *Inst. Mech. E.*, 1949, **160**, 441; *J. Inst. Fuel*, 1954, Melchett Lecture.
Nuclear Reactors and their Applications. Sir J. Cockcroft. *Proc. Inst. Elect. Eng.*, 1953, **123**, 99.
Statistical Summary of the Mineral Industry. 1945–1951. H.M.S.O. 1953.
Solar Energy for Water and Space Heating. H. Heywood. *J. Inst. Fuel*, 1954, **27**, 334

CHAPTER II

THE ESSENTIAL PROPERTIES OF FUELS

In the sense of present-day usage, the fuels available are those which have been stored in the earth's crust by the decay of organic matter, supplemented by water power and relatively very small amounts of vegetable waste materials. They consist mainly of coal in its various forms, petroleum and natural gas, bituminous shales, and " tar " or bituminous sands. Coal and natural gas are used in their natural forms, but petroleum and the shales require distillation and refinement to form usable fuels. Secondary fuels are obtained from coal or oil in the form of non-natural gaseous fuels. The entire range consists mainly of the following.

Solid Fuels

Vegetable wastes.
Wood and charcoal.
Coal :
  Lignite, brown woody, and black with conchoidal fracture. Bituminous coal, ranging from non-caking to highly-caking. Semi-bituminous or carbonaceous coal (low-volatile). Anthracite.
Coal briquettes.
Coke, carbonized coal or carbonized coal briquettes.

Liquid Fuels

Petroleum and refined fractions, motor spirit, diesel oil, fuel oil, etc. Shale distillates (shale oil) and similar fractions to petroleum. Tar sand distillates.

Gaseous Fuels

Natural gas from oil measures.
Manufactured gas :
  Coal gas and coke-oven gas.
  Total gasification gas and synthesis gas.
  Producer gas.
  Water gas and carburetted water gas.

By-product gases :
  Blast-furnace gas.
  Methane from sewage.
  Methane from coal measures.

Before proceeding to a consideration of these fuels and their properties it is necessary to consider briefly those properties which are essential to fuels of all types. From an economic point of view it is clear that the choice of a fuel for an industrial or other purpose depends largely upon proximity to the source of supply, and further, that the occurrence of a fuel in a given area has been the deciding factor in making the area industrial or not. The existence of the steel industry of Durham and Yorkshire is due, for example, to the existence there of the high-quality coking coals necessary. Where oil has become available in quantity, such as in South America, and coal is scarce, oil has replaced coal for purposes such as power production.

In certain industries it is difficult to distinguish between the fuel and the raw material. For example, in the blast furnace, coke is the fuel, but it is also an ingredient which takes part in the reactions by reducing the iron ore to metal. The coke therefore requires not only the properties of a fuel but also the special properties of a raw material. To a lesser extent this is true of other industrial processes but, in the main, the general utilization of the stored fuels consists in the production of heat or mechanical energy which is transformed as efficiently as may be into work.

For any substance to be of value as a fuel, therefore, and leaving on one side for the moment the question of its suitability for a particular appliance or machine, it must be capable of being transformed by combustion with air. In the first place it is desirable that it should have a high calorific value and that it should contain the minimum of (inert) constituents which do not contribute to the yield of heat energy. Neither should the inert constituents interfere unduly with the ease of obtaining the heat release.

In the case of the solid fuels the inert constituents are moisture, mineral matter and oxygen chiefly. In the case of the petroleum fuels, which are mainly hydrocarbons, this does not apply. The functions of ash and moisture are largely as diluents, that of oxygen is more fundamental in that calorific value is reduced by oxygen in proportion to the amount of hydrogen in the fuel with which it combines. Since the calorific values of carbon and hydrogen are in the ratio of 1 to 4·25, the fuel importance of low oxygen and high H/C ratio is obvious.

Combustion. The mechanism of the liberation of heat energy from fuel is termed combustion, but is the exothermic heat of reaction between the fuel and the oxygen of the air. This energy is therefore a known quantity and is always calculable from the masses of the reactants and a knowledge of the completeness of the reactions. In combustion the reactions normally take place at a high temperature, and at a high speed, but it follows that the same amount of heat is liberated whatever the conditions provided the end products are the same. Efficiency in the use or application of this heat depends only upon the manner in which combustion is controlled and the liberated heat is applied to the purpose in view, and upon the suitability of the fuel to the process or appliance. In many cases suitability can have more influence than high or low calorific value in determining the effectiveness of a fuel; for example, the octane number of a motor spirit has a greater bearing on efficiency than variations of calorific value.

For the full heat of reaction to be made available the reactions must be as complete as possible, which means that not less than the theoretical amount of air must be supplied in the correct manner. The addition of more than this amount may mean that an undue proportion of the heat is carried away in the waste gases without doing useful work. In practice, the best results are usually obtained at a compromise with a small proportion of excess air, since operation with theoretical air usually means the escape of a small proportion of unreacted fuel or its products. In burning coal incomplete combustion is evidenced by the visual appearance of smoke, and/or by the presence of carbon monoxide and hydrogen, mainly the latter, in the products of combustion. In the case of oil, smoke formation is more easily avoided, and incomplete combustion is normally limited to the escape of carbon monoxide unburned.

Incomplete combustion is avoided by proper distribution of the air supply in such a manner as to obtain intimate contact of air and fuel either at the surface of the latter or through admixture with the gases or vapours first evolved, and by avoiding chilling of combustion gases before the reactions are complete. The methods of achieving this vary with the fuel and the system of combustion and are dealt with later.

Production of Flame. Flame is produced by the combustion of gases and vapours, in the case of solid fuels these being volatilized or formed by heat from the fuel, or by the incomplete combustion of the carbon which gives rise to carbon monoxide, an inflammable gas. The temperature resulting from the combustion must be sufficiently high to maintain the reaction, otherwise the flame is extinguished. In the case of solid fuels, like coal, the amount of flame produced will be dependent largely on the ratio between the volatile combustible constituents and the carbon residue, which is non-volatile. It will be seen later that this ratio is highest with bituminous coals and falls to a minimum with anthracite.

When flame is produced, a proportion of the heat units from one pound of fuel is generated throughout probably several cubic feet of space. High local intensity with such fuels cannot be attained. When this is desired combustion must take place as far as possible on the grate, so that a fuel low in volatile constituents, such as anthracite, coke or charcoal, must be employed.

In general, flame is inefficient for heating purposes where there is a great difference between its temperature and that of the surface being heated, as in a boiler. This is due to two causes, the checking of combustion by lowering of temperature, and the formation of a thin layer of gas, which is a poor conductor of heat, along the surface of the plate. Much depends, however, on the luminosity of the flame. Owing to the presence of highly-heated particles of solid carbon, to which most of the luminosity of all ordinary flames is due, the radiant effect of such flames is higher than that of non-luminous flames.

The latter radiate heat as infra-red energy. Oxygen, nitrogen and hydrogen do not radiate, but carbon dioxide and water vapour radiate strongly and contribute appreciably to heat transfer at high temperatures.

The rate of radiation is a function of the projected area of the flame, its absolute temperature, and emissivity. The emissivity of luminous flames is not readily calculable.

Ignition Temperature of Fuels.   For active combustion to be initiated the temperature of the fuel must be raised to a definite level which is characteristic of the fuel.   Such temperatures can be determined, but their application to practical conditions must be made with a certain amount of care. For example, finely-divided coal will ignite near its ignition temperature in almost any circumstances, but a lump of the same coal will not readily ignite near this temperature, or without prolonged heating, under adiabatic conditions.

The ignition temperature of solid and liquid fuels cannot be given precisely since they depend upon the conditions under which the fuel is heated. In the case of coal, rapid heating is necessary since otherwise distillation intervenes and what is measured is the temperature of ignition of the coke formed.

The ignition temperature of coal has been determined by dropping 5 to 6 gm. of powdered coal into the bottom of a heated crucible through which a current of oxygen is passing.   The start of active combustion is indicated by a visible glow and followed later by an explosion or flame. Allowing 10 sec. as a suitable time for the coal to reach the temperature of the crucible, the i.t. for anthracite is recorded as 340° C., and for a bituminous coal as 270° to 290° C.   In air the temperatures are higher, anthracite 500°, Welsh steam coal 470°, bituminous coal 380° to 420° C. In general, ignition temperature decreases progressively with decreasing carbon content from anthracite to lignite.

The ignition temperature of carbonized fuels is readily determined by passing heated air through a bed of the material and raising the temperature until the bed temperature shows a sudden jump.   In the case of coke the temperature depends upon the temperature of carbonization of the coal, varying from 420° C. to about 620° C., with increase of carbonizing temperature from 500° to 1050° C.   The temperature for wood charcoal may be as low as 220° C.

Gases and Vapours.   In this case the actual values for spontaneous ignition temperature also depend upon the conditions of the method employed but are more exact than those of the solid fuels.   Four methods mainly have been used :

(1) The dropping of oil-drops into a heated crucible (Moore, Holm).

(2) The adiabatic compression method (Dixon, Tizard).

(3) The admission of an explosive mixture into an evacuated, heated vessel (Mallard and Le Chatelier).

(4) The concentric-tube method (Dixon and Coward).

In view of these differences of method the accepted values for hydrocarbons have been subject to considerable change. Values obtained by Method 3 in air using theoretical mixtures, are as follows :

Methane 600° C., pentane 510°, octane 250°, benzene 700°, *cyclo*hexane 510°, propane 493° C.

Values obtained in oxygen are lower, and comparative values in air and oxygen are given below for a number of hydrocarbons. These are recently-accepted values (1952) and some of them differ quite widely from those of Method 3 above.

SPONTANEOUS IGNITION TEMPERATURE (° C.)

	In air.	In oxygen.
Benzene	580	566
Carbon disulphide . . .	120	107
Ethane	472	432
n-Pentane	218	208
Toluene	552	516
Hydrogen sulphide . .	292	220
Gasoline, 73 octane . .	300	290
Diesel oil, cetane 60 . .	247	242

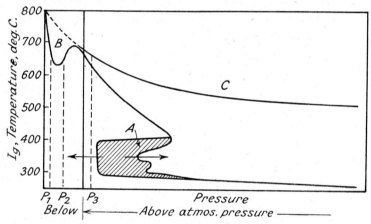

FIG. 3.—The Effect of Pressure on the Ignition Temperature of Gases and Vapours.

Below atmospheric pressure some gases show the phenomenon of ignition in area B, but above this point the simpler gases, methane, ethylene, etc., show a decrease in ignition temperature with increasing pressure (C). With hydrocarbons above C_3 the low-temperature system occurs (A), which gives the phenomenon of cool flames within the range 300° to 400° C. These can bring about complete ignition, but above 400° C. the ignition temperature is that given by curve C.

In the case of fuels for the diesel engine, where good performance depends upon a low value, an ideal method would be to make the determinations in air under the pressure and temperature conditions of the engine. This was embodied in the method of Foord (*J. Inst. Pet. Tech.*, 1932, **18**, 533) in which the time lag between injection and ignition was measured with precision. Usually the S.I.T. is taken as the lowest temperature at which the fuel, after any delay, will ignite—this may amount to seconds and clearly the " wait " period is important. Naturally it is reduced by rise of temperature, and should not be more than one- or two-fifths of a second for the high-speed diesel engine.

From curves given by Foord the following delay times and ignition temperatures (in air) have been deduced :

Seconds.	3	2	1	$\frac{1}{5}$
Gas oil . . . . (mainly paraffin)	340° C.	350° C.	375° C.	500° C.
Diesel oil . . . . (mainly naphthene)	390	412	450	575
Creosote	485	505	533	620

In the case of gases, ignition temperature varies with concentration but, in the neighbourhood of stoichiometric proportions, small variations have little effect. Method 4 is most commonly used, with preheated streams of the gas and air or oxygen, the values with oxygen being again lower. Values for the simple gases are given by Dixon and Coward as :

IGNITION TEMPERATURES OF GASEOUS MIXTURES IN °C. AT ORDINARY
PRESSURES

Gas.	In oxygen.	In air.
Hydrogen	580–590°	580–590°
Carbon monoxide	637–658	644–658
Methane	556–700	650–750
Ethane	520–630	520–630
Ethylene	500–519	542–547
Acetylene	400–440	406–440

It will be noted that, whilst in the case of simple gases like hydrogen and carbon monoxide the ignition temperature variation is small, in the case of hydrocarbon gases the temperature is uncertain to over 100° C. Further, whilst there is close agreement between the values in oxygen and in air in some cases, in other cases there is a marked discrepancy.

Limits of Combustion or Inflammability. Combustible gases or vapours are capable of burning in air or oxygen only within closely defined limits of concentration. To ensure combustion it is necessary first that sufficient heat shall be developed to raise the temperature of the gases in the vicinity to the ignition temperature, and secondly, that the heat contained in the products of combustion of this gas shall in turn raise the temperature of the next increment of gas to the ignition temperature.

Two limits are recognized, of high and low concentration of fuel, which are termed the "upper" and "lower" limits respectively. The lower limit is the smallest proportion of combustible which will enable the above propagation to continue. The upper limit is similarly represented by the mixture which contains the minimum amount of air which will liberate sufficient heat to enable the combustion to continue. The range of mixtures thus included is sometimes referred to as the "explosive range" and is of importance in connection with accident risks by the escape of inflammable gases or vapours into air ; it also has an important bearing upon the practical usage of such mixtures in the internal combustion engine.

The factors which affect the limits are (1) calorific value, (2) the relative volume and specific heat of the diluent gases and (3) ignition temperature. In addition, both are affected by the shape of the containing vessel, the direction of propagation, pressure and temperature. Upward propagation in a tube of 7·5 cm. diameter gives almost optimum conditions. Limits of inflammability of certain combustibles are given below from Coward and Jones (*U.S. Bureau of Mines*, Bull. 279) as determined under these conditions.

TABLE VI
LIMITS OF INFLAMMABILITY OF GASEOUS AND LIQUID FUELS AT ATMOSPHERIC TEMPERATURE AND PRESSURE

(Per cent. by volume)

	Lower.	Upper.
Blast-furnace gas	35	74
Coal gas	5·3	31·5
Natural gas	4·8	13·5
Water gas	6·0	55
Petrol	1·4	6
Benzene	1·4	7·4
Alcohol, ethyl	3·6	18·0

The magnitude of the effects of variation of tube-diameter, and direction of flow, are seen in the following table for acetylene, U, D and H meaning upward, downward and horizontal directions of flow.

	Tube 7·5 cm.			5 cm.			2·5 cm.		
	U.	H.	D.	U.	H.	D.	U.	H.	D.
Low	2·6	2·68	2·78	2·6	2·68	2·8	2·73	2·87	2·9
High	>80·5	78·5	71·0	78·0	68·5	63·5	70·0	59·5	55·0

With hydrocarbons above C_3 the situation is complicated by the phenomenon of cool flames. The normal flame range centres about the theoretical mixture for complete combustion, but the cool-flame range centres about the composition most reactive in slow combustion, i.e. on the rich side.

Increase of temperature widens the normal-flame range appreciably ; increase of pressure also widens the range except in the case of carbon monoxide where it is narrowed. These effects are illustrated below for hydrogen, methane and carbon monoxide in air.

TABLE VII

EFFECTS OF TEMPERATURE AND PRESSURE ON INFLAMMABILITY LIMITS IN AIR

Temp. °C.	H_2.	CO.	CH_4 up.	CH_4 down.
17	9·4–71·5	16·3–70·0	6·3–12·9	6·0–13·4
100	8·8–73·5	14·8–71·5	6·0–13·7	5·4–13·5
200	7·9–76·0	13·5–73·0	5·5–14·6	5·0 13·8
400	6·3–81·5	11·4–77·5	4·8–16·0	4·0–14·7
Press. atm.				
10	10·2–68·5	17·8–62·8	6·0–17·1	
50	10·0–73·3	20·6–56·8	5·4–29·0	
125	9·9–74·8	20·7–51·6	5·7–45·6	

The effect of downward propagation for methane is included for comparison ; in these circumstances pressure has a more marked effect on the limits. The effect of temperature and pressure on the limits is of importance to the internal combustion engine since the charge is always under compression at the moment of ignition and is also heated by the hot walls of the cylinder. With hydrocarbon/air mixtures pressure raises the upper limit considerably, while the lower limit is first reduced up to 50 atm., and then increases again. These latter effects are small, however, and the overall effect is a considerable widening of the limits.

The limits for a mixture of combustible gases can be calculated from Le Chatelier's Rule ; the rule is of value in certain industrial processes where the explosion risk can be reduced by the introduction of another ingredient which has a low upper limit.

Rule : $L = a + b + c$, etc., divided by $\dfrac{a}{A} + \dfrac{b}{B} + \dfrac{c}{C}$, etc.

where a, b, c, are the proportions of the constituents and A, B, C, their inflammability limits. The rule applies more accurately to the lower limits. An elaboration of the calculation has been made by Jones (Tech. Paper 450, *U.S. Bureau of Mines*), in which the mixture is split into simpler components and these calculated ; graphs are supplied.

Velocity of Flame Propagation. The speed at which a flame will travel through a gas/air mixture has an important effect upon the design of burners and combustion spaces. Too high a speed may mean overheating of the burner or too localized heating, while too low a speed may lead to extinction of the flame. It is influenced by the proportions of the reactants and by the shape of the chamber in which the combustion takes place.

The usual method of determination is to pass the combustible mixture through a tube at such a rate that the flame, started at the outlet end, just fails to strike back.   Such conditions simulate those of gaseous combustion but not those of the internal combustion engine where there is always turbulence.   Except in the case of very weak mixtures turbulence greatly increases the velocity.   The increase is greater for weak mixtures than for rapidly-burning mixtures.   The highest velocity is not found at the point when the fuel and air are in theoretical proportion for complete combustion but approximately halfway between the upper and lower limits of combustion.   At these limits it has been shown that the rate is about 20 ft. per sec. for the first five members of the paraffin series of hydrocarbons.

When flame propagation is studied by the above tube method it is found that the rate decreases with the diameter of the tube to a marked extent, the speed in a 1-in. tube being less than half that in a 12-in. tube.   If comparisons of the different fuel gases are made under more than one set of conditions the curves are found to be of the same general shape but of very different dimensions.   At low gas percentages the rate of propagation is low ; as the percentage increases the rate increases to a maximum and then decreases again as the upper limit of inflammability is approached.   The lowest speeds, those of the limiting mixtures, are the same for all gases at about 0·65 ft. per sec.   The velocity is also affected by the presence of moisture, that of carbon monoxide, for example, being considerably decreased.

Experimental values obtained in a 2·5-in. tube are given in Table VIII for a number of combustible gases.   The variation with concentration is illustrated in Figure 4.

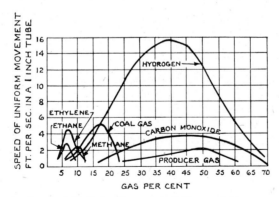

Fig. 4.—Speed of Uniform Movement of Flame of Gases in Air.

The outstandingly high velocity for hydrogen makes this gas a very valuable constituent of low-grade gases without which it might be difficult to sustain combustion in the absence of heated surfaces.

The Le Chatelier formula can be used to calculate maximum velocity

TABLE VIII

MAXIMUM SPEED OF UNIFORM MOVEMENT OF FLAME IN MIXTURES WITH AIR IN HORIZONTAL TUBES

		Vel., cm./sec. at tube diam. of	
	Per cent.	2·5 cm.	5·0 cm.
Hydrogen	38	490	—
Methane	9·5	66	91
Ethane	6·5	86	130
Propane	4·6	80	112
Butane	3·7	83	113
Pentane	3·0	82	115
Ethylene	7·2	142	—
Acetylene	8·9	282	—

in the case of rich gases. It is not accurate for lean mixtures such as producer gases.

Flame Temperature. Flame temperature is of importance in gas heating partly because the higher the flame temperature the more rapid the rate of heating and partly because the higher the flame temperature the greater the thermal efficiency of the process.

Actual flame temperatures are difficult to measure and the values normally used are those of the "theoretical" temperature, i.e. that which would be developed if the heat of combustion heated only the products of combustion. Theoretical flame temperatures can therefore be calculated from the heat of combustion, specific heats, and volumes of the gases. These values are, of course, higher than the practical values, but are of importance in being strictly comparable and serve for the calculation of effects of pre-heating, excess air, etc. Values for certain of the common gases are :

	B.Th.U.* per cu. ft.	Flame temp. ° C.
Coal gas	560	2160
Water gas	310	2300
„ „ carburetted	529	2250
Producer gas	128	1680
Blast-furnace gas	92	1460
Hydrogen	320	2045
Methane	995	1880
Carbon monoxide	318	1950

* Gross at 60° F. and 30 in. satd.

In calculating flame-temperature values the lower (net) heat of combustion of the gases is used since latent heat is not available at temperatures above 100° C.

The flame temperatures of mixed gases can be calculated from tables or graphs showing the total heat content of the products of combustion which are mainly CO_2, N_2 and H_2O. The "theoretical" temperatures are for cold gas and the theoretical amount of cold air. They are decreased by the addition of excess air and increased by pre-heating either air or gas. In practice, the calculated flame temperature is not realized because : (1) the data, especially specific heats, used for calculating are not too exact, (2) some dissociation of the products CO_2 and H_2O occurs, (3) the flame radiates heat to the extent of 5–20 per cent. and (4) heat is lost by convection and conduction since combustion takes an appreciable time.

The losses under (3) and (4) depend upon specific conditions, but those under (2) can be calculated from known data and should be applied wherever possible by deducting the heat of dissociation from the heat of combustion of the gas. Since heat is absorbed by the dissociation the corrected temperatures are appreciably lower than the uncorrected; that for CO, for example, is reduced by 400° C.

In practice, high flame temperature is achieved (1) by rapid combustion, (2) by reducing excess air to a minimum, and (3) by pre-heating. An increase of excess air from 0 to 100 per cent. reduces the flame temperature of producer gas by some 30 per cent. The same gas pre-heated to 500° C. and burned with pre-heated air at 500° C. shows an increase of flame temperature of about 20 per cent. Since dilution and pre-heating are such important factors in practice, arrangements are made in most modern furnaces for heat interchange from flue gas to combustion gas or air and, where dilution is necessary, to achieve this by the circulation of hot flue gas rather than by increasing the excess air.

Heat interchange is achieved either by regeneration or recuperation. The former process is discontinuous, the hot gases giving up their heat in a checker brickwork chamber for a short period and the chamber giving up its heat again to the gas or air. Two chambers operated alternately at short time intervals form a complete system. Recuperation is a continuous process, heat being given to the gas or air from the hot flue gases through brick or metal partitions, the gases flowing counter-current to one another.

Speaking generally, a regenerator is used where a high degree of pre-heat is required; it does not suffer from possible leakage of flue gas into the air stream but does have a greater operating cost and suffers from the variability of the air temperature.

Effect of Dissociation in Flames. At the high temperature at which gaseous combustion takes place some dissociation occurs of the carbon dioxide and water vapour. This has the same effect as if the hydrogen and carbon monoxide were not completely burned, so that the flame temperature achieved is less than the theoretical. Correction for diffusion effects is laborious, involving the solution by trial and error of two simultaneous equations, and has been simplified to a graphical basis by Underwood (*Tech. Data on Fuel*, 1950, 305). The data required for the calculation are:

(1) The composition of the waste gas assuming no dissociation.
(2) The heat derived from the calorific value of the fuel and any pre-heat supplied, expressed in terms of kilo-calories per cubic metre of waste gas (undissociated) at 0° C. and 760 mm.

The use of the charts then enables the corrected flame temperature to be calculated. A further correction can be added to allow for flame radiation, normally about 10 per cent. At a temperature of 2000° C. carbon dioxide dissociates to the extent of about 6 per cent. and water vapour about 1·9 per cent. when the pressure is one atmosphere.

Calorific Value. The basic property of a fuel is its calorific value, although other properties may assume major importance at a later stage by making the heat units more readily available, or more efficiently convertible into useful work.

The calorific value of a combustible material as determined is the heat liberated by its complete combustion with oxygen and the condensation of the products to the temperature of determination. The values may be expressed in any standard heat units.

The calorific value of a gas is expressed as the number of heat units liberated by the combustion at constant pressure of unit volume, saturated with water vapour, both air and gas being at standard temperature, and the products being cooled also to this temperature. Combustion must be complete, i.e. there shall be no products other than carbon dioxide, sulphur dioxide, water and nitrogen.

The net calorific value is the gross calorific value recalculated on the assumption that the effluent gases are cooled to the standard temperature but that all the water vapour remains in the vapour state.

In Great Britain the standard temperature is 60° F. and the heat unit the British Thermal Unit; in Europe these are 15° C. and the calorie.

The British units are :

(1) The mean British thermal unit or the 1/180th part of the heat required to raise the temperature of a pound of water from 32° to 212° F.

(2) The cubic foot, the gas being measured at 60° F. under a pressure of 30 in. of mercury (at 60° F.) and saturated with water vapour at 60° F.

The barometer reading is corrected to 45° latitude with the mercury at 32° F., the brass scale at 62° F., and at sea-level. The humidity of the air is not specified.

The calorific value of a solid or a liquid fuel is normally determined at constant volume in a calorimeter capable of withstanding the pressure developed. Since the products are cooled to the temperature of the calorimeter the value obtained is the gross value. The method of determination is described in Chapter XIX.

One mean British thermal unit is equal to 251·996 mean gram-calories ; the latter may be defined as 1/100th of the heat required to raise the temperature of one gramme of water from 0° C. to 100° C.

The 15° calorie is the amount of heat required to raise the temperature of one gramme of water from 14·5° C. to 15·5° C. and is used as the international standard in calorimetry. It differs from the mean calorie by only one part in 4000, which is not significant in the examination of fuels.

The kilogramme-calorie (K) is 1000 calories and is equivalent to 3·96 B.Th.U. and is 4·180 ergs of energy.

A fourth unit of heat—the *pound degree centigrade unit*, being the amount of heat required to raise 1 lb. of water 1° C.—is frequently employed in stating the calorific value of solid and liquid fuels. It is related obviously to the B.Th.U. as are the Centigrade and Fahrenheit thermometer degrees, namely

$$\frac{\text{Fahrenheit degree}}{\text{Centigrade degree}} = \frac{180}{100} = 1·8$$

A concrete practical example will make this evident : 1 gram of coal burnt in a calorimeter raised the temperature of 3000 grams of water 2·5° C. Its calorific value = 3000 × 2·5 = 7500 calories. 1 lb. of coal would have obviously raised 3000 lb. of water 2·5 × 1·8 = 4·5° F., or its calorific value = 3000 × 4·5 = 13,500 B.Th.U. The calorific values of all solid and liquid fuels referred to subsequently have this ratio between B.Th.U. and calories.

It is frequently convenient to express these values in foot-pounds

```
1 kilogram degree centigrade = 3087 foot-pounds
1 pound degree centigrade   = 1400      ,,
1 British Thermal Unit      = 778       ,,
```

Gross and Net Calorific Values. When a fuel containing hydrogen is burnt, water is produced invariably, and if this water is condensed it gives up its latent heat as steam together with the heat liberated on cooling from its condensation point to the temperature of the calorimeter. The total calorific value, *gross*, or higher heating value of a fuel is the number of heat units liberated when unit weight of fuel (or volume, in the case of gases) is burnt and the products of combustion are all cooled to 60° F., the water vapour in them being condensed.

In many cases, however, this heat carried by the water produced from hydrogen during combustion, or stored in water evaporated from the fuel, is not available for conversion into work. Thus, it plays no part in raising the flame temperature of burning gases, or in developing energy in a gas engine. For all such computations it must be eliminated, and the value after this deduction is termed the *net* calorific value. This may be similarly defined to the gross value except that whilst the products are assumed to be cooled to 60° F. it is further assumed that *the water vapour does not condense.*

The figure taken for the deduction from the gross calorific value to represent the latent heat of evaporation could be the actual latent at the temperature of evaporation (970 B.Th.U. at 212° F.), plus the heat liberated in cooling the water to 60° F. (152 B.Th.U. from 212° F.), but it is considered that this value would be too great. The problem was considered by the Heat Engines Trials Committee of the Institution of Civil Engineers in 1925, which concluded that the value to use should be the latent heat of condensation of the vapour down to a reference temperature of 60° F. The value recommended was 1055 B.Th.U. per lb. of water, and this value is still used in general practice whenever thermal calculations are based on the net value.

The British Standards Institution has published definitions of gross and net calorific values (B.S. 526—1933) and recommends that they shall be respectively designated by the symbols H_s and H_i.

For many thermodynamic calculations the net value is of service, but its real value must not be misconstrued. The error has arisen that the net value is the true measure of the practical heating value of the fuel. Flue gases and exhaust gases are seldom cooled to anything approaching 100° C. (212° F.), and must carry away not only the latent heat units in the uncondensed steam, but all the additional sensible heat units in the flue gas, which will depend primarily on their temperature. The net value is a useful convention but is in reality an artificial figure.

Although the net calorific value at one time received official recognition as a standard in the case of coal gas, it is agreed generally that the gross value is the proper one to take, and the Gas Regulations Act (1920), which altered the whole system of charging consumers from one of cubic feet to " therms ", specifies the gross value. The inability of most appliances to convert all the heat units into other forms of energy is no logical basis for rating fuels on a value which is not their true one ; indeed in some cases it is practicable to utilize at least a considerable proportion of the latent heat units. The general opinion is, therefore, that the gross value is the correct one to consider in thermal calculations.

When it becomes a question of comparison between different samples of coal (unless of very different water content) or of oil, the net value offers so little advantage over the gross as to be negligible, because with coals of the same class, or oils of the same character, the hydrogen content is so similar in different samples, that the difference between the gross and net values is nearly constant. The extra labour involved in determining the hydrogen by the combustion process—the only method available giving the requisite accuracy—is not commensurate with the gain.

Calculation of Calorific Value. In general, actual determinations in some form of calorimeter are preferable to calculated values ; comparison between the methods is dealt with under Calorimetry (p. 496), but the general method of calculating the values is referred to here in order that other points may be elucidated.

It is assumed in practically all such calculations that the heating value of the constituent elements of the fuel is the same as the value for these same elements in the free condition, and that no heat is generated beyond this, or no heat utilized in setting free the constituent elements in a condition for their combustion by oxygen, assumptions which certainly cannot be substantiated.

When carbon is burnt in oxygen with the formation of carbon dioxide, the weights of material involved and the heat evolved may be expressed by a *thermo-chemical equation*, thus :

$$C \quad + \quad O_2 \quad = \quad CO_2 \quad + \quad 97{,}644$$

12 grams Carbon 32 grams Oxygen 44 grams Carbon dioxide calories

and when hydrogen burns with the formation of water at constant pressure as :

$$H_2 \quad + \quad O \quad = \quad H_2O \quad + \quad 69{,}000$$

2 grams Hydrogen 16 grams Oxygen 18 grams Water (condensed) calories

Water (as steam) + 58,100

It follows that 1 gram of carbon gives 8137 cals. (14,646 B.Th.U. per lb.), and 1 gram of hydrogen 34,500 cals. (62,100 B.Th.U. per lb.), if the steam produced is condensed to water at 0° C. ; if the steam remains as such at 100° C., 29,050 cals. (52,290 B.Th.U. per lb.).

The calculated calorific value (gross) of any fuel containing only these two elements will be found from the equation :

$$\frac{(\text{Carbon \% } \times 8137) + (\text{Hydrogen \% } \times 34{,}500)}{100} = \text{calories (gross)}$$

A large number of fuels already contain oxygen,[1] and therefore a smaller quantity of this gas will be required for their combustion, and the heat produced will be proportionately less. The assumption is made that any oxygen present is already wholly in combination with hydrogen ; again, this is certainly not the case, but since nothing is definitely known as to the actual distribution of oxygen between the hydrogen and other elements present, it affords the only possible working hypothesis. Since it is known that in water 8 parts by weight of oxygen are combined with 1 part of hydrogen, it is customary to deduct from the total hydrogen an amount equal to one-eighth of the oxygen present, calling the remainder the *available hydrogen*. The formula thus becomes :

$$\text{Calories (gross) per gram} = \frac{(C \text{ \% } \times 8137) + \left\{\left(H - \frac{O}{8}\right) \times 34{,}500\right\}}{100}$$

In the most complete form, such as may be applied to coals, the following extended formula is employed :

$$\text{Calories} = \frac{(C \times 8137) + \left\{\left(H - \frac{(O + N - 1)}{8}\right) \times 34{,}500\right\} + (S \times 2220) - (H_2O \times 600)}{100}$$

[1] In combination.

Here a fixed deduction of 1 per cent. is made for the nitrogen present in the fuel, this being regarded as a fair average, although somewhat low for British coals ; sulphur, in the form of pyrites, is regarded as furnishing heat, and an approximate deduction is made for the evaporation of the moisture present in the fuel.

In the case of gaseous fuels the calorific value must not be calculated from the elementary constituents, but from the sum of the calorific values of the constituent gases themselves, the values for which are well established, and are given in Table LXXII, Appendix.

Exothermic and Endothermic Compounds. If the simplest of the formulæ on page 31, namely, that for a fuel containing carbon and hydrogen alone, be applied to the two gases, methane or marsh gas (CH_4) and acetylene (C_2H_2), it is found that in the case of methane the calculated value is much higher than that found by a calorimeter, whilst in the latter case it is considerably lower. Some of the heat is expended in breaking down the methane before combustion ; in the case of acetylene heat is actually evolved.

The explanation is to be found in the conditions attending the formation of the two gases. When methane is formed from its elements, carbon and hydrogen, heat is evolved, and to separate these elements again and enable them to enter into fresh combination with oxygen during the combustion, as much heat must be supplied as was given out originally. Compounds which evolve heat on formation are termed *exothermic*. Acetylene, conversely, absorbs heat on formation ; this heat is evolved on decomposition, and adds to the heat generated by the combustion of its constituent elements. Compounds whose formation from their elements requires the supply of heat are termed *endothermic*.

It follows that all formulæ for calculating calorific values must fail unless the heat of formation of the fuel is either only slightly positive or negative. Such formulæ apply fairly well to most coals, simply because coal is very slightly endothermic, its endothermic character increasing with the amount of oxygen present. In the case of gaseous fuels, where the heat of formation of the constituent gases may be either markedly positive or negative, calculation from elementary composition will obviously give misleading results.

With gaseous fuels the results calculated from the values for the constituent gases at constant volume are found to be in good agreement with determinations made in calorimeters of the usual pattern—Chapter XIX.

It is important to note that the calorific value is higher when the fuel is burnt at constant pressure than it is at constant volume, for example, in cases where the final products occupy a less volume than the original, e.g. with hydrogen, where the steam occupies two-thirds of the former volume, and may ultimately condense to a negligible volume. In the case of actual determinations of calorific values of solid and liquid fuels in a bomb calorimeter, the difference is negligible, a few calories per gram in the case of coal.

Calorific Intensity. Whilst any given fuel is capable of developing on combustion a given number of heat units, the actual temperature attained by the combustion will depend not only on the calorific value but on a number of other conditions—the weight of the products of combustion and of any excess air, their specific heat and the heat losses which take place. Assuming that the whole of the heat is utilized without loss in raising the temperature of the products, then it is possible to calculate the maximum theoretical temperature attainable. Accurate knowledge of the actual variation in specific heat of gases with rise of temperature was for long wanting. Only in recent years has sufficiently accurate data on the specific heat of gases at high temperature been available. In practice it is seldom possible to attain the theoretical maximum because of inevitable heat losses through radiation and as sensible heat in the products.

Certain practical considerations however arise. Imagine that a fuel is burning under a boiler, and a steady temperature has been attained, that is, the heat production and losses have reached a certain equilibrium. Increase of the rate of combustion by increasing the draught will not raise the amount of heat given out per pound of fuel, but the production of heat increases proportionately much faster than the loss of heat, consequently a higher calorific intensity is attained. Again, the use of too much air for combustion will greatly lower the temperature owing to losses of sensible heat. The effect may be illustrated with approximate figures for the combustion of hydrogen. With the theoretical volume of pure oxygen the theoretical attainable temperature is over 6000° C. (say 11,000° F.) ; with the theoretical volume of air 2300° C. ; with twice the theoretical air 1400° C.

In the case of regenerative furnaces, where the waste heat from the gaseous products is utilized for heating up the air required for combustion (with the poorer gaseous fuels the fuel is heated also) it will be seen how greatly this must add to the calorific intensity of the reaction ; indeed, the success of such low calorific value fuels as " producer gases " is dependent entirely on this possibility of increasing the intensity by regeneration. For example, the theoretical temperature for the combustion of carbon monoxide with twice its volume of air, both gases supplied at ordinary temperatures, is less than 1600° C., but if by regeneration the initial temperature of the combustible gas and the air is 500° C., then a temperature of a little over 2000° C. is theoretically attainable.

Evaporative Values. It is sometimes the practice in steam engineering to state the thermal value of a fuel in terms of its power of evaporating

F.—C

water from a temperature of 100° C. (212° F.) into steam at the same temperature.

The evaporative value will therefore equal the calorific value divided by the latent heat of steam, which at atmospheric pressure is 539·3 cal. per g. or approx. 971 B.Th.U. per lb.

The latent heat of steam (or latent heat of vaporization of water) falls with increase of temperature (i.e. higher boiler pressure). According to Regnault, up to 230° C. (404 lb. absolute pressure), it equals 606·5 — 0·695t, where t equals the boiling temperature. The important point, however, in practice is the total amount of heat in steam at a given temperature. This obviously will be the sum of the latent heat of vaporization and heat required to raise the water from feed temperature to its boiling-point. According to Regnault, the feed being 0° C. (32° F.), the value for the total heat up to 230° C. is equal to 606·5 + 0·305t calories. From this value the temperature of the feed water must be deducted. The value in B.Th.U. will be 1·8 times as great.

As an example, a boiler is worked at 115 lb. absolute pressure ; the feed water is at 15·5° C. (60° F.). At this pressure the water boils at 170° C. (338° F.). The total heat equals 606·5 + (0·305 × 170) = 658 cals. or 1184 B.Th.U. The heat required to convert 1 kilogram of water to steam under these conditions will be 658 − 15·5 = 632·5 cals., or 1 lb. of water 1138 B.Th.U. If the coal has a calorific value of 7500 calories (13,500 B.Th.U.), the theoretical evaporative power will be 11·8. Regnault's values illustrate the calculation but, in practice, the engineer to-day uses the modern values contained in Callendar's Steam Tables in which the heat quantities are set out in terms of absolute steam pressure.[1]

Theoretical Air for Combustion. This is a most important consideration, governing to a large extent the arrangements for the supply of air, especially in internal combustion engines, and, further, enabling the theoretical composition of the flue or exhaust gases to be determined, which, as will be dealt with fully later, has an important bearing on fuel economy.

Custom has established somewhat firmly the calculation of the air required in pounds, and weight units do not involve corrections for temperature, but since gases are measured in cubic feet and thought of in terms of volumes and not weight, it seems more reasonable to consider their consumption in such units. In either case the calculation is simple, being based on the known combining values of oxygen with the individual combustible constituents, using their ordinary expression in the form of chemical equations for convenience.

The following data are of great service in such calculations, since they apply to all cases of chemical combination where gases are involved.

---

[1] A short version of the Tables is included in *Technical Data on Fuel*, see page 37.

	At 0° C. and 760 mm. pressure.	At 60° F. and 30 inches pressure.
The molecular weight in grams always . . . } =	22·4 litres	23·62 litres
The molecular weight in ounces always . . . } =	,, cubic ft.	,, cubic ft.
The molecular weight in pounds always . . } =	359 cubic ft.	378 cubic ft.

Conversely, the weight of 1 cu. ft. in pounds will equal $\dfrac{\text{molecular weight}}{359}$ at 0° C. and 760 mm., and $\dfrac{\text{molecular weight}}{378}$ at 60° F. and 30 in.

Further, the composition of air is taken as :

	By weight.			By volume.		
	Per cent.	Ratio N/O	Ratio air/O	Per cent.	Ratio N/O	Ratio air/O
Nitrogen . .	77	3·35	4·35	79	3·76	4·76
Oxygen . . .	23	1	1	21	1	1

Full information as to the weight and volume of both oxygen and air for combustion, the products of combustion, etc., for elementary fuel constituents, and the principal constituent gases of ordinary gaseous fuels, will be found in Table LXXIII, Appendix. An example of the method of calculation of these values is given below, the instance chosen being the combustion of carbon to carbon dioxide.

$$
\begin{array}{lccc}
& \text{Carbon.} & \text{Air.} & \text{Flue gases.} \\
& \overbrace{\text{C}} & \overbrace{+\ O_2\ +\ (\text{nitrogen})} & =\ \overbrace{CO_2\ +\ (\text{nitrogen})} \\
\text{Weight in}\} & 12 & +\ 32\ +\ (107) & =\ 44\ \ +\ (107) \\
\text{gm. or lb.}\} & 1 & +\ 2·66\ +\ (8·93) & =\ 3·66\ +\ (8·93) \\
& & \underbrace{}_{11·6} & \underbrace{}_{12·6}
\end{array}
$$

Volume in litres.

At 0° C. and 760 mm.} 12 grams + 22·4 + (84·2) = 22·4 + (84·2)
           1 gram + 1·86 + (7·0) = 1·86 + (7·0)
                        8·86 litres   8·86 litres

At 60° F. and 30 in.} 12 grams + 23·60 + (88·7) = 23·60 + (88·7)
           1 gram + 1·96 + (7·36) = 1·96 + (7·36)
                        9·37 litres   9·37 litres

Volume in cubic feet.

At 0° C. and 760 mm.} 12 lb. + 359·0 + (1350) = 359·0 + (1350)
           1 ,, + 30·0 + (112·5) = 30·0 + (112·5)
                       142·5 cu. ft.   142·5 cu. ft.

At 60° F. and 30 in.} 12 lb. + 378·0 + (1421) = 378·0 + (1421)
           1 ,, + 31·5 + (118·4) = 31·5 + (118·4)
                       149·9 cu. ft.   149·9 cu. ft.

Composition of flue gases (by volume).

$$CO_2\% = \frac{30·0 \times 100}{142·5} = 21·0 \qquad\qquad N_2\% = \frac{112·5 \times 100}{142·5} = 79·0.$$

The volume (or weight) of oxygen or air for any fuel will be arrived at by the sum of the volumes (or weights) required by the ultimate constituents per lb. in the case of solid or liquid fuels, and in the case of gaseous fuels from the like quantities required for the separate combustible gaseous constituents per cubic foot of the whole gas.

In regard to gases Haslam has shown that it is approximately true that the theoretical amount of air required for combustion of a fuel is a function of its gross calorific value. His equation for calculating the number of cubic feet of air required to burn 1 cubic foot of the gas is:

$$\text{cu. ft. air} = \frac{(\text{B.Th.U.})^{1 \cdot 06} - 52}{100}$$

Where less accuracy is required it can be taken that the heating value of rich fuel gases calculated in terms of heat units per cubic foot of theoretical gas-air mixture is approximately the same, i.e. 100 B.Th.U. The relationship is less true in regard to low-grade gases, e.g. it is about 87 B.Th.U. for water gas and 65 for producer gas.

The It Diagram. A more precise relationship than that of Haslam is contained in the It (heat content-temperature) diagrams of Rosin which are based on two facts.

(1) Statistical relationships exist between the net calorific value of all industrial fuels, their air requirements, and the volume of combustion gases which they give.

(2) Equal heat contents of the theoretical combustion gas per unit volume correspond to equal temperatures.

The heat content of the combustion gas as formed can, therefore, be obtained without calculation from ultimate analyses or fuel gas composition. Also, the combustion gas temperature can be derived from its heat content, or vice versa. Tables of air requirements, and volumes and heat contents of the combustion gases from all fuels, are available and the It diagrams to which they apply (*Tech. Data on Fuel*, 1950, 431–55). These include data for combustion with oxygen or oxygen-enriched air, with which the dissociation factor has obviously a greater effect. The air diagrams are also corrected for diffusion.

In using the diagrams for designing furnaces or combustion appliances a figure for excess air must be assumed, while in practical tests the excess air is calculated in the usual way from the composition of the waste gases. Where the gross calorific value only of the fuel is known the net value must be obtained by calculation (p. 29).

The tables of " Technical Data " also relate to the complete combustion of fuels at atmospheric pressure with air and increasing percentages of oxygen up to pure oxygen. The total heat content in the combustion gases is the sensible heat plus the latent heat of dissociation of CO_2 and H_2O, neglecting that of N_2 and the formation of traces of NO. This varies with oxygen content and with a factor r depending upon the fuel C/H ratio and equal to the ratio $CO_2/(CO_2 + H_2O)$ in the undissociated gas. The method of calculation of the true composition of the dissociated gas is too complicated for discussion here and reference should be made to the original papers or to *Technical Data*. As an example of the variation of total heat in the undissociated gases, the following example is quoted of the data for solid and liquid fuels.

TABLE IX

It Diagram Typical Data

B.Th.U. per " n " cu. ft. of Combustion Gas ($r = 0.75$)

Temp. °C.	Air	$O_2 = 60\%$	$O_2 = 100\%$	
1500	66	80	91	Total heat
	—	1	2	Latent heat
2000	96	121	141	Total heat
	7	14	18	Latent heat
2500	151	207	264	Total heat
	36	70	105	Latent heat

The true gas composition is calculable from a knowledge of the dissociation constants of the constituent gases involved. An example of the differences to be expected, which depend upon r and temperature and the percentage of oxygen, is as follows for anthracite ($r = 0.8$) :

Undissociated Gas—Air . . . . CO_2 18.25, H_2O 4.55, N_2 77.2%
 ,,   ,, —Oxygen . . ,, 80.0 , ,, 20.0 , — %

Dissociated Gas	° C.	CO_2	CO	H_2O	H_2	OH	O_2	O	H	N_2
Air	1500	18.1	0.1	4.3	0.1	0.2	0.04	—	—	77.1
	2000	16.0	1.7	4.0	0.1	0.5	0.9	—	—	76.8
	2000	10.0	7.2	2.9	0.2	2.0	3.3	0.9	0.4	73.1
Oxygen . .	1500	79.6	0.3	19.9	—	0.1	0.2	—	—	—
	2000	73.0	4.7	19.0	0.2	1.1	2.0	—	—	—
	2500	49.0	20.0	13.0	0.7	5.3	9.5	1.8	0.5	—

These values illustrate the very considerable allowances which must be made in the calculation of available heat at the high temperatures at which dissociation is well advanced.

LITERATURE

The above is only a very brief summary of the varied properties and the many facts which must be known to the modern fuel technologist. It is essential for his daily work and the many calculations involved that he should have available a general data book but should refer to original papers for new data ; this is particularly important in the field of gaseous combustion where there is presently considerable activity. The general data book recommended is *Technical Data on Fuel*, published by The British National Committee of the World Power Conference, and kept up to date by continuous revision.

CHAPTER III

WOOD, PEAT, AND MINOR SOLID FUELS

Classification of Fuels. Fuels are employed in the solid, liquid and gaseous condition. The solid fuels are essentially naturally occurring materials, principally wood, peat, and coal, although for special purposes they are carbonized for the production of charcoal and coke. Liquid fuels are mostly direct natural products, such as the petroleum oils, but considerable quantities are obtained as the result of destructive distillation of solid fuels (tars, etc.). Gaseous fuels occur naturally locally as natural gas, but are also the result of destructive distillation of solid fuels (coal gas, coke oven gas) or liquid fuels (oil gas), or the result of the incomplete combustion of solid fuels in gas producers either by an air blast (producer gas), steam (water gas), or a combination of air and steam (semi-water gas).

With such a large variety of materials available classification is difficult, but the following is a general scheme.

GENERAL SCHEME OF CLASSIFICATION OF FUELS

Natural or "stored" fuels	Unchanged	Wood ; spent tan ; coconut shells, etc. Fatty oils—fish, palm, etc. Natural gas.
	Metamorphosed	Peat (slightly). Coal (in varying degree). Mineral oils (completely).
Prepared fuels	By destructive action of heat on natural fuels	Charcoal, coke. Tars, benzole (shale oil). Coal and coke oven gas.
	By " limited " combustion	Producer gas ; water gas.
	By fermentation	Ethyl alcohol.
	By synthesis	Methyl and ethyl alcohol, motor spirit.
	By hydrogenation	Motor spirit ; tetralin.

The chief solid fuels are as follows :

Wood	Wood charcoal
Peat	Peat charcoal / Briquettes
Lignites and coal . . .	Coke / Briquetted fuels

In addition to the above fuels, relatively small amounts of various waste materials are frequently available locally in certain industries—spent tan, bagasse (the residue of canes after sugar extraction), Nile sud, coconut and other nut shells, etc.

WOOD

Composition and Thermal Value of Wood.   The abundance of wood throughout man's existence, its comparatively rapid growth and reproduction, and the ease of obtaining supplies, naturally made it one of the earliest and most generally used of all fuels.   At the present time it is only of importance as a fuel in countries where forests still remain and other fuels (coal, oil) are not readily available.

The combustible portion of all woods consists of a modified form of cellulose, *lignin*, which contains a higher percentage of carbon and oxygen than the cellulose from which it was derived.   Cellulose approximates to the empirical formula $n(C_6H_{10}O_5)$, the percentage composition being $C = 44.4$; $H = 6.2$; $O = 43.4$ per cent.   In   many   woods,   more particularly the coniferous, considerable quantities of resinous substances of much higher calorific value than lignin are found.   In cellulose the hydrogen and oxygen are present in the proportions existing in water—in other words, as far as calorific effect is concerned the hydrogen is negligible, and the heating value is dependent on the carbon and any resinous constituents present.   The average calorific value of cellulose is 4150 calories per g. (7500 B.Th.U. per lb.).

The average composition and thermal value of dry wood is given in Table X.

TABLE X

Composition and Calorific Value of Dry Woods

	Lb. per cu. ft.	Carbon.	Hydrogen.	Oxygen.	Ash.	Calories per g.	B.Th.U. per lb.
Ash	46	49·2	6·3	43·9	0·6	4450	8000
Beech . . .	43	49·1	6·1	44·2	0·6	4500	8100
Elm	35	48·9	6·2	44·2	0·5	4470	8040
Oak	52	50·2	6·0	43·4	0·4	4360	7850
Fir . . .· .	—	50·4	5·9	43·4	0·3	4770	8580
Pine	30	50·3	6·2	43·1	0·4	4820	8680

In general, resinous woods such as fir, pine, etc., exhibit a higher calorific value, a pine knot for example giving about 6005 calories (10,860 B.Th.U.).

Even *dry* wood, therefore, is but a poor fuel from the point of view of thermal value.   In practice it would normally be used in air-dried condition containing 10 to 15 per cent. of moisture when its calorific value would be correspondingly lower than those of Table X.   When freshly cut, the moisture content is much higher, and varies over quite a wide range from 25 per cent. in willow to 50 in poplar.   Moisture content also varies with the season of cutting.

Wood is therefore a very variable fuel so far as heating value is concerned and its present-day usage is largely limited to places where better fuels are expensive and to domestic heating where its ready ease of ignition, pleasant burning quality, and freedom from ash, make it a popular fuel in certain circumstances.

For burning in the open fire the quality of wood logs depends partly upon whether they are green or dry. A quite general appreciation is as follows :

	Green.	Dry.		Green.	Dry.
Ash	excellent	excellent	Elm	poor	sparks
Oak	slow	good	Holly	good	excellent
Beech	slow	good	Larch	scented	sparks
Birch	good	too fast	Yew	good	good
Chestnut . . .	poor	too slow	Fir	poor	poor
Pear	good	scented	Apple	good	excellent
Cherry . . .	good	scented	Hawthorn . . .	poor	slow

Wood has been used in emergency for the production of town gas. Dry firwood, carbonized at 1200° C., will yield 30,000 cu. ft. of gas per ton, at a gross calorific value of 360 B.Th.U. per cu. ft., or 108 therms.

The composition of the gas is CO_2 13, C_nH_m 2, CO 24, H_2 45, CH_4 15, N_2 1 per cent.

The yield of charcoal is about 20 per cent. of the dry wood.

Wood, and more especially hard wood, is used successfully for the manufacture of producer gas. The producers are of special design and will treat wood up to 50 per cent. moisture content. A typical wood producer gas has a calorific value of 143 B.Th.U. per cu. ft. and contains CO_2 9, CO 25, H_2 10, CH_4 3, and N_2 53 per cent.

Wood Charcoal. Wood charcoal is obtained by the destructive distillation of wood which, if carried to completion, leaves a residue retaining the original shape and structure of the wood, and which consists almost entirely of carbon. In practice, distillation is carried out at a relatively low temperature of about 600° C. and the charcoal contains about 2 per cent. of residual hydrogen.

The loss on distillation is high, only about 20 per cent. of the air-dry wood is recovered as charcoal, but since this has lost the high proportion of combined oxygen the calorific value is high, of the order of 14,500 B.Th.U. per lb.

Charcoal was formerly a fuel of great importance in the metallurgical field, but has now been replaced by coke in all but special applications because of shortage of supply. Its main usage to-day is in the sorption of gases or vapours in purification plant and for the recovery of solvents from gas or air streams in industry. It is also used in the treatment of solutions (or effluents) for the removal of noxious constituents or colouring matter by sorption.

Production of Charcoal. This was at one time carried out entirely by restricted combustion in heaps, a portion of the wood furnishing the necessary heat for the carbonization of the remainder. This process is necessarily wasteful, the yield seldom exceeding 15 per cent., and at present it is confined to countries where waste is not considered or where deforestation is a desired object. If the wood had a calorific value (dry) of 8500 B.Th.U., the yield of charcoal was 20 per cent., and of the high calorific value of 13,000 B.Th.U., the percentage of heat units remaining in the product would be about 30.

The production of charcoal by dry distillation of wood in closed retorts, externally heated, enables valuable by-products to be recovered. Where charcoal production is the primary object the distillation is carried out at a high temperature, and the liquid distillate is Stockholm tar or wood creosote, which, owing to its great preservative value, is employed widely for creosoting timber.

Distillation of wood, however, is now largely practised, especially in the United States, more particularly for the valuable liquid products, and charcoal is the by-product. In order not to impair the value of these products the temperature employed is lower than for complete carbonization. In practice oil-heated retorts are used with an initial temperature of 200° C. and finishing temperature 330–340° C. The yield of the various products per cord of wood (4000 lb.) is :

Turpentine	.	.	.	.	.	.	.	40 gallons
Light oils	.	.	.	.	.	.	.	16 ,,
Heavy oils	.	.	.	.	.	.	.	128 ,,
Charcoal .	.	.	.	.	.	.	.	950 lb.

In addition to the liquid products of distillation, large volumes of gas are liberated of the composition CO_2 30, C_nH_m 8, CO 35, H_2 11, CH_4 12, and N_2 4 per cent.

The chemicals and solvents obtained vary in yield with the type of wood distilled ; typical yields are shown in Table XI.

TABLE XI

PRODUCTS FROM WOOD DISTILLATION

Products.	Rich wood (4 cords = 16,600 lb.).	Lean wood (4 cords = 16,000 lb.).
Charcoal	4280 lb.	4400 lb.
Refined turpentine	42 gal.	22 gal.
Pine oil	12 ,,	4 ,,
Resin spirit	21 ,,	12 ,,
Resin oil	140 ,,	65 ,,
Creosote oil	45 ,,	21 ,,
Wood alcohol	6 ,,	10 ,,
Calcium acetate (80 per cent.) . . .	300 lb.	350 lb.
Pitch	1400 ,,	625 ,,

Composition and Properties of Charcoal. Charcoal is used as a fuel in the form in which it is produced, but for use as an adsorbent or purifier, it may be granulated in specific size grades or even pelleted. It is a fibrous black solid of distinctly friable character. It is light and porous and, owing to its very large surface area, has a high adsorptive capacity for gases. The surface area varies considerably, up to 10,000 m.^{2} per g., but is usually within the limits of 150 to 450 m.^{2} per g. Coal varies from 20 to 200 m.^{2} per g.

After the 1914–18 war special attention was directed by the French Government to the production of charcoal for use in small portable producers for driving automobiles with producer gas. The utilization of waste wood in the French forests was expected to replace an appreciable amount of the imported petrol. Governmental support gave an impetus in 1927 to the building of portable kilns and the design of producer-driven vehicles in France. Such vehicles are also of interest in our colonies where wood is available in quantity. Information regarding progress in this direction is available in the Reports of the Rallyées des Carburants Nationaux of the Automobile-Club de France. At this stage it was found that 16 lb. of charcoal were equivalent to one gallon of petrol, a motor lorry, for example, using 0·24 lb. of charcoal per ton-mile as against 0·144 lb. petrol.

During the last war a considerable impetus was given to the design of better road producers and to the production of reactive cokes as an alternative to charcoal. A new cross-draught producer was designed which, with a sisal or slag-wool filter, and a steam-air blast, gave a very satisfactory performance with no more engine wear than was found with petrol.

In this producer, charcoal gave the following performance in comparison with a graded anthracite, using a 3-ton Bedford lorry fully loaded. The size grading of the fuel was 1¼ to ¼ in. Comparison is made with an anthracite specially graded and activated for the same purpose. The charcoal was delivered in 3 to ¼-in. pieces, and when graded to the desired size of 1¼ to ¼ in. gave a yield of 80 per cent. The graded material had a moisture content 5·6 per cent., and its volatile matter and ash content were 16·9 and 2·3 per cent. respectively. This volatile matter is rather high for this purpose since the tar formed on combustion can give trouble in filtration of the gas. The potential tar was actually 32 oz. per ton, but was found to be controllable during an observation period of 1250 miles. The bulk density was 12 lb. per cu. ft., the C.A.B. value 0·007 (very low) and the calorific value 13,700 B.Th.U. per lb. dry.

	Ignition time (sec.).	Engine on gas (min.).	Lb./mile.	Average speed (m.p.h.).
Charcoal	20	1–2	1·35	24·3
Progasite	30	2	1·32	23·6

Time in gear, per cent. :	I.	II.	III.	IV.
Charcoal	0·2	13·0	27·1	59·1
Progasite	0·3	14·4	31·5	53·8

Gas analysis:	CO$_2$.	CO.	H$_2$.	N$_2$.	B.Th.U./ cu. ft.
Charcoal . .	1·6	32·4	13·0	53·0	145
Progasite . .	4·1	28·3	9·7	57·9	121

The general behaviour of the fuel was very satisfactory, confirming the fact that good charcoal is an excellent material for motor traction in areas where petrol is either expensive or difficult to obtain or good hardwood and suitable labour are readily available.

Over the same course the corresponding figures for petrol were as follows :

Average speed, 29·4 m.p.h. Petrol consumption, 12 m.p.g.
Time in gear 1, nil ; gear 2, 1·0 ; gear 3, 4·5 ; gear 4, 94·5 per cent.

PEAT

Importance of Peat. It is estimated that the stored reserves of peat in the world are approximately one-sixtieth of those of coal. These are, however, being worked at a rate which is less in proportion, and their utilization could be increased with advantage. This is particularly true in countries such as Russia and Eire, where the reserves are considerable and coal has to be imported. Production is most advanced in Russia where about 10 million tons of air-dried peat are now produced per annum.

In Europe the peat areas are estimated at 140 million acres. In Great Britain there are several million acres of varying depths, probably 6 million acres to a depth of 30 ft. In practice it would not be economical to recover all this peat and it is considered at present that probably only one million acres could be exploited, and to a depth of 6 ft. This would recover, however, some 1000 million tons of air-dried peat containing 25 per cent. of moisture, which would be a considerable contribution to fuel production.

The utilization of peat on any appreciable scale is mainly dependent on the cost of excavation and handling of the very large quantities of very wet raw material and the removal of the large excess of water which is at present a necessary preliminary to the usage of the peat as a fuel.

A comprehensive review of the position in Great Britain is available in a special Report of the Fuel Research Station, " The Harvesting and Winning and Utilization of Peat " (H.M. Stationery Office, 1948).

Formation of Peat. It is usual to distinguish between bog peats and forest peats. In the former, principally found in high altitudes, the main contributors to the decayed vegetation are the smaller forms of vegetation. These form the main deposits in Great Britain and Northern Europe and in Canada and Siberia. The latter are formed mainly from tree growths and therefore occur chiefly in the dense forests of the tropical and sub-tropical rain belts.

In the bog, peat consists of partially-decomposed vegetable matter, the result of luxuriant growth of lower forms of plant life, mostly mosses, under such favourable conditions as high moisture and temperate climate. While the lower part of the stem dies off, the upper part continues its growth, so that in the course of time a thick deposit results ; as the under portions become buried deeper and deeper in the swamp, decomposition through bacterial and other agencies progresses. The result is that whilst the upper parts of the bed are a matted, water-saturated sponge, the lower portions have largely lost their vegetable characteristics, and have become a semi-solid brown to black mass, in which greatly disintegrated vegetable structure is visible under the microscope.

Forest peats are different in character as coming mainly from the decay of tree growths under high-temperature conditions. It is considered that it is this material which formed the basis of the main deposits of carboniferous coals.

Other influences such as the inorganic matter present, the acidity of the mass, and the presence of bacteria and fungi, have produced types of peat which show characteristic differences. " Fen peat " has been formed in a basic environment from material containing alkaline mosses. " Moor, bog and moss peats " have been formed in an acid environment due to the development of organic acids. These may be divided into :

Valley peat collected in water, blanket moss formed on high moorland with an abundant rainfall, and hill peat similar to blanket moss but formed under condition of better drainage.

Moisture in Peat. It is apparent that the moisture content in an undrained bog must be very high ; and in fact the amount of solid matter is not much more than 5 to 8 per cent. When drained, however, the solid content can be raised to 12 per cent. when the upper parts can be cut by hand into blocks and air-dried to give a bulky and porous fuel. Hand-cut sods will usually contain from 88 to 90 per cent. of water. P. Purcell in the Report of the Director of Fuel Research (H.M. Stationery Office, London, 1922–3) defines *water/dry peat* ratios as follows :

Very wet peat	19
Undrained bog	13–14
Cut peat	9
Lowest for raw peat	6–7
Air-dried peat	0·33

These ratios show clearly the amounts of water associated with, say, one ton of dry peat at different stages. Raw peat consists of two distinct materials, plant residues and peat humus. The latter swells greatly in water but forms a hard mass on drying. Shrinkage is prevented in the hand-cut peat by the presence of plant remains, but when these are macerated in the case of machine-cut peat greater shrinkage becomes possible and the fuel becomes denser. In addition, the humus after drying will no longer absorb water to the same extent. The increase of density may be as much as from 0·4 to 0·8.

On complete air-drying, peat reaches an equilibrium with the air at from 13 to 18 per cent. of moisture. In practice the water content is seldom below 20 per cent. and the inner portions of the blocks of peat seldom reach so low a figure. It has been estimated that, for domestic requirements, the moisture content should not exceed 30–35 per cent. and, for industrial purposes, not more than 30 per cent.

Winning and Harvesting of Peat. Peat is still won by the old-established method of hand-cutting because of local markets and cheap labour in country districts. In Ireland, for example, out of 5 million tons produced in 1948 only 100,000 tons were obtained by mechanical means. The method suited for full-scale production is machine-excavation, maceration of the product, the spreading of the paste on a drying-ground and the final collection and stacking of rectangular blocks, the spreading of these on a drying floor, and the final collection and stacking of the air-dried blocks.

Hand-cut peat dries more slowly than macerated peat but drying can be accelerated by building the blocks into heaps as soon as they can be handled, the blocks being arranged so as to give maximum access of air. In this way the drying time can be reduced to about half. Even then the relative drying times are 30 to 60 days in favour of macerated peat.

The moisture content of peat cannot be reduced by pressure ; a pressure of 800 lb. per sq. in. will not reduce the water content below 75 per cent. and any filter medium is rapidly choked by colloidal matter. The use of steam helps only a little. It is for these reasons that the chief mechanical method has become maceration and air-drying.

The excavating machine is a rotating chain of scrapers which dredge a layer of peat from the inclined face of the bog and feed it to the macerator. The finely-divided product is extruded, cut into blocks, and spread by conveyer on the surface of the bog. Drying takes about 6 to 7 weeks in Eire. The finished blocks are 10 in. long by $2\frac{1}{4}$ in. across and weigh 1·75 lb. In Russia the layers are spread at an original thickness of 20 cm. and after drying to the following schedule are approx. $25 \times 5 \times 5$ cm., weighing 0·7 kg.

	Start.	Turning.	Stacks of five.	Heaps.	Dumps.
Moisture per cent. .	88	84	79	70–50	25
Time (days) . . .	—	7–12	7–10	14	28–36 Total
Shrinkage V_o/V_t . .	0	1·5	2·6	3·4–4·0	4·3

Other processes which are less well developed are that of Milled Peat, and the Peco and Hydro-Peat processes.

In the Milled Peat process, half-inch layers of peat are milled from the surface of the bog by a machine and allowed to air-dry with occasional harrowing. After a few hours the moisture content falls to 45 per cent. and the peat may then be briquetted or used directly as a power-station fuel. In the Peco process the milled peat at 50 per cent. moisture is dried to about 10 per cent. moisture and briquetted warm at a pressure of 5 tons per sq. in. Fuel consumption in the process is about 20 per cent. of the material treated. In the Hydro-Peat process high-pressure water jets wash the peat from the bog and spread the pulp on a cambered surface to assist drainage. Pumping is easy at 5 per cent. solids and the depth of layer is about 8 in. After a few days the plastic mass can be cut into sods for drying. Three crops can be obtained in a season. The addition of gypsum is stated to accelerate drying.

An adequate survey is a necessary part of the preliminary work of peat winning by mechanical means since drainage can be an expensive operation in many cases. In Eire in 1948 the average drainage cost was about £27 per acre.

Physical and Chemical Properties of Peat. The composition of the peat substance, i.e. with water and ash eliminated, varies over only a moderate range. The following data are mainly from analyses by Bunte on Bohemian peats, and by Brame on British peats.

	Limit.	Average.
Carbon	56–63	57·5
Hydrogen	5·7–6·3	6·1
Sulphur	0·6–1·0	—
Nitrogen	1·3–2·7	—
Oxygen	31–38	34·9

An analysis of a typical Irish Peat is given in Fuel Research Technical Paper 4 (1921) as carbon, 60·1 ; hydrogen, 5·8 ; sulphur, 0·6 ; nitrogen, 1·4 ; oxygen, 32·1 per cent.

The mineral matter in peat is uniformly distributed ; dirt bands are not present as in coal seams. The amount is variable ; it is exceptional to find less than 3 per cent., but not uncommon for over 10 per cent. to be present, most of which is undoubtedly due to infiltration. The lower layers will contain usually high ash as compared with the upper felted peat.

The volatile matter in peat varies with its position in the bog. Purcell gives an example for different Irish peats :

	Volatile matter	Ash.
Brown peat, Ticknevin	67·2	1·0
Black ,, ,, ...	65	7·8
Dense black peat	65·5	7·1
Light fibrous peat, Denbigh Moor . .	70·4	0·7
Dense black peat ,, ,, .	61·8	15·2

The calorific value of dry peat of normal ash content varies between the limits of 9000 and 9500 B.Th.U. per lb. In practice the high moisture of air-dried peat does not make this heat fully available and as a fuel it suffers in comparison with bituminous coal of, say, 8 per cent. moisture.

The specific gravity of air-dried peat varies with the method of its preparation. Hand-cut peat varies from 0·25 to 0·7 with an average of 0·5. Macerated peat varies from 0·85 to 1·0.

The bulk density of coal is from 45 to 48 lb. per cu. ft. In comparison, peat is 20 lb. or 2½ times as bulky, an important factor in transport costs.

Utilization of Peat. In Great Britain the main use of peat has been as a domestic fuel although considerable experiment has been made in Eire to develop its use for steam-raising. Other uses have been as cattle litter and as a soil ameliorant, for thermal insulation and packing, and for gas purification. On the Continent there has been much greater utilization for steam raising in power stations and in locomotives.

Peat is an excellent fuel for the open domestic grate. It is easy to ignite, burns freely with a low rate of supply of primary air, and gives a pleasant fire with long flames. The rate of radiation is lower than with coal bulk for bulk. Other domestic appliances such as cookers and slow-combustion stoves are being developed by the Industrial Council of Eire. One aspect of the use of peat in the home is that its low bulk density makes it require 2½ times as much storage space as coal.

There are three methods by which peat is utilized for steam generation on the Continent.

(1) Combustion under boilers of peat blocks or coarse powder.
(2) Combustion as dried pulverized fuel.
(3) Complete gasification in producers with combustion of the gas under boilers.

In the U.S.S.R. a considerable proportion of the electrical power stations are operating on either hydro-peat or milled peat at reported high efficiencies. In recent stations of large output (200,000 kW.) hydro-peat is burned in water-tube boilers using a Marakev shaft-chain grate which is a combination of gas-producer and a chain grate. The best results have been obtained at 30 per cent. moisture content. For burning milled peat the Shirshnev grate is used in which the peat, flowing from the top of the combustion chamber, is maintained in suspension in preheated air until combustion is complete.

Steam-raising with peat briquettes has been successfully applied in Germany. Recent experiments in Eire have employed " Turbine " furnaces with forced-draught fans and have achieved efficiencies of 61 per cent. At the Fuel Research Station an equivalent evaporation of 5·18 lb. of water has been obtained at an efficiency of 65·4 per cent. The additional labour required to maintain the rated capacity of the boiler was noticeable and could be an important drawback in handling peat.

As pulverized fuel, peat has been used with success in locomotive-firing. The Swedish State Railways report 4·7 lb. of steam per lb. of peat having

a calorific value of 7740 B.Th.U. per lb.   The pulverization of peat is more
difficult than of coal owing to the presence of fibrous material which has
to be withdrawn from the system.   For this reason and since the load
on the drier is so much heavier, it seems unlikely that this technique will
be adopted to any large extent.

The combination of producer gas and steam raising has been successfully demonstrated in Eire using Wollaston producers in association with
shell-type boilers.   This producer is fixed in front of the boiler and the hot
producer gas (900° F.) passes directly into the combustion chamber.   In
one trial 3·76 lb. of steam were raised from the boiler and 0·31 lb. from the
jacket of the producer, making 4·07 lb. per lb. of peat or 75·4 per cent.
efficiency.   Ammonia recovery is an important feature of the use of gas
producers for power purposes and peat, with a nitrogen content of 1·5 per
cent., is giving a recovery of 75 lb. per ton in large Mond producers.   The
other yields, calculated to a basis of dry peat, are as follows :

		Per metric ton (dry peat substance).
Cubic feet of gas at 0° C. and 760 mm. .	. .	99,000
Calorific value per cubic foot .	. . . .	157 B.Th.U.
Tar	. . .	110 lb.
Calcium acetate	. .	9 ,,

Taking 8500 B.Th.U. per h.p.hr., the gas would produce electrical energy
at the rate of 1·6 lb. of dry peat per kWh.

Carbonization of Peat and Peat Coke.   The denser forms of air-
dried peat lend themselves to gasification in retorts and several processes
have been proposed to recover those products of distillation which would
otherwise be lost when the peat is burned as a fuel.   These have been
carried out on a moderate scale in Europe for the recovery of peat coke for
metallurgical purposes and gas producers, but no applications have been
made in Great Britain.

Since peat has no binding properties the material must be fed in lump
form in order to produce a sized coke.   This coke is denser than the original
peat and has a high mechanical strength.   This, and high reactivity, make
it valuable for some metallurgical processes, particularly where a low sulphur
content is desirable.

The yields of peat coke and other products vary quite considerably with
different forms of peat as shown in the following table of Gray-King assay
tests.

Sample.	Somerset.	Devon.	Scotland.	Eire.
Coke, cwt. . .	6·2	5·2	6·7	6·1
Tar, gal. . . .	18·7	34·7	20·2	18·2
Liquor, gal. . .	95·1	94·6	96·0	98·2
Gas, cu. ft. . .	4,790	4,620	3,960	4,330

These tests were made on peat containing 30 per cent. of moisture ;

similar yields would be obtained on a large scale with the exception of the tar, which would be about 70 per cent. of the assay yield.

Peat tar is a thick semi-solid material which on distillation yields paraffin wax, oils, tar-acids and pitch. Yields per ton of air-dried peat would be, oils 8 to 15 gal., tar-acids 2 to 3 gal., wax 6 to 12 lb., pitch 40 to 50 lb. The liquor would yield ammonium sulphate 8 to 12 lb., methyl alcohol 10 to 15 lb., acetone 8 to 12 lb., acetic acid 10 to 15 lb.

Experiments on the production of town gas are described in Fuel Research Technical Paper 4 (1921). Irish block peat was carbonized in Glover–West continuous vertical retorts and gave very satisfactory results. At a carbonizing temperature of 980° C. a throughput of 4 tons per retort per day was achieved. The rated throughput of these retorts on coal is 2·5 tons per day. The gas is low in yield and has also so low a calorific value that in industry it would require enrichment before it could be suitable for town use. The yields were as follows, the coke was hard, dense and reactive and had a calorific value of 12,600 B.Th.U. per lb. dry.

Carbonizing temperature			980° C.	850° C.
Yields per ton of peat (20 per cent. H_2O)—				
Coke	.	cwt.	5·4	5·4
Gas .	.	cu. ft.	14,900	13,760
,, .	.	B.Th.U.	325	340
,, .	.	therms	48·4	46·8
Tar .	.	gal.	12·6	21·3

Other Uses for Peat. Peat has a number of uses which are not associated with its fuel value but which could contribute to a production scheme. It is a satisfactory cattle litter in the form of peat moss. In horticulture it is a useful soil ameliorant. Wax of the Montan type (ester wax) can be extracted in fair yield from certain types of peat. The yields vary very widely from 3 to 19 per cent. by weight of the dry peat from British sources, the best yields being obtained from heather peats. The best solvent is a mixture of benzene and ethyl alcohol. The extracted peat would of course still be a satisfactory fuel. The high commercial value of such wax (about £70 per ton) might well assist peat-production schemes.[1]

Ethyl alcohol can be obtained by the hydrolysis of peat with dilute sulphuric acid, neutralization with lime and fermentation with yeast. So far the process has proved too costly for industrial application.

MINOR SOLID FUELS

As these are closely allied to either wood or peat, consisting chiefly of cellulose, they may be considered here conveniently.

Bagasse is a fuel of considerable importance in cane-sugar-producing countries, and consists of the residual crushed cane after the extraction of

[1] See also lignite, page 119.

the juices. It is usually burnt under boilers on the sugar plantations but could have wider applications if it could be made available in a portable form, either baled or briquetted. Attempts are being made to expand its use by increasing the fuel efficiency of sugar plants to make more bagasse available, and either baling this in a machine working on the principle of the hay press, or briquetting it in a press of the type used for brown coal (p. 118). The working of 130,000 tons of cane will give 100,000 tons of wet bagasse, which on fermentation during storage for some months will

Fig. 5.—Ward Bagasse Furnace.

dry to 10 to 15 per cent. moisture. The briquetting proposals are not yet satisfactory but baling is ; the baling machine used is capable of producing 50 tons per hr. of fairly solid material in sections 1 ft. square by 2 ft. long and weighing 90 to 100 lb. When used for firing locomotives the blocks are broken by hand into flat layers of about 2 in. in thickness.

The fermented bagasse, at 15 per cent. moisture content, contains about 60 per cent. of fibrous material and about 15 per cent. of residual sugar and has a calorific value of about 3800 cal. per g. at an ash content of 2 per cent. It is easily ignited and is very free-burning.

On the plantation the raw bagasse is consumed for steam raising in its air-dried condition in very modern equipment. In this form it is in narrow strips 3 to 8 in. in length and containing about 45 per cent. of moisture.

For efficient combustion it requires a special form of furnace, but this can be used with water-tube boilers of standard type. The common furnace was formerly of the horseshoe Dutch-oven type, but this has been modernized to the Ward type as shown in Figure 5. Other furnaces such as the step-grate type are also in use. In the modernized horseshoe type the fibre stalks are charged on to the hearth so as to form a cone about 5 ft. in height. Combustion takes place round the edges of the cone, using both primary and secondary air at 1 to 2 in. pressure. The ash collects on the hearth and is removed at intervals of about 24 hours.

Boilers are normally of the Babcock water-tube types; they may be quite large, up to 60,000 lb. of steam per hour at 600 lb. pressure, and may be equipped with economizers and superheaters in the usual way. In some cases they have arrangements for auxiliary firing with oil fuel for use in times of shortage of bagasse.

Rice Husks. This material, like bagasse, has a considerable fuel value at the centres of production of the crops, and furnaces have been developed for their efficient combustion in order to provide heat for the drying of the rice crops. The material is high in ash content and burns unevenly except in these furnaces. Despite this failing, the surplus finds some application in domestic cooking appliances.

Some 10,000 quintals (1000 tons) of husks are produced in the winning of 56,000 q. of rice. At a mean calorific value of 3500 cal. per g. 3 kg. of husks will dry 1 kg. of rice paddy so that the saving of coke by using husks can be as much as 2 cwt. of coke per ton of rice made.

Using a sloping grate for the preliminary drying of the rice hulls, steam-raising furnaces have been designed which have given an output of 2·7 kg. of steam per kilogram of hulls.

Peanuts " hulls " when dry have a calorific value of 4000 cal. per g. and a low bulk density of about 0·08. They can, however, be burned successfully on a mechanical stoker if a high ratio of primary to secondary air is maintained of ten to one. An efficiency of 80 per cent. of the net calorific value can be obtained.

Other Vegetable Wastes. Other vegetable fibres can also be utilized on the site of production. In Java the preparation of 3 tons of usable *sisal* from 100 tons of leaf gives 95 tons of waste material which, after drying in air, forms a reasonable fuel which can be produced at the annual rate of 2 tons per acre under cultivation. The power equivalent of this is about 1200 kWh.

In the Argentine the over-production of *corn*, principally barley, has made it an indigenous fuel for steam raising for the generation of electrical power. In 1941 the Argentine Electric Co. consumed 8 million bushels, and in 1942, 20 million bushels. This material has also been used for the heating of houses. Over-produced maize has been used for the firing of locomotives.

Vegetable Oils for the Diesel Engine. A considerable amount of work has been done to find the best conditions of running a diesel engine on ordinary vegetable oils, the idea being to utilize in this way any over-produced material.

Vegetable oils have a calorific value of only 9200 cal. per g. as compared with 11,000 for petroleum diesel oils, but this is not a serious disability if the engine can be made to run smoothly. It has been found that the only alteration necessary is the provision of a pre-heater to reduce the rather high viscosity of the oil and to prevent separation of solid fatty acids. With this provision, good results, and even easy starting, have been obtained with soya-bean, arachis and cotton-seed oils and there is no reason to suppose that other oils would not be equally satisfactory.

Cotton seeds as such have also been used with success in the suction gas producer to give a power output of one b.h.p. hr. per 2·5 to 3·0 lb., a figure which is comparable with that obtained with hard woods.

Town Refuse. The disposal of the waste material from dustbins, etc., is an important sanitary problem, and its destruction by burning in suitable "destructors" is not only a satisfactory method from a sanitary point of view, but can generally become remunerative when the heat is utilized for steam raising. As an adjunct to the ordinary boiler plant in electricity generating stations "destructors" have considerably reduced fuel consumption, and with a good type of destructor little nuisance from dust, etc., should be experienced.

Refuse varies considerably in character according to the town, and with the season; the average amount of combustible matter for London is stated to be about 38 per cent.

	Winter.	Summer.
Fine dust	35	17
Fuel cinders	32	15
Putrescent material	9	24
Paper	10	23
Metal	3	5
Rags	1	2
Glass	2	3
Bones	2	1
Miscellaneous	7	9

The raw mixture contains from 10 to 40 per cent. of moisture and has a net calorific value of 3000–4000 B.Th.U. per lb. In the northern towns, where the refuse contains more cinders, the calorific value is higher, 4000–5000 BTh.U per lb.

Several types of refuse destructor have been described by E. W. Smith (*J. Inst. Fuel*, 1932, **6,** 88), who states that thermal efficiencies of over 64 per cent. on the *net* value can be obtained. The thermal losses are waste gases, 18 ; unburned fuel, 7, and radiation, etc., 11 per cent. A modern unit destructor will handle 30 tons of refuse per day. The material is all handled mechanically, passing over magnetic separators to remove iron, and being forcibly charged to the destructor cells which may be either of the high-pressure blast type or the rotary-kiln type. Special grates are generally necessary to dispose of the large proportion of non-combustible matter; these may be rocking or rotatable grates to keep the burning mass in motion. Boilers are of the water-tube type.

It is regrettable that this source of fuel saving is now falling into disuse, probably owing to the high labour cost of collection and separation. In Huddersfield, for example, the raising of steam from 27,000 tons of refuse annually was estimated to save 8000 tons of coal. It is also estimated that the amounts available in cities are about 300,000 tons per million of population, or say 2·4 million tons in Greater London. If this were all dealt with on a fuel-economy basis the saving could be 800,000 tons of coal annually. Nevertheless, in 1951 there were only three waste-heat generating stations altogether representing 4·8 million kWh or 3500 tons of coal, and one of these has since been closed down.

REFERENCES

The Winning, Harvesting and Utilization of Peat (H.M.S.O.), pp. 47–142.
Producer Gas for Road Transport. T. F. Hurley and A. Fitton. *J. Inst. Fuel*, 1947, **21,** 283.
Peat Deposits in Scotland. Geological Survey, Scotland. H.M.S.O. 1943.
Peat Resources of Ireland. Purcell. Fuel Research Board. H.M.S.O. 1920.
Winning, Preparation and Use of Peat in Ireland. H.M.S.O. 1931.
Brown Coal. H. Herman. State Electricity Commission of Victoria. 1952.
Wood Products, Distillates and Extracts. Dumesny and Noyer. Scott Greenwood. 1921.

CHAPTER IV

COAL AND ITS CONSTITUENTS

Coal is a stored fuel, occurring in layers in the earth's crust, which has been formed by the partial decay of plant materials accumulated millions of years ago and further altered by the action of heat and pressure. This definition excludes bituminous shales which contain fuel material, and, to an extent peat. The latter is however generally included in the coal series since it is regarded as the raw material of a stage in the formation of coal.

Two theories have been advanced for the method of accumulation of the plant remains. The first or " in situ " theory holds that the coal seam marks the area in which the original material grew and accumulated. The second or " drift " theory holds that the material was transferred by rivers to a lake or estuary before deposition. Either theory can account for the wide area occupied by seams, for their uniformity of thickness, and for the relative absence of inorganic material.

The best modern example of the in situ theory is the Great Dismal Swamp of North Carolina, which is an area of some 1000 square miles fed by rivers and draining into the sea. Below 15 ft. of water, 10–15 ft. of decaying trees and leaves have collected. Coastal swamps of a similar character are found in many places in the tropics.

The drift method is seen in the large quantities of plant material which are carried downstream by present-day rivers and sometimes deposited near the estuary. Should a swamp be developing at this estuary it is clear that both methods could be operative at the same time.

The drift theory is favoured by the similarity between coal and the sedimentary rocks. During the period of deposition of the plant debris there could be periods during which heavy quantities of mud were carried down to form intervening layers ; this is a feature of many seams. This theory also explains most satisfactorily the occurrence of very thick seams. It has been estimated that from 15 to 20 ft. of vegetable matter is necessary for the production of 3 ft. of peat, or only 1 ft. of coal. When it is realized that many coal seams reach 10 ft. in thickness the immense size of the original deposits of vegetable debris are realized.

Conversion of Vegetable Matter into Coal. On dry ground, fallen vegetable matter is attacked by the oxygen of the air and gradually converted into water and carbon dioxide so that eventually no trace remains. Under water, however, the course of decomposition is different and at first is influenced by the action of bacteria. This action continues until decomposition is complete, or until the products of decay become so concentrated that the action is stopped by the destruction of the bacteria. It is clear that the action could continue longer in a swamp where the acid products of decay are carried away by drainage. A second theory is that the acids may be neutralized by the nature of the associated mineral strata. The course of decay is then, as stated by Mackenzie Taylor, through two courses of bacterial action.

(i) Action not truly anaerobic, leading to the formation of peat.

(ii) Continuous anaerobic fermentation under alkaline conditions leading to the formation of bituminous coal. The alkalinity necessary for absorption of the carbon dioxide produced has been maintained by base exchange in the layer of alkaline clay which Taylor suggests covers every deposit of coal. Differences in the alkalinity of the clays have created the different types of coal recognized ; lignites, where low alkalinity has limited the extent of fermentation, and bituminous coal where the roof is sodium clay of high alkalinity. This theory indicates how all types of coal can be formed without presupposing the aid of high temperatures or pressures.

Certain parts of plants are more resistant to decay than others and in coal these can be recognized as only slightly-altered fragments, particularly spore exines, bark and cuticle.

Fischer and Schrader differed from Taylor in suggesting that the bacterial action converted the cellulose of the plant to gaseous and liquid products, and the lignin to humic substances (coal ulmins), and that it was mainly the latter that became transformed into coal through various stages which could be recognized by high solubility in alkali solution as in brown coals and lignites. Continued transformation then produced bituminous and anthracitic coal, in which the transformed ulmins are no longer alkali-soluble. It is of interest to trace the origin of the term " ulmins ". In Brande's *Manual of Chemistry* (1841) it is stated that " the peculiar brown matter which may be extracted from bog-earth, peat and turf is frequently termed ' humus ' . . . there is also a brown exudation found upon the bark of trees, and especially of the elm, and hence called ' ulmin,' which contains a similar matter combined with potassa . . . by digestion with weak solutions of caustic or carbonated potassa, a brown liquid is obtained from which acid throws down ' ulmin.' "

Whatever may be the truth, it is an experimental fact that coal-like material can be made from both cellulose and lignin. Bergius converted cellulose in the presence of water at 340° C. and at 140 atm. pressure, to a black substance (C 84, H 5, O 11) which in some respects resembled coal. A conclusion from his experiments was that lignin was a transformation product of cellulose. Gropp and Bode in similar work concluded that heat and pressure could convert cellulose to dull coal, and lignin to bright coal. Berl, heating these substances in alkali at 300° to 400° C., concluded that lignites originated from lignin and bituminous coals from cellulose, but the conditions were probably too drastic, as almost any plant material will give a coal-like product under these conditions. They record the fact, however, that cellulose and lignin coals are essentially different as shown below, and it may be that the truth is a matter of degree and that plants rich in cellulose give bituminous coals, while plants rich in lignin resins and waxes lead to lignites.

	Cellulose. coal.	Lignin coal.
Bitumen soluble in benzene	15	0·5 per cent.
Coal yield	33	65 ,,
Phenols in distillation	3·6	0·5 ,,

These artificial coals were not entirely like bituminous coals in being of lower density and in giving rather different products on distillation and an imperfect coke. If there is any conclusion from the work it is that both cellulose and lignin are contributory in coal formation.

It is generally accepted that the action of bacteria was limited to the early stages. Part of the plant substance was severely broken down to simpler substances, but part resisted decay and retained at least some of its identity. The vegetable sludge thus formed was in time converted into peat-like material. At this stage heat and pressure became the operative factors. At the depth of the coal measures, and in the absence of volcanic action, the maximum temperature was probably less than 200° C.; the pressure would be very variable owing to earth movement, but that due to depth alone would be about 1200 lb. per sq. in. per 1000 ft. of depth. Neither factor alone is sufficient to transform peat-like material into coal and a third factor must be the very long period of time to which the decayed vegetable material has been subjected under these conditions.

Support for this theory is found in Hilt's Law (more correctly hypothesis) which observes that, at a given point in a coalfield, carbon content increases and volatile matter decreases, with increase of vertical depth. This observation is certainly general, although there are exceptions. The effect of variation of pressure is seen in regions in which there was, at some time after the vegetable matter was buried, considerable earth movement which set up severe stresses among the rock formations. A good example of this is found in South Wales, where in one seam there is marked lateral change in the degree of coalification which corresponds with depth and with probable earth movement; the greatest changes occur in the areas of most intense disturbance.

A variant of the theory is found in the action of molten volcanic rocks; where these have been in contact with the coal measures the degree of coalification is markedly advanced even to the stage of similarity to anthracite. Naturally such coals are found in isolated places only; the Central Coalfield of Scotland is one.

The increase of carbon content as coalification advances is, of course, accompanied by the gradual decrease of volatile matter of which hydrogen and oxygen are the main components. The decrease of these components through the stages of coal formation is illustrated in Table XII. The accelerated change in the anthracite has been attributed by Roberts to abnormal heating of a local character though not actually by molten rock as in the case of Scottish anthracite.

TABLE XII

STAGES IN COALIFICATION (CARBON = 100)

	Hydrogen.	Oxygen.	Available hydrogen. $\left(\text{Hydrogen} - \dfrac{\text{Oxygen}}{8}\right)$
Cellulose, pure	13·9	111·0	0·0
Wood, average	12 0	88·0	1·0
Peat	10·0	57·0	3·0
Lignite (Khirgis Steppes) . . .	7·8	54·0	1·1
Brown coal (Europe)	7·9	36·0	3·4
Lignite (Europe)	6·9	30·0	3·5
Bituminous coal (Staffs.) . . .	6·0	21·0	3·4
Steam coal (Welsh)	5·0	5·5	4·3
Anthracite (Welsh)	4·75	5·2	4·1
Anthracite (Penns.)	2·8	1·8	2·6
Graphite	0·0	0·0	0·0

The regular progression of these changes is clearly illustrated in Figure 6, given by H. G. A. Hickling (*Trans. Inst. Min. Engs.*, 1926, **72**, 261), where

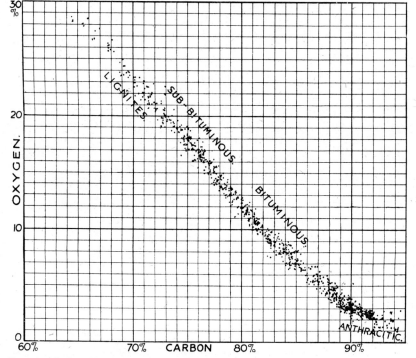

FIG. 6.—Carbon-Oxygen Content of Pure Coal Substance from Lignites to Anthracites (Hickling).

until the anthracite zone is reached, the concentration of the carbon and oxygen may be represented by a straight line. The more rapid concentration in the anthracite region *may* be due to abnormal heating.

These considerations lead to the conclusion that the differences between coal types is due to the following causes :

(1) Differences in the original vegetable matter and its separation by the levigating action of the water.

(2) Differences in the extent of bacterial decay.

(3) Differences in the extent of devolatilization of the decayed material by heat and pressure.

There seems little doubt that these causes all acted together and that the differences now found are the result of variation of the extent to which each cause operated.

There has been considerable difference of opinion regarding which particular substances in the original plant tissues ultimately became coal, but since opinions are based upon the study of coal constitution they are dealt with later in the course of this discussion. It is important to realize at this stage, that there are certain types of vegetable matter which are more resistant to decay than others, and that the existence of these in coal gives a clue to the origin of the original material. Plant spores are the most resistant, cuticles next and algae least. Certain coals are found to abound in spore remains and fragments of cuticle.

Coal Measures. The consolidation of the coal deposits is best explained by a brief consideration of the earth's geological history. The oldest rocks known—the Archean—were formed largely from molten material derived from some distance down in the earth's crust. The parts exposed at the surface, particularly at higher levels, were gradually broken down and disintegrated by the forces of nature (rain, frost, etc.) and the rock particles so formed were carried to lower levels by rain and rivers. Here they collected and gave rise to a series of sedimentary rocks (sandstones and shales) known as the Cambrian formation. These rocks are variously estimated to have been produced from 400 million to 500 million years ago. Since that time the earth has suffered many upheavals, between each of which the process of disintegration and formation of new rocks has been repeated. Thus, following the Cambrian, were deposited the Ordovician, Silurian, Devonian or Old Red Sandstone, and Carboniferous series of rocks.

Very little evidence of plants is found in the rocks of the Cambrian and immediately following periods, and it is probable that plant life was not then abundant. Later, in the Devonian period, thin seams of coal appear, but it is not until the next or Carboniferous period that the seams become thick. From this period onwards all the stratified formations contain carbonaceous materials, but in Great Britain valuable coal seams are found only in the Carboniferous strata. The coals in later formations are mainly lignitic in character.

During the early part of the Carboniferous period the area occupied by the British Isles was for the most part covered by a deep sea, in which a great thickness of limestone was formed. In central Scotland, however, conditions were somewhat different, for the limestone there contains considerable thicknesses of shales with a number of valuable coal seams—the Limestone Coals. Later, conditions over the whole area became shallower, probably resembling a huge delta, and the massive sandstone known as the Millstone Grit was deposited. The last part of the period was a time of gradual subsidence, with occasional fluctuations and pauses. Sedimentation more or less kept pace with the subsidence, shales and sandstones being formed, but periodically the area was converted into wet muddy flats at about sea-level. Conditions were then similar to those of the Great Dismal Swamp already described : vegetation flourished and the material of the coal seams accumulated. Eventually subsidence continued, and the coal-forming material was buried beneath further sandstones and shales, the process being repeated many times. Gradually, however, the seams became thinner and less frequent, and finally, at the end of the Carboniferous period, the rocks formed were devoid of coal seams. The whole of these coal-bearing rocks are collectively known as the " Coal Measures ".

Types or Species of Coal. Peat is usually considered as outside the true coal series but it must be mentioned at this point as being the parent substance of the coal series. It is considered more fully in Chapter III.

Lignites belong to the Tertiary geological formations and occur widely in Europe, North America and Australia. Only limited deposits are to be found in Great Britain, principally at Bovey Tracy, Devonshire.

Normally they occur in thick seams near the surface and can be quarried at a low cost. Two forms are recognized, brown and earthy, and black and pitchlike. The former contains 30 to 50 per cent. of moisture as mined and is dried and briquetted before use. Black lignite, or sub-bituminous coal in the U.S. classification, differs from the brown variety in showing no obvious woody structure. On exposure to air black lignites oxidize readily and disintegrate and their effective utilization also involves briquetting or carbonization. The black lignites develop through the lignitous coals to the bituminous species, showing from 40 down to 20 per cent. of volatile matter and 84 to 92 per cent. of carbon. As devolatilization proceeds in this direction there is an increase in the ability of the coal to form a hard coke on heating out of contact with air.

The transition from the bituminous coals to anthracite is represented in this country by the steam coals of South Wales, the carbonaceous species. At one end of the scale these coals have marked caking power and those containing 20 per cent. of volatile matter form coking coals. The range from 15 to 10 per cent. volatile matter and 4·5 to 4·0 per cent. hydrogen are steam coals, and household stove coals which are relatively smokeless in burning and yet have free-burning qualities. The last member of the species is anthracite, in which devolatilization has proceeded to such an extent that the product shows less than 8 per cent. of volatile matter. The composition and properties of these types are dealt with more fully later.

One type is rather outside the regular series in containing more hydrogen than normal for its carbon content ; this is *cannel*. Cannel is a dull, hard material composed mainly of only slightly-changed plant remains, which makes it high in volatile matter and yields a higher-than-usual proportion of liquid products (tar) on distillation. A form of cannel, Boghead coal or torbanite, is similar in appearance and properties but, in addition to spore remains, contains a large number of round, flat, yellow bodies which are taken to be the remains of algae.

MACRO- AND MICRO- COMPONENTS OF COAL

Visual examination of coal in the seam or in large pieces shows that it is not homogeneous throughout its mass. With most coals differences in texture are apparent, some bands having a dull and others a bright appearance. These bands may be separated from one another by " dirt " bands or may merge into one another without visible partings. These differences are most marked in the case of bituminous coals but can be traced in lignitous coals, in certain black lignites and, to a less extent, in carbonaceous coals. The macroscopic constituents in bituminous coal which are identifiable by eye have been termed by Stopes vitrain, clarain, durain and fusain, and by Thiessen, anthraxylon (vitrain and clarain) and detritus (durain). Similar terms in German nomenclature are glanzkohle, mattkohle and faserkohle.

Vitrain. Vitrain is the bright black brittle coal which normally occurs in very thin bands. It breaks with a conchoidal fracture and, when viewed in very thin sections (0·0005 in.), is generally translucent and amber-red in colour. It is almost free from plant structures but shows a faintly defined cellular structure. A typical thin section of vitrain is shown in Figure 7 (*a*). The cells of vitrain are generally filled with ulmins (see p. 55) and often consist of complete pieces of bark. Bark tissues are more resistant to decay and form a larger proportion of coal than might be expected owing to the fact that bark formed a larger proportion of the tree then than it does now.

Clarain. Clarain is bright black but less bright than vitrain. It is often finely banded so that it tends to break irregularly. In thin sections it shows partly the same appearance as vitrain in thin bands, but these are interbanded with more opaque bands consisting largely of fragmented plant remains among which can be identified cellular material, spore exines and cuticle. A typical clarain structure is shown in Figure 7 (*b*).

Durain. Durain is the dull greyish-black coal which is hard and tough and breaks irregularly. In thin sections it is fairly opaque and shows large and small spore exines and woody fragments in a matrix of opaque grains. Figure 7 (*c*) shows a typical durain structure with large flattened macrospores.

In the coal seam, durain bands are often thick, and can be followed throughout the area of the seam. The fragmentary nature of the plant remains in durains suggests that its origin was the vegetable mud carried into the coal basin by water flow; the presence of a higher proportion of

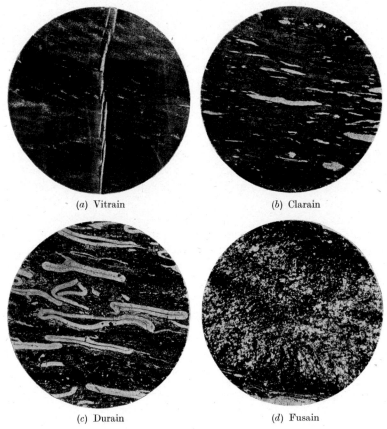

(*a*) Vitrain   (*b*) Clarain

(*c*) Durain   (*d*) Fusain

FIG. 7.—Sections of Bituminous Coal taken perpendicular to the Bedding Plane.
(× 20)

clay supports this. With very high proportions of clay, this material becomes " carbonaceous shale " and with very high proportions of spore material it becomes the variety of coal known as *cannel.*

Fusain. Fusain is the soft black powdery material which occurs in very thin layers in the coal and at which fracture tends to occur. It shows the original cell structure of wood, though considerably deformed, and is considered to be woody fragments which have undergone a different process of decay from the rest of the coal. See Figure 7 (*d*).

Resins. Different woods vary rather widely in their resin content, conifers, for example, being rich. Since resins are resistant to decay they are frequently found as such in coal. In certain lignites and brown coals fragments can readily be separated by hand. In bituminous coals the resinous bodies are normally of microscopic size and can be seen in thin sections as spherical or oval globules of a yellow-red colour. Occasionally it is possible to pick out small fragments of resin.

Spores. It appears certain that the bulk of the plants from which coal was formed were propagated by means of spores, some large (macrospores) and others of microscopic dimensions (microspores). During the process of decay the contents of these spores have disappeared, but the resistant cuticle has survived and can be seen in microsections (Figure 7 c). In transverse section these spore exines appear as flattened double-walled discs having been compressed during the consolidation of the matrix, but in sections along the bedding planes they are nearly circular.

Macerals. The above banded constituents of coal are, by definition, those visible to the unaided eye. The eye is not capable of distinguishing particles of less than 1/500 in. (50 μ) and it is understoood that differences of smaller size may occur. These differences do exist and can be distinguished by the microscope in thin transparent sections. Stopes originally called the components separable by eye " rock " types (U.S. *primary* types), indicating that they were layers of material different to the eye but not necessarily more homogeneous at microscopic level than mineral rock layers such as sandstone or clay. It was not, however, until a much later date (1935) that she actually pointed out the existence of areas within the rock types which differed under the microscope. By analogy with minerals she called these " macerals " and used the term " -inite " to distinguish them from the rock types ending in " -ain ". Thus the chief component of vitrain was *vitrinite*, plant remains *exinite* from spore exines of which they were often composed, and the main component of fusain *fusinite*.

Seyler has since taken the nomenclature a step further in terms of chemical composition and defined three groups of each :

Perhydrous—rich in hydrogen—spore remains, etc., cuticle.
Orthohydrous—medium hydrogen—vitrinite with similar intermediates.
Subhydrous—low in hydrogen—fusinite and similar intermediate bodies.

He states that in vitrinite the structure of the lignified tissues has largely disappeared (collinite) but can sometimes be seen (tellinite). In fusinite the plant structure is very clearly defined. There are many intermediate forms between the two. Micrinite is an opaque granular material characteristic of durain, and is probably a mixture of vitrinite and fusinite in a finely-divided state.

Durain and clarain are therefore complex mixtures of vitrinite and fusinite and their interpretation by petrological analysis is difficult and often misleading if too exact correlation with coal properties is attempted. The component vitrinite is however distinctive in forming the greater part of vitrain and as used by Seyler (p. 76) in his optical reflectivity examination of coal components as being the component which typifies coal *rank* or degree of metamorphism.

Composition of the Visible Banded Constituents of Coal. Quite marked differences in the proportions and properties of these constituents are found in British coal seams. In five Lancashire seams the differences in proportions are shown by Sinnatt to be as follows :

	Vitrain.	Clarain.	Durain.	Fusain.
1	14·6	65·9	18·1	1·4
2	9·8	53·1	35·2	1·9
3	7·0	70·0	21·2	1·8
4	1·3	98·7	nil	nil
5	73·0		26·5	0·5

The proportions in coal seams generally are typical of the seam and vary widely.

There are important differences in the composition and properties of these constituents, but in general the vitrain and clarain have a higher hydrogen content and more volatile matter than the durain of the same seam. The caking properties of the durain are also less than those of the bright coal ; this difference has suggested the physical separation of coal by crushing and screening to provide a fraction of appreciably higher caking power than the average of the seam. Owing to the relatively-hard character of durain this segregation occurs to some extent in the normal procedure of coal mining and preparation for the market.

Typical differences in properties are shown in Table XIII.

TABLE XIII

ANALYSES OF COAL CONSTITUENTS FROM THE SAME SEAM

	Vitrain.	Clarain.	Durain.	Fusain.
Moisture	1·7	1·4	1·2	0·9
Volatile matter	34·6	37·6	32·2	19·1
Ash	0·6	3·5	4·6	9·6
Carbon	84·4	82·2	85·8	88·7
Hydrogen	5·4	5·7	5·3	4·0
Sulphur	1·0	2·3	0·9	1·0
Nitrogen	1·5	1·9	1·4	0·7
Oxygen	7·7	7·9	6·6	5·6
B.Th.U. per lb. (dry, ash-free)	14,790	14,790	15,100	14,840

On carbonization the vitrain gave a grey, slightly-swollen coke, the clarain a similar but more swollen coke, the durain a dull-black friable coke and the fusain a pulverulent residue.

Further differences are brought out by the behaviour of the constituents on carbonization. Table XIV shows the yields of products obtained in the Gray-King assay from one set of sections of the Lancashire Arley seam. The results are calculated to dry coal at the same ash content.

TABLE XIV

GRAY-KING ASSAY OF BANDED CONSTITUENTS OF COAL

(Arley Seam, Lancashire)

	Coke.	Tar.	Liquor.	Gas (ml.).	Type of Coke.
Vitrain	69·0	16·2	4·6	13,440	G_3
Clarain	71·5	14·5	4·2	12,800	G
Durain	76·2	11·2	3·6	11,340	F/G

The higher caking power of the vitrain is noticeable and also the higher yield of tar and volatile matter. The clarain is more or less intermediate in behaviour to vitrain and durain.

The differences in caking power between " hards " and " brights ", which are respectively rich in durain and vitrain, are marked in other seams which are high in caking power but hardly noticeable in the seams of weakly coal. Some examples are quoted below.

Caking Coals	Beeston, Yorks.	Barnsley, Yorks.	Middleton, Little, Yorks.	Ince, Roger, Lancs.	Kent 1	Kent 2	Kent 3
Whole seam	G_4	G_5	—	G_4	G_7	G_5	G_3
Brights	G_6	G_6	G_6	G_6	G_8	G_6	G_4
Hards	E	G	E	E/F	F/G	F/G	D/E

Medium-caking Coals		Notts. T.H.			N. Wales, Quaker.
Whole seam	F	C/D	D/E	E/F	F
Brights	G	E	E/F	G_3	G
Hards	C/D	B	C	C/D	E

INORGANIC CONSTITUENTS OF COAL

The inorganic constituents of coal can be seen in part as (i) thin dirt partings separating the coal and layers and forming lines of weakness at which lump coal breaks readily ; (ii) lump pyrites in the form of dull gold nodules ; (iii) disseminated pyrites in the form of glistening scales ; (iv) white " ankeritic " partings, usually perpendicular to the bedding plane of the coal and the coal bands, consisting mostly of calcium magnesium carbonates deposited by infiltration in the shrinkage cracks in the coal substance. The distribution of these inorganic constituents and of those not visible to the eye can be seen clearly in an X-ray photograph (Figure 8). The British pioneer work in this field has been carried out by C. N. Kemp

(*Trans. Inst. Min. Eng.*, 1929, **177** (**2**), 175), to whom this photograph is due. Even in those parts of the coal which are most free from inorganic constituents the ash content is 2–3 per cent. The variations in distribution generally follow the horizontal coal bands, but the presence of constituents

ASH
%

} 5·2

} 3·3

} 2·8

} 5·2

} 3·1

} 11·3

} 8·2

} 3·2

Fig. 8.—X-ray Photograph of Coal showing the Distribution of the Inorganic
Constituents.

of high atomic number in the shrinkage cracks is particularly noticeable. These are the so-called ankerites. With the exception of the pyritic section, which shows 11·3 per cent. of ash, the whole of this inorganic matter shown would be regarded as inherent and not adventitious.

The impact of these inorganic constituents on the observed ash content of coal is discussed more fully in Chapter V.

THE CHEMICAL CONSTITUTION OF COAL

A considerable volume of research work has been carried out in order to determine the physical and chemical constitution of the complex substance which constitutes coal. It is apparent that the problem is one of great complexity owing to the heterogeneous character of coal and it is not surprising that many different techniques have been adopted. Much of the work is academic in character and has little apparent bearing upon the use of coal as a fuel. In this review, therefore, only the broad outlines of the researches are described. In some cases the objective of the work has been utilitarian, and in such cases and where the results may be thought to have a bearing on practical usages, more detail has been given. The work is divisible first into chemical and physical methods, and later into divisions of each.

(1) Decomposition of the coal by heat and the chemical examination of the products.

(2) Separation into fractions by the use of solvents and the chemical examination of these.

(3) Oxidation by air and stronger reagents followed by the study of the products. These reagents have been oxygen, potassium permanganate, nitric acid, sulphuric acid, ozone, chlorine dioxide, sodium hypobromite, ferric chloride, and boric acid.

(4) Fusion with caustic alkali under reducing or oxidizing conditions.

(5) Treatment with the halogens, chlorine or bromine.

(6) The artificial production of coal-like substances has been attempted at elevated temperature and pressure.

(7) Physical methods have included ;
    X-ray diffraction,
    Refractive index,
    Surface reflection of light,
    Study of structure and porosity of coals.

In addition to these there might be added certain work on the physical properties of different coals which has value in explaining differences in their properties. These are :
    X-ray studies of mineral matter,
    Surface area measurement by the heat of wetting,
    Infra-red absorption of thin sections.

Action of Heat on Coal. In this field much of the work has a double significance, coal constitution on the one hand and carbonization on the other. There is no clear distinction between the search for knowledge as regards the constitution of coal and investigations relating to its coking properties. When coal is heated it gives as volatile products tar, liquor and gas, and as a residual product coke, which may be weak and friable or hard and cellular according to the nature of the coal. The composition and nature of these products vary with the temperature, the pressure, the rate of heating and the nature of the coal.

Since Delesse in 1857 there have been a number of workers in this field, but the greatest volume of work emerged from the researches of Wheeler and his collaborators during the period 1910 to 1930. When bituminous coal is heated the sequence of events is as follows : There are first evolved the occluded gases, composed mainly of higher paraffin hydrocarbons, followed by substantial amounts of water at about 200° C. Thereafter appear at intervals sulphuretted hydrogen and olefines (270°), oils unaccompanied by marked gas evolution (310°), and finally, commencing at about 350°, a continuous gas evolution together with much viscous oil. The nature of the evolved gas alters as the heating progresses. Below 450° it largely consists of paraffin hydrocarbons, but these cease to be evolved at temperatures above 700°, whilst this latter temperature marks a sudden rapid increase in the quantity of hydrogen evolved.

The groupings which contain sulphur begin to decompose with evolution of hydrogen sulphide and mercaptans between 200° and 300° C. Those which contain nitrogen decompose at 300° C. with evolution of ammonia. The oils which appear in the early stages of heating in very small amount are probably liquated from the coal substance and are not products of decomposition in the normal sense. These appear from peat at 180°, from lignite at 235°, and from bituminous coals from 215° to 245° C., depending upon the caking power of the coal ; the lower values obtaining with the coals of higher caking power (lower oxygen content). The temperature of active decomposition of the coal shows the same variation with coal rank between 290° and 360° C. in the bituminous species.

The nature of the liquid product (tar) produced in the initial stages of decomposition has been closely examined by Wheeler, Pictet, Morgan, and others. The compounds identified have been hydrocarbons up to paraffin wax, bases from aniline to quinaldine, olefines up to nonene, aromatic hydrocarbons including benzene and from naphthalene to tetramethylanthracene, naphthenes, and phenols from phenol itself to xylenol.

In considering these products the question which arises is which part of the coal substances they come from. It is evident that they are the result of progressive decomposition, by the action of heat, of the complex substances of higher molecular weight which comprise the coal. In order to make the decomposition as little severe as possible a high vacuum was used in most cases. At very high vacua (0·001 mm. Hg) condensible oils are not obtained until the point of active decomposition is reached and it has been concluded that if there are any actual chemical entities of a distillable character in coal they cannot be isolated in this way owing to their low vapour pressures. In order to follow up the question of which part of the coal contributed to the recognizable products of thermal decomposition, Holroyd and Wheeler examined the products of thermal decomposition of the fractions of coal obtained by separation with organic solvents (q.v.) and studied the products obtained from different types of coal. From the results they were able to deduce the contribution of each constituent group as shown in Table XV.

TABLE XV

RESOLUTION OF BITUMINOUS COALS BY HEAT

(Holroyd and Wheeler, *Fuel*, 1930, **9**, 40)

Constituent.	Principal gaseous products.	Principal liquid products.		
		Character.	Quantity.	Temperature range, deg. C.
Free hydrocarbons	Paraffins in small quantity.	Saturated and unsaturated hydrocarbons in nearly equal amount.	Equal to original amount of free hydrocarbons in the coal.	225–300.
Resins . .	Paraffins and higher olefines.	Resins and unsaturated hydrocarbons.	Usually rather less than original amount of resin in the coal.	325–375.
Structured plant entities (e.g. spore exines).	Oxides of carbon and some paraffins.	Unsaturated hydrocarbons, neutral oxygenated compounds and water.	About 30 per cent. of original plant entities in the coal.	300–320.
Ulmins . .	Paraffins and some oxides of carbon.	Phenolic and acid oils, unsaturated hydrocarbons, aromatic and hydro-aromatic compounds and water.	Decreases with the "rank" of the ulmin 6·1 per cent. of water and 3–0·05 per cent. phenols with coals ranging from 77–90 per cent. carbon.	Decomposition point increases with "rank" of ulmin from 290–365 with coals ranging from 77–90 per cent. carbon. All oils distilled below 400.

The hydrocarbon and resinic constituents contribute extensively to the liquid (tar) products of distillation of coal. The extractable hydrocarbons of solvent separation are the source of the hydrocarbon oil which distils out of coal without marked decomposition as shown by little evolution of gas. The resins are responsible for the tar constituent which is insoluble in light petroleum but soluble in ether and is distillable from coal in the temperature range 330° to 370° C. The resinic material distilled at higher temperature is similar to the resin extract (γ_2), but is evidently produced with decomposition since the amount obtained is not proportional to the amount of resinic material in the coal. The hydrocarbons on the other hand are shown to distil without decomposition, by the fact that the solvent-extracted hydrocarbons distil without decomposition and are similar in character and analysis. The ulmin material is seen to decompose at temperatures which rise with increasing coal rank.

It may be concluded from the above that the study of the thermal decomposition of coal has not been particularly illuminating with regard to the chemical constitution of coal. It has, however, provided useful information to the carbonizing industries regarding the stages of thermal destruction, and the factors which affect the nature of the tars produced at the different levels of temperature used in industry.

Extraction of Components by Organic Solvents

At first it would appear that the separation of coal into fractions by the action of solvents should be a promising method of attack, especially if the fractions obtained should be capable of more precise chemical examination than the original coal. For this reason a number of solvents have been tried, but the results have not given information of any positive value in this connection. They have been of value in the utilization of coal, and a brief account of them is necessary here.

The two solvents with which most work has been done are benzene and pyridine, although some binary mixtures have been tried.

Benzene was first used by F. Fischer in 1916 and later by W. A. Bone in 1924–37. It will be of interest to describe their techniques.

Fischer heats the coal in an autoclave in contact with benzene at 205° C. for one hour, and repeats the procedure with fresh solvent until no more extract is obtained. The concentrated extract is poured into 3–4 times its own volume of light petroleum (b.p. 40–60°) and the precipitate of " solid bitumen " filtered off, the filtrate being evaporated to give a residue of " oily bitumen ". Bone's procedure is to extract the coal in an autoclave of the Soxhlet type, in an inert atmosphere. The extract is concentrated and poured into five times its own volume of light petroleum (b.p. 40–60°) and filtered.

The filtrate is evaporated to give the oily bitumen, but this is fractionated to give Fraction Ia, Ib and II.

Fraction Ia, volatile in steam, soluble in light petroleum.
Fraction Ib, not volatile in steam, soluble in light petroleum.

Fraction II, insoluble in light petroleum, soluble in a 1 : 4 mixture of benzene and light petroleum.

The precipitated solid bitumen is extracted with absolute ethyl alcohol to give :

Fraction III, soluble in ethyl alcohol.
Fraction IV, insoluble in ethyl alcohol.

These fractions are characteristically different. Fraction I is a viscous, neutral oil low in oxygen and free from nitrogen. Fraction II is a red-brown solid softening below 60° C. and having a C/H ratio of 13. Fraction III is a red-brown solid softening below 150° C. and having a C/H ratio of 12·5. Fraction IV is an amorphous brown powder which softens between 150° and 250° C. and has a C/H ratio of 15.

Fischer claimed that his " oily bitumen " was responsible for the caking properties of the coal and his " solid bitumen " for swelling under heat. Bone claimed that his fraction IV was a measure by yield of the " coking " power of the coal. These views were in disagreement since the fractions I and II corresponded to the oily bitumen. In the case of lignites the fractions III and IV are not present and their place is taken by phenols and esters. It is not held by either, however, that the caking property is due entirely to the presence of certain constituents but that other factors intervene ; this could well have been the cause of the disagreement. Bakes has in fact pointed out that the nature of the infusible portion of the coal is very important, since this does not act by any means as an inert diluent.

A conflicting piece of evidence, the meaning of which is not clear, is found in the fact that fine grinding of coal suddenly increases the amount of extract when the size of particle reaches one μ (0·001 mm.). The amount may be increased to as much as 10 times.

Pyridine as a Solvent. The use of pyridine as a solvent has been investigated mainly by Wheeler and his colleagues. The yield of extract obtainable from a bituminous coal, provided the solvent is pure and anhydrous and that the extraction is carried out in an inert atmosphere, amounts to 20 to 25 per cent. on an average, as against 7 to 15 per cent. for benzene under pressure. The pyridine extract is further fractionated with other solvents, the method being shown diagrammatically on page 71.

Whether these fractions have any real significance or not is open to doubt, but they do possess different properties which are characteristic of the different qualities of coal. It is suggested that the *alpha* fraction which is similar to the *beta* fraction, in consisting of ulmin material, contains undispersible ulmins of high molecular weight ; the beta fraction contains the dispersible ulmins. Examination by X-ray diffraction confirms this.

The *gamma* fractions contain the hydrocarbons, phenolic esters and the *gamma* resins.

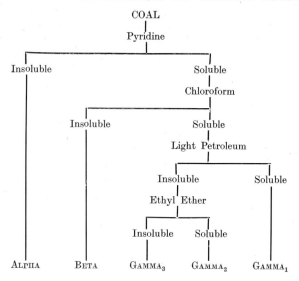

*Gamma*₁ was of vaseline-like consistency, and was found to consist of—
(*a*) Saturated hydrocarbons, 40 per cent., containing C, 87·40 ; H, 11·13 per cent. These contained hydrocarbons of other than straight or branched chain structure.

(*b*) Unsaturated hydrocarbons, 40 per cent.

(*c*) Resins (dark red in colour), 20 per cent., containing C, 84·21 ; H, 7·31 per cent.

*Gamma*₂ was a brick-red powder, m.p. 100–110° C., containing 15 per cent. of saponifiable matter consisting of phenols and carboxylic acids (as esters), some of which contained hydroxyl groups. The unsapionfiable portion, m.p. 90–100° C., resembled the resin from gamma₁. Its composition was C = 84·0; H = 7·2; O = 8·8 per cent. Nitrogen and sulphur were absent. No carboxylic, ketonic, aldehydic, or alcoholic group was present, and the oxygen was probably present as non-reactive bridge linkages.

*Gamma*₃ was a brown powder insoluble in alkali.

Hoffmann and Damm (1922) examined the neutral oil obtained from the pyridine extract of an Upper Silesian coal, and isolated a number of paraffins (including heptacosane), saturated and unsaturated hydrocarbons and also methyl anthracene. These were the same substances as had been isolated in the benzene extracts by Pictet and their easy separation suggests that the part of the coal molecule which contains least oxygen is most lightly bound.

The claim of greatest importance in this work is that the ability of coal to form a coherent coke is closely concerned with the proportion of γ constituents 1 and 2. Remixing of the components showed that the original caking power of the coal was scarcely changed and that it was fair to assume that the components had been obtained with very little chemical change.

When, however, the *alpha* and *beta* fractions were blended separately with the *gamma* 1, 2 and 3 fractions, the first two gave strong hard cokes—*gamma* 2 more swollen—while the last gave a pulverulent residue. Examination of a series of coals of increasing rank however does not disclose any relationship between the rank, and the proportion of either *gamma* 1 or the ratio of *gamma* 1 to *gamma* 2 and 3. This problem was further examined by Bakes in a research in which the effects of both benzene and pyridine extracts were examined from three bituminous coals which could be described respectively as strongly-caking, medium caking and non-caking.

The results of benzene-pressure and pyridine extraction are shown in Table XVI, in comparison with the very considerable differences in caking power as measured by the Campredon index.

TABLE XVI

BENZENE AND PYRIDINE EXTRACTS AND THE CAKING POWER OF COAL

Fraction.	I.	II.	III.	IV.	Gamma 1.	Gamma 2.	Gamma 3.	Caking index.
Mitchell main :								
Bright	2·7	1·8	1·1	10·9	3·9	3·1	1·5	24
Dull	1·8	1·7	0·9	10·9	1·3	1·9	2·7	16
Dalton Main :								
Bright	2·9	2·7	1·7	9·0	1·9	4·1	2·0	15
Dull	2·2	3·0	1·1	7·9	1·8	1·5	2·0	14
Warwick Slate :								
Bright	1·3	2·2	1·3	5·0	1·2	1·7	1·5	3
Dull	3·5	0·8	1·0	7·2	1·5	2·2	2·5	4

There is here a rough correlation between the caking power of the coal and the amount of extract component—IV. in the case of the benzene extract and *gamma* 1 and 2 in the case of pyridine—to which the power of inducing caking is attributed. Bone has claimed that a coal has caking properties when the amount of fraction IV exceeds 2 per cent., and is strongly-caking above 5 per cent. The above data suggest that these limits should be increased to 6 and 9 respectively. The differences between the proportions of *gamma* 1 and 2 are more regular, from 7·0 per cent. to 1·7 for a decrease of caking index from 24 to 3.

These conclusions do not take into account the differences in the structure or surface area of the supposed " inert " components, and it may be finally concluded that the proportions form only a general guide to the properties of swelling and caking and that these are probably more easily assessed by the empirical methods which are available (q.v.).

Other Solvents. The effects of many other solvents on coal have been tried, including mixed solvents.

In some cases the objective has not been coal-constitution research ;

in the Pott-Broche process extraction of coal with tetrahydronaphthalene at the decomposition point brings over 90 per cent. into solution and allows of the making of an ash-free material for such a process as the hydrogenation of coal, or for the internal combustion engine.

Most of the other solvents have been used either to evaluate caking constituents, as in the case of benzene and pyridine, or to separate and identify organic substances.

The general conclusion to draw from all the work done is that it adds considerably to the knowledge of coal behaviour but does not really disclose anything outstanding as to the chemical constitution of the so-called coal molecule. A very complete study of the literature of the subject up to the year 1933 was prepared by W. E. Bakes (Fuel Research Tech. Paper 37) to which reference can be made.

Humic Acids in Coal

Some examinations of the " ulmins " of coal have been made separately on the understanding that they are in a sense chemical entities. That they are not homogeneous, however, is shown by the fact that they can be separated into fractions by the selective action of solvents.

The equivalent weights of humic acids are variously reported from 150 to 400. Molecular weight determinations vary widely from 2350 to 26,000.

It is accepted that the molecule has phenolic, carboxylic and ketonic groups, but the nature of the main part of the molecule is still a matter for speculation. It was considered by Wheeler that the original alkali-soluble ulmins (present in peat and brown coal) and the insoluble ulmins of a bituminous coal have the same nuclear structure but differ in their external groupings. Whatever may be the truth of this assertion, it is a fact that mild oxidation, say with air, largely transforms a bituminous coal into alkali-soluble material closely resembling alkali-soluble ulmins. This procedure has been called by Francis and Wheeler " regeneration " of the ulmins. These authors have shown that vitrain can be oxidized with air at 150° C. and rendered soluble in dilute caustic alkali to the extent of 97 per cent. of the coal substance. The ulmins, natural and regenerated, are readily recovered from solution in alkali by precipitation with mineral acid and washing free from electrolyte.

From a consideration of these " separates " the authors conclude that the molecular weight of the coal ulmin was about 680 or a multiple of this number, each unit containing one nitrogen atom, one hydroxyl and four carboxyl groups. The further oxidation of regenerated ulmins gives rise to oxalic, succinic and benzene-carboxylic acids.

Chemical Degradation Methods

The greatest insight into the constitution of coal has been gained from the examination of the chemical degradation products of coal or natural or regenerated ulmins. It will be readily understood that chemical degradation leads necessarily to the formation of substances less complex in type than those originally present in the coal so that the characterization of degradation products can only give information of the presence of structural units with which the complex coal structure has been built and can give little or no information concerning the complexity of the structure. Nevertheless, a knowledge of the building units is important from many aspects, not the least of which may be the more scientific utilization of our coal resources.

Although a great variety of reagents has been employed in the attack on coal, yet only in a very few instances has the examination of the products been prosecuted with any thoroughness, and even in some of these cases assertions have been made on very meagre evidence concerning the identity of certain constituents. Of the many methods employed, oxidation has proved to be the most useful. Other methods have employed hydrogenation, halogenation and the action of alkali.

Oxidation Methods. The first step in the oxidation of coal substance is the rendering of the ulmins soluble in alkali, and the second the breaking down of these complex bodies into recognizable chemical entities.

The pioneer work was done by F. Fischer who, by air oxidation, obtained benzene carboxylic acids ranging from phthalic to mellitic acid in addition to simple fatty acids. Improved technique using oxygen under pressure in an alkaline medium has led in the U.S.A. to a practical method for the manufacture of a considerable range of these acids. Other workers have confirmed these findings and have speculated upon the mechanism of the reactions, concluding mainly that the first step in oxidation is the formation of carboxyl groupings.

Potassium permanganate has been used either in alkaline, acid or neutral solution. Bone was the first to identify oxalic, acetic and succinic acids and all the benzene-carboxylic acids with the exception of benzoic. The amounts of acids made varied from 10 per cent. for lignite, to 50 per cent. with anthracite, i.e. increasing with the rank of the coal. This led to the conclusion that the structures probably present in coal were unreduced benzene rings linked through side chains or hetero-cyclic rings. Other workers have reached similar conclusions, and the method has also been applied to the classification of coal by rank.

Nitric acid may also be used as an oxidizing agent but, as might be expected, the products are nitrated to some extent. Reaction at room temperature with 5N acid renders brown coal entirely soluble in acetone as a presumed isonitroso derivative from the grouping $CH_2CO—$. More drastic oxidation gives again benzene carboxylic acids, etc. Sulphuric acid in certain circumstances will act as an oxidizing agent, but in the cold it acts as a sulphonating agent. Bituminous coal will absorb up to 10 times its weight of concentrated acid to give a dry product which when freed from excess acid has the properties of base exchange. Sodium hypobromite may also be used as an agent and leads to the same products, although there is also evidence of bromination.

Treatment with Caustic Alkali. Under oxidizing conditions, the same carboxylic acids are identified but, in the absence of oxygen, paraffin hydrocarbons (waxes) have been identified including for example n-octacosane ($C_{28}H_{58}$).

Hydrogenation

The action of hydrogen on coal under pressure has been used as a means of studying the transition of coal to a liquid product, and has also thrown some light on coal constitution. The oxygen groupings are in the main readily removed, and the proportion of such oxygen to that less readily removed decreases with increasing rank. Under the action of the hydrogen under heat, bituminous coal liquefies readily, the first sections to go being the plant remains. With lower-rank coals an increasing proportion of the oxygen is liberated as water.

Other agents have been used in the resolution of coal but without adding to the above findings. These include chlorine and bromine which have also been used to attempt the measurement of the degree of unsaturation, though without positive result. If bromine is allowed to act on coal dispersed in an organic solvent both substituted and additive products are formed and the solubility of the material in other organic solvents is increased. In some cases the caking power of the coal is appreciably increased, particularly by chlorine, despite the fact that there is also evidence of oxidation.

Physical Methods of Examination

Physical methods have been used to examine coals for such properties as porosity, electrical conductivity, dielectric constant, equilibrium moisture content, etc., but others have been employed in order to obtain insight into the constitution of the molecule which has not been obtainable by chemical methods. These have included paleobotanical methods, X-ray diffraction and reflectivity of light.

X-ray Diffraction. The first work by Mahadevan showed that all banded coals had a lattice structure similar to graphite. The vitrain pattern showed only diffuse haloes suggesting only colloidal graphite crystallites, while durain showed a similar pattern with strongly-marked haloes and evidence of mineral constituents. These findings have been confirmed by many others, and it is indicated that the coal series from peat to anthracite all contains a basic aromatic ring-structure of which the diffracting crystallites increase with rank until they approach graphite in the case of anthracite. The size of the crystallite is reported to be about 10 Å for lignite and ranging from 15 to 60 Å for coals. A considerable volume of work on these lines has been done by H. L. Riley and his colleagues, in which the coals have been studied alongside their cokes made at different temperatures, and cokes made from complex pure organic substances. In the first place, he confirms the effect of rank, and states that the a dimension of the crystallites increases with rank but the c dimension increases to a maximum at 92 per cent. carbon and then decreases.

In a study of carbon black it has been found by Briscoe that one particle is apparently a packed structure of graphite layers of carbon atoms parallel to, and equidistant from, one another, but oriented in a random manner to each other. To this he has given the name " turbostratic ", i.e. of unordered layers. Riley claims that coals show the same structure with the addition of an extra (γ) band. From this he has obtained a picture of the structure of coal as consisting of flat, aromatic lamellae of layered carbon atoms which form turbostratic crystallites with an inter-layer spacing of 3·5 Å, together with other ring systems with side chains attached to the peripheral carbon atoms and forming another turbostratic system with a plane spacing of 4·5 Å. The growth of the c dimension is explained on carbonization by assuming that the layers become mobile on heating and build on one another. This theory provides a physical picture of the structure of coals and can be used to explain the differences in their properties. For example, the ability of caking coals to intumesce and form a hard coke can be explained by postulating the development under the influence of heat of a highly-mobile turbostratic system.

Reflectance of Light. Since coal is an opaque substance, the only optical property which can be measured is its power of reflecting light. In 1929 Stach was the first to discover that the reflectivity of coal appeared to vary with rank, but later this observation was limited to vitrain as this is the only homogeneous component of coal. Indeed, it was also observed that the refractive index also varied with rank, increasing from 1·7 to 1·9 in the bituminous class with increase of carbon content.

The most comprehensive work has however been done by Seyler, who measures the proportion of vertically-incident light which is reflected, using a microscope with oil-immersion lens and a suitable photometer. In this way he has identified ten components of coal which have distinct reflectivities in a series of steps and without intermediates, ranging from 0·26 to 4·41 per cent. and forming a geometric series with a ratio of 1·363. The exinites form the only exception in having abnormally low values.

The surface of a piece of coal seen in this way consists of a pattern of areas of irregular shape and size, the reflectivity of which can be summed into a number of groups. Normally one coal does not contain more than 3 or 4 of the components, so assessment of their areas is not so laborious as might be supposed. Further, a vitrain or clarain will contain one component predominantly ; this is the vitrinite component which designates the rank of the coal. This is nearly always the component of lowest reflectivity in each coal. The components of lowest value are found in the coals of lowest rank and the highest in anthracitic coals ; fusain shows a high value which suggests that it is an advanced product of coalification. In view of this the term fusinite is used to designate the highest degree of coalification of vitrinite.

An example of the type of classification diagram which is obtained by the analysis of coal in this way is shown in Figure 9. This diagram actually represents the Nine Foot seam of South Wales which changes in analysis from west to east because of geological disturbance effects. The percentage of each component is the height of the block—drawn on a square-root scale to accentuate small amounts. Each block represents a component of definite reflectance (N_r) and the percentage of this on a spore-free basis, i.e. vitrinite. In this example the three most eastern coals, varying in carbon content from 86·9 to 88·2 per cent., show a vitrinite component of $N_r = 4$ or 0·92 per cent. reflectance. In each sample the only other

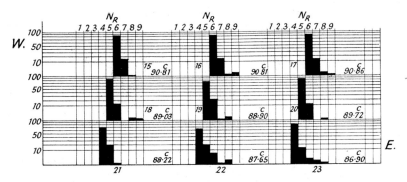

Fig. 9.—Seyler Somatic Diagram of the Nine Foot Seam of South Wales.

component is the next in the series, N_r5, or 1·26 per cent. reflectance. When the carbon exceeds 89 per cent. as in the next three samples above, the vitrinite suddenly jumps to N_r5 and the other component becomes N_r6. At 91 per cent. carbon another jump occurs to N_r6 and N_r7. This sudden change is normal in coal and a jump always occurs with increase of rank or metamorphosis as indicated by carbon content.

The true significance of these observations has not yet been fully explained, probably because of the meticulous character of the examination required. It is apparent, however, that there must be some basic explanation for the absence of intermediate components and the strange variation of percentage reflectance with change of rank of the vitrinite. So far as practical usage of the data is concerned it would seem that the same information can be obtained by less intricate methods. Seyler has claimed that they could have real value in coking practice, or in coal hydrogenation, but empirical tests would be much easier to make and would be just as illuminating.

Miscellaneous Physical Tests. A number of other physical properties of coal have been examined but mainly for technical reasons, and the
results have in the main little bearing on the constitution of coal.

It is claimed that the *refractive index* of coal varies with its rank, referring
again to the vitrinite as the component representing rank. The inference
is that the micelles in the coal substance become more closely packed with
increasing rank. The coals of highest rank become anisotropic, showing a
higher index in a direction perpendicular to the bedding plane of the coal
in the seam. It may be assumed that this is due to the closer packing of
the atoms in this direction. Approximate values for the refractive index
vary from 1·6 at 78 per cent. carbon to 1·85 at 90 per cent. carbon using
Wratten filter 70 at 7000 Å.

The *heat of wetting* of coal has been studied in order to arrive at a measure
of its internal surface. It is necessary to use an organic liquid of small
molecular size first to enter the very fine pores and secondly to displace
the layer of methane which is adsorbed on all fresh coal surfaces. The heat
of wetting is liberated rapidly (20 min.) and accurate calorimetric measurements can be made. The amount varies from 8 cal. per g. for anthracite
to 18 for a weakly-caking coal of about 80 per cent. carbon content. If
the heat of wetting is plotted against volatile matter or carbon the typical
coal rank curve is obtained (see Figures 13 and 14), which shows a minimum
value at about 90 per cent. carbon. In view of this it is apparent that the
values have significance in relation to the basic properties of coals. It is
also possible to deduce from the data a value for the size of the coal micelle
using a determined figure for the heat of wetting of unit coal surface of
10 cal. per 100 sq. m. Assuming surfaces of 20 to 200 sq. m. per g., and
one continuous layer of micelles of cubical shape, the length of side of these
varies from 200 Å to several thousands, with an average value of the order
of 500 Å.

From this work, Bangham suggested a structure for coal as a colloid
composed of spherical and ellipsoid micelles of the above size, increasingly
crushed together with increasing rank, but having continuous pores. This
theory is not necessarily incompatible with the graphite crystallite theory
of Riley if it is considered that the crystallites build up into macromolecules
or micelles.

Electrical conductivity measurements of fusain suggest that it has the
same physical structure as graphite. The measurement of the dielectric
constant shows that coal is a colloid affected both by variation in composition
and in the proportion of water present.

Physical Structure of Coal

Certain other physical methods have been used to examine the properties
of coals, not so much to arrive at its constitution as to obtain knowledge
regarding its general physical make-up.

X-ray shadow photography has been used to investigate the distribution of mineral matter (Figure 8) and has shown the existence of shrinkage cracks both vertical to, and in line with, the bedding plane. If a piece of coal is partly immersed in a solution of a lead salt the salt is drawn up into the remainder by capillary action. On photographing later, the position of the fine cracks and pores in the coal mass can be seen. The mean diameter of these fine pores is of the order of 500 Å, i.e. of the same order as the supposed coal micelle. As would be expected, vitrain shows a less porous structure than clarain and this in turn than durain (see p. 60).

Conclusions

This brief review of the work done on the constitution of coal suggests that the complex character of coal has defeated the objective and that little has been learned that cannot be assessed for all usual purposes by simpler empirical methods. The separation of the coal into simple fractions to facilitate analysis was an obvious approach but none of the methods used have altogether avoided decomposition in the process. The wider use of new physical methods is now indicated, if greater knowledge is to be obtained.

Oxidation has proved the most effective weapon in leading to the identification of actual chemical entities from coal, but the action is too strong and no identifiable substance has been isolated which shows more than one benzene ring in the molecule. Steps between this and the macromolecule of Bangham have still to be established.

Finally, it would seem that further work can only be of academic interest in the present-day utilization of coal as a fuel, and that continuation of research should be aimed at new applications of coal regarded as a raw material.

REFERENCES

The literature of work on the constitution of coal is very wide and it would be out of place to attempt to reproduce it here. It is considered sufficient to list the papers which give references and which are more general in their approach.

L. Horton, R. B. Randall and K. V. Aubrey. *Fuel*, 1944, **23**, 65. Complete biblio. to 1944.
Coal. Bone and Himus. Longmans Green and Co. 1936. General account of Coal research.
Chemistry of Coal Utilization. H. H. Lowry (editor). Chapman and Hall. 1945. Comprehensive survey, particularly of U.S. work.
The Ultra-Fine Structure of Coal and Coke. B.C.U.R.A. Conference, 1943. H. K. Lewis. 1944. Series of papers on physical properties.
Progress in Coal Science. D. H. Bangham. Butterworths. 1950. Series of specialized papers.
The Nature and Origin of Coal and Coal Seams. A. Raistrick and C. E. Marshall. Eng. Univ. Press. 1939.
Coal and Coalfields in Wales. F. J. North. Press Bd. Univ. Wales. 1931.
Constitution of Coal. M. C. Stopes and R. V. Wheeler. H.M.S.O. 1918 and *Fuel*, 1924, **3**, 3. Summary and biblio. of early work.

M. C. Stopes. *Proc. Roy. Soc.*, 1919 (B), **90, 470**. Original paper on the banded constituents of coal.

Melchet Lecture, 1941. C. A. Seyler. *J. Inst. Fuel*, 1943, **16,** 134.

Coalfields of Great Britain. Trueman. Edward Arnold (Publishers) Ltd., London. 1954.

Coal Mining. Statham. Eng. Univ. Press. 1951.

Coal. Grenfel. Gollancz. 1947.

Coal. Francis. Edward Arnold (Publishers) Ltd., London. 1954.

CHAPTER V

COMPOSITION AND CLASSIFICATION OF COAL

PHYSICAL PROPERTIES

It will now be realized that coal as mined consists of the coal substance itself associated with certain mineral constituents and mixed with a variable amount of inorganic material (dirt), which comes mainly from the roof and floor of the seam, and is mixed with it during mining. In order to compare types of coal one must consider the coal substance only, but in assessing the value of the coal for certain purposes it is necessary also to consider the amount and properties of the inorganic constituents which form ash on combustion. There are also certain minor constituents which are not included when comparing types of coal but whose presence and amount may limit the uses to which a coal can be put.

This chapter deals not only with the comparison of types of coal, i.e. coal classification, but with the chemical and physical properties of coal, and the effects of these on the behaviour of coals during usage. The methods of analysis and testing are dealt with in Chapter XIX and in the other chapters concerned with industrial procedure.

Moisture in Coal. The moisture in coal may be divided into accidental or " free " moisture, and the moisture due to the hygroscopic properties of the coal itself. The distinction between these is not definite but depends upon the condition of the coal and the humidity of the atmosphere. The free moisture is easily lost by drainage and evaporation and, except during very wet weather, the coal which reaches the consumer usually contains only 2 to 3 per cent. except in the case of small washed coal. Large amounts of free moisture in coal are obviously undesirable from the point of view of the customer, but for certain uses a small amount of free moisture may improve the performance of the coal in an industrial process. One example of this is the addition of water to small, dry coal to improve combustion on a boiler grate. A certain minimum of moisture is advantageous, from 5 to 12 per cent. according to particle-size distribution, giving optimum efficiency of combustion. Also in the coking of coal the best results are obtained with 3 to 5 per cent. moisture.

The hygroscopic moisture is more firmly held on the coal surface and in the fine pores and, given time, will establish an equilibrium with the moisture of the atmosphere. It is also termed " inherent " moisture or, as a result of its method of determination, " air-dried " moisture. The value obtained for a given coal depends upon the humidity of the drying air used, but if the determination is made at a controlled humidity the result is typical of the coal.   In general, the value at say 99 per cent. humidity for a series of coals decreases with increasing rank from 20 per cent. with lignites to 10 per cent. with bituminous coals of 80 per cent. carbon, which are non-caking, to 3 to 4 per cent. with strongly-caking coals (85 per cent. C), and 1 to 2 per cent. with anthracites.   The " air-dried " moisture content of a coal is therefore an approximate measure of its rank and therefore of the other qualities which are indicated by rank.   The relation between air-dried moisture and the porosity of the coal is dealt with more fully later.

Mineral Matter and " Ash " in Coal.   All coals contain a proportion of inorganic material which, since it is determined as the weight of residue obtained on complete combustion, is usually referred to as " ash ". It is derived in part from the mineral matter present in the original vegetable substance (inherent), in part from material carried by flood water, etc., amongst the decaying vegetable matter, and may also be due partly to shale, etc. (extraneous), derived from the strata adjacent to the coal seam, which it has been impracticable to remove by picking or washing. Since changes of composition take place during ashing, i.e. the minerals present become fully converted to oxides, the weight of ash is less than that of the mineral matter to the extent of about 10 to 15 per cent.   With low-ash coals this is not important and an analysis quoted to a basis of dry, ash-free material more or less represents the coal substance, and is often used in comparing coals or assessing the properties of an unknown coal. With coal containing more than about 5 per cent. of ash comparison should be made on a basis of " mineral matter-free " material.   The changes which occur are the dehydration of shales and clays, the loss of CO_2 from carbonates of Ca, Mg, or Fe, the oxidation of pyrites to Fe_2O_3, and the volatilization of alkalis and chlorides.   Formulæ are available for the calculation of the determined ash content to mineral matter (p. 477), but these are subject to some variation from one coalfield to another because of variation of the water of hydration of the inherent clays, and other reasons.

Several methods have been proposed for determining the proportions of mineral matter in coal.   If the oxygen content could be determined directly, and a reliable method will no doubt be evolved sometime, the mineral matter could be the difference figure in the ultimate analysis.

Alternatively it has been proposed to burn away the coal at a low temperature (350° C.) at which decomposition of the mineral matter would not occur ; this is however very slow and not very accurate.   Another method is to remove the mineral matter in stages by flotation methods without losing any coal, determine the ash contents at each stage, and extrapolate the curve to zero.   Faults in this method are the separation of some coal also and the variation of composition of the mineral matter from one stage to another.   The removal of the bulk of the mineral matter by extraction with inorganic acids may be a useful preliminary procedure.

The use of an established formula for calculation is at the moment the best approach, and, if all the facts are known, is accurate to a marked degree. Of the two available formulæ, King-Maries-Crossley, and Parr the latter is suspect because it makes the assumption that all the sulphur is associated with the mineral matter and it is not at all certain that this is justified. The former is reliable, but for high accuracy local or district factors must be known for the water of hydration of the shale, etc.   There seems no reason, however, why this should not be done in a systematic manner and a list of factors compiled to cover all coals in due course.   Its only fault is that the amount of analytical work necessary is rather great for ordinary use and cannot always be done.   The full formula can however be shortened for use in such cases since a statistical analysis has shown that each of the six factors can be correlated with one of the others, e.g. SO_3 (ash) with CO_2.   The shortened forms due to Fereday and Flint are satisfactory when the full analysis cannot be made, but accuracy is always in danger from the freak coal.   These formulæ are given in Chapter XVIII. A further formula has been proposed to copy Parr and calculate coal to a pure basis which excludes sulphur, but this is only an attempt to justify the use of the Parr formula in certain researches, and is not sound.

Mineral matter or ash is certainly inert and valueless so far as fuel value is concerned and has the first disadvantage of having to be paid for at coal prices.   It may have other disadvantages during combustion, for example, in boiler practice using a grate, it may seriously restrict the passage of the primary air and lower the rate of combustion and in turn reduce the output of steam.   In addition, frequent cleaning of the fires is necessary with the accompanying losses through open fire doors ; the loss of carbon carried through into the ash pit may be considerable ; deposits are caused in tubes and flues, and in addition, if of a fusible character, are especially troublesome through the formation of clinker.   In boiler plants using powdered coal the ash generally necessitates the provision of special plant to trap the dust and grit.   In producer gas practice fusibility poses a serious question, and coals otherwise suitable may be unworkable except with such excessive steam supply that the efficiency is adversely affected.   In chain-grate stokers a certain amount of ash is desirable in order that the back-end of the grate will remain covered and not allow the formation of air-holes.

The average ash content of British coal in the seam[1] is about 4 per cent., but very clean seams are known which contain less than 1 per cent.   Of the banded constituents the vitrain is of low ash content (1 to 2 per cent.), the clarain higher (3 to 5 per cent.) and the durain still higher (5 to 8 per cent.). The high ash content of fusain is due to the infiltration of hard water into this porous material, and may be very high.

[1] Excluding dirt bands.

The extraneous ash is derived from dirt partings in the coal, which may be clay or pyrites, ankeritic material deposited in shrinkage cracks from water (CaMg carbonates) and roof and floor. The appearance of mineral matter is seen in Figure 8.

Finely divided " inherent " mineral matter, whether from the plants or muds, cannot be removed by mechanical methods, washing, etc., but the higher specific gravity of undispersed shale, pyrites, etc., enables washing to be successfully carried out.

With coal from a given seam, the amount of ash is usually highest in the smaller sizes, due to the easy separation of pure lump coal and the consequent concentration of mineral matter in the fines.

Where the coal in the seam is hard and the dirt is friable the above is true. In some cases the coal is friable and the dirt hard, when the increase of ash with decreasing size may not be so marked or may even be reversed. The hard coals of Nottingham, Lancashire, Staffordshire, Cumberland and Scotland show this segregation, but the softer coals of Durham, Kent and Yorkshire (partly) are more variable. Chapman and Mott (*The Cleaning of Coal*) quote the following ash contents for sizes of Yorkshire coals :

Size (in.).	Over 1.	$1-\frac{3}{8}$.	$\frac{3}{8}-\frac{1}{8}$.	$\frac{1}{8}-\frac{1}{25}$.	$\frac{1}{25}$.	Average.
Silkstone	6·4	8·1	14·4	21·5	11·8	14·3
High Hazel	1·8	5·6	9·0	15·7	20·8	7·2

and for one Durham coal:

Size (in.).	Over 1.	$1-\frac{1}{2}$.	$\frac{1}{2}-\frac{1}{4}$.	$\frac{1}{4}-\frac{1}{8}$.	$\frac{1}{8}-\frac{1}{16}$.	$< \frac{1}{16}$.
Ash per cent.	4·8	18·6	19·5	19·5	15·6	15·8

With infusible ash, the value of two coals of similar character will be fairly proportional to their relative ash content, but it is quite otherwise if one gives a fusible and the other an infusible ash. A low ash content of a fusible character may be far more detrimental than a high ash of infusible character.

Essentially the mineral matter consists of silicate of alumina together with the basic oxides lime (CaO), magnesia (MgO), and iron (Fe_2O_3), together with traces of sulphates, carbonates and phosphates. Wood ashes are characterized by the presence of high proportions of alkalis, potash (K_2O), and soda (Na_2O), in combination with carbonic acid with little or no alumina. Peat ash contains a high percentage of lime and a little alumina. Coal ash is characterized largely, then, by the high percentage of alumina which is present. It may be noted that alumina as a constituent occurs in any quantity only in those plants existing to-day which are allied to those of the coal formations. Silicate of alumina (clay), however, would be the principal substance carried amongst the decaying vegetable matter when in a partially submerged state, judging by the usual shale beds accompanying the coal seams.

The composition of coal ashes varies widely ; the following are quoted by King and Crossley (Fuel Research Tech. Paper 28, 1933) as normal limits relating to British and American coals :

Constituent.	Per cent. of ash. American.	British.
Silica	40–60	25–40
Alumina	20–35	20–40
Ferric oxide	5–25	0–30
Calcium oxide	1–15	1–10
Magnesium oxide	0·5–4	0·5–5
Titanium oxide	0·3–3	0–3
Alkalis	1–4	1–6
Sulphur trioxide	—	1–12

Whilst it is difficult to correlate composition of the ash with clinkering property, it is certain that the nearer the composition approaches that of aluminium silicate ($Al_2O_3 . 2SiO_2$; $Al_2O_3 = 45·8$ per cent., $SiO_2 = 54·2$ per cent.), the more infusible it will be ; that on replacement of part of the alumina by other bases, such as lime and magnesia, and more particularly iron oxide, the more easily fusible will it become, due to the formation of double silicates, which are far more fusible than the simple ones.

The fusion temperatures of certain selected ashes in relation to their composition are shown in Table XVII.

TABLE XVII

Composition and Fusion Temperature of Certain Coal Ashes

Constituents.	SiO_2	TiO_2	Al_2O_3	Fe_2O_3	MnO	CaO	MgO	K_2O Na_2O	SO_3
1. Lancashire coal	27·1	0·9	23·2	29·2	0·1	7·1	2·7	3·2	7·3
2. Yorkshire coal .	49·2	1·2	35·9	3·5	—	2·7	0·7	5·0	2·1
3. Durham coal .	48·9	–1·4	38·8	2·1	—	4·9	0·6	2·1	2·1
4. S. Staffs coal .	47·3	1·3	38·2	1·1	—	6·3	0·8	1·3	3·6
5. Scottish coal .	48·3	2·8	31·8	9·3	—	1·9	2·1	2·5	1·5
6. Anthracite . .	37·4	1 8	31·9	19·7	—	3·7	1·7	1·6	2·5

Fusion temperature ° C.		1	2	3	4	5	6
Oxidizing atmosphere	a . .	1220	—	—	—	—	1315
	b . .	1310	—	—	—	—	1340
Reducing ,,	a . .	1115	1520	1550	1550	1430	1215
	b . .	1155	1555	1605	1600	1470	1285

(a) Temperature of softening.   (b) Temperature of fusion.

The high iron content of Nos. 1 and 6 are responsible for their low values and for the larger difference between oxidizing and reducing atmospheres ; ferrous silicate has a lower fusion temperature than ferric silicate. For this reason red ashes are recognizable as probably of low fusion temperature, but the reverse is not always the case since an unduly high proportion of lime will also give a low value.

In industrial usage the softening temperature is probably a better guide to the behaviour of coal during combustion than the final fusion temperature, and the following limits may be regarded as typifying behaviour in a mildly-reducing atmosphere.

Above 1450° C.   Very refractory for all uses.
1450° to 1350° C.   Refractory for most uses and unlikely to give trouble except in unusual circumstances.
1350° to 1250° C.   Require care in arranging primary air and more exact fire-cleaning schedules.
Below 1250° C.   Always likely to lead to clinkering ; both stoking and fire-cleaning must be of a very regular type.

In the United States the following limits are recognized : Refractory —over 1430° C. ; medium—1430° to 1200° C. ; fusible—below 1200° C. It is recognized that an ash which shows a large difference between the values obtained in oxidizing and reducing atmospheres is more likely to give trouble with clinker than one which shows only a small difference even when the fusion temperature is the same in the two cases.

The use of catalysts in the hydrogenation of coal has directed attention to the rarer constituents of coal ash. It has been found that most ashes contain appreciable amounts of boron, chromium, molybdenum and vanadium, whilst in some, notable quantities of germanium, tin and zinc have been found. The presence of some of these elements may prove to be of some importance. Ba up to 6 per cent., Ge up to 1·1 per cent. and V up to 4·5 per cent. of the ash have been reported. Certain gas-producer flue dusts now provide most of Britain's germanium.

CHEMICAL COMPOSITION AND PROPERTIES OF COAL

Proximate Analysis of Coal. The simplest form of analysis of coal has become known as the " proximate " analysis and consists in the determination of the moisture and ash (dealt with above) and of the volatile matter. To this is often added the determinations of sulphur content and calorific value. This examination provides a good deal of information regarding the coal and is often sufficient for the requirements of industry. The moisture figure is that determined on the coal in an air-dried condition and mineral matter is reported as ash. The volatile matter is the loss of weight of the coal as heated to a standard temperature for a standard length of time out of contact with air. It is therefore an arbitrary figure and its determination can only be made under rigidly standard conditions.

The solid residue left after the determination of volatile matter, and after deducting the ash, is termed the "fixed carbon". This is to some extent a confusing term since it bears no relation to the true carbon content and contains small amounts of sulphur, nitrogen and oxygen. The complete "proximate analysis" therefore consists of moisture (air-dried coal), ash, volatile matter, fixed carbon, all adding to 100 per cent.

Ultimate Analysis of Coal. By ultimate analysis is meant the determination of the elements carbon, hydrogen, sulphur, nitrogen and oxygen. For strict accuracy and comparison the results should be calculated to a basis of mineral-matter-free coal but, for the majority of coals of fairly low ash content, it is satisfactory if the calculation is made to a basis of dry, ash-free coal. The methods of analysis are given in Chapter XVIII and are all precise methods except in the case of oxygen which, in the absence of a positive method, is given as the difference from 100 per cent., of the sum of the others.

Since some coals contain an appreciable amount of carbonates the proportion of carbonate carbon must be determined separately and deducted. The observed hydrogen value may also be high if the coal contains hydrated silicates which are not decomposed on drying the coal, but this error is usually very small. The sulphur remaining in the ash should be deducted from the total sulphur and the "volatile sulphur" value used in the calculation.

Carbon, Hydrogen and Oxygen. These three elements together make up the true coal substance and their proportions are a guide to the properties of any coal. This fact is made use of in the various classifications of coal which are explained below.

Oxygen in Coal. The amount of oxygen in coal has an important bearing upon its properties and, as will be shown later, can be used in coal classification systems. Regarding coal solely as a fuel, oxygen is more undesirable as a constituent than moisture or ash ; an increase of 1 per cent. in oxygen content reduces the calorific value of a bituminous coal by about 1·7 per cent. Increase of oxygen content in bituminous coals is also associated with decrease of caking power and increase of moisture content ; high-oxygen coals are non-caking and hold over 10 per cent. of moisture even when air-dried ; low-oxygen bituminous coals are strongly caking and hold only 1 to 2 per cent. of moisture when air-dried.

Nitrogen in Coal. It is unusual to find less than 1 per cent. of nitrogen in the coals of Great Britain or more than 2·5 per cent. ; indeed, it is exceptional to find a coal giving a higher figure than 2 per cent.

When coal is distilled or carbonized about 15 per cent. of the nitrogen is converted into ammonia together with small amounts of cyanogen and pyridine bases. More than 50 per cent. normally remains in the coke.

When ammonia recovery from carbonization processes was of economic importance the percentage of nitrogen in the coal used was also important. Now that most of the industrial ammonia is made synthetically the nitrogen content of coal is not of particular significance.

Sulphur in Coal.   This element is found to about the same extent as nitrogen, viz. 0·5 to 2·5 per cent.   It occurs in three forms : in combination with iron as pyrites, FeS_2, which on heating under oxidizing conditions becomes iron oxide (Fe_2O_3) with liberation of sulphur dioxide ; as organic sulphur compounds, from which the sulphur compounds in tar and gas are mainly derived ; as sulphates, principally calcium sulphate ($CaSO_4$), forming a constituent of the ash.   In some cases it is desirable to distinguish between the fixed sulphur (occurring in the coke) and volatile sulphur.

Sulphur is of great importance in fuels, especially those used for metallurg cal purposes, since it may pass into the metal under treatment.   Pyrites loses part of its sulphur by distillation on strongly heating, hence, when raw coal containing pyrites is burnt part of the sulphur set free may be absorbed by the grate bars, and since the sulphide of iron formed is comparatively fusible, may give rise to serious trouble, whilst, if the sulphur be burnt to sulphur dioxide, serious corrosion of copper tubes, etc., with which the gases come in contact may occur.

When coal containing sulphur is distilled in retorts or coke ovens the sulphur found in the coke is always somewhat less than in the coal, the actual loss probably being dependent mainly on the organic sulphur compounds present.   Pyrites also may lose some of its sulphur, becoming iron mono-sulphide (FeS), and calcium sulphate may be reduced by contact with the hot carbon to the sulphide.   In the majority of cases the coke will still contain over 80 per cent. of the original sulphur of the coal, and this residual sulphur may not be as objectionable in its altered condition of combination.   It is quite conceivable that pyrites gives off elementary sulphur vapour which is readily absorbed by iron or other metal, but that iron sulphide loses sulphur only as the dioxide which may have little effect on the metal.

Numerous processes have been proposed for the further reduction of the sulphur left in the coke, but the most satisfactory method is that of washing the crushed coal, when a fair proportion of the pyrites may be mechanically separated.

Iron pyrites has been credited with the main responsibility for the spontaneous ignition of coal, but little importance is now attached to this theory.   The question is fully discussed later.

Some discussion has arisen as to whether sulphur present in pyrites should be regarded as a heat-giving constituent in fuels, an important consideration when the calorific value is calculated from the elementary composition.   Whilst calcium sulphate cannot undergo combustion, sulphur in organic combination and as pyrites may do so and add to the calorific value. The calorific effect of sulphur should find a place in formulæ used in such calculations.

Arsenic and Phosphorus. Arsenic and phosphorus occur in small quantities in most solid fuels, the former probably as arsenical pyrites. Their presence has no significance when the fuel is used for steam-raising or gas making, but in process work, as for example, the metallurgical use of coke, even small quantities can have a very undesirable effect on the product. The presence of arsenic may also lead to poisoning in certain industries. During the inquiry into arsenical poisoning from beer (Royal Commission, 1901–3) it became known that malt had, on occasions, been dangerously contaminated with arsenic from the fuel used in the kiln, also, of the various types of fuel examined gas coke appeared to be the least desirable. Since that period interest has abated, and there has been very little published information of the distribution of arsenic in fuels. Hence, many of the published figures available are probably not representative. These vary, however, from nil to as much as 2·9 grains As per lb. of coal.[1] The upper limit for malting use is 0·02 grain of " volatile " arsenic ; any " fixed " As is not important. In a number of anthracites examined the " fixed " As was 0·03 grain, and the " volatile " As 0·01 grain on the average.

The amount of phosphorus in coals is important if they are to be used for the manufacture of coke for metallurgical purposes. If the phosphorus in the coke is too high (see p. 246) it may have a deleterious effect upon the metal produced. In clean British coals 0·05 per cent. is seldom exceeded and in most cases the amount of phosphorus is less than ·005 per cent. Extreme cases of 1 to 2 per cent. have been reported.

Gases in Coal. In the undisturbed seam, coal contains a considerable amount of methane adsorbed or occluded under pressure. A good deal of work was done on the subject because of its relation to safety in mining and in recent years a process has been developed for its recovery and utilization. This latter is dealt with in Chapter XV (p. 369).

When the coal is disturbed during mining the methane is liberated and the freshly-mined coal contains only part of that originally present. The remainder is evolved on crushing the coal or during exposure to the atmosphere.

The most reliable work on the subject is that of F. Fischer and his colleagues, who examined certain Ruhr coals at different intervals after mining. The samples of coal were crushed to μ size (0·001 mm.) and evacuated in a specially-constructed gas-tight ball-mill from which gases were pumped off continuously ; it was found that very large quantities of gas could be removed and also that the amount removed was independent of the temperature. They also showed by analysis of the nitrogen in these occluded gases that it contained argon to the same extent as the air, and

[1] Expressed as As_2O_3.

hence proved that the nitrogen and oxygen in the gases are adventitious. Their results are tabulated on a nitrogen-free basis in Table XVIII.

It is to be noted that the composition of the gases obtained is very much the same for caking coal and for anthracite, but the volume of gas obtained from the latter is the remarkable figure of 10 times the volume of the coal itself.

TABLE XVIII

GASES REMOVED FROM COALS GROUND TO μ SIZE IN A VACUUM BALL-MILL

Coal.	Caking coal from Mathias Stinnes Mine.					Anthracite from Sophia-Jacoba Mine.	
	Banded coal 4 hrs. after mining.	Banded coal stored 1 week.	Banded coal cut from a large piece.	Durain coarse powder <3 mm.	Vitrain picked pea size.	20–30 mm. particle size.	
Time of grinding, hrs.	1·5	10	4	4·5	3	7 = 5 hrs. at Room temp.	20·5
Temperature	Room	Room	100°	Room	Room	2 hrs. at 100°	Room
c.c. gas/100 g. coal .	125	196	130	68	125	880	890
Analysis of Gas :							
CO_2	1·7	2·0	7·4	8·8	5·3	4·2	5·2
CO	1·3	0·5	0·3	0·7	1·0	0·5	0·5
H_2*	[2·5]	[3·0]	[2·5]	[3·7]	[3·6]	[4·0]	[2·7]
CH_4	93·8	93·5	88·6	85·2	89·3	91·1	90·8
C_2H_6	0·7	0·9	0·6	0·8	0·4	0·2	0·8
C_3H_8	0·0	0·1	0·6	0·8	0·4	—	—

* The hydrogen figures are doubtful owing to the method of analysis.

THE CLASSIFICATION OF COAL

The properties of coal as revealed by proximate and ultimate analyses, and later by the inclusion of certain other factors, have been made the basis of a number of systems of classification of coal into types. The intention has been partly to illustrate the transition changes from one type to another, but mainly to show how a knowledge of certain essential properties will allow of the prediction of others by reference to the classification.

The general description of coals by name forms the first rough classification, but the terms lignite, bituminous coal, anthracite, etc., are not sufficiently definite for more than casual use. A system based on the normal usage of the coal is also unsatisfactory as quite different types can sometimes be used efficiently for the same purpose. It does serve a useful

purpose, however, to designate certain types as coking, gas, steam, navigation, household, etc., provided this definition is based on more precise
knowledge, and separation into the subdivisions of each industry is
understood.

Commercial coals also vary in size and ash content and these factors can
sometimes outweigh even such a basic quality as caking power in the choice
of coal for a given purpose. For this reason the most successful systems
have been based on the evaluation of the quality of the coal substance,
leaving the influence of size and content of ash or other impurity to be
assessed as a secondary matter by the expert within the industry.

A number of such systems have been evolved and, since each of them
has something to recommend it, they are described briefly below. As a
first step, however, it is desirable at this stage to give a brief description
of the popularly-recognized types.

Peat, as explained in Chapter II, is not, strictly speaking, a coal, but it
does represent the starting-point of the coal series. Its appearance and
occurence is described in Chapter II. On a dry, ash-free basis it represents
a carbon level of 62 to 64 per cent. with about 30 per cent. of oxygen. Its
main usage is as a block fuel for the domestic fire, but it can be used in
emergency, or locally, as a boiler fuel, or even for the production of town gas.

Lignites mark the transition of peat to coal and form the lowest rank
of the true coals. Lignites may be black, or brown and earthy, with a pronounced woody structure ; on air-drying they tend to disintegrate and are
commonly marketed in a briquetted form. The air-dried material has a
moisture content of 15 to 20 per cent. The dry, ash-free content of carbon
and oxygen varies from 60 to 75 per cent. C and 25 to 20 per cent. O_2. Their
uses are dealt with in Chapter VI.

Sub-bituminous coals form a group between lignites and bituminous
coal, although the term has sometimes been applied to the subdivision
between the latter and anthracite. They have high moisture and volatile-
matter contents and no caking power. Carbon and oxygen range from
75 to 83 per cent. C and 20 to 10 per cent. O_2.

Bituminous coals are black and banded in appearance. They cover
a wide range of properties and for this reason the term bituminous is usually
associated with the prefix caking, or medium, strongly, weakly or non-
caking. Their carbon contents range from 75 to nearly 90 per cent., with
a change of volatile matter of 45 to 20 per cent., and a marked variation of
caking power. They form the general-purpose coals of household and
industrial demands. It is in this group, therefore, that the closest definition
is necessary in any classification system.

Semi-bituminous coals form a group between bituminous coal and
anthracite. Their carbon contents range from 90 to 93 per cent carbon,
volatile matter from 20 to 10 per cent., and oxygen from 4 to 2 per cent.
Their uses include steam raising (dry, steam coal), domestic stoves and,

since those of highest volatile matter possess considerable caking power, the production of metallurgical coke.

Anthracites form the highest rank of coal and therefore the extreme of metamorphosis from the original plant material. Carbon content is over 93 per cent., volatile matter less than 8, and caking power zero.

Unusual types of coal are the cannels and torbanites ; these are described in Chapter VI.

The general relationship between these types is shown in Table XIX, in which the data are given in terms of pure coal free from mineral matter.

TABLE XIX

STAGES IN THE TRANSITION OF COALS

	Wood.	Peat.	Lignite.		Bituminous.				Carbon-aceous.	Anthra-cite.
			Brown.	Black.	1	2	3	4		
Air-dried.										
Moisture	20	20	18	15	10	3	1	1	1	1
Volatile matter, less moisture . . .	—	50	47	41	35	34	32	30	11	8
Fixed carbon . .	—	27	28	32	45	58	62	64	84	88
Ash	0·5	3	7	12	10	5	5	5	4	3
B.Th.U. per lb. . .	6,400	7,700	9,900	10,200	10,700	13,900	14,300	14,400	15,000	15,000
Ash-free dry.										
Carbon	50	60	67	74	77	84	85·6	87	92	94
Hydrogen . . .	6·5	6	5·5	5·4	5	5	5	5·3	4	3
Oxygen	43	32	26	19	16	8	5·4	4·7	2	2
Sulphur and nitrogen	0·5	2	1·5	1·6	2	3	4	3	2	1
B.Th.U. per lb. . .	8,000	10,000	13,200	13,900	13,400	15,100	15,200	15,300	15,800	15,600

Bituminous 1.　Lignitous, long-flame steam and house coal.
,,　　　2.　Para-bituminous, hard steam and house coal. ⎫
,,　　　3.　Para-bituminous, gas and coking coal. ⎬Seyler.
,,　　　4.　Ortho-bituminous, coking coal (Durham). ⎭

It is clear from this table that the proximate analysis provides an easy means of differentiating between diverse types such as lignite and bituminous coal, but that a knowledge of the elementary composition is essential if there is to be differentiation within the limits of types. Even then, further knowledge may be necessary regarding caking power, since there may be variations at the same carbon content. In using the table it is necessary to remember that each class or type merges into its neighbour and that there is no sharp division. Indeed, the figures show the gradual elimination of oxygen from 40 per cent. in wood to 2 per cent. in anthracite and the change in hydrogen content from 6·5 to 3 per cent. These two factors have an additive effect on the carbon figure so that the C/H ratio increases steadily, e.g. from 14·5/1 to 16·4/1 within the bituminous class.

The regular nature of these variations was a clear lead to the evolution of a classification system. The first real attempt was made by Regnault in 1837 in terms of carbon, hydrogen and oxygen. This was modified in 1874 by Grüner, who added volatile matter and caking power. He was particularly interested in the bituminous type and divided this into five classes as shown in Table XX.

TABLE XX

REGNAULT-GRÜNER CLASSIFICATION OF BITUMINOUS COALS

No. of class.	Character of coal.	Carbon.	Hydro-gen.	Oxygen.	Ratio $\frac{O}{H}$	Volatile matter.	Nature of coke.
I.	Dry, long flame, non-caking	75–80	4·5–5·5	15–19·5	4–3	40–50	Powdery or slightly coherent.
II.	Fat, long flame	80–85	5·0–5·8	10–14·2	3–2	32–40	Caked, but friable.
III.	Fat, properly so called	84–89	5·0–5·5	5·5–11·0	2–1	26–32	Caked, moderately compact.
IV.	Fat, short flame	88–91	4·5–5·5	4·5–6·5	1	18–26	Caked, very compact, lustrous.
V.	Lean coals—anthracite	90–93	4·0–4·5	3–5·5	1	10–18	Powdery or slightly coherent.

This arrangement was not entirely suitable for British coals and was further modified in 1925 by Brame, and enlarged to include other types of British coals. Among the coals of low rank, although lignite proper only occurs in very small quantity in Great Britain, there are " dry " coals, with high oxygen content, between the lignites and the usual steam " non-caking long flame coals ", which seem to demand special groupings, and for these the terms lignitous and ligno-bituminous have been adopted. Brame's modified and extended form of Grüner's classification is given in Table XXI.

TABLE XXI

GRÜNER CLASSIFICATION MODIFIED FOR THE COALS OF GREAT BRITAIN

No. of class.	Name of class.	Carbon.	Hydro-gen.	Oxygen.	Volatile matter.
I.	Lignitous	75–80	4·8–5·5	12–20	35–47
II.	Ligno-bituminous . . .	78–84	4·5–6	8–13·5	35–45
III.	Long flame, non-caking (steam, etc.)	82–86	5–6	6–12	30–40
IV.	Long flame, partly caking (gas)	82–86	4·5–5·5	5–9	30–40
V.	Short flame (coking) . .	85–89	4·5–5·5	4–7·5	20–30
VI.	Semi-bituminous	89–92	4–5	2–4·5	13–20
VII.	Semi-anthracite	91–93	3–4·5	3–5	8–13
VIII.	Anthracite	over 92·5	below 4	below 3	below 8

A closely allied classification on the basis of the Grüner system has been adopted by W. A. Bone, the main groupings being lignites, bituminous, semi-bituminous and anthracites, with sub-division of the bituminous into non-caking long flame, caking long flame, hard coking and hard coking short flame, and the anthracite group into anthracitic and anthracite.

It must again be emphasized that no such system can be rigid ; for example, a gas coal towards the lower limit of volatile matter may be satisfactorily worked for coke in a suitable oven, and a semi-bituminous caking coal may be equally good for coking whilst not so well suited for burning owing to its caking properties.

A number of other classifications have been attempted since. The most important of these are described below.

1. Frazer (Pa. 2nd Geol. Survey, Rept. M.M. 879).

In this scheme the ratio of fixed carbon to volatile matter was used. The system failed mainly because of considerable overlapping of classes and limitation to one particular coalfield.

	Ratio.
Anthracite	100/1 to 12/1
Semi-anthracite	12/1 to 8/1
Semi-bituminous	8/1 to 5/1
Bituminous	5/1 to 1/1

2. Campbell (U.S. Geo. Survey, Paper 48, 1906).

Campbell considered that the above ratio was of little value except for coals of low volatile matter and suggested instead the ratio of carbon to hydrogen together with a descriptive record of the appearance of the coal and its behaviour on weathering. This was adopted by the U.S. Geological Survey in 1902.

3. Ralston (U.S. Bureau Mines Tech. Paper 93, 1915).

This was the most comprehensive system to date and included the percentages of carbon, hydrogen and oxygen in a triangular diagram. The percentages of the three elements were plotted on trilinear co-ordinates as shown in Figure 10.

This diagram shows in a striking manner the variation in oxygen content from wood to anthracite.

4. Parr (Univ. of Illinois Bull. 180, 1928).

Parr classifies coal in terms of the calorific value of the coal substance (pure coal or unit coal) plotted against the percentage of volatile matter. The calorific value of a coal is given by :

$$\frac{\text{Indicated B.Th.U.} - 5000\,S}{1 \cdot 00 - (1 \cdot 08\,A + 22/40\,S)}$$

and the volatile matter by :

$$\frac{\text{Determined volatile matter} - (0 \cdot 08 + 0 \cdot 4\,S)}{1 \cdot 00 - (1 \cdot 08\,A + 22/40\,S)}$$

Where A = ash and S = combustible sulphur expressed as fractions, the water of hydration of clays being taken as 8 per cent.

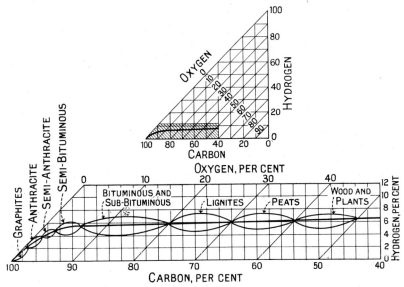

Fig. 10.—Ralston's Classification of Coal.

The following table (XXII) shows the types of coal and the limits of volatile matter and unit calorific value characteristic of each type.

TABLE XXII

Parr's Classification of Coal

Class of coal.	Unit volatile matter.		Unit B.Th.U.	
	Low.	High.	Low.	High.
Anthracite	0	8	15,000	16,500
Semi-anthracite	8	12	15,000	16,500
Bituminous A	12	24	15,000	16,500
,, B	24	50	15,000	16,500
,, C	30	55	14,000	15,000
,, D	35	60	12,500	14,000
Lignite	35	60	11,000	12,500
Peat	55	80	9,000	11,000
Cannels	60	80	15,000	16,500

W. Francis (*J. Inst. Fuel*, 1933, **6**, 301) has proposed as a method of classification rational analysis, i.e. the determination and ultimate analysis of what Wheeler and his co-workers regard as the primary constituents of coal, (1) free hydrocarbons, (2) resins, (3) plant entities, (4) ulmins. The original paper should be consulted for further details of what appears to be a promising scheme for a really scientific classification of coal.

It is apparent that the changes of composition of coal through the various types can be represented graphically. When pairs of property factors such as carbon and hydrogen, or carbon and calorific value, volatile matter, or caking properties, are plotted, nearly all the points fall within a narrow band which has a distinctive shape. This has been termed " the coal band " and one form of it has already been shown in Figure 6 for carbon/oxygen. The distance along the band indicates the rank of the coal. The width of the band is a measure of the variation of hydrogen which appears in coal as a result of variation of the nature of the plant material contributing to it.

A similar system, but which allows of greater differentiation between types, is now the most commonly recognized and used, certainly in Great Britain ; it is due to C. A. Seyler. From 1900 onwards he examined Grüner's system in relation to British coals and made it applicable by further sub-division of the bituminous species according to caking properties. Coking coals of the South Wales type he termed *meta-*, of the Durham type *ortho-*, and of the gas coal type *para-*bituminous. Bituminous coals of low caking power he termed lignitous as approaching the type of lignite.

The final system divided each species of coal into genera in which the variation of hydrogen was considered in relation to the variation of carbon content in the species. The complete system took the form shown in Table XXIII (*Analysis of British Coals and Cokes*, 1924).

The system can conveniently be expressed graphically on carbon-hydrogen axes. Seyler draws an analogy between his chart and a geographical one, the hydrogen lines corresponding to parallels of latitude and the carbon lines to those of longitude ; just as the position of a place is defined geographically by defining latitude and longitude so the position of a coal can be defined by quoting its C : H values. Then, by reference to a chart the nature of the coal is at once clear. Such a system of definition should be clearer than a system of names.

Seyler has worked continuously since on his system and has from time to time added other factors to it. These include isovalent lines showing the regular variation of different properties such as calorific value, capacity moisture, and caking power.

In the chart, the common types of coal fall within the rectangular areas to the left and together form a curved band which is sometimes termed the coal band and resembles that of Parr. Coals of higher hydrogen content (*perhydrous*) are bogheads and cannels of less common occurrence. *Sub-hydrous* coals are fusain and certain durains.

The isovalent lines are as follows. The lines of equal calorific value (isocals) slope upwards from left to right while those of equal volatile matter (isovols) cross these at right angles. The former are parallel, equally spaced lines, following Dulong's law, but the latter are less regular outside the region of 10 to 40 per cent. volatile matter. In themselves these lines have no great significance, but their insertion indicates means of correlating

TABLE XXIII

SEYLER'S CLASSIFICATION OF COAL

Carbon.	Anthracitic.	Carbonaceous.	Bituminous.			Lignitous.	
			Meta-	Ortho-	Para-	Meta-	Ortho-
Carbon.	Carbon over 93·3 per cent.	93·3–91·2.	91·2–89·0.	89·0–87·0.	87·0–84·0.	84–85.	80–75.
Per-bituminous genus. Hydrogen > 5·8 per cent.	—	—	Per-bituminous (per-meta-bituminous)	Per-bituminous (per-ortho-bituminous)	Per-bituminous (per-para-bituminous)	Per-lignitous	
Bituminous genus Hydrogen 5·0–5·8 per cent.	—	Pseudo-bituminous species	Meta-bituminous	Ortho-bituminous	Para-bituminous	Lignitous Meta	Ortho
Semi-bituminous genus Hydrogen 4·5–5·0 per cent.	—	Semi-bituminous species (ortho-semi-bituminous)	Sub-bituminous (sub-meta-bituminous)	Sub-bituminous (sub-ortho-bituminous)	Sub-bituminous	Sub-lignitous Meta	Ortho
Carbonaceous genus Hydrogen 4·0–4·5 per cent.	Semi-anthracitic species Dry steam coal	Carbonaceous species (ortho-carbonaceous)	Pseudo-carbonaceous (sub-meta-bituminous)	Pseudo-carbonaceous (sub-ortho-bituminous)	Pseudo-carbonaceous (sub-para-bituminous)		
Anthracitic genus Hydrogen < 4 per cent.	Ortho-anthracite True anthracite	Pseudo-anthracite (sub-carbonaceous)	Pseudo-anthracite (sub-meta-bituminous)	Pseudo-anthracite (sub-ortho-bituminous)	Pseudo-anthracite (sub-para-bituminous)		

calorific value and volatile matter. The isocals are also lines of equal air requirements for the combustion of the coal and have been correlated by Seyler (*loc. cit.*) and Rosin and Fehling (*Das It. Diagramm*, Berlin, 1929), with flue gas volumes, calorific intensity and flame temperature under

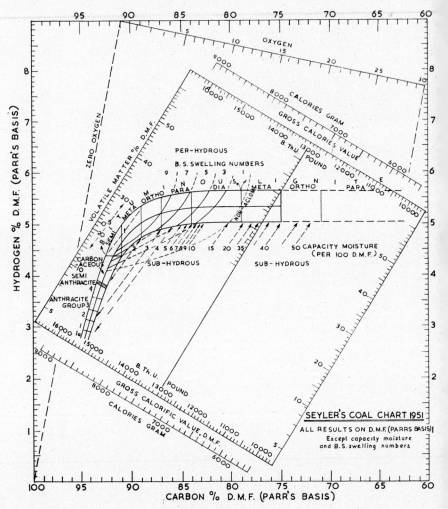

Fig. 11.—Seyler's Classification of Coal.

conditions of adiabatic combustion. A number of scales show the combustion characteristics appropriate to the isocal lines. The top and bottom scales are metric and British units respectively. It should be noted that, in order to be sure that his coal data were as representative of the coal substance as possible, Seyler calculated his analyses to a basis of " pure " coal using the Parr convention (p. 478) for calculation to a mineral-matter-

free basis. It would have been much more satisfactory had he used the
K.M.C. formula (p. 478), which includes sulphur in the coal substance,
particularly because of its impact on British coals. Unfortunately this
latter formula requires rather detailed analyses which are more difficult to
obtain and in their absence an opportunity was lost.

A recent form of the chart is shown in Figure 11, and a simplified form,
showing C/H axes and the coal band only, is shown in Figure 12.

That there is a discontinuity in the coal band has been shown by E. S.
Grumell (*Trans. Inst. Min. Eng.*, 1931, **81(2)**, 214; **81(3)**, 308). When
the calorific value of a large series of coals is plotted against their carbon

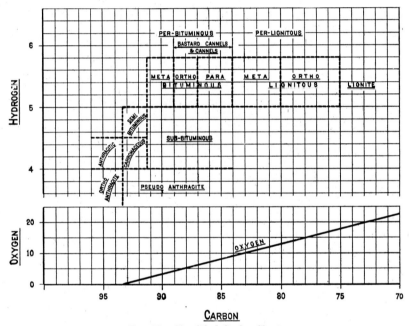

FIG. 12.—Simplified Seyler Chart.

content a coal band is obtained which shows a sharp bend at about 86 per
cent. C indicating that above this point the coals diverge from the Dulong
formula. Below the point agreement of observed calorific value with that
calculated from the Dulong formula is found within reasonable limits.
Grumell prefers to consider dull and bright coals separately as having
different sources and shows that their coal bands do not coincide. A coal
band of this type is a useful guide to fuel composition since it is comparatively narrow in both dimensions below the band at 86 per cent. carbon.
For example, with bright coals the iso-calorific lines may contain coal
differing by 1·2 per cent. of carbon and the iso-carbon lines coal differing
by only 155 calories. It seems probable that even these margins may be
reduced by calculation of analyses on a more accurate basis.

PRACTICAL CLASSIFICATION OF THE FUEL RESEARCH BOARD (D.S.I.R.), AND THE COAL BOARD

During the war years an essentially practical system was suggested in Great Britain for the evaluation of coal reserves. It was hoped to make this as simple as possible and the criteria chosen were volatile matter and caking power (on the Gray-King scale), with the intended addition of reservations for particle size and ash content and, for metallurgical purposes, sulphur and phosphorus. The objective was therefore to use volatile matter as the criterion of rank and to define caking power as an additional usage classification. In order to make this clear the relationship between volatile matter and caking power is reproduced in Figure 13 from the paper making the original suggestion.

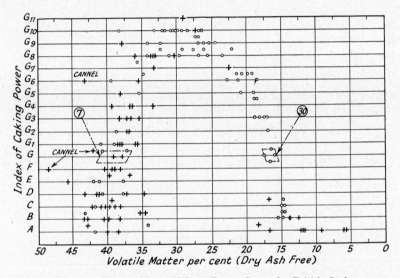

Fig. 13.—Volatile Matter/Caking Power Curve for British Coals.

The close connection between volatile matter and coal rank is shown by the similarity of the curve of Figure 13 to that of Figure 14, where caking power is graphed against the carbon content of the pure coal.

In this figure it is seen that caking power develops at 15 to 20 per cent. volatile matter, reaches a maximum at 22 to 33 per cent., and disappears again at about 40 per cent. At lower values of volatile matter the band is narrow, showing a close correlation, but at the other end it is very broad and wide variations of caking power are possible in coals of the same volatile matter. This suggests that the use classification should divide the bituminous class in which caking power is predominant into (horizontal) sections corresponding to several ranges of caking power and in turn to compartment these into, say, two or three ranges of volatile matter. This would then give sufficient compartmenting in the right place, and is in fact what was done in the Fuel Research Paper on the subject (Survey Paper 58, 1946), which has classified the reserves of British coals in this way. The system has been adopted, with some modification, by the National Coal Board and is now implicit in their coal marketing schemes. A somewhat shortened version of the Coal Board arrangement is given below with a few additional explanatory notes.

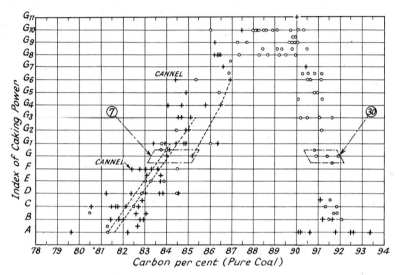

FIG. 14.—The Variation of Caking Power of Coal with Rank.

Coal Rank Code Numbers (National Coal Board). The system was developed with a numerical background in order to facilitate mechanical handling of the data, but the same numbers have through familiarity provided a useful code description which is short and convenient to use. The volatile matter is expressed on dry, ash-free coal and the caking power is that of clean material containing not more than 7·5 per cent. of ash. The method of determining this is described in Chapter XVIII.

100	Anthracite, non-caking	.	. . .	. V.M.	9·5% or less
100a	,,	,,	coke type A	. .	4·0– 6·5%
100b	,,	,,	coke type A	. .	6·6– 9·5%
200	Low-volatile steam coal	.	. .	. V.M.	9·6–20·0%
201	Dry steam coal, non-caking type A/B	.	.		9·6–14·0%,
201a	. . .	. . .	. .	.	9·6–12·0%
201b	. . .	. .	. .	.	12·1–14·0%
202	Coking steam coal.	Weakly-caking type C–G	.		14·1–15·5%
203	,, ,, ,,	Medium-caking type C–G$_4$			15·5–17·5%
204	,, ,, ,,	Strongly-caking type G$_4$–G$_8$			17·6–20·0%
206	Scottish anthracite.	Weakly-caking type A–B			9·6–15·5%
		A–D			15·6–20·0%

Medium Volatile Coals

300	Heat-altered coal.	Weakly-caking type A–G$_3$ V.M.	20·1–30·0%
300a	,,	,, Medium-caking type C–G$_3$.	,, ,,
300b	,,	,, Weakly-caking type A–F.	,, ,,
301	Coking coal.	Strongly-caking type G and over	20·1–30·0%

High Volatile Coals

400	Coking/gas coal. Strongly-caking type G$_9$ $_+$. V.M.	30·0% +
401	Coking coal	30·1–37·0%
401a	,, ,, ...	30·1–33·0%
401b	,, ,, ...	33·1–37·0%
402	Gas coal	37·0% +
500	Strongly-caking coal. Strongly-caking type	
	G$_5$–G$_8$ V.M.	30·0% +
501	. . . .	30·1–37·0%
	For Durham only :	
501a	. . . .	30·1–33·0%
501b	. . . .	33·1–37·0%
502	. . . .	37·0% +
600	Medium-caking coal. Medium-caking type	
	G$_1$–G$_4$ V.M.	30·0% +
601	. . . .	30·1–37·0%
602	. . . .	37·0% +
700	Weakly-caking coal type E–G . . . V.M.	30·0% +
701	. . . .	30·1–37·0%
702	. . . .	37·0% +
800	Very-weakly-caking coal type C–D . . . V.M.	30·1% +
801	. . . .	30·1–37·0%
802	. . . .	37·0% +
900	Non-caking coal type A–B . . . V.M.	30·0% +
901	. . . .	30·1–37·0%
902	. . . .	37·0% +

The separation of coals for the market in this manner will lead to a wider knowledge of their properties and it should become easier for industry in the future to obtain the best type of coal for its purpose. It must be emphasized that separation is by type only and that the other factors of ash content and size grading must be dealt with also. To take one example of the application of the system we have the separation of coking and gas coals. The users of the former prefer high caking power, low volatile matter, low sulphur and perhaps phosphorus, and low ash content, and can use (perhaps prefer) coal of small particle size. The users of the latter desire good caking power and prefer high volatile matter and graded sizes ; ash and sulphur are less important. Now the industries overlap in their demands but it is apparent that the scheme could make a very efficient first separation by allocating clean caking coals of small size to coking, and graded coals to gas. This is indeed done already to a very considerable extent. There could be added, however, the subdivision of caking coals into close ranges of volatile matter and their redirection. For example, the gas industry should not be allowed to have any of grade 401*a* if it is clean enough for making coke even if it means crushing large coal of this grade or greater transport on other coals. Distribution plans are already moving in this direction.

PROPOSED CLASSIFICATION OF THE ECONOMIC COMMISSION OF EUROPE

In order to facilitate trade in coal in Europe the Commission appointed a committee to prepare a commercial system which would exactly define the properties of all European coals and arrange them in groups or classes. The work of the Committee is not yet complete and the following brief statement is not necessarily what the final system will be.

It is proposed to divide coals into ten classes on parameters of volatile matter of the dry, ash-free coal, and the calorific value of the moist, ash-free coal, the moisture content being the " capacity " moisture determined at 30° C. and at 97 per cent. relative humidity.

Each class is then divided into four groups representing degrees of caking power as measured by the " free-swelling index " of the French coal specification, and the Roga Index. These groups are in turn divided into sub-groups which are decided by the type of coke obtained under carbonizing conditions, it being considered that this measures a different property than the F.S. and Roga indices. The test methods selected are the Gray-King assay and the Audibert-Arnu dilatometer test.

The descriptions of the tests specified are given partly below and in Chapter XVIII.

Although the tests do not measure exactly the same mechanism of caking or swelling, there is a rough correlation between the results of test, as follows :

The Roga Index falls on both sides of the line representing the index against ten times the Free-Swelling index.

In the Audibert-Arnu test dilation does not occur until the coal corresponds to type G to G_1 of the Gray-King assay. Thereafter the agreement is :

G_1 to G_4 gives a maximum dilation from 0 to 60 per cent.
G_4 to G_8 ,,   ,,   ,,   ,,   60 to 130 ,, ,,
G_8 to G_{12} ,,   ,,   ,,   ,,   130 to 400 ,, ,,

The A.-A. method is, therefore, probably more discriminating in the range of very strongly-caking coals.

The Roga Index correlates with the Gray-King assay approximately as Index 0–5 = AB ; 5–10 = BD ; 20 = G ; 45 = G_4.

PHYSICAL PROPERTIES OF COAL

Coal has certain physical properties which vary to a greater or less degree with each type, and some of these, such as porosity, have been used in studies of coal constitution. Others such as specific gravity or bulk density have a bearing mainly on their industrial uses.

Porosity. Porosity measurement as a guide to coal constitution is dealt with above. It is realized that, in general, coal is interspersed by capillaries and pores of different size which give it a sponge-like structure.

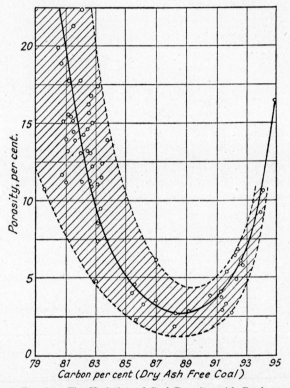

Fig. 15.—The Variation of Coal Porosity with Rank.

If the porosity of coal is measured by impregnating it with water, allowing the surface film just to disappear, and calculating the retained water as a measure of the total volume of the capillaries, a relationship with carbon content is found as shown in Figure 15, which is approximately the reverse of the caking power curve of Figure 14, and is therefore a measure of coal rank. The dispersion of the points is quite large, but this is, as explained already, typical of the coal band drawn on any ordinates. It shows a minimum value at about 88/89 per cent. carbon and both high porosity and greater variation with lower-carbon coals. Porosity values obtained in this way are not of course absolute values but are strictly comparable with one another. As would be expected, the shape of the curve is the same as the Bangham " heat of wetting " curve (p. 78), and it appears that one per cent. porosity is equivalent to about one cal. per g. as heat of wetting. Since Bangham has shown that this is also equivalent to 10 m.^{2} per g. coal, the mean diameter of the capillaries must be about 40 Å.

The sorption of moisture by coal shows characteristic hysteresis loops as shown in Figure 16. The width of the loop increases from high-rank coals (anthracite, C, almost zero) to a wide loop with coal, A, of about 82 per cent. carbon and maximum porosity. If this loop is due to the slow

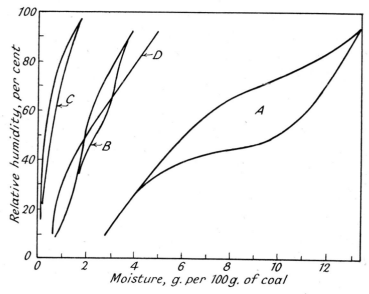

FIG. 16.—Moisture Sorption by Coal of Different Rank.

rate of emptying of the finer pores it is possible to calculate the spacing of these. In the figure the relative loops for the four coals are 5, 4, 0·1, and 0 ; taking 30 Å as their mean diameters their spacings become 150, 500, 1000, and 1000 + Å respectively. These dimensions agree with the size of the Bangham micelle and the increase of size with rank agrees with Riley's theory of molecular condensation in the metamorphosis of coal. In the case of the banded components of coal, vitrain shows a wide loop, and durain and fusain narrow loops. Since their overall porosities are about the same, it follows that the pores in vitrain are of less diameter. This has been confirmed by the X-ray study of the rate of penetration of inorganic salts from solution.

Caking Power. The behaviour of coal on heating, and whether the solid product is pulverulent or massive, is of special importance to many industrial processes, and many methods have been suggested for its measurement or definition.

There has been some confusion in the use of the terms " caking " and " coking ", but there need be none if the latter when applied to coals is limited to mean that a coking coal is simply one that is used for the manufacture of metallurgical coke. That leaves the term caking in the abstract and allows it to be qualified (strong, weak, non-, etc.) according to the method adopted for test. The method must always be stated, however, as most methods measure slightly different properties and their results are not all capable of more than approximate correlation.

Some of these methods are described in Chapter XVIII, but attention is particularly directed to the Gray-King Assay coke type which has been referred to above as an instrument in a practical coal classification system. In this method the coal (20 g. passing a 72 B.S. sieve) is carbonized under standard conditions to 600° C. If the carbonized residue is pulverulent with no sign of coherence the coal is termed " non-caking type A ". Coal which gives a hard, compact, non-fissured coke of the same volume as the original coal is termed G, while the intermediate letters designate coals whose coke-friability decreases within this range. Coals of higher caking power are blended with 72-mesh carbon to give a coke corresponding to type G, and termed G_1 to G_{10} respectively, the subscript numbers indicating the number of grams of carbon necessary in the 20-g. blend.

The present standards of coke type are referred to a photographic series in which A appears as a powder, E to F a series of decreasing friability, G the basic standard of unit volume and hardness, while G_1 to G_9 show the increased swelling which would take place if admixture with carbon were not done. Several of these cokes are shown in Figure 17.

The correlation with the coal types of the National Coal Board's classification of coal has been discussed but is repeated below :

Gray-King Assay. Coke type.	National Coal Board. Coal type.
A, B	100(A), 201, 206, 300b, 901, 902. Non-caking.
C, D	202, 206, 300b, 801, 802. Very weakly caking.
E, F, G	202, 203(G), 300b(EF), 300a(G), 701, 702.
G_1, G_2, G_3, G_4	203, 204(G_4), 300a(G_{1-3}), 301(G_4), 601, 602. Medium caking.
G_5–G_8	204, 301, 501, 502. Strongly caking.
G_9 and over	301, 401, 402. Very strongly caking.

Correlation of the Gray-King scale of caking power with the results obtained by other methods has been attempted, but the agreement is not very close. The excellent agreement which the G-K scale shows with the variations of the coal band is, however, a strong recommendation in favour of its usage. This is shown above on a volatile matter basis in Figure 13, and on a basis of carbon content in Figure 14. In the latter case the precaution has been taken to show the curve on the basis of mineral-matter-free coal. It is evident that a fairly narrow band can be drawn to enclose

B

E

G

G$_2$

G$_4$

Fig. 17.—Selection of Standard Cokes of the Gray-King Assay.

all the points ; it could actually be narrower if it were confined to the examination of vitrinites only. It is also noteworthy that the curve is an inverse reflection of the carbon/porosity/heat of wetting curves which suggests a correlation between caking power and internal structure.

It is important that the assay should not be made on dirty coals since the presence of too much mineral matter will reduce the observed value. In addition, the presence of pyritic sulphur will reduce the value by one index for each one per cent. of sulphur present in the form of FeS_2.

The correlation with the B.S. swelling index is perhaps better than with other tests, and is as follows :

Gray-King Coke Type	A	B	C	D	E	F	G	G_1	G_2	G_3	G_4	G_5	G_6	G_7	G_8
B.S. Swelling No.		1	$1\frac{1}{2}$	2		3		4	5	6	7	8	8	9	

The lack of definition in the early part of the swelling-number scale is of course due to the fact that this method was not intended to cover weakly-caking coals.

Studies of the Plasticity of Coal during Heating. A number of studies have been made of the behaviour of caking coals when passing through the various stages of plasticity which occur with rise of temperature up to the point of coke formation. The objectives have been the devising of a means of predicting the behaviour of coal in carbonizing plant from a laboratory test, and to a less extent in studies of the classification of coals.

The techniques have varied ; J. D. Davis has measured the resistance to stirring of coal heated at a controlled rate of $3 \cdot 4°$ C. per minute. Damm and Agde measure the expansion of a briquette heated at $4 \cdot 2°$ C. per min. under a load of 10 lb. per sq. in. and record the temperatures for the beginning of contraction and expansion. Gieseler has used a penetrometer to measure the softening temperature and the solidifying temperature. G. E. Foxwell passed a stream of nitrogen through a column of coal and measured the softening temperature as that at which resistance developed to the passage of the gas ; he observed also the temperatures of (a) maximum resistance to flow and (b) when resistance subsided with the inception of porosity as coke formation began. He defined in this way the plastic range of coal and also obtained a measure of the maximum resistance to flow measured in millimetres of water.

A method more closely related to practice is aimed at the measurement of the swelling pressure which might be developed in an oven during the carbonization of the coal charge. Laboratory methods do not provide such information with any certainty, probably because the difference of scale cannot be overcome. The method now adopted is to carbonize the suspected coal in a model oven (12 in. wide : 400 lb. coal) with a movable wall connected to a device for indicating the pressure. This wall pressure is compared with the gas pressure developed within the charge as measured by the insertion of a special pressure pipe into the centre of the charge.

Using this technique, it has been found that coking coals fall into groups which show pressure/time curves of typically different shapes.

(a) Slight wall pressure rising to 0·75 lb. per sq. in. ; almost negligible internal pressure showing a slight rise at the time when the plastic layers meet at the centre of the charge, again to 0·75 lb.

(b) Higher initial wall pressure rising to 4 lb. and reaching 5 lb. as the plastic layers meet ; internal pressures rising to about 8 lb.

(c) Continuous rise of wall pressure to a maximum of about 8 lb. ; very high internal pressure rising to over 15 lb.

These groups are not sharply defined and many intermediate types of coal are found. Correlation of the results to practice is not yet fully established, but the method is finding useful application in the study of coal blending in order not only to modify dangerous coals but also to conserve coking coals by the wider use of weaker-caking coals and coke breeze.

The whole subject of the plasticity of coal is full of complications and is too diffuse to discuss here. The reader is referred for a more complete account to *The Quality of Coke* by Mott and Wheeler.

Specific Gravity and Stowage Capacity. The specific gravity of coal is dependent upon two variables—the character of the combustible portion and the proportion of ash ; the latter is of much higher density than the coal substance, and consequently exercises considerable influence on the specific gravity of the whole coal. The specific gravity varies between 1·27 and 1·45 for bituminous coal ; only in exceptional cases will it fall outside these limits. On an average, anthracite is from 10 to 15 per cent. denser than bituminous coal and varies from 1·4 to 1·7.

The bulk density of coal, and therefore its stowage capacity or the amount which can be stored in a given volume, depends upon a considerable number of factors. These include the size and grading of the material, the shape of the particles, the amount of free water present, and the shape of the container and the method of packing of the coal in it. Shape of coal is probably the least important since it does not vary greatly from one coal to another. Table XXIV (page 110), from *Technical Data on Fuel*, gives a comparison of the effects of both size of coal and size of container for dry, loosely-packed material.

Compacting the coal may increase these values by amounts up to 20 per cent. Small coal decreases in density with increasing free moisture to a minimum value which depends on the amount of fine material present. This minimum occurs at 4 to 6 per cent. of free moisture for normal small coals and is about 15 per cent. lower than the density of the dry coal.

Angle of Repose. This is of interest in the storage of coals and in ensuring the flow of coal in conveyers and feed hoppers. The angle is not an exact figure since it depends upon other factors such as the roughness of the surface and the presence of water. For this reason values may

TABLE XXIV

BULK DENSITY OF DRY COAL

Size of coal.	Side of container (in.).			
	Large	18	12	6
		lb. per cu. ft.		
2×1 in.	40 ± 4	42	41	38
$1 \times \frac{1}{2}$,, ...		42	41	$39\frac{1}{2}$
$\frac{1}{2} \times \frac{1}{4}$,, ...		39	$38\frac{1}{2}$	38
$\frac{1}{4} \times \frac{1}{8}$,, ...		38	$37\frac{1}{2}$	37
2 in., small	52	51	$50\frac{1}{2}$	50
1 in., small	50	49	$48\frac{1}{2}$	$47\frac{1}{2}$
$\frac{1}{2}$ in., small	$47\frac{1}{2}$	47	46	$45\frac{1}{2}$
$\frac{1}{8}$ in., small	44	44	$43\frac{1}{2}$	43
Dust $< \frac{1}{8}$ in.	30 to 36			
Pulverized	25 to 31			

vary by as much as $2°$ to $3°$. For dry coal in bulk the following data indicate the order of things :

Size of coal	$1\frac{1}{4}$–$\frac{3}{4}$ in.	$\frac{3}{4}$–$\frac{1}{2}$	$\frac{1}{2}$–$\frac{1}{4}$	$\frac{1}{4}$–0
Angle with the horizontal (deg.)	41	40	38	32

Coherence. The resistance of coals to breakage on handling is an important factor in industrial usage. Certain valuable coals are limited in their applications, and are less efficient than they might be, because they form an undue proportion of fines on handling and these fines tend to accumulate mineral matter to such an extent that they cannot be used for the purposes for which the quality of the clean coal substance should make them suitable. In some cases the friability is such that the coal cannot be efficiently sized and it has to be marketed as " run of mine " material. Durham coals are an example of this. The fines normally find their way into a cheaper market or, as in the case of some anthracites, are briquetted before sale. In shipment, formerly, there was considerable deterioration of size, but to-day anti-breakage loading devices are in common use.

Lump coal tends to break during storage, through oxidation and other reasons. The extent of breakdown varies with the type of coal ; in the case of black lignite the rate is high and complete disintegration to a powder may occur in a few days, particularly if assisted by alternate wetting and drying. A measure of the tendency of a coal to disintegrate on storage can be obtained in this way by applying standardized conditions of wetting and drying and measuring the proportion of fines produced after a given number of times. Such a test has been developed for U.S. coals by the U.S. Bureau of Mines.

Thermal Properties. Calorific value is obviously one of the most important properties of a fuel. Methods of determination and calculation from analysis are described in Chapter XIX. Until recently many of the published calorific values were open to question owing to the faulty methods of determination used, but now it is recognized that the only reliable means is a calorimeter of the bomb type and standardized conditions. In considering calorific values of coal from the same source it is often of value to calculate the calorific value to the dry ash-free fuel if the ash content is not high and to use this value as a check. All consignments of the same coal should conform to the same dry ash-free calorific value, although small variations may occur in mixed consignments.

A more reliable check is obtained by using the dry, mineral-matter-free analysis ; in this case remarkably close checking can be done. This also serves for the checking of series of analytical results on the same or similar coals.

When coal is carbonized as in gas or coke manufacture the thermal changes involved (heats of reaction) are small. The complex bodies in the coal are broken down to simpler bodies in the products of carbonization, and since there is a difference in the heat of formation of the original and final bodies, the distillation is accompanied either by an evolution or absorption of heat. Mahler and Euchène were the first to attempt to estimate the magnitude of the thermal changes, the former by determining heats of combustion of the coal and of proportionate amounts of products, and the latter by preparing a thermal balance of a large-scale carbonization. In more recent years the tendency has been to carry out experiments in specially designed calorimeters.

In nearly all cases the thermal effect is small and variable, exothermicity or otherwise depending on the temperature of carbonization. In general, it may be said that peats, lignites and younger coals are more exothermic than the older coals, exothermicity apparently being somewhat connected with the oxygen content. The following figures, which refer to a carbonizing temperature of $700°$ C., may be regarded as giving the order of the heat release.

Wood	+ 168 to + 323 cal.
Lignites	+ 103 to 112 "
Brown coal	+ 25 to + 98 "
Bituminous coal	+ 30 to − 57 "

Below $600°$ C. some coals are exothermic and some endothermic, but above that temperature there is a general tendency towards endothermicity which is more pronounced above $800°$ C. The difficulties of experimental determination of definite values are very great and cannot readily be eliminated. They rather tend to show that the amount of labour necessary in this determination is out of proportion to the reliability of the results obtainable.

Terres (Bituminous Coal Conference, 1928) has also provided figures for the " coking heat " of coal. The " nett coking heat " is the number of Calories required to convert 1 kg. of coal at $20°$ C. into coke at a definite temperature, including the energy in Cal., corresponding to the external work performed by the distillation products. The "gross coking heat" includes the radiation loss from the ovens and the sensible heat content of the flue gases. The temperature normally adopted is 1000° C. The "heat of decomposition" is the net coking heat at the temperature in question minus the sensible and latent heat content of the coke and volatile products, and the heat equivalent of the work performed by these products against the atmosphere. In exceptional cases this heat of decomposition may vary from + 110 at 930° C. to − 75 Cal. at 1010° C. Such a coal would require a long coking time. The net coking heat varies between 450 and 200 Cal. per kg. of air-dried coal. Coking heats are highest in the case of coals having a high endothermic heat of decomposition. The more exothermic the decomposition, the lower is the coking heat and the more endothermic the decomposition, the higher is the coking heat. When the heat of decomposition is zero the normal coking heat is approximately 325. The time required for coking coal in a coke oven can be calculated from Terres' data. This is still the classic work on this subject.

Specific Heat. The specific heat of coal is of interest in connection with carbonization problems generally. Coles (*J.S.C.I.*, 1923, **42,** 425T) gives the following values for dry ash-free coal at normal temperature :

Fusain	.	.	.	.	.	0·21–0·22 gm. cals./gm./° C.
Anthracite	.	.	.	.	.	0·22–0·23 ,, ,,
Bituminous coal	.	.	.	.	0·24–0·26 ,, ,,

The specific heat of coal ash varies from 0·16 to 0·17. Further, the specific heat of coal increases with increase of volatile matter and with decrease of the C/H ratio. The relationship between specific heat and ash or water content is linear and any combination can be calculated from the appropriate formula. In the case of coke Terres has also shown that specific heat varies with the ash content and has given values of which the following are typical :

$t°$ C.	Mean sp. heat in gm. cals./gm./° C.
600	0·325–0·00081 A⎫
1000	0·382–0·00135 A⎭ where A = ash per cent.

Thermal and Electrical Conductivity. Terres has also provided formulæ for the mean thermal conductivity of certain coals between 0 and $t°$ C.—t being the temperature of carbonization.

For coking coals giving a coke of high density (low porosity)

$$k = 0.0003 + 0.0016 \times \frac{t}{1000} + 0.0016 \times \left(\frac{t}{1000}\right)^2.$$

For gas coals giving a coke of average density

$$k = 0.0003 + 0.0013 \times \frac{t}{1000} + 0.0015 \times \left(\frac{t}{1000}\right)^2.$$

For gas coals giving a spongy coke

$$k = 0\cdot0003 + 0\cdot0013 \times \frac{t}{1000} + 0\cdot0010 \times \left(\frac{t}{1000}\right)^2.$$

Processes have been suggested for the electrical carbonization of coal in which case the conductivity or *specific resistance* of coal and coke is of special interest. A certain number of determinations of resistance have been made, but the values appear to vary within very wide limits and can as yet be accepted only with reserve. They vary for bituminous coal from 5×10^7 to 4×10^6 ohms per cm. per cm.^{2}. Fusain, 362 ohms, and cokes, $0\cdot004$–$0\cdot007$ ohm, have values of quite a different order.

Solubility. Organic solvents are capable of dissolving coal in part, the amount dissolved depending upon the solvent and varying from about $0\cdot1$ per cent. with cold benzene to $47\cdot3$ per cent. with boiling quinoline. The most complete solution is assured in any solvent by acting upon finely divided coal at the boiling-point of the solvent or under pressure. Solubility in solvents has been made use of in separating constituents from coal which confer special properties such as caking power upon the coal. The two most commonly used have been pyridine at $118°$ C. and benzene under pressure at $275°$ C. The solubility of coal in pyridine varies with the type of coal from $7\cdot5$ to 42 per cent. and with benzene under pressure from $3\cdot5$ to 21 per cent. Further information regarding the properties of the extracts obtained is given in Chapter IV. The effect of other solvents also varies with the type of coal. The more important of these are : acetone up to 3 per cent., aniline up to 12 per cent., phenol up to 35 per cent., tetralin up to 45 per cent., alcohol, carbon disulphide and ether all less than 1 per cent.

Softening or Melting-point. When a coking coal is heated it passes through a series of stages, softening, swelling, setting and shrinking. The softening stage may be due to the liquefaction of the soluble fractions and is described variously as softening, melting or fusion of the coal. The temperature of inception varies with the type of coal and increases with the maturity of the coal within the range $320°$ to $420°$ C. As would be expected, the actual temperature varies considerably with the rate of heating of the coal ; slow heating might give a value of $350°$ C. while heating at the rate of one degree per minute might give $420°$ C. This matter is further discussed above and in the section on research on the constitution of coal. It is clear, however, that the temperature bears a relation to that of the rapid evolution of gas and that both are of importance in coking practice in deciding the optimum conditions for the treatment of coal in general and coal blends in particular.

Grindability. The behaviour of coals on grinding has become of importance in connection with the production of pulverized fuel, where the coal is reduced in size so that 90–95 per cent. will pass a 240 B.S. sieve.

On grinding, all coals give particles of the same irregular shape, but the particles from air-swept mills have generally a rounded appearance, as distinct from the sharp edges seen in particles from the other mills. The behaviour of six types of coal in six typical mills has been examined at a final particle size of 80 per cent. passing a 240 B.S. sieve (Fuel Research Tech. Paper 49, 1947). The distribution of particle size is the same for ball, ring-ball, and emery-type mills and the curves agree with the Rosin-Rammler exponential law.[1] The other mills showed wide variations owing mainly to agglomeration of particles but also due to the action of the classifier in the case of impact mills. Particle shape covered a wide range of irregularity, but the product of any mill could not be readily distinguished except in the case of the flaking of tube-mill products and in the rounding of particles from air-swept mills.

The distribution in the case of a Yorkshire coal was as follows, the figures being the percentages remaining on the sieve-sizes stated.

Sieve opening, B.S.				36	72	120	200	240	300
,,	μ	.	.	422	211	124	76	66	53
Ball-mill	.	.	.	—	0·4	1·4	10·1	20·4	31·3
Tube-mill	.	.	.	0·3	2·6	5·8	14·5	21·9	30·6

The distribution of ash between coarse and fine fractions varies both with type of mill and hardness of coal. The tube-mill gives uniform distribution of ash with all the coals (bituminous) examined, but the other mills cause a concentration of ash in the coarser fractions which becomes more marked as the softness of the coal increases. The air-swept mill in which the oversize is recirculated is an exception ; in this case the coarser fractions are of lowest ash content.

Since the bright coal of banded bituminous coal is generally softer than the dull durain bands, pulverization gives a separation of these in the various size fractions, generally in the direction of more bright coal in the finer material. The effect is quite marked and is very noticeable in the case of the hammer-type mill using the softer bituminous coals. In one example the bright coal in the fraction B.S. 72 to 120 was 20 per cent., in the fraction B.S. 200 to 240 was 70 per cent., and in the fraction below 300 B.S. was 85 per cent.

In grinding coal to the necessary degree of fineness for firing as pulverized fuel it is apparent that a large proportion will be very much finer than the upper limit set. Normally the largest particles are not larger than 300 μ while some 30 per cent. has a particle size smaller than 6μ.

In the United States the A.S.T.M. has developed a method of measuring the " grindability " of coals by (a) the amount of work done in grinding

---

[1] $R = 100e^{-bx^n}$, where R is the percentage of powder remaining on a sieve of aperture x in. b and n are constants for a given powder and vary with coal from $b = 120$–180 and $n = 0.8$ to 1.1—J. Inst. Fuel, 1933, **7**, 29.

to a uniform size or (b) the increase of surface produced by the application of a standard amount of work, on the assumption that Rittinger's Law holds that the rate of increase of surface is proportional to the power applied in grinding. Two special mills are used in which the power applied is mainly that used in the grinding.

In (a) a small ball-mill is used and the energy used to grind 500 g. of coal so that 80 per cent. will pass a 200 A.S.T.M. sieve (74 μ) is measured as the number of revolutions required. A percentage index is calculated as : 500 g. $\times$ 100/revs.

In (b) the Hardgrove ring-ball mill is used and 5 g. of coal graded 1190 to 590 μ is treated for 60 revs. and the proportion passing a 74 μ sieve measured. The results are compared with those of a standard coal and an index calculated as 13 + 6·93w, where w is the material less than 74 μ. The indices compare as follows :

Ball-mill.		Hardgrove mill.		Ball-mill.
20 .	 29	20 .	. . . . . .	14
30 .	 43	30 .	. . . . . .	21
50 .	 68	50 .	. . . . . .	36
70 .	 90	70 .	. . . . . .	53
100 .	 118	100 .	. . . . . .	90

REFERENCES

The Ultrafine Structure of Coals and Cokes. H. K. Lewis. 1944.
Coal, Its Constitution and Uses. W. A. Bone and G. W. Himus. Longmans Green. 1936.
Technical Data on Fuel. World Power Conference Committee, London. 1950.
The Quality of Coke. R. A. Mott and R. V. Wheeler. Chapman and Hall. 1939.
British Coke Research Association. Conference Reports 1952, 1953, and Director's Reports.
Melchett Lecture, 1944. J. G. King. J. Inst. Fuel, 1944, 18, 5.
Melchett Lecture 1943. C. A. Seyler, J. Inst. Fuel, 1943, 16, 134.
The Actions of Solvents on Coal. W. E. Bakes. Fuel Research Tech. Paper 37, 1933.
The Constitution of Coal. L. Horton, R. B. Randall and K. V. Auybrey. Fuel, 1944, 23, 65.
British Coal Utilization Research Association Bulletins. Reviews 123 and 125, 1953.
Agglutinating and Swelling Power of Coal. H. E. Blayden, H. L. Riley and F. Shaw. Fuel, 1946, 25, 13.
Chemistry of Coal Utilization. Lowry. Chapman and Hall. 1945.

CHAPTER VI

VARIETIES OF BRITISH, DOMINION AND COLONIAL COALS

In Chapter V it has been explained that the properties of coal are such that they form a continuous band if carbon content is graphed against decreasing oxygen and increasing degree of metamorphosis. Coals can be found to correspond with any position on this curve so that it might be considered invidious to divide coals into smaller groups. It is true, nevertheless, that parts of the band exhibit distinctive characteristics which have caused them to become known commonly, and certainly commercially, by these group names. Excluding peat, although it is the parent substance of coal, these groups are, as explained on pages 59, 91, brown coal and lignite, lignitous or sub-bituminous coal, bituminous coal, semi-bituminous or anthracitic coal, and anthracite. The occurrence and properties of the industrial coals marketed from these groups are described below.

LIGNITE

Nature and Occurrence of Lignite. Reference has been made already to the intermediate position which lignites occupy naturally between peat and coal. Lignites vary very widely in character and composition according to the metamorphosis which the lignin of the plant has undergone, from bituminous wood to material so closely resembling " dry " bituminous coal that it is difficult, if not impossible, to distinguish between them. They are characteristic of formations more recent than those of the true coal formations, but frequently have become so altered by local conditions as to merge into bituminous coals or even semi-coked material resembling anthracite.

Lignites are of later (Tertiary) geological formation than coal. In Great Britain there are only limited deposits, the brown lignite of Bovey Tracy, Devonshire, but in Europe, North America, Australia, New Zealand and India the deposits are extensive, brown lignites being sometimes found in seams 100 ft. thick so near the earth's surface that they can be quarried at relatively low cost.

Lignites occur in a number of well-defined forms and can be classified by their physical characteristics :

(1) Woody or fibrous brown coal having the structure of wood.

(2) Earthy brown lignite, compact but friable.

(3) Brown coal, having a slight woody structure, a slaty cleavage and dark-brown colour.

116

(4) Bituminous lignite or "pitch-coal" is black and breaks with a conchoidal fracture. It resembles coal and sometimes anthracite in appearance. This form has been classified by the U.S. Geological Survey as "sub-bituminous" coal.

Composition of Lignite. The first general distinction between lignites is that between the black form, and the earthy forms containing a proportion of relatively unchanged woody material. The former contain a relatively low proportion of moisture as mined (14 to 16 per cent)., but the latter are characterized by high moisture content of the order of 45 to 55 per cent. The range of chemical composition in this group is very wide, as may be illustrated by the analyses of European lignites shown in Table XXV ; the mean values are shown in bold type and the extreme variations in smaller type.

TABLE XXV

COMPOSITION OF LIGNITES (European). (Calculated to the dry, ash-free fuel)

Range of carbon.	No. of samples.	Carbon per cent.		Hydrogen per cent.		Oxygen per cent.	
Below 60 per cent. . .	5	**57·1**	59·2 55·1	**5·8**	6·1 5·1	**37·1**	38·9 34·8
60–65 per cent. . . .	8	**63·3**	64·8 62·0	**5·6**	6·6 4·7	**31·1**	32·5 29·2
65–70 ,, . . .	25	**67·1**	70·0 65·2	**5·5**	6·7 4·8	**27·4**	29·7 25·0
70–75 ,, . . .	19	**72·6**	75·0 70·6	**5·8**	7·4 4·6	**21·6**	24·0 18·2
75–80 ,, . . .	2	**76·3**	76·6 76·0	**7·3**	8·3 6·3	**16·4**	17·7 15·1
Above 80 ,, . . .	3	**84·4**	86·6 82·2	**5·4**	6·6 3·9	**10·2**	13·2 9·0

Of these samples over 90 per cent. contain under 75 per cent. of carbon and over 20 per cent. of oxygen. The last three have a composition in good agreement with a large number of English coals for which the term "lignitous" has been accepted. Since classification based on geological evidence is thus capable of including totally dissimilar fuels, it is agreed that lignites proper contain under 75 per cent. of carbon and over 20 per cent. of oxygen.

The volatile matter in lignites falling within the above range is seldom less than 48 per cent. ; it usually exceeds 50 per cent., but in a large number of cases the ratio of volatile matter to fixed carbon is approximately 1 to 1.

The following analyses (Table XXVI, page 118) are typical of the most important lignite deposits : in view of the wide variations in composition these are given in ranges rather than in precise figures.

The calorific value of lignites corresponding to the above depends upon the degree of metamorphosis of the woody components and can vary quite widely, from about 9000 to about 11,000 B.Th.U. per lb. calculated to the dry, ash-free basis. In practice, however, the high moisture content of the material as mined means a very low net calorific value and the thermal

TABLE XXVI

ANALYSES OF LIGNITE DEPOSITS (dry, ash-free)

	Carbon.	Hydrogen.	Sulphur.	Nitrogen.	Oxygen.
Brown :					
Germany	70–68	5·2–5·8	1·5–3·0	0·7	18–22
Australia, Victoria . . .	70–66	4·5–5·0	0·3	0·5	25–28
,, South . . .	66–64	4·5–4·8		0·5	
Canada	71–68	4·6–5·0	1·2–1·5	1·0	23–25
N. Dakota	75–72	4·5–5·0	1·0	1·0	20–22
Bovey Tracey, Devon . .	67	5·6	2·6	1·0	24
Black :					
Canada	71–68	4·5–5·0	1·0–1·5	1·0	22–24
New Zealand	72–70	5·0–5·4	0·5	1·0	20–22
Burma	72–70	4·5	1·0	1·0	21–23

efficiency of its utilization as a fuel is greatly reduced by the necessity of removing the greater part of this moisture before the point of application.

Brown lignites yield, by solvent extraction, from 2 to 10 per cent. of " montan " or ester wax having a high melting-point of 75 to 85° C.

The Utilization of Lignites. Although the reserves of lignite and brown coal are quite large, over 400,000 million tons, their utilization has been limited so far to those districts where there is a scarcity of coal of the bituminous type. No doubt this will be changed in due course when advantage will be taken of the pioneering work done in Germany in particular, in Russia and in Australia. The extent of the production of lignite in the U.S.S.R. is not known, but of the 208* million tons produced annually elsewhere Germany produces 147, Czechoslovakia 20 and Australia 6 million tons. The lignite deposits are relatively near the earth's surface and are very thick. In Germany they vary from 20 to 30 metres deep, up to as much as 100 metres; in Australia the coal series reaches 600 metres while the main seams are 50 to 130 metres thick. The depth of the overburden decides whether the winning of the material is done by quarrying (open-cut working) or deep mining. At one time the limit economic for the former was at a ratio of overburden to coal of 2·5/1, but this has now been raised by improved methods to as high as 7/1. This is an important consideration in the recovery of the lignite since the losses in deep mining may be 35 per cent. as against only 10 per cent. in open-cut mining. The overburden is removed by cutting from the surface and by using scraper and bucket conveyers ; the face of the seam is exposed for some hundreds of feet as in a large quarry.

The raw material obtained in this way contains, as stated above, about 50 per cent. of moisture and the important step in preparation is the drying

* 300 in 1954.

of this to about 15 per cent. moisture and its conversion into a sized or granular material. In Germany over two-thirds of the output is actually briquetted, either in small size ($\frac{1}{20}$ kg.) for industrial use, or in large size (1 kg.) for domestic use.

The work of treatment is done on a very large scale (2000 tons per day) and forms a continuous process. The drying is done by steam or combustion gases on the lignite crushed to under 4 mm. size, and the dried material is briquetted in high-capacity presses in which the pressure necessary is obtained by the forcing of the material through the dies of the press. Alternatively, heavy ring-roll presses are used, of which the best known is the Krupp Ring-Roll press.

The finished briquettes have a density of 1·2 to 1·3 and a breaking stress of 15 to 20 kg. per sq. cm. At 15 per cent. moisture content their calorific value varies between 4500 and 5000 cal. per g.

In Australia the German methods have been copied and, although applied to a smaller output, have been improved upon. The account of work at Yallourn and Morwell (Victoria) by Dr. H. Herman is very complete and the reader is recommended to it for all the details of the plant and operations of the utilization of brown coal.

As a fuel the raw lignite is at a disadvantage in comparison with bituminous coal as regards its small size, high moisture and low calorific value. At Yallourn one unit of the power station, using a predrying shaft, has achieved a steam-raising efficiency of 67 per cent. of the net calorific value. On the pre-dried and briquetted material, burned on a mechanical grate, the efficiency rises to 80 per cent., but it must be remembered that heat is consumed in the preparation of the briquettes.

Other uses for the brown coal are as pulverized fuel for steam-locomotives and in the production of town gas. For use as pulverized fuel the lignite must be dried to 5 per cent. moisture or less. Experiments in Victoria on an experimental locomotive on the railway have indicated that an efficiency of 80 per cent. can be obtained. Air-dried granular lignite can be utilized for the production of town gas. At atmospheric pressure the Lurgi Spülgas low-temperature carbonization process produces a gas of 200 B.Th.U. calorific value and a smokeless fuel of excellent quality. At an elevated pressure (20 atm.) the Lurgi high-pressure process can gasify the coal completely with oxygen to give a gas of 450 to 480 B.Th.U. per cu. ft. and directly suitable for distribution as town gas. This process is described more fully in Chapter X.

The Spülgas process gives a very high yield of tar (17 to 25 per cent. of the dry lignite), and during the last war this was a valuable raw material in Germany for the production of motor spirit by hydrogenation. The coke, because of its high reactivity to oxygen, was also a successful fuel for the mobile gas producer.

Black lignites weather badly on exposure to the air and disintegrate into slack. This disability has militated against their industrial usage ; even attempts to make a solid fuel by carbonization have so far failed.

CANNEL COAL

As explained above (p. 60), the characteristic difference between cannel and bituminous coal of the same carbon content is associated with the original plant material of abnormally high spore content from which it was formed. This gives it an abnormally high hydrogen content of the order of 6 per cent. so that it falls appreciably outside the normal classification coal band (Figure 28) and is not in the direct line of transition of the main bulk of coals from lignite to the bituminous species.

The amount of cannel in reserve is relatively very small and it is only in special applications that it has any interest. It occurs normally in bands or lenticles and, when it does occur in a separate seam, this is of limited extent—a few square miles. In Great Britain the main reserves are in the Scottish coalfields, where its occurrence in bands is common, but it is also found in the coalfields of Lancashire and Cannock.

Cannels vary widely in ash content from 2 to over 40 per cent. and in volatile matter from 50 to as much as 85 per cent. of the dry, ash-free material. The normal hydrogen content of 6 per cent. may rise to 10 per cent., as in the " boghead " cannels, because of their high content of algae. In general appearance they are dense, greyish-black and hard, and break with a conchoidal fracture. In texture they are smooth and can be polished to a smooth shiny surface.

Cannel was at one time of great value when the important quality in town gas was its illuminating value. Its high hydrogen content made cannel give a high yield of hydrocarbons on distillation and it was in great demand as an enriching agent for blending with normal bituminous coal in order to raise the illuminating power of the gas. The advent of the incandescent mantle spoiled this market and since then its presence in a coal seam has been undesirable rather than otherwise.

Typical analyses of cannels are given in Table XXVII, calculated as percentages of the dry, ash-free material.

TABLE XXVII

Composition of Cannel and Boghead Coals

	Carbon.	Hydrogen.	Oxygen.	Volatile matter.	Ash on dry coal.
Boghead	78·1	10·4	11·4	87·8	33
Newbattle * . . .	84·5	6·6	5·0	43·5	4
Lancashire . . .	79·0	6·0	15·0	52·7	3

* S 2·4, N 1·4.

On distillation, cannels yield a tar of a more paraffinic character than bituminous coal and in much higher yield. The boghead cannel of Torbanehill (Scotland) yielded as much as 120 gal. per ton despite its high ash content. The entire deposit was worked for its oil content and is now of historic interest only. Less rich cannels of the Newbattle type yield from 40 to 80 gal. per ton, depending upon their ash content. This fact has made them an object of interest to promoters of systems of low-temperature carbonization in order that the high yield of "oil" would improve the economics of the production of a smokeless domestic solid fuel. The sporadic character of cannel and the small amounts available have militated against this and to-day there is no plant operating on this material. Had cannel been more plentiful there is no doubt that at least one process would have been successful and valuable tar products would have been available.

It has been shown also that suitably-sized cannel of reasonably low ash content can be carbonized in continuous gas retorts at a high throughput to give town gas of a suitable composition, and a liquid distillate of 42–55 gal. per ton. In this work the cannel used was Newbattle (Midlothian) of the composition shown in Table XXVII. In the laboratory it gave a mean potential yield of tar of 28 per cent. of the dry, ash-free cannel and in actual gas-making 24 per cent. The thermal yield of gas was 45 per cent. higher than that of normal Scottish gas coal and the coke was of a saleable quality. On refining, the tar produced the following valuable products :

```
Motor spirit, octane No. 68     .    .    .    .     4·9 gal.
Diesel oil, cetane No. 46  .    .    .    .    .    10·0  ,,
Fuel oil   .    .    .    .    .    .    .    .    11·0  ,,
Tar acids  .    .    .    .    .    .    .    .     4·0  ,,
Paraffin wax, m. pt. 55° C.      .    .    .    .    24·0 lb.
Pitch      .    .    .    .    .    .    .    .   160·0  ,,
```

If cannel were made available in quantity, separated properly from the bituminous coal associated with it, there is no doubt that this would be the most economic way of making the best use of it.

BITUMINOUS COAL

As stated above, the black lignites merge into a class of lignitous coals. These in turn merge into the bituminous coal species without any clearly defined division. The lignitous coals and the bituminous coals are normally regarded as one class of widely divergent properties which vary gradually and regularly from one end of the class to the other. The bituminous species comprise coals containing from 24 to 40 per cent. of volatile matter and 84 to 91·2 per cent. of carbon. Lignitous or non-caking bituminous coals contain over 10 per cent. of oxygen, while the high-rank coking coals at the other end of the scale contain less than 5 per cent. As devolatilization of the coal increases, the ability of bituminous coal to form a hard coherent coke when carbonized also increases.

In the seam, all bituminous coals exhibit a banded structure, the coal showing alternate bands of bright and dull coal arranged parallel to the bedding plane. Four types of band have been defined in this country by Stopes as vitrain, clarain, durain and fusain and two bands have been defined in American coals by Thiessen as attritus and anthraxylon. The anthraxylon corresponds to the vitrain and clarain, and the attritus to the durain.

Vitrain has a glassy lustre and normally occurs in very thin bands about 0·2 in. thick. In thin sections it is pale brown and translucent and microscopically appears almost devoid of structure. Clarain appears in thicker bands and is less bright and less brittle than the vitrain. It is translucent in thin sections and shows disintegrated plant remains when examined under the microscope. Durain is the dull hard coal which occurs in definite bands from a fraction of an inch to sometimes a large proportion of the seam. It is hard and strong. Microscopically it contains plant remains embedded in a granular matrix which is opaque in thin sections. Fusain occurs chiefly in lenticles and forms points of weakness in banded coal. It is dull, granular and fibrous and usually very friable. Microscopically it consists of woody tissue, opaque in thin sections.

Photomicrographs of typical sections are shown in Figure 7, and other data on page 60.

The measurement and examination of the bands in bituminous coal seams form a means of exploring the variations which occur in the different parts of the coalfield.

Utilization of Bituminous Coal. Bituminous coal may be regarded as the all-purpose species in that its essential properties cover a wide range and therefore meet the requirements of most users. These essential properties, apart from a reasonable freedom from ash and a suitable size of particle, are primarily represented by the percentage of volatile matter and the level of caking power. That these are related to one another and to the rank of the coal has already been explained (p. 100) and it is possible to deduce the properties of any bituminous coal for a given purpose if its analysis is known and its position on the coal band can be assessed.

Taken by itself the proportion of volatile matter in a coal is of importance in that it largely governs the character of the combustion in steam raising and furnace work, the condition of " flaming " in domestic usage, the yield of gas in carbonization, and so on. In combustion it affects the design of both the grate or the method of combustion and of the combustion space of the furnace used. This subject is dealt with later under steam raising.

In carbonization practice a reasonable level of caking power is an essential but, granted this, high volatile matter is preferred for gas-making coals and low volatile matter for the manufacture of metallurgical coke. The former industry therefore uses bituminous coal of fairly high caking power, high volatile matter, and suitably sized to fit the method of gasification and the level of caking power. The coke industry prefers coal of high caking power, low volatile matter and does not require sized coal. It does however require low ash content and low sulphur and phosphorus. The two industries tend therefore to overlap in their choice of suitable coal so far as essential properties are concerned, but the adjustment in demand is made on the basis of sized coal for gas, and clean slack for coke.

In producer gas practice the deciding factors are volatile matter, caking power, size distribution, and fusibility of the ash. Volatile matter is again important in determining the yield of gas, caking coals are admissible only in certain types of producer in which there are means for breaking up fused lumps in the coking zone, and good sizing means good freedom of passage for the gases. Coals with ash of low fusion temperature are always to be avoided even if the total ash content is low.

For domestic usage the choice of coal in this class is much wider. For the open grate the preferred bituminous coal is of high volatile matter and low to medium caking power. Free-burning qualities are usually associated with decrease of caking power and this is generally true but, depending upon the nature of the ash, some slight caking is generally an advantage in house coals.

These are the main uses of bituminous coal, but it is apparent that any process can have a wide choice of properties within the class, or select for a given type of coal the appliance best suited to it. Other factors in the choice and utilization of bituminous coals are dealt with later under the processes concerned.

Caking Power. In the bituminous class of coal perhaps the most important single property is caking power. The relation between this and rank has been discussed (p. 100) and shown graphically in Figures 13, 14, 15. The incidence of caking power is at about 81·5 per cent. carbon on the dry, mineral-matter-free basis (d.m.m.f.) and its disappearance at about 91·5 per cent. at 14 per cent. volatile matter. The variation of caking power with rank is not uniform ; with increasing carbon content it rises to a maximum between 81·5 and 87·5 fairly steadily, between 87·5 and 89·5 it is at a maximum but tends to be variable, between 89·5 and 91·5 it decreases very sharply to zero. Typical analyses to illustrate these steps are shown in Table XXVIII (p. 124).

In practical usage the evaluation of the effect of caking power is complicated by the fact that bituminous coal is not homogeneous and does not always behave as it does in the laboratory in a state of intimate mixture. The best method of assessment for any given purpose is to use one or more standardized tests and interpret the meaning of these in terms of earlier correlations with practice. In the case of coking coals a model oven is an intermediate step, but in other uses a model might give a misleading result. Methods of assessment of caking power which are in common use are the Swelling Index, the Gray-King Assay, and the sand Agglutinating Value, but to these are now added the Roga Index, and the Audibert-Arnu Dilatometer test. These methods of test are described in Chapter XVIII. Any

TABLE XXVIII

VARIATION OF CAKING POWER OF BITUMINOUS COALS WITH CARBON CONTENT
OR RANK

(Calc. to mineral-matter-free coal)

Volatile matter.	C.	H.	S.	N.	O.	Gray-King Index.
40	82	5·4	1·5	1·2	9·7	B
38	84	5·4	1·5	1·2	7·7	G
36	85·5	5·3	1·5	1·2	6·5	G_4
33	87·5	5·2	1·5	1·0	4·8	G_9
25	89·5	4·8	1·2	1·0	3·5	G_9
20	91	4·5	1·0	1·0	2·5	G_4
14	91·5	4·3	1·0	1·0	2·2	B
7	93	3·6	0·8	0·8	1·8	A
2·5	94	2·6	0·8	0·8	1·8	A

or all of them may be used in the assessment of coal properties, but only correlation with the process in question and consideration of the effect of size of particle will give a reliable result.

NAVIGATION, BUNKER AND SMOKELESS STEAM COALS

No term descriptive of coal is employed so widely as " steam coal "; it includes all coals other than strongly-caking coals and anthracites. Any of the bituminous steam coals already described can be used for navigation and bunker purposes, but the most valuable are the semi-bituminous or carbonaceous coals. These coals represent the transition stage between bituminous coking coals and anthracite and occur chiefly in South Wales although similar seams occur in East Kent. Those containing about 5 per cent. of hydrogen and 20 per cent. of volatile matter are caking steam coals ; those containing up to 4·7 per cent. hydrogen and 18 per cent. volatile matter are second-class steam coals ; those containing 4·0 to 4·5 per cent. of hydrogen and 10–15 per cent. of volatile matter form the celebrated Welsh steam coal, formerly termed " first-class Admiralty steam coal ".

Coal of this latter type is particularly valuable in having a low ash content and a high calorific value (15,800 B.Th.U. per lb. on the dry, ash-free fuel) and for its smokelessness and free-burning qualities on the boiler grate.

ANTHRACITE

Anthracite is the least widely distributed of the coals and one of the most valuable. The most notable deposits are those of South Wales and Pennsylvania, in both of which anthracite of very high quality is obtained. Anthracite is hard and lustrous, and does not soil the fingers. The ash is lower than in bituminous coals. Owing to its low content of volatile matter it burns almost without smoke and does not soften or cake. This, with its high density, makes it a particularly valuable fuel for use in stoves.

The anthracite area in South Wales is a comparatively narrow belt along the north and north-west of the coalfield. Over this area, which is about 25 miles long, the change in volatile matter in the coal substance is from 9·5 to 4·5 per cent., but in this small range no less than five varieties of anthracite are recognized commercially. The varieties can be recognized empirically, but the best exact definition is in terms of hydrogen content as follows.

	Hydrogen per cent.	Volatile matter per cent.
1A	2·95	4·5 to 5·0
1	2·95 to 3·10	5·0 to 6·0
2	3·10 to 3·35	5·5 to 6·5
3	3·35 to 3·60	6·0 to 7·5
4	3·60 to 3·90	7·5 to 9·5

In other parts of the country coals of similar composition to anthracite are found, which have resulted from the intrusion of igneous rocks into bituminous coal measures. Here the ash is higher than in the unaltered coal, and such coal may be regarded almost as a semi-coke. True anthracite appears to derive its special characteristics from the nature of the original deposited carbonaceous matter, or from changes brought about in it very shortly after deposition, and existed as anthracite before denudation or serious disturbance of the strata took place. Where great subsequent disturbance of the strata has taken place, the anthracite still has the same characters and composition, but has become broken down into a coarse powder called " culm ".

Anthracites proper contain less than 8 per cent. of volatile matter with 93 per cent. or over of carbon. Pseudo-anthracites, e.g. the Scottish anthracites, are higher in volatile matter and approximate to about 12 per cent.

The chief industrial uses of anthracite are steam-raising, domestic stoves and central-heating, and malt and hop drying.

COALS IN THE BRITISH COMMONWEALTH

In Great Britain itself fuel reserves are limited to coal ; the proportions of other fuels available are negligible in comparison. This does not however apply to the Dominions and Colonies, in some of which oil and natural gas are available, and in the following accounts of coals available, there is included a brief statement of the general fuel situation as a whole.

Coal in Great Britain

The coal seams of Great Britain are practically all contained in the Carboniferous geological formation. In this there are three main phases of deposition of rock, (1) Carboniferous Limestone, (2) Millstone Grit and

(3) Coal Measures.   The first or oldest is about 300 ft. thick and in England contains no coal excepting a few seams in Northumberland ; the second varies from 300 to 3000 ft. over the country, but again coal is found only in a few local deposits.   The third provides over 95 per cent. of our coal production and is of variable thickness, reaching 8000 ft. in the South-west, and consists of varied successions of sandstones, clays, shales, fireclay and coal.

The seams of coal vary in thickness from fractions of an inch to the 30 ft. of the Warwickshire Thick coal, but the general average is several feet.   In normal coal mining, a seam is not worked below 2 ft. in thickness.

The coal measures were originally deposited in four main tracts if one excludes the few unworkable seams of Devon and Cornwall and the relatively poor field of Eire.   These are shown in the coalfields map, Figure 18.

(1) Scottish Group.   Fife and Clackmannan, The Lothians, Central (Lanarkshire) and Ayrshire.

(2) Northern Group.   Northumberland and Durham, Cumberland.

(3) Midland Group.   Lancashire and Cheshire, N. Wales, N. Stafford-shire, Shrewsbury, Coalbrookdale and Forest of Wyre, Cannock Chase and S. Staffordshire, Warwickshire, Leicester and S. Derby, and Yorkshire, Notts and Derby.

(4) Southern Group.   S. Wales, Forest of Dean, Bristol and Somerset, and Kent.

The heavy earth movements of the later Carboniferous period caused severe folding of the coal seams and exposure and denudation in some places, resulting in the separation of the main tracts into some 40 areas, of which 20 are coal-bearing.   In the latter, the coal measures may be at the surface (exposed coalfield) when the coal will lie in a basin and outcrop at the boundaries, or they may be overlaid by the newer (Cambrian and Jurassic) rock formations, or older rocks, forming a *concealed* coalfield.   In the latter case more seams than are yet known may still be found in the Midlands and S.E. England under the newer rocks, and in the West and North under the older rocks.   Prospecting by drilling will no doubt deter-mine this in due course and the seams will be worked up to 4000 ft. in depth or more if improved methods of deep mining are found.

Scottish Group.   This comprises the fields given above and shown in Figure 18 to lie across the narrow part of Scotland between Ayrshire and Fife and to form three main basins.

An important difference from the fields of England lies in the fact that workable coals are to be found in the Carboniferous Limestone, and in some areas seams are found which have been altered by the action of volcanic rocks so that they resemble anthracite.   The Limestone coals form about 45 per cent. of the total output of Scotland and consist of normal bituminous coals, in some seams of reasonably high-caking power. Many seams contain thick bands of durain of a very hard character.   The

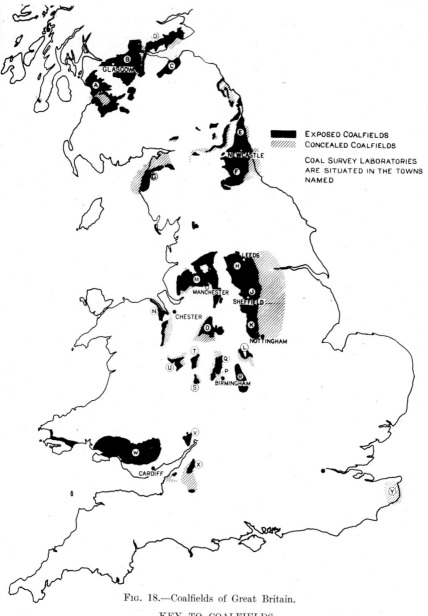

FIG. 18.—Coalfields of Great Britain.

KEY TO COALFIELDS

(A) AYRSHIRE
(B) CENTRAL
(C) LOTHIANS
(D) FIFE AND CLACKMANNAN
(E) NORTHUMBERLAND
(F) DURHAM
(G) CUMBERLAND
(H) WEST YORKSHIRE
(J) SOUTH YORKSHIRE
(K) NOTTINGHAMSHIRE AND
    DERBYSHIRE
(L) LEICESTERSHIRE AND
    SOUTH DERBYSHIRE
(M) LANCASHIRE AND CHESHIRE

(N) NORTH WALES
(O) NORTH STAFFORDSHIRE
(P) SOUTH STAFFORDSHIRE
(Q) CANNOCK CHASE
(R) WARWICKSHIRE
(S) WYRE FOREST
(T) COALBROOKDALE
(U) SHREWSBURY
(V) FOREST OF DEAN
(W) SOUTH WALES AND
    MONMOUTHSHIRE
(X) BRISTOL AND SOMERSET
(Y) KENT

local name is "splint" coal and the lumps are frequently segregated for use in locomotives.

The *Fife and Clackmanan* coals are characterized by high volatile matter and weak to moderate caking power and are good household and steam-raising coals. Those of lowest caking power are in favour as power-station fuels. Many of the seams contain cannel bands and in some localities pseudo-anthracites are found.

The *Lothian* field works mainly the Limestone coals which are of high volatile matter (40 per cent.) and low caking power and low ash and sulphur content; their uses are household, general industry, gas manufacture where the caking power is highest, and railways in the case of splints.

The *Central* coalfield has worked the Coal Measures but the main seams are now largely worked out and production is moving to the Stirlingshire area. The coals are bituminous but their caking power is more marked so that they find an outlet for the manufacture of coke. The Limestone coals of the eastern sections form the best coking coals of Scotland. In many areas the seams are affected by igneous intrusion and then the coals find a sale for navigation purposes and for brewing.

The *Ayrshire* field works mainly the Coal Measures to produce weakly-caking, high-volatile coal which is popular as house coal. Splints and pseudo-anthracite are marketed separately.

Northern Group. The Northern Group includes the Northumberland and Durham coalfield to the east of the Pennines and the Cumberland field on the west. These formed one basin at the time of deposition and extend beyond the present coastal boundaries. The uplifting of the Pennines caused the division into two fields.

The *Northumberland and Durham* field forms a triangular area of about 800 square miles and has an output of about 50 million tons per annum. The Tyne marks a sharp line of demarcation across the field in that the high caking quality of the Durham coals is not continued north of the river, and seams begin to appear in the Limestone Formation. North of the Tyne, therefore, the coals are weakly-caking to non-caking in character. The change takes place gradually so that the coal nearest the Tyne has quite strong caking power and can be used for gas manufacture and even in some cases for the making of metallurgical coke.

Geographical changes take place in the same way over the Durham field but are gradual. In West Durham the coals are soft, bright, contain 26 to 30 per cent. volatile matter and are best-quality coking coals. To the north, east and south there is a gradual increase in hardness and volatile matter and an accompanying decrease in caking power so that the coals change slowly to steam and house coal in the north and to coking-gas and gas coals in the south and west.

Formerly the best coking coal was obtained from the three lowest seams, Victoria, Busty and Brockwell in West Durham, but these are not likely now to last more than another 40 years.   Improvements in coking practice and blending will bring into use the coals of higher volatile matter.

All the coals of the Durham area tend to be friable and for this reason are usually marketed as " run of mine " coal.   Even in this form the proportion of fines may be large, say 50 per cent. passing a ½-in. screen.

The exposed Coal Measures in the Cumberland coalfield form a coastal strip and a north-east extension, together covering 85 square miles.   A westerly dip carries the seams under the sea to a large undersea field whose boundaries are not yet known.   Mining at present reaches only five miles under the sea.

About 20 seams are workable, but the main output comes at present from only eight of them.   There is little variation in quality and all the seams give high-volatile, strongly-caking coals suitable for coking and for gas manufacture.

Midland Group.   This group, as stated above, contains a large number of fields which were at one time all part of a large area in which the Coal Measures were deposited as one continuous sheet.   Now the chief seams occur in the Middle Measures, two or three in the Lower Measures, but none of any value in the Upper Measures.

The *Lancashire and Cheshire* field, about 500 square miles in area, lies in a basin-fold on the west flank of the Pennines.   This whole area was strongly disturbed by earth movement and the seams are badly folded and faulted.   The coals are all bituminous but, as might be expected, cover a wide range of the class from non-caking coal of high volatile matter to strongly-caking coal almost up to the quality of Durham coal.   For this reason they supply all markets although in this area the heavy demand is for industrial coal.

The *Yorkshire, Nottingham and Derby* fields are among the largest producers with about 70 million tons of coal annually.   They consist of a main basin lying between Leeds in the north and Nottingham in the south.   On the west the Coal Measures lie on the surface but to the east they dip below Permian and Triassic rocks to form a concealed coalfield ; the boundary of this is not yet known but it does extend beyond Lincoln, where the Measures lie at a depth of 4000 ft.

About 30 workable seams contain coal of good quality and low inherent ash.   An important feature of the seams is that they contain bands of " hards " or durain which are much harder but less strongly-caking than the bright coal.   All the seams are bituminous but vary widely in quality as evidenced by variation of volatile matter from 30 to 40 per cent., and of caking power from non-caking to highly-caking.   There is a general tendency for volatile matter to increase and for caking power to decrease from north to south.   This is not regular but is very marked over the field as a whole ; Yorkshire, for example, supplies graded gas coals and coking smalls while Derby, and Notts in particular, provide free-burning house

F.—F

and industrial coals. In general, the " hards ", when separated, are used on the railways. The change from north to south is exemplified by the following analyses from points 40 miles apart in the Barnsley area.

	C.	H.	O.	N.	S.	Volatile matter.	Gray-King coke type.
Elsecar . . .	84·6	5·2	7·5	2·2	0·5	35·0	G$_4$
Watnall . . .	80·2	4·8	13·0	1·3	0·7	42·6	B

The *North Wales* coalfield covers an area of 90 square miles in the counties of Flint and Denbigh. In the latter the Coal Measures are exposed in a strip on the south of the Dee estuary, and travel under the river to a small area on the Wirral. In the former they pass under the Triassic rocks in Cheshire. Altogether the field is only the outcrop of the larger field under the Cheshire Plain ; folds and faults are numerous. The coals vary from medium- to strongly-caking bituminous and are of very good quality ; the output is about 2 million tons annually.

The *North Staffordshire* coalfield covers about 100 square miles at the base of the Pennines. The Coal Measures lie in two major folds, a basin on the east and an arch on the west, which diverge southwards. The arch is very steep-sided so that many of the seams lie vertically and cause great difficulty in mining. The south tilt of the folds carry the seams into a concealed field under newer rocks. To the west are a series of large faults which must lead to the concealed field of the Cheshire Plain.

The upper seams of coal are non-caking and the lower seams are caking in the west and non-caking in the east. There are a large number of seams of more than average thickness and the future of this field should be bright. Typical analyses of the same seam from west and east are :

	C.	H.	O.	N.	S.	Volatile matter.	Gray-King type.
West	85·0	5·4	5·9	1·8	1·9	33·5	G$_4$
East	82·2	5·3	8·9	1·7	1·9	40·3	A

Because of the wide range of caking power the coals supply the industrial and household markets while the caking varieties supply the gas and coking markets. The output is about 6 million tons annually.

The *Cannock Chase and South Staffordshire* fields occupy an area of 150 square miles to the west of Birmingham in the Coal Measures. A broad belt of faulting divides the basin, which to the east and west is faulted to lower depths, and to north and south passes under the newer rocks of the Triassic.

There are 20 seams of good quality and one in South Staffordshire which has a thickness of 20 to 30 ft. of coal through the thinning of the intervening strata ; this is the Thick Coal seam.

All the coals are relatively low-rank bituminous coals with high inherent moisture, high volatile matter and low caking power. They are excellent house and industrial coals. The output is about 6 million tons annually.

To the west of this field lie the smaller fields of *Shrewsbury, Coalbrookdale* and *Forest of Wyre* which produce about one million tons of coal of the same type.

In *Warwickshire*, to the east of the South Staffordshire field the Coal Measures lie deeply buried under newer rocks, but emerge through a series of faults into the narrow basin of the Warwick field. The sequence carries 15 seams of good thickness which in the middle of the field provide the Thick Coal by the thinning of intervening strata ; the composite seam is 20 to 30 ft. thick. The quality of the coal is the same as that of the coal of Leicestershire but some seams contain thick bands of dull, hard coal (spires) which is of low ash content and is in demand for special purposes such as baking. The output is about 5 million tons.

The *Leicestershire and South Derbyshire* field covers an area of about 100 square miles but only about 25 square miles of this is exposed, since the Coal Measures dip north and south below the Triassic rocks. Some twelve seams occur, averaging from 3·5 to 15 ft. in thickness. The coals are bright and soft, weakly-caking and of high volatile matter (40 to 45 per cent). They show the same hard bands as Yorkshire seams though less markedly. Their main uses are, lump coal for household purposes and small coal for power stations. Sometimes the hards are separated for locomotive use. The output is about 6 million tons annually.

The Southern Group. The coalfields of South Wales, Forest of Dean, Bristol and Somerset, and probably Kent were originally part of one Coal Measure basin separated from the north by a land area.

The *South Wales and Monmouthshire* coalfield forms an oval basin, 56 miles long from east to west and 15 to 20 miles wide. An extension 4 miles long extends into Pembrokeshire. The northern boundaries of the field are the older rocks and there are no buried extensions. The field is faulted and cut by deep valleys into which the seams outcrop, and which complicate mining operations.

The Coal Measures in some cases reach 8000 ft. in thickness. The Lower Coal Series contains the important seams ; the overlying Pennant Series is barren of coal and the Supra-Pennant occurs only in patches and provides only a small proportion of the coal output. The coal seams vary in proper-ties across the field more than they do vertically so that the place of origin of a coal is more significant as regards coal properties than the seam. The change is gradual and consists in a transition from bituminous coking and gas coal in the east and south-east to semi-anthracites and anthracites in the west and north-west. The following analyses illustrate the change.

		C.	H.	O.
E.	Glamorgan	87·7	6·1	4·4
	Aberdare Valley	88·4	5·3	5·1
↓	Rhondda Valley	92·0	4·3	2·4
W.	Carmarthen	94·4	3·3	1·3

The volatile matter of the coal is closely related to other properties, and in South Wales an exact picture of the variation of properties over the field can be seen in a chart tracing the variation of volatile matter from place to place. The " iso-vol " lines trace a regular geographical pattern. Although these changes are gradual certain dividing lines are recognized which give the following classes :

Volatile matter.

Anthracite	. . . .	5·0– 9·0	C/H to 94·5/2·5.
Sub-bituminous coal .	. .	9·0–13·5	⎧Carbonaceous coal ; dividing line
Semi-bituminous coal	. .	13·5–17·5	⎩ is 4 per cent. H.
Bituminous coal : I .	. .	17·5–20·0	Coking coals.
II .	. .	20·0–23·0	,, ,,
III .	. .	23·0–30·0	,, ,,
IV .	. .	30·0–35·0	Gas and industrial coals.

The best way to study these changes is to consider Figure 19, which shows a curved band into which the coals fall. It is seen that the coal

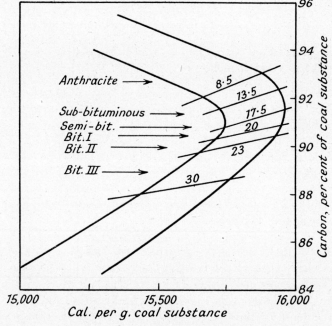

FIG. 19.—The Coal Band for South Wales Coals. The crossing lines and figures represent the percentage of volatile matter.

substance has a maximum calorific value about 91 per cent. carbon and 18–20 per cent. of volatile matter. Divisions of the anthracite species are also recognized (see p. 125). The sharp changes of caking power are peculiar to South Wales ; the property first appears between 13·5 and 14·0 per cent. volatile matter, increases rapidly as the latter increases, and by 18 per cent.

gives almost a coking coal. In terms of the Gray-King coke type we have at 14 per cent. type C, at 16 per cent. type F/G, and at 18 to 19 per cent. type G_3. At about 25 per cent. a maximum of G_7 is reached and above this level the caking power decreases.

Anthracites and the next group both find their uses for gas producers and domestic stoves, those of low arsenic content are used for hop drying and malting. Coals between 13·5 and 20 per cent. volatile matter form the caking-steam group which contains the best coals for this purpose in the world ; they are also suitable for domestic use. Coals from 17 to 30 per cent. volatile matter are used, either alone or blended, for coking, and from 30 to 35 per cent. for gas manufacture. The annual output of the field is about 25 million tons, of which 3 are anthracite. The output of the latter could be much higher if a market could be found.

The *Forest of Dean* coalfield lies in Gloucestershire between the rivers Wye and Severn in two basins of which the largest is 9 × 3 miles. It contains 12 workable seams totalling about 30 ft. of coal but most of the output comes from the High Delf seam. The second basin is smaller and contains only the lower seams. The coals are all high-volatile bituminous coals but their caking power varies ; the High Delf for example is strongly-caking near the middle of the field and weakly-caking near the outcrops. The output is about one million tons.

The *Bristol and Somerset* coalfield has several areas of exposed Coal Measures totalling about 50 square miles which form part of the larger concealed area of 240 square miles. The Measures are divided by 2000 ft. of Pennant sandstone ; the upper contains 15 seams and the lower 25. The latter are valuable coals but are not greatly worked because of their depth and severe faulting, and contribute only 10 per cent. to the output. The Pennant Sandstone contains several seams but these are not worked. The seams in this field all tend to be thin but some of them are worked down to 2 ft. thickness.

The coals are all bituminous and mostly of the gas and coking type ; the output is about one million tons but is increasing, because of less transport costs, for local use.

The *Kent* coalfield is entirely concealed below newer rocks varying in thickness from 1000 to 3000 ft. and has a known area of 200 square miles, which may be larger since the Measures extend under the sea to the east and south. Twelve seams have been proved and five are being worked, but the field has not been explored and little is yet known about the development of the seams except in the neighbourhood of the pits. A resemblance to the coals of South Wales is recognized and, excepting anthracite, the coals range from the carbonaceous to the bituminous type as in Wales. Also, the low-volatile coals, which are non-caking, achieve some caking power at about 14 per cent. volatile matter and become highly-caking at about 28 per cent. Beween 22 and 30 per cent. they would be quite suitable for

TABLE XXIX

Analyses of British Coal Seams (percentages of the dry ash-free coal). Fuel Research Board Survey Reports

	Carbon.	Hydrogen.	Nitrogen.	Sulphur.	Oxygen and errors.	Volatile matter less moisture.	Calorific value B.Th.U. per lb.	Type.	Gray-King coke type.
Scotland :									
Lanarkshire : Main and Ell	80·1	5·3	1·3	1·6	11·7	36·5	14,520	Household, slightly caking.	A
,, Virgin	81·4	5·4	2·1	0·8	10·3	41·5	14,600	Household and gas, medium caking.	A
Linlithgow : Six Foot (Kinneil)	84·1	5·2	1·6	0·4	8·7	36·9	14,920	Gas or steam, slightly caking.	G
Clackmannan : Hawkhill (Tullygarth)	80·9	5·5	1·8	0·9	10·9	43·5	14,270	Household, non-caking.	A
Northumberland :									
Yard (Ashington)	83·1	5·3	2·0	0·9	8·7	37·7	14,570	Household.	F
Main (Seaton)	80·8	5·5	1·7	1·2	10·8	40·6	14,580	Bunker, steam.	A
Beaumont	84·6	5·4	1·7	1·5	6·8	37·1	15,200	Household.	G₉
Durham :									
Brockwell (Durham)	87·4	5·2	1·7	0·8	4·9	28·3	15,480	Coking.	G₉
Hutton (Chester-le-Street)	87·0	5·3	1·6	1·1	5·0	32·6	15,510	Gas.	G₉
Busty	87·8	5·3	1·4	0·9	4·6	29·4	15,660	Coking.	G₉
Cumberland :									
Main	84·8	5·4	1·5	1·0	6·3	33·0	15,250	Coking.	G₃
Lancashire :									
Arley (Atherton)	83·8	5·1	1·4	2·0	7·7	37·6	15,040	Coking, gas.	G₃
Ravine (Bickershaw)	83·4	5·3	1·6	3·5	6·2	38·8	15,170	Coking, gas.	G₃
Smith (Atherton)	83·3	5·3	1·7	1·7	8·0	39·9	15,090	Coking, gas.	G₃
King (Burnley)	82·9	5·2	1·6	3·5	6·8	36·2	15,190	Manufacturing, medium coking.	F
Wigan, Four Foot (Garswood)	82·4	4·9	1·8	2·0	8·9	40·2	14,720	Coking, gas.	G
Lower Mountain Mine (Altham)	85·4	4·9	2·1	0·7	6·9	32·0	15,020	Coking.	G₄
North Wales :									
Main	82·9	5·2	1·6	1·1	9·2	38·0	14,670	Gas, house.	E

134

Yorkshire									
Beeston	83·8	5·5	1·5	1·5	7·7	33·0	15,050	Steam, household.	G
Parkgate (Rotherham)	82·3	5·2	1·7	2·8	8·0	34·4	15,480	Gas, coking, steam (Hards).	G₂
Barnsley " Hards "	84·8	5·1	1·6	0·9	7·6	33·7	14,920	Gas, coking.	G₃
Barnsley " Hards "	85·1	5·1	1·5	0·8	7·5	34·7	14,940	Household steam (Hards).	G₃
Silkstone	86·3	5·2	1·6	0·9	6·0	34·0	15,470	Gas, coking, household (Hards).	G₅
Haigh Moor	84·1	5·6	1·8	1·4	7·1	35·0	15,100	Household.	G
Notts and Derby :									
Top Hard	82·5	5·5	1·8	2·0	8·2	38·2	14,730	Household, steam (Hards).	C
Deep Soft	80·7	5·8	1·8	1·3	10·4	38·7	14,590	Ditto.	A
Waterloo (Chesterfield)	81·8	5·4	1·5	2·0	9·3	39·9	14,570	Household.	A
Tupton	81·4	4·9	1·7	3·1	8·9	39·0	15,050	Household and steam.	A
High Hazel	80·0	5·5	2·0	1·4	11·1	38·8	14,230	Household.	A
Deep Hard (Alfreton)	83·1	5·2	1·8	0·9	9·0	37·7	14,800	Steam, gas, household.	G
North Staffs :									
Banbury Seven Foot	81·4	5·4	1·7	1·6	9·9	38·6	14,420	Household, steam, manufacturing.	A
Cockshead or Eight Feet Banbury	83·0	5·4	1·9	0·7	9·0	36·2	14,820	House, steam, gas mnfg.	E
Great Row	81·4	5·5	1·9	1·2	10·0	40·0	14,490	Pottery, steam, household.	A
Warwick, Leicester and S. Staffs :									
Warwick : Slate	79·7	5·3	1·0	1·2	12·8	43·7	14,060	Non-caking, steam.	B
,, Two Yard	80·5	5·5	1·4	0·7	11·9	39·6	14,190	Household.	B/C
,, Seven Feet	79·4	5·5	1·3	2·2	11·5	47·0	13,920	Household and steam.	A
Leicester Main	74·5	5·7	1·5	2·8	15·5	39·7	—	Household, mnfg. (non-caking).	A
South Wales :									
Craigola	91·5	4·3	1·5	0·8	1·9	14·5	15,800	Steam and stove.	B/C
Pentre and No. 3 Rhondda (Llanharan)	83·9	5·2	1·5	1·4	8·0	36·4	14,780	Coking and gas.	G₂
Peacock Vein (Swansea)	92·5	3·5	1·2	0·9	1·9	5·0	15,700	Anthracite.	A
Bristol and Somerset :									
" Parkfield Large Gas " (mixture of Hard Vein, Top Vein, Great Vein, Hollybush)	84·5	5·4	1·8	1·8	6·5	37·7	15,030	Coking and gas, household.	G₉
East Kent :									
Milyard	88·6	4·5	1·2	1·9	3·8	22·8	15,540	Coking.	G₈
Seam H (Betteshanger)	91·0	4·2	1·3	0·7	2·8	15·4	15,700	Steam.	A

coking. All but one of the seams now being worked give very friable coal which is a disadvantage for general purposes, though not for coking, or for gas making in static retorts or ovens. The output is about one and a half million tons annually.

Analyses of British Coals. It is not possible in this volume to reproduce many analyses of the diverse varieties of coal found in this country but a selection of coals representative of the different fields are given in Table XXIX. Detailed information about the principal seams are, however, available in the reports of the D.S.I.R. surveys of the coal resources which are obtainable from H.M. Stationery Office. These reports also contain data regarding commercial grades of coal on sale up to the year 1944 ; after this time the work was taken over by the National Coal Board and no further reports have been issued.

Australia and New Zealand

Australia is dependent upon coal for most of its fuel requirements in having no significant deposits of oil or natural gas, and only limited resources of hydro-electric power. The geological history of the country does suggest that oil might be found and oil has now been struck in Western Australia. Until 1952, shale or torbanite was distilled in New South Wales (Glen Davis) to yield about 10 million gallons of motor spirit annually, but this has been abandoned although the reserves of material might have lasted another thirty years or more. A small amount of industrial alcohol is made from molasses (7 million gallons), but only about one million gallons is used as fuel.

The black coals of Australia, occurring mainly in New South Wales and Queensland, are of Permian to Cretaceous age. The brown coals of Victoria are of Eocene to Miocene age. An estimate of the reserves of these has been given in 1947 as follows, in millions of tons.

	Anthracite and bituminous.	Sub-bituminous and lignite.
Queensland	1704	67
New South Wales	11,668	50
Victoria	33	37,000
Tasmania	244	—
S. Australia	—	650
W. Australia	—	800

In New South Wales the Coal Measures contain over 70 ft. of workable coal in 10 or 12 seams of a bituminous character. In properties the coals vary from good-quality coking coal to hard coal of relatively low caking power which is suitable for industrial and domestic purposes.

In Queensland the coal is very variable owing to the action of severe faulting and all types are found from anthracite to caking and gas coal. Lignite is also found in seams of moderate thickness.

AUSTRALIA AND NEW ZEALAND 137

In Victoria there is practically no bituminous coal but very large deposits of lignite. These have been described above (p. 116). It is likely that the solid fuel requirements of the State will be modelled on the use of lignite in the future.

The total general production of coal in Australia in the year 1951-2 was 27 million tons, of which 14·7 millions were in New South Wales, 2·7 in Queensland, 1·7 other black coal and 8·1 millions of brown lignite in Victoria. The analyses of certain typical coals are shown in Table XXX. The very low sulphur content of some of the seams is most remarkable.

TABLE XXX

ANALYSES OF AUSTRALIAN BLACK COALS

	Moisture.	Volatile matter.	Ash.	Sulphur.	Calorific value (dry, ash-free).
Newcastle (coking) .	1·9	32·5	13·2	0·3	14,580 B.Th.U.
Greta (gas) . .	2·9	32·6	6·7	0·8	15,080 ,,
Lithgow (general) .	3·4	30·6	13·3	1·0	14,720 ,,
Newcastle (general) .	2·9	33·9	11·6	0·3	13,900 ,,
Bulli (coking) . .	2·1	21·7	13·1	0·3	15,100 ,,
Aberdare (gas) . .	3·0	30·4	13·6	0·2	14,400 ,,

In *New Zealand* the production of coal in 1951 was 2·4 million tons, of which nearly one-third was obtained by open-cast working. Of this, 667,000 tons was bituminous, 1,420,000 tons was sub-bituminous and 288,000 tons was lignite.

A good deal of oil-prospecting has been done from time to time but only in two places has this led to commercial production. At Motoroa 4·4 million gallons and at Taranaki 0·3 million gallons are produced annually. Considerable reserves of oil-shale are available, but these are not rich in oil and it is questionable whether they would pay for treatment ; they yield only about 12 gallons of oil per ton on distillation.

TABLE XXXI

COMPOSITION OF NEW ZEALAND COALS (dry, ash-free)

	Volatile matter.	Carbon.	Hydrogen.	Nitrogen.	Sulphur.	Oxygen.	Cal. Value B.Th.U. /lb.
Semi-anthracite :							
Paparoa Mine . .	17·7	89·0	5·0	0·7	0·3	5·0	15,750
Bituminous :							
Brunner Mine . .	39·2	83·3	5·2	0·9	2·4	8·2	15,310
Millerton Mine . .	35·8	84·0	5·5	1·0	3·0	6·5	14,900
" Blackball " . .	50·0	78·3	5·9	1·0	4·4	10·4	13,300
Semi-bituminous :							
Greymouth Mine . .	45·5	76·8	5·0	1·1	0·4	16·7	14,060

New Zealand has some natural gas, which has not been utilized, but extensive plans are being made for utilizing its valuable natural steam supplies. The thermal area is in the North Island and very large quantities of superheated steam are available for the production of power.

The reserves of coal in New Zealand are not large ; about 58 million tons bituminous, 500 million tons sub-bituminous and 370 million tons lignite. The analyses of typical varieties are given in Table XXXI (page 137). Certain of the caking coals are remarkable for a very high fusibility and have to be blended before they can be utilized for coke or gas manufacture.

Canada

The fuel situation in Canada has changed very much for the better since 1938 owing to the accelerated development of the oilfields in Alberta, and of the natural gas associated with them. Canada has also considerable reserves of coal but these are not evenly distributed and in the past it has imported a high proportion of its industrial coal into the central provinces from the more accessible fields of the United States. In 1949 the relative figures were 28·2 million tons imported and 15·6 millions mined, or 30 per cent. of the total.

The greatest production of petroleum is taking place in Alberta, but it is impossible to assess the reserves since prospecting is only in an early stage so far as the remainder of the country is concerned. There is no doubt that the total reserve must be large. Prospecting is also taking place with success in Saskatchewan, Manitoba, and British Columbia, Ontario, Quebec, Newfoundland and the North-west Territories. In 1930 the total production of oil was about 20,000 tons and of natural gas about 30×10^{12} cu. ft. ; the high rate of increase since then is shown by the following data.

Year.	Petroleum (thousand tons).	Natural gas (10^{12} cu. ft.).
1930	20	30
1938	93	40
1945	134	—
1948	160	—
1950	385	68
1952	818	88

The sources of the 1952 production were as follows :

	Thousand tons.	10^{12} cu. ft.
Alberta	790	79
Ontario	3	7·9
Saskatchewan . . .	21	1·0
New Brunswick . . .	4	0·2

Canadian petroleum is mainly of an intermediate type and wax-bearing, but several wells give oil of a naphthenic character.

In Athabaska there is an unusual deposit of oil-bearing material which has been called " tar-sands " but is really sand saturated with a petroleum of high asphalt content. The sands cover an area of about 30,000 square miles and vary in depth from several feet to about 200 ft. The oil is recoverable by treatment with hot water, but now that the petroleum reserves in Canada have been tapped it is not likely that the utilization of these sands will be pushed forward. In some places the possible yield is estimated at 200 million barrels (35 gal.) per square mile but it is true that a high proportion of the total area will yield at least 100 million barrels per square mile. Further data regarding these deposits are given in Chapter X.

Canadian Coals. The coals of Canada cover a wide variety of types from lignite to anthracite but the distribution of these is unequal since much the greatest reserves are in Alberta, Saskatchewan and British Columbia. Taking the provinces from east to west the estimated reserves are given in Table XXXII, in comparison with the production figures for the year 1945.

TABLE XXXII

COAL RESERVES AND COAL PRODUCTION IN CANADA

Province.	Type.	Reserves (million tons).	Production 1945 (million tons).
Nova Scotia	. Carboniferous system. Low, medium and high bituminous coal . .	1500–3000	5·11
New Brunswick	Carboniferous system. High volatile bituminous coal	50–100	0·36
Ontario .	. Lower Cretaceous system. Lignite, brown coal	100–150	—
Manitoba .	. Lignite	50–100	—
Saskatchewan	. Lignite	12,000–24,000	1·54
Alberta .	. Upper Cretaceous system. Low, medium and high volatile bituminous, sub-bituminous, lignite, semi-anthracite	24,000–48,000	7·80
British Columbia	Jurassic system. Low, medium and high volatile bituminous, sub-bituminous and lignite . .	10,000–18,000	1·70
			16·51

Of the total coal production at present Alberta has 48 and Saskatchewan 24 per cent.

Analyses of typical coals are given in Table XXXIII (page 140). The figures for ash and moisture are typical of the commercial coals but the other data are given on a basis of dry, ash-free coal in order to facilitate comparison with other coals.

It is apparent from this table that Canada has good reserves of coal of all types and that the only complication is that the distances over which the coal has to be hauled to the market, say from Alberta to the west, are very considerable. The coals of New Brunswick do however present some

TABLE XXXIII

ANALYSES OF TYPICAL CANADIAN COALS

	Moisture.	Ash.	C.	H.	S.	N.	O.	Calorific value (B.Th.U./lb)	Volatile matter.
			On dry, ash-free coal.						
Alberta :									
Semi-anthracite	1·0	5·0	89·8	4·2	0·8	1·3	3·9	15,000	11·0
Bituminous l.v.	1·8	7·9	89·0	4·5	0·8	1·8	3·9	14,520	15·7
Bituminous m.v.	5·0	12·0	87·5	5·0	0·3	1·3	5·9	—	24·2
Bituminous h.v.	7·0	10·0	85·0	5·3	0·6	1·3	7·8	—	29·3
New Brunswick .	3·0	16·0	82·2	5·4	0·7	6·8	4·9	—	37·6
Nova Scotia . .	4·0	8·0	82·2	5·4	3·4	1·5	7·5	—	38·3
British Columbia	4·5	8·0	86·4	5·0	1·4	1·0	6·6	—	27·6
Vancouver Island	3·7	10·7	83·2	5·0	1·1	1·0	9·7	—	35·1

problem because of their high sulphur content and their liability to spontaneous combustion on storage.

South Africa

In South Africa there are considerable reserves of coal, some torbanite
and bituminous shale, but no petroleum or natural gas. The reserves of
coal are estimated to lie between the following limits.

	Millions of tons.	
	Proved.	Estimated.
Natal (bituminous)	855	1710
(anthracite)	233	—
Orange Free State (bituminous) . . .	1010	1025
Transvaal (bituminous)	21,540	28,000

Coal in South Africa lies in the Karroo or Permo-Carboniferous formation
and the fields cover a wide area over the Transvaal, Natal, and the Orange
Free State in what is essentially a continuous field. Production is limited
at present to the Ecca Series but seams are available also in the Beaufort
and Stromberg Series.

The most important coalfield is the Witbank-Middleburg (Transvaal)
which produces 50 per cent. of the present production of 30 million tons
annually. The field contains five seams all containing non- to weakly-
caking coal of a dull appearance except one in which the coal is more banded
and has appreciable caking power. The same five seams are in the Ermelo-
Breyton field but only one is worked to provide a non-caking steam coal.

In Natal the seams are thinner but the coal is of higher rank than in
either the Transvaal or the Orange Free State. They are friable, however,
and give more fines on handling. There are two important fields, the
Klip River to the north-west and the Vryheid to the north-east. In the
former, two seams of bright, banded coal lie close together some 600 ft.
from the surface ; the lower seam has caking properties. Five seams occur

in the Vryheid field, all of coal of fair quality ; one seam has caking properties but the others contain non-caking steam coal.

The coalfield of the Orange Free State is separated from that of the Transvaal only by the Vaal river. At this point there are three seams of low-grade coal but of exceptional thickness in some places up to 40 ft.

In the Cape there is little coal and this is of poor quality and high ash content and serves only a local market of a few thousand tons annually.

Of the undeveloped fields the Waterburg is the most important. It is in the Transvaal adjoining Bechuanaland and contains altogether 23 seams in the Upper and Middle Ecca Series. These seams will in due course provide useful coals ; the steam coal seams are thick, ranging from 4 to 15 ft., and although the caking coal seams are thinner their caking power is considerable.

The composition of the coals of South Africa are given as typical examples in Table XXXIV. The typical ash and moisture content is given of the commercial coals but, for comparison with other coals, the other data are calculated to the dry, ash-free coal.

TABLE XXXIV

ANALYSES OF SOUTH AFRICAN COALS

Transvaal :	Moisture.	Ash.
Witbank	2·2–3·0	9·7–17·0
Middleburg	2·0	11·0
Ermelo-Breyton	2·5	15·0
Natal :		
Vryheid (bituminous)	1·1	13·5
(anthracite)	1·6	7·2
Klip River	1·5	15·1

(Dry, ash-free coal)

Transvaal :	C.	H.	S.org.	N.	O.	Calorific value.	Volatile matter.
Witbank	82–85	4·5–5·3	0·4	2·0	8–10	14,300	30–38
Breyton	80–83	5·0	0·5	2·0	9–13	14,100	37–40
Waterburg gas . . .	80–81	5·6	0·8	1·7	11–12	14,400	40–42
Waterburg steam . .	84–85	4·5	0·5	1·8	8–9	14,300	27
Natal :							
Vryheid (bituminous) .	86–88	4·7–5·0	0·5	2·2	4–7	15,400	20–28
(anthracite) .	90	4·0	0·5	2·4	3·0	15,300	9–12
Klip River . . .	83–88	4·7–5·3	0·8	2·2	4–9	15,000	21–37
Orange Free State . .	76–80	4·2–4·8	0·4	2·0	13–17	13,200	32–36

India and Pakistan

India has large reserves of coal, chiefly in the fields of Bengal, Bihar, and Madya-Pradesh [1] which lie along the 24° N. parallel and extend some 25 miles south of it. No survey has been made of actual reserves but these must be large in relation to the present rate of production of 30 million tons annually.

[1] Former Central Province.

Wood and charcoal are widely used. It is estimated that each family consumes about 1–3 tons of firewood per annum, a total of 50 million tons, or the equivalent of 25 million tons of coal. Wood is also supplied from the national forests to the extent of 4 million tons annually and some 1·5 millions of this is converted into charcoal for domestic purposes.

Mineral oil is not found in India except in Assam, where 163,000 tons are produced annually. The countries therefore import the greater part of their oil requirements of 2·5 million tons. Alcohol is also produced from molasses to the extent of 11 million gallons, and about one-quarter of this is used as motor spirit in an alcohol/petrol blend.

Methane from sewage should be a good prospect in the warm climate of India (mean 27° C.) but has not been exploited yet to any extent.

Indian Coals. The coals occur chiefly in the Damuda Series of the Lower Gondwanas in two main horizons, (1) the Lower or Barakar Measures and (2) the Upper or Raniganj Measures separated by 1500 ft. of ironstone shales. From east to west the fields are Raniganj, Jharia, East and West Bokhara, and South Karanpura, with some extensions to the south and west. Other coal-bearing areas are found elsewhere but are of much less significance. One area of lignite is found 100 miles south of Madras. At the present time the Raniganj and Jharia fields provide 13 million tons of coal annually and the Bokhara fields 4 millions.

Generally speaking, the Indian coals are of the weakly-caking bituminous type and contain mineral matter in such a fine state of dissemination that they are difficult, if not impossible, to clean by present-day methods to a low level of ash content. Some of the seams are of coking quality, if of high ash content; these are mainly in the Jharia field, and in Girindih.

Indian coals in general contain a high proportion of hard durain bands and, although low in sulphur content (0·5 per cent.), are inclined to be liable to spontaneous combustion. Some of the coking coals have the disability of a high phosphorus content of the order of 0·1 to 0·3 per cent.

In the Raniganj field the coals in the upper measures change in an east to west direction from weakly-caking to caking, but in the lower measures are all caking.

	East (Upper).	West (Upper).	Lower.
Carbon . . .	78·5–82·5	82·0–84·5	85–89
Hydrogen . . .	5·0–5·7	5·1–6·0	4·5–5·5
B.Th.U./lb. . . .	14,000–14,500	14,500–15,000	14,700–15,700

In the Jharia field low, medium and high volatile bituminous coals are found conforming to the following general analyses of the coal substance :

Volatile matter.	Carbon.	Hydrogen.	B.Th.U./lb.
<30	89–92	4·2–4·6	15,500–15,800
30 to 33	87–90	4·5–5·5	15,200–15,800
>33	83–88	4·8–5·8	15,000–15,700

The Bokhara coals are p-bituminous (Seyler) with 85·5 to 88 per cent. carbon and vary in volatile matter from 31 to 36 per cent.

The Karanpura coals are weakly or non-caking *meta*-lignitous coals with 35 to 39 per cent. volatile matter and with carbon contents between 81 and 84 per cent. The Jharia field should develop for South India.

Pakistan Coals. Coal seams of Tertiary age occur mainly in Baluchistan and West Punjab (Pakistan) and in Assam (India) in Eocene formations. The main Punjab coals are those of Dandot and Makerwal.

The Tertiary coals of both India and Pakistan are sub-bituminous or lignitic. Most of the Punjab coals are high in ash (10–18%) and of high volatile matter (55–60% d.a.f.) ; the Assam coals are of lower ash content. The seams are narrow, 2 to 8 ft., and the coal is non-caking and very friable and has the defect of high sulphur content (2–8%). Most of the sulphur is " organic " and it is not possible to reduce it by any known treatment.

Effective utilization of these coals calls for special coal-cleaning methods, followed by either carbonization or briquetting. The Assam coals are briquetted without cleaning for railways and tea-garden fuel.

Pakistan at present produces 0·4 million tons out of the 1·8 million tons it requires, and has to import from India either better quality coal or coal of different type for railways and for coke manufacture.

The British Colonies

Deposits of coal and lignite occur in several of the Colonies, but commercial production is so far confined to Nigeria and Malaya. Quite large reserves of coal have been proved in Tanganyika and exploration work is going on in Borneo, Rhodesia, Bechuanaland, Swaziland and Nyasaland and on the lignite deposits of Nigeria.

Nigeria. Sub-bituminous coal of Cretaceous age is found in Onitsha Province and other areas, but only in the Enugu field (5 ft. seam) of Onitsha is it being worked. This is being done at several places using adits, and pillar-and-stall mining.

The coal is dull black, with a conchoidal fracture, and weathers very badly on exposure, a fact which makes its efficient utilization difficult. Its normal moisture content is of the order of 8 per cent., its ash content 7, and its volatile matter 35 per cent. The composition of the dry, ash-free coal is : carbon 79·8, hydrogen 5·9, sulphur 1·1, nitrogen 2·0, and oxygen 11·2 per cent. On the same basis the volatile matter is 47·5 per cent. and the calorific value 14,700 B.Th.U./lb. Production in 1952 was 581,000 tons, of which two-thirds were shipped from Port Harcourt.

Nigeria also possesses extensive deposits of lignite of Tertiary age. This outcrops in the Benin and Onitsha Provinces near the river Niger.

Malaya. Two seams of coal of Tertiary age have been worked at Batu Arang in Selangor by both open-cast and mining methods. The coal is brownish-black in colour and lustrous and breaks with a conchoidal fracture.

It has a high moisture content (21 per cent.) and breaks down on drying in the typical black-lignite manner. Proved reserves are about 50 million tons and the present rate of production is about 350,000 tons annually.

Tanganyika. Coals of Karroo age are found in many places but only in small basins so that the reserves are not large. An exploration in the south-west at Ruhuhu suggests 300 million tons there, of which one-sixth is of good quality but non-caking. Probably other seams will be found.

Sierra Leone. Reserves of about 1·5 million tons of brown lignite have been proved in the neighbourhood of Freetown. This is of normal quality and could be utilized by briquetting or as a fuel for brick kilns.

Borneo. Tertiary coals ranging in rank from anthracite to lignite are widely distributed in the islands of Sarawak, Brunei and North Borneo. These have been worked for a number of years but are now not being produced. Survey work is however going on and has already disclosed that the reserves are considerable and that they contain caking coals of the highest quality. The latter are in the area of Silantek-Abok in Sarawak. This suggests that this area may be of considerable interest in the future particularly as a source of coking coals. The analyses of the caking coals are shown below in comparison with others of lower rank from the same area. These are quoted to the basis of dry, ash-free material.

	C.	H.	S.	N.	O.	B.Th.U./lb.	Volatile matter.	Gray-King type.
Silantek . . .	83·9	4·7	1·8	2·4	7·2	14,900	29·8	G_7
Silimpopon . .	80·2	6·2	4·9	1·5	7·2	14,500	51·0	G_5
Sadong . . .	77·1	5·3	0·9	1·7	14·9	13,850	48·9	E
Brunei . . .	70·3	4·3	2·7	1·3	21·4	13,100	47·0	A

Bechuanaland, Swaziland, Nyasaland. Coal seams in the Karroo system have been found in these colonies, but only exploration work has been done.

Rhodesia. In the north no coal of any value has yet been found. In the south, however, one coalfield (Wankie) has been in production for some time and quite considerable reserves are believed to exist in the basins of the Zambesi, Limpopo and Sabi rivers. The reserves at Wankie are thought to be of the order of 4,000 million tons and annual production now exceeds 2·5 million tons. The coal is bituminous and has marked caking properties. Its ash content is about 10 per cent. but it can be cleaned to a much lower figure. The composition of the dry, ash-free coal is carbon 87, hydrogen 5, sulphur 2, nitrogen 1·5 and oxygen 4·5 per cent.

Exploration has indicated that the reserves are much larger over the colony than at Wankie, but that the coal is likely to be of inferior quality and non-caking.

REFERENCES

Resources of the British Empire : Coal. Andrew. E. Benn. 1924.
Oil Shale and Cannel Coal. Inst. of Petroleum. 1938 and 1951.
Brown Coal. Herman. State Electricity Comm. of Victoria, Australia. 1952.
Evaluation of Commonwealth Coals. Francis. *J. Inst. Fuel*, 1952, **25**, 15.
Coal : Its Formation and Composition Francis. Ed. Arnold (Publishers) Ltd. 1954.

CHAPTER VII

TREATMENT AND STORAGE OF COAL. BRIQUETTES. COAL-OIL SUSPENSIONS

PREPARATION OF COAL

A small proportion of the coal mined is sold directly without further treatment (run-of-mine coal), but by far the greater proportion passes through some form of treatment before being marketed. Such treatment may consist of (1) separation of types of coal, (2) grading into size, (3) washing and/or cleaning, (4) mixing.

In a thick coal seam there may be more than one type of coal, i.e. brights and hards, and these may be brought to the surface separately. Similarly, sections of the seam which are high in ash or sulphur content may be kept separate. Grading consists of separating the coal into fractions of different size, each size being suitable for a specific purpose. Washing and cleaning consist in removing from the coal extraneous dirt introduced as pieces of the roof or floor, or dirt bands, imperfectly separated at the coal face. Finally, mixing or blending is used to modify the properties of coal to suit one purpose. It should be realized that screening is also a mixing operation if a number of seams are being worked at one colliery, since one screen size will contain varying proportions of the coal from each seam.

Coal grading is to-day of the utmost importance. Coal cleaning, although not so important if clean seams are being worked, is important for small coal and will increase in importance as the thicker coal seams become worked out.

The first operation in dealing with coal at the surface is preliminary screening.

The chief requisite of the screening plant is that it should require little attention, that it should produce as little breakage of the material as possible, that it should be uniform across its surface and that the screen apertures should not tend to clog. Screening plant consists of several types, revolving screens, shaking screens and vibrating screens, and the apertures in the surface may be either round or square holes. In screening, the shape of the coal and dirt is of importance and the greatest accuracy in screening is achieved when dealing with large dry coal on a vibrating horizontal screen, the material containing no flat pieces. The most common type of screen, however, is the longitudinal belt screen in which the angle of inclination is about $45°$. The capacity of a 6-ft. screen of this type operating on $1\frac{1}{2}$-in. coal, is about 100 tons per hour.

After screening, the large coal (over $3\frac{1}{2}$ in.) is passed over picking belts where foreign material is removed by hand. On a 100-ft. belt, six workers can pick as much as 100 tons of coal per shift.

The smaller coal may be sold without further treatment or it may be cleaned and sized. In 1931, 66·7 million tons of this coal was cleaned, representing 30·4 per cent. of the coal mined and perhaps 70 per cent. of the small coal available. In 1927 the percentage was only 20·5 ; by 1951 it had risen to over 50 per cent., when the amounts cleaned by different methods were :

Washing processes	.	95·7
Dry cleaning	.	12·6
Froth flotation	.	1·3

109·6 million tons or 51·6 per cent. of production.

Screening or Grading

The coal industry has always adjusted its screening plant to meet market demands and this has given rise to a wide variety of sizes and caused considerable confusion. In order to remedy this, rationalization of sizes was attempted in 1946 and has since been widely applied. The chosen sizes are as shown below and may be either square or round apertures. Certain degrees of latitude are laid down which vary with the size handled, for example, that 2×1-in. doubles (round sizes) must not contain more than 25 per cent. through a $\frac{7}{8}$ in. sq. screen or 3 per cent. through a $\frac{3}{16}$ in. sq. screen.

	Large cobbles.	Cobbles.	Trebles.	Doubles.	Singles.	Peas.	Grains.
Size, in., round hole	6×3	4×2	3×2	2×1	$1 \times \frac{1}{2}$	$\frac{1}{2} \times \frac{1}{4}$	$\frac{1}{4} \times \frac{1}{8}$

The large coal was to be defined as " over x inches " and slacks as " smalls " with a rider stating, for example, " $\frac{1}{2}$ inch 50 " meaning a maximum size of $\frac{1}{2}$ in. with 50 per cent. passing a $\frac{1}{8}$-in. screen.

The distribution of size varies over the whole country for reasons associated mainly with the hardness of the coal. The average for 1951 is shown below in comparison with figures for the friable coals of Durham and the Yorkshire coals of more average hardness. The figures are percentages.

	Million tons.	Large.	Unscreened.	Graded.	Slacks. Cleaned.	Not cleaned.	Others.
Total 1951	195·4	30·7	7·1	21·0	17·1	19·8	4·3
Durham	24·7	6·3	42·2	9·7	16·5	24·5	0·8
Yorkshire	40·1	29·7	0·8	30·3	25·2	12·8	1·2

Many types of screen are used for coal grading, from gravity-bar screens to trommel, jigging or vibrating screens ; a description of these is beyond the scope of this book.

Coal Cleaning

The advantages of clean coal are obvious, but the extent to which cleaning can be practised depends on the character of the coal and the ultimate cost. In 1945 it was estimated that cost was of the order of 15 pence per ton.

Cleaning processes depend chiefly upon differences in specific gravity between clean coal and dirt, the specific gravity of coal being about 1·3, of shale about 2·5 and of pyrites over 4·0. Other physical properties which differ are coefficients of friction, resilience, shape and surface tension. Density differences are the most important and coals can be assayed for cleaning purposes by density separation, using mixed liquids of different densities for floating off the coal in fractions. Such liquids may be mixtures of carbon tetrachloride and toluene, or solutions of calcium chloride. An example of such a separation is shown in Table XXXV of a coal containing 15·3 per cent. of ash.

TABLE XXXV

FLOTATION ASSAY OF COAL

Sp. gr. of liquid.	Floating material.		Sinking material.	
	% yield.	ash %.	% yield.	ash %.
1·25	5	0·8	95	16·0
1·30	65	2·4	35	39·3
1·35	75	3·1	35	51·8
1·40	79	3·8	21	58·5
1·50	82	4·5	18	64·1
1·60	85	5·6	15	70·0

If clean coal of less than 5 per cent. ash were required it would be necessary to " cut " at 1·50 sp. gr. in which case the yield would be 82 per cent. of coal at 4·5 per cent. ash.

These results can also be expressed graphically as shown in Figure 20.

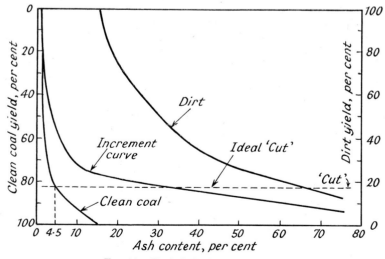

FIG. 20.—Typical Washability Curves.

The clean coal and dirt curves are drawn from the figures in Table XXXV while the increment curve shows the ash content of the dirtiest particle which is included in the " clean " coal. In Figure 20 this is 31 per cent. ; if the cut were made nearer the elbow of this curve, say at 75 per cent. clean coal, it would be 12 per cent. only.

In order to obtain clean coal it is apparent that the cut should be made at the elbow of the clean coal curve, i.e. about 5 per cent. ash and a yield of over 80 per cent. of the coal.

In practice, cleaning is not so easy as this since some of the " dirt " may be intergrown with the coal and cannot be separated from it without a degree of crushing which cannot be allowed. The coal may contain :

(i) free dirt derived from the roof or floor or mineral bands in the coal which separate in mining or in screening. This dirt may be almost free from adherent coal.

(ii) mineral matter in the coal from the original plant materials and entangled clay, silt, etc., and partings which have avoided separation during breakage. Some coals in this country have an ash content as low as 0·8 per cent. but the general average of "inherent" ash is of the order of 4·5 per cent.

In dealing with sized coal the main difficulty in cleaning is associated with the particles which consist of coal and intergrown dirt. These " middlings " could be cleaned by crushing to liberate this dirt but normally this is not an economic procedure. Indeed at the present high cost of coal it is not economic to clean material which has too high a content of middlings and departs unduly from the theoretical curves above. To-day, therefore, the performance of a washery can be assessed from the degree to which it works to the assay results.

Most coal-cleaning plants now operate on the principle of gravity separation though not necessarily by the use of dense liquids. They may be separated into groups as follows :

Wet Processes.
    (a) Jig washers.   (b) Trough washers.   (c) Dense media washers.   (d) Concentrator tables.   (e) Froth flotation.

Dry Processes.
    (f) Air tables.   (g) Spirals.   (h) Berrisford process.

The most common type is the jig washer. The principle is that the coal is fed to a screen which is submerged in water, and the latter is caused to pulsate through the bed of coal. This produces a stratified bed from which the clean coal can be taken from the top layer and dirt from the lower layer. One type, the Baum washer, is described later.

In trough washers the coal is caused to flow down a launder in such a manner that stratification according to density takes place and mechanical separation becomes possible. In the Rheolaveur type the trough contains slots specially arranged to separate the dirt. In the Blackett washer the trough is a spiral on the inside of a horizontal rotating drum.

The " dense medium " washer applies the principle of the assay but uses, not a liquid of high density, but a water-suspension of dense fine particles. These are readily separated from the clean coal by means of a water spray. The particles can be recovered for re-use by settling. A variety of substances are used including sand (Chance), barytes and clay (Barvoys), iron oxide (Tromp and others), tailings (Dutch State Mines).

The pioneer dense-medium process, that of Lessing, employs a solution of calcium chloride in water. In most commercial washing processes, however, the principle employed is the rate of settling of the particles in a fluid, such as water or air. This rate reaches a constant or terminal velocity when the resistance of the fluid equals the weight of the particle. Neglecting shape, increase of size or density affects the terminal velocity. The principle is applied directly in upward current washers of which the best known is the Draper Tube. If the velocity of the upward current of water is slightly greater than the terminal velocity of the coal, the heavier dirt will sink and the clean coal will be carried forward in the water stream. The great difficulty with this type of plant is the obvious necessity for close sizing. In practice the size range cannot be more than 2 to 1. For this reason this type of plant has not a wide application in coal cleaning.

Concentrator Tables are identical in action to those used in ore dressing. The table, which is fitted with wood riffles, is oscillated lengthwise while coal is fed to the top and water flows transversely. The combined action of the oscillations and the water stratifies the coal, the clean coal riding over the riffles and the heavier dirt being carried along the riffles to the far end.

None of the wet processes is suitable for the cleaning of fine coal (say below 0·1 in.) because the forces tending to separate the coal and particles are not great enough. In Froth Flotation processes the property which is utilized is wetability. Shales are preferentially wetted by water while coal is preferentially wetted by oil in the presence of water. Thus if a suitable oil is added to a slurry of dirty coal the coal particles absorb the oil as a thin film and, if the mixing takes place in an aerated water stream, the bubbles attach themselves to the coal particles and bring them to the surface where they can be separated. A number of slightly-different systems are in use but in all of them the separation is continuous and the amount of oil necessary is only of the order of one pint per ton of coal treated. Suitable oils are light lubricating or " spindle " oils for the coating of the particles and a cresol for creating the necessary froth.

The Baum Jig Washer. As a practical example of an industrial washer one must take the jig type, of which the Baum plant is the most common in Great Britain ; indeed, it is used in some fifty per cent. of British plants. The essential part of it, the wash-box, is shown diagrammatically in Figure 21. The box consists of a main tank divided by a grid so that in cross-section it appears " U " shaped. The narrower limb connects to a pulsating air supply while the wider limb contains a grid which supports a 1-ft. bed of coal. The coal enters at one end and passes along to the other, subjected meanwhile to the jigging action of pulsations at the rate of about 30 to 60 per minute. The clean coal passes over a weir at the end, the heavy dirt, which separates at an early stage, passes downwards through a slot to a collecting extractor, and the middlings pass also downwards through a similar mechanism. Fine dirt, which passes through the grids, is collected from the bottom. The process is regulated

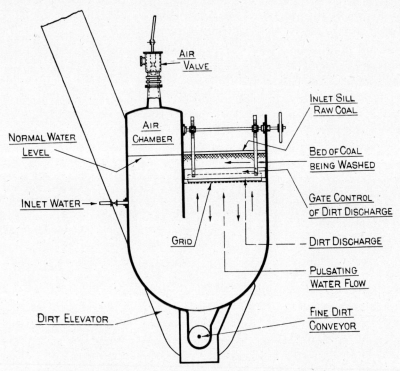

FIG. 21.—Diagrammatic Section of British Baum Wash-box.

to suit the coal and to maintain a uniform bed ; this can be done automatically by a float which is weighted to take up a position near the coal/dirt interface.

Dry processes of cleaning are not favoured in comparison with wet, despite the fact that they avoid the complication of a very wet product, the difficulty of handling wet slurries, and the large volumes of washery water which must for cost reasons be separated and re-used. The main reasons are that they must work to very close limits of sizing, which greatly limits their applicability. The most common type is the air table, in which the water of the concentrator table is replaced by an upward current of air. The raw coal is passed in a thin layer over a perforated table with longitudinal riffles about $2\frac{1}{2}$ in. high. The surface of the table is tiled cornerwise from the feed end, the air current may be steady or pulsating and the table may be steady or jigging. The air current segregates the coal and the dirt, the riffles trap the latter and carry it to a suitable exit port, while the clean coal flows over the riffles to another collecting point.

The depth of the riffles is from $1\frac{1}{4}$ to 2 in. at the inlet end, depending on the side of the coal, and about $\frac{3}{32}$ in. at the outlet end. The spacing varies from 1 in. for very small coal to a greater width for larger coals and to 6 in. for special coals. The capacity of a table varies with the size of the coal, for example from 55 tons per hour for 4 to 2 in. coal to 30 tons for coal 1 to $\frac{1}{2}$ in. and to 20 tons for coal $\frac{1}{4}$ to $\frac{1}{8}$ in.

Taking an example of a Durham gas coal containing in the raw state 8·5 per cent. of ash in the material over $\frac{1}{16}$ in., this gave 92·8 per cent. of clean coal at 3·7 per cent. ash and 7·2 per cent. refuse at 66·4 per cent. ash and containing only 1·2 per cent. of coal.

Size (in.).	Raw coal %.	Ash %.	Ash % in Clean coal.	Dirt.
2–1	30·0	9·3	4·5	66·5
1–$\frac{1}{4}$	42·7	8·1	3·2	67·0
$\frac{1}{4}$–$\frac{1}{16}$	27·3	8·1	3·8	66·9

There are a number of designs of air table but the total number of plants in use is very small in relation to the number of wet washers.

Other dry-cleaning processes make use of differences in the physical properties of coal and shale. The Spiral Separator makes use of the difference in the coefficient of friction, which is lower for coal. The separator is a tall, vertical spiral with a pitch varying from 28 to 38 in. depending upon the type of coal. As the raw coal slides down, the coal particles move to the outside of the spiral while the dirt particles slide down near the axis ; the two fractions are collected separately. The process is not in wide use since its effectiveness is so easily affected, even by patches of moist coal, or by deterioration (rusting) of the surface of the spiral if there is any interruption of use.

The Berrisford process makes use of differences in resilience. If a mixture of coal and dirt particles is projected by a jigging feed on to an inclined plane the former tend to bounce and gather speed while the latter slide down close to the surface. If, then, the plane contains a gap or opening of the right width, the dirt can be separated as it falls through. The height of the initial fall on to the plane, the shape of the lip, the space before the gap, and the angle are all critical. An example of these for two sizes of coal are as follows :

	Height of fall.	Length of plane.	Width of gap.
Coal 2 to 1 in. . . .	5 in.	12 in.	8 in.
Coal $\frac{1}{8}$ to $\frac{1}{32}$ in. . . .	$\frac{7}{8}$ in.	3 in.	1 in.

Processes employing other physical properties exist but their application to the preparation of coal is very limited.

Dustproofing

In the handling of dry coal the projection of dust into the atmosphere can sometimes be a serious nuisance and attempts have been made to render fine coal dustless. This can be done effectively by spraying the surface with oil or a solution of calcium chloride. Coal is porous, however, and in order to keep a proportion of the oil on the surface for a sufficient length of time it is necessary to vary the amount with the type of coal. It is interesting that the oil requirement follows the porosity curve of Figure 14 with a minimum at 85 per cent. carbon. The oil is applied with a high-pressure spray in amounts varying from 5 to 10 lb. per ton ; with this amount the effect will last at least ten weeks. A light spindle oil is effective but proprietary oils are available which also contain 1–2 per cent. of rubber, or iso-butylene polymer or similar substance.

Auxiliary Processes

In all cleaning processes the fine coal (less than $\frac{1}{20}$ in.) is the cause of much trouble. In wet processes, it forms a slurry which requires special auxiliary plant for its separation from the washery water since this has to be kept below a certain percentage of solids in suspension. In dry processes it necessitates the installation of elaborate dust-collecting plants.

Dedusting. Processes normally involve fine screening and/or winnowing with collection of the dust. If this is not of high ash content it can be remixed with the clean coal. If of high ash content it must find some other outlet such as pulverized fuel. Dedusting cannot of course be done with wet or even damp coal. Where possible, dedusting is done prior to washing since the efficiency of the washer is increased and the water problems reduced.

Flocculation. Washery waters are normally settled for the recovery of the fine material and the re-use of the water to as large an extent as possible. In practice the rate of settling is increased by the addition of chemical flocculating agents such as glue and starch. Only a small quantity is necessary (5 to 10 lb. per ton of (dry) suspended solids) but the rate of settling of the solids can be increased to 16 times in the early stages and over 7 times when the proportion of solids has reached 40 per cent. The effect is due to the modifications of the surface properties of the coal particles by the adsorbed layer of colloid so that on collision the particles tend to adhere. The hydrophilic colloids (gelatin, starch) are satisfactory alone but can be improved by the addition of a wetting agent such as turkey-red oil. Although electrolytes will not flocculate coal particles larger than 0·07 mm. (240 mesh), starch will work up to 0·3 mm. diameter, which is its particular value.

For the recovery of the solids a common form of plant is the drum filter. This is a slowly-rotating wire-cloth drum which dips into the slurry and, by internal suction, collects a layer of solids ; this is dewatered by the suction and scraped off at a suitable point in the revolution.

Dewatering of Washed Coal. All washed coal is freed from water to the greatest possible extent before it leaves the washery. For graded coals special dewatering screens are used ; for fine coals it is necessary to use drainage bunkers.

Coal Breaking

The term " breakage " applied to coal means the reduction of large coal, for which there may not be a market, to graded coal, with the minimum wastage due to the formation of fine material. The general principle of coal winning must always be to employ the minimum of breakage consistent with the supplying of markets, but there must always be circumstances, particularly with hard, massive coals, when breaking into commercial grades must be done.

Two types of breaker are in common use in Great Britain, the pick type and the roll type. In the pick type the coal passes under a steel plate, faced with specially-arranged spikes or picks, which moves up and down. In order to reduce the formation of fines the spacing of the picks is very open to start with and close enough later to give the required maximum size of coal particle.

The roll breaker may be of three types : (i) single rolls in which the teeth on the rolls press the coal against a spring-loaded breaker plate, (ii) double, toothed rolls arranged side by side between which the coal passes, and (iii) a series of double rolls in which the size of the teeth and the spacing of the rolls can be progressively reduced. With rolls of this type the most efficient performance is obtained by not attempting to break the coal too severely in one passage but by screening out the oversize after one pass and recycling it to the breaker.

An example of the performance of a typical breaker is given below, by quoting from experimental work on a pick-type breaker, with secondary picks arranged at 2-in. centres. In Table XXXVI is given the size analyses

TABLE XXXVI

BREAKAGE OF LARGE COAL IN A PICK BREAKER

Coal.	1	2	3	4
Over 4 in. . . .	0·2	0·4	0·6	0·7
1. 4–3	5	8	10	13
2. 3–2½	14	21	18	20
3. 2½–1¾	28	28	27	28
4. 1¾–1	24	21	22	17
5. 1–½	14	10	11	9
6. ½–3/16	8	6	6	6
7. Under 3/16 . . .	6·8	5·6	5·4	6·3

of products from four coals of increasing hardness, all over $2\frac{3}{4}$ in. in size and containing particles varying in weight from 0·5 lb. to 45 lb. Coal 4 was a particularly hard coal, rich in durain.

The similarity of effect is quite marked although the effect of increasing hardness $(1 \rightarrow 4)$ is shown in the increase of the proportions of fractions 2 and 3.

Experiment on the action of the pick breaker has shown that the size of the coal has no effect over a weight of lump of 10 lb., but below 10 lb. the mean particle size of the product increases. From data obtained by breaking definite particle sizes the end product for a given set of conditions can be calculated, i.e. each size acts as if it were alone.

With the pick breaker the proportion of fines is affected by the thickness of the picks and their spacing, and variations of these must be made for different coals. For example, with a given spacing, the reduction of the cross-section of the picks by one-third reduced the percentage of fines in one coal by about 3 per cent. It follows that decrease of clearance of picks also increases the formation of fines. Finally the larger the maximum size of the coal being broken, the higher the proportion of fines formed.

Other breakers all give comparable results but do not quite approach the efficiency of the pick breaker in reducing the formation of fines. Finally, breaking in stages, with recirculation of the oversize from the first, gives a better result from the point of view of avoiding fines, than one-stage breakage.

The avoidance of breakage in the handling of coal is almost as important a part of coal preparation as any, and precautions are taken in handling coal to avoid all unnecessary shocks. Spiral shoots are used to fill deep bunkers and inclined belt conveyors are used to convey coal from one point to another and to fill rail cars. In loading ships special movable hoppers are used and anti-breakage chutes. One of the latter resembles a one-sided escalator arranged vertically and adjustable in height to give the minimum final fall to the floor of the hold.

Breakage in transport, apart from loading, is not serious, as can be seen in the following example of two screened South Yorkshire coking coals transported from the colliery to London and rescreened there.

	$+ 2$ in.	$2\text{--}1\frac{3}{4}$	$1\frac{3}{4}\text{--}1\frac{3}{8}$	$1\frac{3}{8}\text{--}\frac{5}{8}$	$\frac{5}{8}\text{--}\frac{5}{16}$	$- \frac{5}{16}$
(1) Before	36·2	28·3	25·5	7·4	1·0	1·6
After	37·6	24·5	24·1	9·3	0·7	2·8
(2) Before	52·3	45·2		1·6	0·4	0·6
After	51·0	43·5		3·4	1·0	1·3

If the serious breakage be taken as the reduction of pieces to pass $\frac{5}{8}$ in,. these figures indicate the formation of (1) 1·9 and (2) 1·3 per cent. more fines of this size—not a serious increase.

STORAGE OF COAL

The storage of coal is undoubtedly a costly procedure but it is essential to our national economy for a number of reasons of which the most important are avoidance of shortages at the point of usage and the levelling out of the different seasonal rates of consumption. The latter effect is equivalent to 30 per cent. between summer and winter.

A further disadvantage to cost of stacking is the deterioration of the quality of the coal and the possibility of serious loss or damage by spontaneous combustion. It is true to say that coal will deteriorate under bad conditions of storage in respect of :

Reduction of size by disintegration in addition to the accidental breakage which will occur on double handling.

Loss of calorific value by oxidation.

Loss of caking power by oxidation. This is more significant than the loss of calorific value.

Loss of gas yield in the case of gas-making coals.

It is also true that the liability of coals to oxidation during storage is not uniform and that precautions have generally to be taken to meet the worst case.

Oxidation cannot be prevented altogether and the first consideration in arranging storage conditions is to reduce the rate of oxidation to a minimum and also to make certain that the heat liberated is adequately dispersed so that the temperature cannot rise to the point of inflammation. It is clear, therefore, that the oxidation of coal, its consequent liberation of heat, spontaneous heating, and conditions of storage, are all interconnected.

Oxidation of Coal. Coals, when freshly mined or broken to expose fresh surfaces, liberate adsorbed hydrocarbons, chiefly methane, varying in amount from 0·02 cu. ft. per lb. for bituminous coal to 0·15 cu. ft. in the case of anthracite. This factor introduces a first precaution in coal storage in that surface ventilation is necessary in bunkers to allow this inflammable gas to escape.

After the escape of these adsorbed gases the coal is particularly liable to oxidation, but after some time in storage and the adsorption of the oxygen in the first stages is complete the rate decreases and the liberation of heat becomes more easy to control. Oxidation may be considered to take place in three stages :

(i) the sorption of oxygen with liberation of heat ;

(ii) the imperfect dissipation of this heat leading to rise of temperature and accelerated rate of oxidation ; the rate of a chemical reaction is doubled by a rise of temperature of 10° C ;

(iii) the breakdown of the sorbed phase with rise of temperature, with liberation of water and oxides of carbon and increased liberation of heat. The heat liberated is about 90 B.Th.U. per cubic foot of air reacting.

The sorption of oxygen (i) is accelerated by slight rise of temperature suggesting the formation of a complex by chemical reaction with the coal. This becomes significant at about 27° C. with bituminous coal and, as the temperature rises, it is augmented by the reactions of (iii) and the whole system can continue to heat up, if escape of heat is prevented. It is not until a temperature of about 120° C. is reached that carbon dioxide and water vapour make their appearance, indicating that a slow combustion has started. Under suitable conditions the process accelerates until a temperature of 140° to 160° C. is reached, when the rate of increase of temperature becomes much greater, until between 200° and 275° C. a self-sustained process of combustion sets in with very rapid rise of temperature until the ignition point, which may lie between 300° and 400° C., is attained, when active combustion is set up.

The temperature cannot rise, however, if the heat liberated is dissipated to the surrounding atmosphere, so that a dangerous state is attained only when the rate of generation of heat exceeds the rate of dissipation.

All types of coal are liable to atmospheric oxidation, with the exception of anthracite. The liability increases with decreasing rank, other factors being the same, some lignites being particularly liable and being storable with safety only under water. The banded constituents do not show any particular liability nor does any constituent which has been separated by solvent action.

As stated, slow oxidation of coal reduces its tendency to heating. The changes which occur in bituminous coal can be recognized by the increased solubility of the coal in caustic soda solution. This is due to the regeneration of soluble ulmins (p. 73), but it is believed that the nucleus of the coal molecule is not altered. The formation of soluble ulmins becomes progressively more difficult as the rank of the coal increases—this indeed can be a measure of rank—and could be used to measure the liability of coal to spontaneous heating. Unfortunately the physical factors greatly outweigh any chemical factors in the progress of oxidation of coal in the bituminous class and it is these which determine the conditions of storage of coal. It is true, however, that the appearance of soluble ulmins is a measure of reduction of caking power which is much more illuminating than any small change which can be detected in, say, the carbon content.

Moisture has apparently no significant effect on the rate of oxidation of coal. Pyrites was for long held to be an important factor because of its own readiness to oxidize in the finely-divided state with liberation of heat. It is now recognized that the important factor is the character of the coal substance and that the presence of pyrites is only a contributory factor. Pyrites may occur in the form of veins or lumps but, though these oxidize slowly, they are not a factor; it is only the disseminated pyrites which contributes.

The physical factors which are of importance are particle size and distribution, the availability of the oxygen supply, the degree of ventilation and the maximum temperature which may be reached. Since the first step in oxidation is the sorption of oxygen it is obvious that the area of surface exposed is of prime importance and that the first generality which can be stated is that coal which contains a high proportion of fines is more liable to oxidation than graded coal.

It has been established that the rate of adsorption of oxygen by coal is not directly proportional to the area of the exposed surface but it does increase with increasing surface and therefore with the proportion of fines. This increased rate, combined with the fact that fines retard the dissipation of the heat, makes the amount and distribution of fines the strongest factor in coal heating. Distribution is important in that a high local concentration of fines can be developed in a stack by the method of stacking, or in the hold of a ship by the method of loading. This concentration of fines then becomes a danger spot which can affect the whole. Mass is also a factor in that it is only in places where the surface area of a considerable quantity of coal in relation to its mass is very great, that is, where there is an accumulation of fines and dust surrounded by sufficient material to give the necessary heat insulation without cutting off the supply of oxygen, that heating can ever arise. With larger coal slow oxidation of the exterior faces only is possible and, beyond causing slow deterioration, can do no harm.

A solid mass of coal is of a low order of thermal conductivity, and, when broken up, the air spaces further greatly lower its conductivity. Given a sufficiently large mass of coal with generation of heat taking place some distance from the surface, the escape of heat is prevented and the temperature at the affected part will rise until the self-sustained stage of oxidation is reached, ultimately resulting in firing if the supply of oxygen is sufficient to sustain rapid combustion. If this is not the case oxidation will proceed only to the limit of available oxygen, the rate will fall practically to zero, and the heated portion gradually cool off.

Experience shows that a large mass of coal in which conditions are favourable is far more likely to heat and finally ignite than smaller masses.

Accessibility of oxygen (air) plays an important part in determining the rate of oxidation and in the localization of areas in which oxidation may proceed rapidly. If no ventilation at all took place the oxygen present in the voids would soon be used up and oxidation would cease. In slow ventilation, where the oxygen content is reduced by interaction with the coal, the rate of oxidation is slowed; it has been shown that the rate varies with the square root of the concentration of oxygen. In the reverse case, where free circulation of air is possible, oxidation will proceed at the slow rate corresponding to a lower temperature since the heat developed will be freely carried away.   Somewhere between the extremes there is a condition of ventilation and heat transfer at which the rates of generation and removal of heat balance.   In an experiment with Pittsburg coal Davis and Byrne found that at 127° C., under the conditions of the experiment, this balance was reached at an air flow of 1·64 cu. ft. of air per hour, per cubic foot of coal and a heat liberation of 148 B.Th.U.   Other coals would give different values, but these figures show the order of the conditions which define the critical conditions for a *bituminous* coal.

Deterioration of Coal during Storage.   The extent of deterioration of coal which occurs in storage must of course depend upon the extent to which it has been oxidized.   The nature of the deterioration may be any of the following :

(i) Loss of heat units, i.e. reduction of calorific value.

(ii) Physical breakdown of size.

(iii) Loss of caking power.

(iv) Increase of friability.

(v) Reduction of gas yield in gas-making with increase of breeze formation in the coke.

Loss of calorific value is of importance to the power station, and to the industrial and domestic user, since all of them are concerned in the best utilization of the heat units in the coal.   Losses of heat units are sometimes ascribed to loss of calorific value when they are more strictly due to the effect of another factor such as, for example, a deterioration of size which reduces the efficiency of utilization.   Loss of calorific value alone is therefore often less serious than is supposed ; if the coal is properly stored so that it does not " heat " unduly the loss should not be more than 0·8 per cent. per annum.   The following figures are quoted from Fuel Research Station experiments on a Forest of Dean coal to demonstrate further that size is a factor.

Size of coal (in.).	Loss of calorific value per cent.	
	One year.	Two years.
2–3	0·11	0·24
$1\frac{1}{2}$–$\frac{1}{8}$	0·5	1·0
$\frac{1}{80}$–$\frac{1}{120}$	1·0	2·1
$\frac{1}{400}$–zero	1·8	3·0

Other data record the loss of calorific value of Scottish gas coals as 0·7 per cent. during three to four years.   That the loss is continuous for a long period is shown by figures for Yorkshire and Derbyshire locomotive coals. These are 1·8 to 2·8 per cent. for the former, and 1·8 to 4·2 per cent. for the latter, for periods of one and seven years respectively.   Should conditions be such that spontaneous heating occurs, even if it is immediately dealt with, the loss may be very large, even up to 10 per cent.

The deterioration of size of coal can also be exemplified from Fuel

Research data regarding four types of British coal which had been screened above a given minimum size. The table shows the amount of material above this size at the end of periods of six, nine and twelve months.

	Per cent. over the minimum size after			
	0	6	9	12 months.
South Wales steam, $2\frac{1}{2}$–$1\frac{3}{8}$ in. . .	100	93·2	91·6	90·7
Warwickshire, $2\frac{1}{2}$–$1\frac{3}{8}$ in. . . .	100	91·4	90·0	87·3
Nottinghamshire, $2\frac{1}{2}$–$1\frac{3}{4}$ in. . . .	100	82·2	73·1	69·4
South Yorkshire gas, over 2 in. . .	54	46·3	48·2	47·8

The relatively high resistance of the South Wales coal is noticeable and also the speedy breakdown of the lower-rank coal of Nottinghamshire. Some of the breakdown is due to actual disintegration of the coal, but much of it is also due to the splitting of pieces along the bedding plane and at the points where inorganic partings occur.

Friability also increases most markedly in those coals which show disintegration on storage, aggravating the loss of commercial value caused by the latter. For example, the Warwickshire coal above, when subjected to a " trommel " test (see p. 241), showed the following breakdown when fresh and after twelve months' storage.

	Fresh.	After 12 months.
$2\frac{1}{2}$–$\frac{3}{8}$ in. per cent.	87·7	68·1
$1\frac{3}{8}$–$\frac{7}{8}$ in. ,, ...	6·9	16·7
Below $\frac{3}{8}$ in. ,, ...	5·4	15·2

This breakdown of size and increase of friability can affect industrial utilization adversely and coals liable to it should be stored to the minimum extent and always under the most suitable conditions. Since the most serious deterioration takes place in the early stages of storage the timing of deliveries to avoid short-term storage is to be recommended.

Loss of caking power is of special importance to the carbonizing industries but can also affect the burning qualities of furnace coals adversely. Caking power is the most rapidly affected of any of the qualities of coal and can be quite marked before other qualities such as calorific value are measurably affected. Should the temperature of the stack rise unduly the effect on caking power can be disastrous. An example of the changes under good conditions of storage can be quoted from Fuel Research Station data.

Size of coal.	Years stored.	Campredon index. Before.	After.	Gray-King coke type. Before.	After.
Large	5	21	6	G_4	C/D
Small	1+	16	6/7	G	C/D
Small	1+	9	2	F	B
Singles	1+	7	3/4	D	C
Small	1	8	2/3	E	B

Data regarding loss of quality for gas manufacture are recorded by

Jamieson and Skilling for a number of Scottish coals. Taking the more strongly-caking of these as examples the following results emerge.

	20-in. seam.			Bannockburn.			Kilsyth.		
	Fresh.	Months. 24	43	1	2	3	1	2	3
Carbon % d.a.f. .	86·9	—	86·0	86·8	—	86·6	84·9	—	82·6
Gray-King Index .	G$_8$	—	G	G$_8$	G$_4$	G	G$_4$	F	E
Campredon Index .	28	26	16	30	22	15	21	13	10
Gas, therms/ton .	66·4	—	67·4	66·6	—	63·1	66·5	6	62·3
Coke, average size .	2·11	—	2·08	2·59	—	2·56	2·39	—	1·79

Very little change is seen in carbon content after $3\frac{1}{2}$ years but the reduction of caking power is marked. This affects the gas yield only some 2–3 therms per ton but gives a coke of smaller size. Coke deterioration is most noticeable with the coal of lowest caking power as might be expected.

Similar data from the London area (H. Stanier), where the coal was run-of-mine Durham gas coal and more prone to deterioration because of its small size, indicate that the loss of gas thermal yield varies from 0·5 to 2·0 therms per ton of coal after a storage period of 2 years. Storage at a temperature of 120° F., the highest temperature likely to be reached in the centre of a coal heap, showed a much higher rate of deterioration.

	Original.	12 months.	24 months.
Therms loss per ton of dry, ash-free coal :			
Gas	(84)	2–3	3–7
Tar	(22)	1–4	3–6
Coke, breeze increase, %	—	—	5
Swelling index	8	4	0

These data emphasize the serious effect of allowing over-heating of coal to take place during storage. The monetary loss represented by several therms of gas and 1 to 2 cwt. of breeze is considerable.

Conditions of Storage. The optimum condition of storage would be in airtight chambers or under water to avoid oxidation altogether, but the former is impracticable and the latter introduces the difficulty of undue wetting and is justifiable only in very special circumstances. Covered stores are expensive but can be justified sometimes for soft friable coals or for coals such as black lignite which disintegrate very rapidly on repeated wetting and drying.

The practical expedient is therefore to store the coal under conditions in the open which limit the oxidation to the greatest extent ; it will be already clear from the above what these conditions are. Large or sized coal is easy to deal with provided there is no undue formation of fines during deposition. The most careful stacking is necessary with coals of mixed sizes in which the large pieces provide an open texture for the passage of air and the fines tend to segregate and form danger patches. Fine coal without large pieces is less dangerous.

The first considerations are the method of stacking and the size (chiefly depth) of the stack. A completely safe depth is less than 5 ft. but is not practicable, a suitable depth for coal containing mixed sizes is about 8 ft., for sized coal 16 ft., for sized hard coal 20 ft., and for really large coal or anthracite 30 ft. Stacking should be done in stages of depth in order to allow the first rapid stage of oxidation to be completed in the lower layers before they are covered ; in this way a 6-ft. stack can be raised to 10 ft. after the lapse of 6 months. Probably a better method is to add a 2-ft. layer every 3 months. The depth of the coal should follow the contour of the ground so that the hollows of the latter are not covered to a greater depth, and fresh coal should not be added unless temperature measurements in the body of the heap show that heating is not taking place.

In all coal stores, the original floor should be cleared of vegetation, flattened and covered with an impervious layer of ashes or clay ; a concrete floor would be ideal. Undue access of air to a stack can be prevented by packing the sides tightly and either rolling the surface or blanketing it with a layer of fine coal well rolled in. The building of a wall on at least one side is helpful ; even if it is only low enough to protect the base it reduces the intake of air effectively. Since wind aids ventilation the stack should be built with its longest side in the direction of the prevailing wind. The surface may even be sealed by spraying with road-tar. Small stores up to 200 tons are conveniently built on a concrete floor by constructing rectangular bays against a long wall about 5 ft. high ; delivery can be made from the open ends.

The precautions which must be taken with coal stacks are simply to observe the temperature within the coal at frequent intervals. Iron pipes inserted vertically to the floor allow of the introduction of a thermometer to any depth ; these can be made to record but generally it is sufficient to take readings at intervals of, say, a few days. A simpler method is to insert iron rods which can be withdrawn every few days and felt with the hand. The danger temperature is about 70° C. and action should be taken immediately if this is approached. Hot spots will usually occur at a depth of 4 to 7 ft. below the surface and near the outer surface where ventilation is most free. The only really effective method of dealing with the hot spots is to start using the coal, digging away the affected section first. Spraying with water is not effective so far as the fire is concerned but it may help indirectly by sealing off the free spaces and preventing further ingress of air.

The storage of " open-cast " coal is a special case since the coal is of small size and often highly oxidized already. A large part of the site should be used at one time, spreading the coal evenly in thin layers. The coal

F.—G

will vary widely in size and special effort will be necessary to avoid the formation of areas in which large coal can form a freely-ventilating section. Finally the surface should be compacted by the passage over it of the heavy vehicles used in the winning of the coal.

Bunker and Cargo Coal. Outbreaks of fire on board ship through the spontaneous inflammation of coal are a source of special anxiety because of the possible loss of life and of valuable property. A number of investigations have been made into the causes of such outbreaks from the classical work of Threlfall, but the most comprehensive is contained in the work of King and Shaw given in Fuel Research Special Paper 5, 1929. This work recorded and examined 336 outbreaks of fire during the three years 1925–8 and the findings resulted in the British Board of Trade issuing Notice 106 and full instructions to shipowners and masters. It was established that, while the outbreaks were due to spontaneous combustion in the coal, there were in the great majority of cases contributory causes which could be circumvented. Most of the fires occurred in bunkers and more than 60 per cent. were proved to be caused by external heating from the boiler or engine-room, unprotected steam pipes, funnel casing, etc.

A second cause was the loading of fresh coal on the top of small heaps of well dried and well-aerated fine coal at the bottom of the bunker and generally in the corners. The fresh coal prevented escape of heat from this well-aerated surface and local heating resulted. The condition was often aggravated by the heat of wetting of the dry coal from moisture introduced with the fresh coal and by the fact that this often happened in a temporary cross-bunker whose bulkhead was not impervious to air.

A third cause was the slow leakage of air, through wooden bulkheads, badly-plugged holes, or badly-fitting doors, at a rate such that the heat developed was not carried away.

A fourth cause was faulty ventilation. This could take several forms : (i) the carrying of a ventilator shaft down into the coal mass so that air could be forced into the coal, (ii) the trimming of two ventilators embedded in the coal mass so that one introduced and the other withdrew air, thus creating an air-stream across the intervening space, (iii) the difficulty of providing any ventilation in lower and between deck bunkers, (iv) the failure to trim the surface of coal in a hold fitted with surface ventilators so that a mound of coal remained between the ventilators. It can be generally stated that the main issue in ventilation is the adequate removal of gases from the surface of the coal and that no air at all be allowed to pass through any mass of the coal.

The final cause is the actual inherent liability of a coal to ignite spontaneously. Of the cases examined in this investigation only 12 per cent. were so liable to spontaneous ignition that the contributory cause could not be ascertained. There must however have been some cause since oxygen or air is a necessary factor and, in the absence of direct heating, there must have been air leakage from somewhere. Special precautions will always be required with such coals.

The general summary of this investigation of 336 cases of outbreak of fire is of interest though it is probable that later experience has eliminated most of the causes stated.

	per cent.		per cent.
Direct heating alone	45	Junction of coals	8
Direct heating with junction of two coals	8	Junction with air leakage . .	3
		Air leakage	6
Direct heating with air leaks .	7	Bad ventilation	4
All three	2	Unidentified	14
Direct heating and bad ventilation	3		
	65		35

The important precautions which emerged from this work were :

(i) Avoid breakage in loading and/or trim the fine coal so that local concentrations are avoided.

(ii) Prevent the external heating of bunker walls by screening and/or promoting air circulation in the annular space between the wall and the screen ; deflect hot air, insulate pipe supports, lag pipes.

(iii) Trim coal residues in the bunker to a position near the door before loading fresh coal.

(iv) Avoid all possible air paths through the coal. Make any temporary bulkhead of two layers of planks covered with brattice cloth. Tunnels through the bunker must also be airtight.

(v) Avoid bad ventilation. The surface of the coal should be freely ventilated by two ventilators suitably trimmed to the wind and they should not be trunked below the surface of the coal nor should heaped coal impede the passage of air over the surface.

For bunkers in land installations more or less the same advice applies. The leaving of residues can be avoided by arranging that all walls shall slope at an angle of about 60° to the vertical towards the outlet.   The inward leakage of air can be avoided by continuously repairing holes, joints or cracks, and using an airtight outlet-valve which can also be sealed if the bunker is left for any length of time unused.

COAL BRIQUETTES

The need for finding an effective market for the fine coal produced in mining led, before the days of pulverized fuel, to the development of processes of briquetting with a binder. In the utilization of brown coal in Germany it was found possible to consolidate this material without the use of an added binder and the industrial development of both brown coal and carbonized (smokeless) brown coal briquettes has been developed to a very large scale (Chapter VI).

In Great Britain, where the fine material to be consolidated is either bituminous coal or anthracite, briquetting without a binder of some sort is not yet a commercial possibility on account of the high pressures of over 12 tons per square inch which are necessary. Although a certain amount of work has been done in this country, using coal in a fine state of division (85 per cent. below 200 mesh), and some success has been obtained as far as the strength and hardness of the briquettes, the heavy costs of the strong presses necessary have prevented commercial development, and in order to make strong briquettes from bituminous coal and anthracite, a binder is necessary. The most satisfactory for this purpose is pitch prepared either from wood, petroleum or coal tars, especially the latter. The proportion of pitch necessary can be reduced by fine grinding, but this is not normally done owing to difficulty in grinding and to fire risk. The pitch is usually passed through a disintegrator with the coal. The best type of pitch is a soft pitch which has a twist point of 55° C. Too soft a pitch becomes difficult to handle in warm weather and the briquettes made from it are liable to be easily crushed immediately after manufacture and before they have had time to harden. If the pitch is too hard it is sometimes modified by admixture with tar oil or creosote. Apart from this the main consideration in the property of pitch is that it should contain little free carbon, the obvious reason being that this acts simply as a diluent. The free carbon content of low temperature pitch is from 5 to 10 per cent. and of high temperature pitches may vary from 15 to 30 per cent. Normally the most satisfactory percentage of pitch varies from 7 to 8 per cent. of the coal. In the case of coke, the percentage is perhaps 1 per cent. higher.

In the manufacture of briquettes the coal is reduced to coarse powder by disintegration, the pitch being introduced at this stage. If the coal is wet pre-drying is desirable. The crushed mixture, all of which will pass through a $\frac{1}{4}$-in. screen, is passed through a second mixer such as a Pug mill in order to increase intimacy of contact. During mixing the mass is heated by dry or open steam, chiefly the latter, and passes directly to the press. The fusion temperature of the pitch used must be such that melting and spreading are possible at the temperature reached.

Presses may be of several types ; for industrial and power purposes the plunger press forming rectangular briquettes is used, but for special and domestic purposes smaller briquettes are made of prismatic or ovoid shape. Rectangular briquettes have the important advantage that they can be stacked in the minimum of space. The calorific value of briquettes is slightly higher than that of the coal from which they are produced, their specific gravity is approximately 1·2 and the storage capacity of rectangular briquettes is about 50 lb. per cu. ft.

With careful stoking briquettes need not produce more smoke than coal.

The advantages which may be gained by briquetting fuel are not commensurate with the cost of the process, but briquetting forms a means of employing as lump fuel materials which would otherwise be either unsaleable or would command only a low price.

A number of substitutes have been suggested to replace pitch as a binder, the chief reason being the variable price of this commodity. The most important of these are pulp binders produced by the fermentation of vegetable matter, sulphite liquor from the purification of wood cellulose and sea-weed extracts. Briquettes made with pulp binders are weak and are subject to disintegration if wetted. Sulphite liquor briquettes require to be baked after manufacture in order to remove the same tendency to disintegrate on wetting. After baking they are as hard and strong as pitch briquettes. The development of this binder has, however, been retarded by its initial cost and by the limited amount available. Suggestions have also been made for the briquetting of heated coal, making use of the plastic condition of heated coking coal to serve as the binder. This proposal, although sound theoretically, has not met with great success since the temperature to which the coal must be heated causes excessive gas formation and the briquettes break down during cooling.

Since the advent of pulverized coal as a large-scale method of utilization of coal fines the need for a process of briquetting for their usage has passed, but the amount manufactured in this country is still of the order of 1·5 million tons per annum. In 1951, one million of this were rectangular briquettes mainly for industrial use, while the remainder consisted of small ovoids.

Briquetting will always be of interest, however, as a technique since there are places where pulverized fuel cannot be utilized, and since it can be a useful preliminary to other processes such as the manufacture of solid smokeless fuel. The Phurnacite process carbonizes ovoid briquettes of South Wales carbonaceous coal fines at a temperature of about 800° C., and produces some 32,000 tons per annum of a material which gives an excellent performance in the domestic stove.

It seems unlikely that briquetting will advance in this country, but there are a number of British Colonies in which efficient briquette presses of small size (say 1–5 tons per hour) would be a useful asset. Such a machine is the Glomera twin-ram press, which will make strong briquettes from brown coal without an added binder, at an output of 24 tons per day of 65-mm. briquettes, using 18 kWh. The crushing strength of the briquettes is about 2 tons per square inch, and they will withstand alternate heating and wetting for a considerable time.

An important factor in achieving strong briquettes is the grading of the material to such a size distribution that the mixture contains the minimum of voids. This can be done by variation of the grinding process and recycling of material during grinding.

COAL-OIL SUSPENSIONS

During the 1914–18 war it was proposed by Lindon Bates that a mixture of pulverized coal and fuel oil should be prepared for boiler firing in order to burn coal under the advantageous conditions of oil firing. It was claimed that the so-called " colloidal fuel " had advantages over both coal and oil, over coal in ease of firing and over oil in having more heat units per cubic foot. To take an example, twenty-six samples of fuel oil from widely distributed sources had a mean calorific value of 19,200 B.Th.U., and with a sp. gr. 0·94, the B.Th.U. per cu. ft. are 1,124,350. With an air dry coal of sp. gr. 1·35 and 14,000 B.Th.U. the B.Th. U. per cu. ft. are 1,177,450. In this country about 2 million tons of fuel oil are used in ships' bunkers, so that replacement by " colloidal " fuel would increase the yearly consumption of coal by 800,000 tons, using a 40/60 coal/oil mixture.

The mixture of coal and oil does not really constitute a true colloid and a more correct term would be coal-oil suspension. Such suspensions are prepared by mixing pulverized coal with fuel oil up to equal proportions. It is a thick viscous fluid which can be pumped only with some difficulty. It is essential that the coal suspension should be sufficiently stable that no deposition of coal takes place in a reasonable time. This can be achieved :

(1) By creating a gel structure in the oil by the addition of a stabilizing agent such as petroleum soap (Greenstreet patent) or lime-resin soap (Lindon Bates) or an alkali salt of a fatty acid.

(2) By using an oil which has the property of high viscosity at low rates of shear. This property is shown by many viscous oils but particularly by cracked residues.

(3) By dispersing or peptizing the coal with a suitable agent such as creosote so that it imparts to the mixture the property of high viscosity at low rates of shear.

(4) By aerating the suspension, as in the Wyndham process.

It is apparent that stability in the first system is infinite provided the strength of the gel is greater than the force exerted by the weight of the coal particle. This is easily achieved since Manning has shown that a solution of 0·1 per cent. of sodium stearate in oil will hold up coal particles much larger than those of pulverized fuel. In the other systems stability is not permanent and settling must take place. This can, however, be made slow enough for all practical purposes, i.e. no appreciable deposition in the cold in three months.

In all systems the coal/oil mixture must be intimately mixed by means of a colloid mill or similar machine. It is also desirable in systems 2 and 3 that the coal should contain no particles which will not pass a 240 B.S. sieve.

The history of this fuel is interesting. Plauson (*J.S.C.I.*, 1920, **39,** 589A) made the first known suspension in 1913 by means of his well-known mill. During Lindon Bates' experiments sea trials were carried out by the U.S. Scout *Gem* in 1918 on a 30/70 coal/oil mixture containing 1 per cent. of lime-resin soap stabilizer. Land trials were also made at Brooklyn using fuels stabilized with coal tar. During 1922 experiments by the Great Central Railway were reported (Robinson, *Modern Transport*, June, 1922). A variety of fuels containing up to 60 per cent. of coal were tried in a locomotive with satisfactory results.

In 1932 the S.S. *Scythia* of the Cunard Co. voyaged from Liverpool to New York using on one boiler (4 furnaces) 150 tons of a 40/60 mixture of coal and oil. The burners had to be cleaned about twice as often as with fuel oil, but otherwise there were no difficulties. The oil used was a cracked residue and gave perfect stability during five and a half months.

These experiments show that technically coal/oil mixtures of sufficient stability can be made and burned. Against the 4–5 per cent. advantage which coal/oil mixtures may possess in calorific value per unit volume, must be set the cost of grinding, mixing and stabilizing the product. Troubles in pumping cannot altogether be overlooked. Further experience in practice is required before judgment is possible on the economic aspects of the method, but interest in the process has now vanished in the face of petroleum oil development and remains only of academic interest.

REFERENCE BOOKS

Coal, Its Constitution and Uses. Bone and Himus. Longmans Green. 1936.
Chemistry of Coal Utilization. Lowry. Chapman and Hall. 1945.
Coal Preparation. Mitchell. A.I.M.M.E. 1950.
Handbook of Briquetting. Franke. Charles Griffin. 1916-18.

CHAPTER VIII

THE COMBUSTION OF FUELS FOR THE PRODUCTION OF HEAT AND POWER

The first step in the obtaining of energy from fuel is, with one main exception, the combustion of the fuel to provide heat. This heat is then available for application in the following principal ways :

(1) Direct use as thermal energy in heating processes. Furnace work, domestic heating by open fires.

(2) Transfer of the heat to a thermal fluid and the application of the latter for heating or power. Steam for heating processes in industry, or central heating of buildings, steam for power.

(3) Transfer of the heat to a thermal fluid and the conversion of the latter to electrical energy and later to heat, power and light. Electrical energy for heating in industrial processes, for domestic heating, for industrial and domestic power, for lighting.

(4) Direct conversion of fuels to power or electrical energy. The internal combustion engine (oil or gas), the gas turbine.

The exception is the treatment of fuel by a process other than combustion in order to provide a more convenient fuel which may be utilized in one or more of the above ways. The main processes of this type in this country are the production of town gas and coke from coal in the gas industry, the use of petroleum oils for the production of carburetted water gas, and the production of producer gas for industrial process work.

This picture is not complete without including the fuel which is used in chemical processes other than as a fuel even although the method of its use may appear to involve combustion. An important example is the use of coke in the blast furnace for the reduction of iron ores ; others are calcining of cement and other minerals, synthesis gas for synthetic ammonia or hydrogen, and the carburizing of steel. Processes in which the coal or oil is more definitely a raw material rather than a fuel are, for example, the production of active carbon from coal and the production of carbon black from oil or gas.

This book is primarily concerned with fuels and their properties rather than with the actual processes of utilization, but it is necessary to describe the main processes to some extent in order that the story of fuel may lead directly to the text-books of mechanical and chemical engineering. The uses of coal as solid fuel are dealt with in this chapter, the production of town gas and coke in Chapter IX, of producer gas and water gas in Chapters XVI and XVII respectively.

168

The importance of a fuel to the community is not necessarily represented by the tonnage consumed, and indeed in industry the fuel cost of a process is not the main item, but it is helpful to an understanding of fuel economics to be aware of the quantities consumed for each purpose. In this country the quantities consumed in the year 1951 are given for coal in Table V, but may be expressed rather differently as follows.

TABLE XXXVII

CONSUMPTION OF COAL IN BRITAIN

	Million tons.	
Coal mined		225
Consumed at the collieries	14	
Exported in ships bunkers	11	25
Coal consumed in the country		200
Industry, mainly fuel but including process coal .	48	
Household coal including miners' free coal = 5 millions	40	
Town-gas manufacture	27	
Metallurgical coke manufacture	25	
Production of electrical power	35	
Railways	14	
Miscellaneous	111	
		200

The main consumers of coal are therefore the domestic market, which includes offices and large buildings, and general industry. It should be understood, however, that these are not the *totals* of their consumptions of solid fuel since they take also a proportion of the manufactured fuels of town gas and electricity. What the totals are can only be guessed at.

THE COMBUSTION OF COAL

Since the first step in converting coal to usable energy is combustion it is necessary to consider in some detail the principles of combustion as applied to coal and the manner in which they affect the principal processes concerned.

The combustible elements of coal consist of carbon, hydrogen, and a portion of the sulphur, and when their combustion is properly completed the flue gases should contain only carbon dioxide, water vapour, and sulphur dioxide, in addition to the large volume of nitrogen which accompanied the oxygen of the air used in the process. If this were true in practice it would be easy to calculate theoretically the amount of air required for the complete combustion of any coal from a knowledge of its elementary composition. In practice, however, complete combustion cannot be achieved without an excess of air and the whole process is a compromise in which it is attempted to strike the best balance possible between loss of heat units through incomplete combustion on the one hand, and losses through heat units carried away in the flue gases by an excessive supply of air on the other hand. The calculation of the theoretical supply of air and the losses through the last-named causes are dealt with in Chapters II and XX ; here, it is only necessary to deal with the question of incomplete combustion, more particularly in its relation to the formation of smoke.

Theoretically, an average bituminous coal requires 11 lb. of air or 140 cu. ft. per lb. but the best conditions of grate firing cannot be attained without 20 per cent. excess, say 170 cu. ft. Incomplete combustion may occur without visible evidence when carbon is partly burned to carbon monoxide instead of the dioxide, and when hydrocarbon gases escape unburnt. Visible evidence of incomplete combustion is given by the formation of smoke. When carbon is burnt to carbon monoxide, out of the possible 8130 calories per kilogram (or 14,650 B.Th.U. per lb.) only 2490 calories (or 4480 B.Th.U.) are actually produced. Should conditions be such that hydrocarbon gases escape combustion the losses will be proportionately higher. It follows, therefore, that the conditions of firing coal to the best advantage consist in distributing the air required for combustion in such a manner as to avoid the escape of unburned gases while using the minimum excess of air.

In grate firing the air is provided in two or more streams. The primary air through the fuel bed brings about the reactions discussed in the chapter on producer gas (XVI) while the secondary air above the fuel bed burns the volatile products of these reactions. Tertiary air (heated) may be supplied at the end of the grate to ensure more complete combustion of any smoke. When coal is charged to a fuel bed it is subjected to the temperature of the bed and heated by the hot gases of the primary reactions. Under these conditions one pound of coal will liberate some 6 cu. ft. of inflammable gases and vapours (tar, etc.) and this will require some 90 cu. ft. of air as a minimum for its combustion.

In the fuel bed it is apparent that the primary air must be evenly distributed, and holes must not develop through which air can pass without reaction ; in this way unburned gases of uniform composition pass to the surface. Mechanical stokers are designed to achieve even distribution, but in hand-firing, by the addition of increments of coal, the nearest approach to the desired condition is obtained by the careful spreading of the smallest practicable increment.

Above the fuel bed imperfect combustion is caused by uneven distribution of the secondary air or by undue reduction of the bed temperature. It is only with automatic firing therefore that the best conditions can be approached. With hand-firing the coal increment must give a rush of combustible gases which will require more air than the supply while the opening of the fire-doors will cause cooling of the temperature. One expedient which helps is to augment the secondary air with heated air over the bed immediately after the door is closed and to close the supply later when the bed returns to normal. This can of course be arranged to work on a time cycle.

Smoke is a visible sign of incomplete combustion of the gases over the bed and therefore of poor distribution of the air. The tendency towards incomplete combustion is greatest with coal of high volatile matter and pronounced caking properties. The best steam coals are therefore those of low volatile matter which still retain free-burning properties ; such are the steam coals of South Wales. The next best type is bituminous coal of relatively high volatile matter but with low caking power ; such coals give a free-burning coke on the grate which does not form large masses and which allows of uniform distribution of the primary air.

The practical issues of grate firing to achieve the best conditions for a suitable coal are therefore concerned with the secondary air. In the first place an adequate draught is essential, particularly to cover periods when the full loading is not in use. To avoid excessive bursts of volatile matter from freshly-charged coal which is hand-fired there are two methods other than " little and often " as referred to above. These are called " coking " and " alternate " systems ; in the former the coal is charged on to a dead plate just inside the door with suitable air admission above the grate, distillation proceeds slowly, the products passing with the necessary air over the highly incandescent fuel on the bars, where they meet with further excess of air at high temperature. When distillation is completed the coked mass is distributed over the grate. The objection to the method is mainly that it is frequently impossible to burn the quantity of fuel requisite for maintaining steam, but it is certainly the most scientific method of hand-firing.

" Alternate " firing may be either in sections over the front and back of the grate, or sections to the right or left. In either case proper admixture with air and maintenance of the necessary temperature are assured, if the furnace construction is a proper one. Necessarily the more frequent opening of the doors, with the accompanying losses through excess air, are involved, and success with either coking or alternate systems is dependent on the skill of the fireman.

In the case of mechanical stokers all the different forms depend upon the principle of a continuous coal feed with its attendant advantage of the uniform evolution of volatile constituents. It is therefore easy to adjust the air supply so that, whilst ensuring complete combustion, no unnecessary excess is employed, whereby the highest efficiency is secured, providing the arrangement is such that towards the back of the grate air is not able to pass freely in through a residue of nearly completely consumed fuel. The amount of fuel which can be burned per square foot of grate area is higher under these uniform conditions, and consequently the duty of the boiler is increased, which often leads to a reduction in the number requisite for a given output. Again, it is frequently possible to use a cheaper grade of fuel than with hand-firing, and saving in labour costs is also effected.

The second essential for smokeless combustion is efficient mixing of the gases and air. This will reduce the length of the flame and increase its calorific intensity, enabling the combustion to be completed before an inordinate space, with possible contact with cool surfaces, has been traversed. A suitable direction to the in-going air may be given at the door by plates, etc., and sometimes a steam jet or jets can be effectively employed. In an internally-fired boiler there is seldom any difficulty as regards mixing owing to the rapid sweep of the gases and air towards the firebridge.

The third condition of maintenance of a high temperature is of equal importance to the supply of sufficient air. In the domestic fire there can be no question of any deficiency of air, but its smoke-producing powers are obvious and are due primarily to cooling, and to a minor extent to insufficient mixture. In boiler practice it is essential that the mixture of gases, vapours, and air in a state of incomplete combustion shall not come in contact with any surface at a comparatively low temperature, such as that of the boiler plates and tubes. With an internally-fired boiler there must be sufficient space between the grate and plates, which will be governed largely by the character of the fuel to be generally employed, that is, its percentage of volatile hydrocarbons. With cross-tubes it is impossible to avoid this contact. Beyond the grate and divided from it by a firebridge a capacious combustion chamber of firebrick reduces the speed of the gases, and enables combustion to be completed before the gases are drawn into the flues. In a water-tube boiler the incompletely burned mixture must be kept from contact with the lower tubes, by suitable arches, baffles or fireclay covering to the tubes.

The partial failure of one or other of these conditions will exercise an important influence on the character of the smoke. On distillation at low temperatures coal yields chiefly tar-forming bodies and rich hydrocarbon gases, while at high temperatures, after the former have distilled off, other bodies break up, yielding gas very rich in hydrogen. The tarry bodies (existing partly as heavy vapours and gases in the furnace, and possibly even as liquid vesicles) and the hydrocarbon gases will differ very much in their combustion. It will be more difficult to ensure complete admixture of the former with air, especially if liquid vesicles are present, and they will escape with very little alteration beyond combustion of the more volatile portions, giving a *brown* tarry smoke. The hydrocarbon gases will mix more readily with air, and if intensity of combustion is maintained will undergo complete combustion, but should this be checked by cooling, dense clouds of *black* smoke, consisting largely of free carbon, will be produced. Should this free carbon once be produced no excess of highly heated air will cause its combustion, a result which has frequently given trouble in burning liquid fuel. The high-temperature gaseous products of distillation, consisting mainly of hydrogen and carbon monoxide, will offer no difficulties in combustion ; it is the low-temperature products, given off with a rush on firing, and the character of these products which are wholly responsible for smoke. Deficiency of air and improper mixing will result chiefly in brown (tar) smoke with little free carbon ; checking of combustion will be the primary factor in the production of black smoke.

The incidence of heavy smoke from a furnace can mean much more than the escape of unburned carbon although it is the carbon mainly which is the cause of the blackness. A really black smoke corresponding to No. 5 of the Ringleman smoke chart means that the solid matter emitted represents 2 per cent. of the thermal value of the fuel. It has been established, however, that the appearance of smoke is an indication of inefficient combustion which is much more serious than the loss of carbon ; it consists in the escape of unburned gases, mainly carbon monoxide, which may represent as much as 20 per cent. of the heat of the fuel at Ringleman 5. The solid combustible matter in the smoke consists of carbon and tarry matter with some 75 per cent. of the former ; it has a calorific value of the order of 15,000 B.Th.U. per lb.

It is important to consider this loss in relation to the loss as sensible heat which would be brought about by the use of an undue amount of air in order to avoid smoke. The smoke is certainly due either to the use of insufficient air or to bad distribution or both, but it is most important to ensure good distribution and avoid losses as sensible heat. It may be calculated that, if 18 per cent. of the heat of the fuel is carried away as sensible heat when using excess air equivalent to 25 per cent. of the theoretical (normal with coal firing), this will be increased to 24 per cent. at 50 per cent. excess air, and 30 per cent. at 100 per cent. excess air.

Black smoke, and its inner meaning of loss of potential heat, is therefore a more serious menace to efficiency than too much excess air. Both, however, can be overcome by the installation of an efficient hand-firing routine, or by the provision of mechanical stokers and exact air regulation.

These general principles of the combustion of coal in solid form on a grate apply to combustion in general when the different conditions are taken into account. For example, in the firing of pulverized fuel the coal particles are uniformly dispersed by the air so that the proportion is kept as closely as possible to the theoretical amount.

In practice, and particularly in steam raising, the efficiency of the combustion system is enhanced by the recovery of heat units from the gases before they are discharged to the atmosphere. This recovery includes the superheating of the steam and the preheating of the feed water and combustion air. To-day, thermal efficiency is practised in all furnace operations to the greatest extent practicable in the operation concerned. The methods used are explained below in relation to steam raising from both solid and pulverized fuel.

SOLID FUEL AND STEAM RAISING

A detailed account of the technique of boiler firing is outside the scope of this book, but it is considered that a brief account of the most advanced systems is of value in demonstrating the importance of the adequate control of the conditions of combustion of the fuel.

Steam Boilers

There are five main types of industrial boiler and the conditions of firing coal to achieve high efficiency vary in each. These are (1) vertical, (2) locomotive, (3) internal-flue horizontal shell type, (4) multitubular horizontal shell type, and (5) water-tube type.

The vertical boiler is used mainly for small outputs of steam. The grate is at the bottom and the hot gases rise upwards at one side and pass through horizontal tubes in the water space to the flues. Firing and ash removal are done by hand and heat recovery from the waste gases is not attempted. The plant is essentially a utility one which is convenient and inexpensive for light loads up to 8000 lb. of steam per hour ; at 150 lb. pressure the efficiency is about 55 to 60 per cent.

The locomotive boiler for industrial usage is adapted from the railway model and has the particular advantage of a large heating surface in proportion to its output of steam ; it is therefore suitable for conditions demanding rapid changes in steam demand. The coal is fed by hand to the grate at one end and the hot gases are drawn by strong draught through horizontal tubes of relatively small diameter. The need for high draught and the absence of economy by heat interchange is now causing it to be replaced by boilers of the " economic " type.

	Grate area (sq. ft.).	Heating surface (sq. ft.).	Steam per hour (lb. from and at 212° F.).
Vertical	28·5	675	4000
Locomotive	23·5	815	4000

The most popular boiler in this country for general industrial steam raising has been the simple shell type with one (Cornish) or two (Lancashire) internal flues. The coal is fed by hand, and is burned on fixed grates in the flues, which pass through the water space. The combustion gases pass into a brickwork flue below the boiler, travel to the front and then pass along two side flues to the main flue and chimney. Simplicity, reliability and low maintenance costs have been the reasons for its popularity, but in addition it has a large water capacity and is able to cope with the sudden high demands for steam which often occur in industry. The combustion space is small, but this is overcome by the use of induced draught and the design of special mechanical chain-grate stokers.

In the latest form, the side flues are replaced by additional fire tubes incorporated in the shell, and an air preheater. This multitubular or "economic" boiler may have double or treble pass tubes to improve convective heat transfer : these overcome the necessary reduction in water capacity. Boilers are now built up to 25,000 lb./hr. output at an efficiency of 80 per cent.

In water-tube boilers the distinctive feature is that the water circulates *through* the tubes and not *round* them as in the case of shell-type boilers. In view of this, greater care is necessary in the pretreatment of the feed water to avoid blockage. Several designs of boiler are available with the heating tubes connected to two or more drums, but the quantity of water is less than in shell-type boilers and steam can be raised more rapidly. For general reasons the shell-type boiler is more effective in industry and the water-tube type has been developed more for large-scale applications such as the electric power station and large industrial plant. In these, they are equipped with water- and air-heaters and the steam is superheated, so that the waste gases leave to the chimney at the lowest temperature practicable to maintain the necessary draught. Units are now in use which generate more than one million lb. of steam per hour.

Combustion on Boiler Grates. The general principles of firing have been described above but a word is still necessary on the types of equipment which are used for mechanical stoking. These may be divided into the three classes of Underfeed, Overfeed and Chain-grate stoker, but the selection of any one of these is largely a matter of choice since, although one type may give its best performance on a particular type of coal, it can still be made to operate efficiently on other types.

In the Underfeed stoker the coal is conveyed along a trough under the grate and forced up in the middle of the fire bed by a screw or ram feeder. The grate slopes to the sides so that the coal is coked in its passage through the bed and is later burned as it flows down the slope. The air is supplied through tuyères round the grate and unburned material is removed from the edges. This stoker is mostly applied to shell-type boilers and to water-heating installations and is most suited to the combustion of graded coal of low caking power ; highly-caking coals give swollen masses of coke which are difficult to burn evenly.

Overfeed stokers are of the (a) coking and (b) spreader type, although the chain-grate is really also an overfeed stoker. In the coking stoker the coal is fed on to the forward part of the grate (dead-plate or coking-plate) where coking takes place and the liberated volatile matter is carried forward and burned over the incandescent fire. After coking, the coal is pushed forward by shaped firebars which move backwards and forwards. The rate of firing is controlled by the speed of the bars and by the length of travel of the ram. This form of stoker, as its name implies, was designed to obtain the best results from coals which gave trouble on other grates by the formation of masses of coke, but it will give an efficient performance on coals of any type other than low-volatile coals. Close grading is not essential but performance improves with graded coals of 1 to 2 in. in size.

In the Spreader stoker the best conditions of hand-firing are simulated by the use of a mechanical shovel or rotor which projects small increments of coal uniformly over the bed, as shown in Figure 22. In this way the whole surface becomes a flaming bed about one inch deep in which the ash collects below the coal and helps to prevent overheating of the firebars.

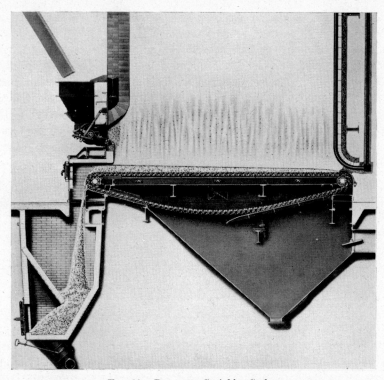

Fig. 22.—Rotograte Sprinkler Stoker.

The grate itself may be stationary with arrangements for the removal by hand of the ash, or it may be stationary with rotating bars for ash removal, or it may move from rear to front of the furnace and deposit its ash at this end. Figure 22 is an example of the last type ; it is noticeable that the ash thickness increases in the direction of travel and helps in the distribution of the primary air where it is most required.

The Chain-grate stoker, as its name implies, consists of an endless chain of refractory links which carries the coal from the feeder through the furnace. Forced air passes through the spaces in the links and the depth of fuel bed and rate of travel of the grate are so arranged that the fuel is completely burned by the time the ash is discharged over the end of the grate. A feed plate controls the depth and uniform distribution of the coal feed. This stoker gives its best performance on weakly-caking bituminous coals of not too high ash content. Caking coals tend to give uneven firing, and low-volatile coals or cokes require a lower arch over the end of the fire to maintain combustion to completion. Coals of very low ash content may cause trouble by the fact that the grate may not be covered at the end and undue leakage of air will occur there; this can be overcome by certain expedients such as partial blanking-off of the air supply at the end.

Large-scale Steam-raising Plant. In large-scale plant to-day (excepting in the case of pulverized fuel, which is dealt with later), all the applications are high-pressure water-tube boilers with chain-grate stokers and the ancillary equipment necessary for attaining of high efficiency by the recovery of heat from the waste gases. Table XXXVIII gives an example of the high efficiency which can be attained by such means, in comparison with a simple installation raising steam for small-scale industrial usage without recovery of waste heat.

TABLE XXXVIII

THE EFFICIENCY OF STEAM RAISING

Coal = 100 heat units

	No heat recovery.	Full heat recovery.
Heat units in coal	100	100
Air preheat	—	4
Lost in ashes . . .	2	2
Radiation, etc., losses . . .	4	4
Waste gases	29	9
Waste gas temperature, ° F. . .	1150	360
Steam % thermal yield . . .	65	85

In the second case the waste gases pass over the tubes of a steam super-heater which abstracts some 40 per cent. of their heat content and reduces their temperature from, say, 1150° to 700° F. The gases then pass through the water heater or " economizer ", to which they impart some 35–40 per cent. of their residual heat with a further temperature drop to about 450° F. Finally the gases preheat the air for combustion with about 30 per cent. of their remaining heat and a final drop in temperature to about 360° F. These three factors may be summarized in terms of the original 100 heat units supplied as coal, as (1) preheat to air 4 units, (2) preheat to water 8 units, and (3) superheat to the steam 16 units. The overall result is an increase of thermal efficiency from 65 to 85 per cent. In some power stations with special equipment over 90 per cent. has been realized, mainly by adding recovered heat from the turbo-generator.

An illustration of the design of a common industrial water-tube boiler of medium size is shown in the frontispiece of the book, Figure 1. This shows in diagram the relative positions of the chain grate, the combustion space above it, the inclined tubes and single drum of the boiler, and the superheater tubes with which the waste gases first come into contact. The feed-water heater or " economizer " is a separate unit of the Green's type. The unit illustrated was designed to raise 15,000 lb. of steam per hour at 250 lb. per square inch pressure and 630° F.

The stoker with which it is fitted can have a maximum area of 324 sq. ft. and will burn up to 9720 lb. coal per hour. The largest units for which stoker firing is considered to be practicable are 890 sq. ft. in area and will burn up to 44,500 lb. of coal per hour. The increase of combustion rate with increase of size is a function of the larger combustion space possible with increase of size. Three examples are :

Grate area (sq. ft.).	Steam (lb./hr.).	Coal (lb./hr.)	Coal (lb./sq. ft./hr.).	Steam
162	25,000	4,050	25	160
324	80,000	9,720	30	250
890	250,000	44,500	45–60	290

The Babcock Cyclone Furnace. A recent development in the search for more economical steam generation is the cyclone system for the burning of coal less than $\frac{1}{4}$ in. in size. It is designed for application to the largest sizes of pulverized-fuel furnace and high outputs of steam.

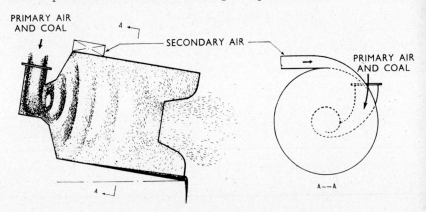

FIG. 23.—Principle of the Babcock Cyclone Burner.

The cyclone itself is a water-cooled cylindrical chamber operating on the principle shown in Figure 23. The construction of the cyclone is unusual ; it is formed of closely-pitched water tubes connected to the normal circulation system of the boiler. At the inlet end is the primary burner into which the coal, carried by the primary air, is fed tangentially. The fuel swirls forward into the main chamber where it meets the high-speed tangential stream of secondary air as shown. The temperature developed is high enough to melt the ash and the globules are carried out to the wall by centrifugal force. After the coating reaches a certain thickness it flows slowly to the discharge end ; the cyclone is set at a small angle to the horizontal to accommodate this. The larger particles of coal are also carried to the outside but, although they may adhere to the molten ash, they are completely burned by the scrubbing action of the secondary air. Fine particles of coal which tend to be carried in the centre of the vortex are assisted to burn by a small proportion of tertiary air which is passed through centrally. In this way a high combustion efficiency is attained with only ten per cent. of excess air and it is claimed as a result that a boiler will give 20 per cent. more output than a conventional boiler occupying the same floor area, and some 3 to 5 per cent. increase in thermal efficiency. The latter is also contributed to by the low carbon content of the slag.

Three cyclone furnaces of 6 ft. diameter would be required for a boiler unit raising 600,000 lb. of steam per hour ; these would be fitted in the lower wall of the furnace of a boiler of the Radiant type.

Two limitations are recognized for this development ; these are that the temperature of fusion of the ash must not exceed about 1370° C. in a reducing atmosphere to ensure complete fusion in the cyclone and that the coal must be sufficiently high in volatile matter to give a long flame ; what the exact limitation is, has not yet been stated.

Boiler Availability. An important factor in steam raising is the number of days in a given year that a boiler can remain in service without being shut down for cleaning and overhaul. The factor has been termed boiler availability and is of special interest to large power stations where the units are large ; it is applied of course to pulverized-fuel firing as well as to grate firing.

The chief factor is the fouling and corrosion of the external surfaces of the tubes and brickwork by the sulphur and inorganic dust carried in the combustion gases. The small proportion of sulphur trioxide (0·003 volume per cent.) is considered to be the chief factor, working in two ways, (1) by hydration with water to form sulphuric acid which corrodes any metal which may be below the dewpoint of the acid, and (2) by undergoing chemical reaction with alkaline dusts to form a low-melting-point solid which adheres to superheater and other tubes and collects ash and coke particles. The growth of the latter may in time impede the flow of gases to unworkable extent. Extensive research work is now being undertaken on this subject to determine the influence of conditions of combustion on the dewpoint of $SO_3 . H_2O$ and the role of smoke and dust particles. With dust-free gases there is a strict relationship between the SO_3 content and the dewpoint, but the presence of dusts causes distinct variations as shown at the top of page 180.

It is considered that the reduction is due to a sorption effect. If certain dusts are added there may also be a chemical effect, as in the case of zinc oxide which appears to act as a neutralizing body and raises the effective

SO_3 % of wet gas $\times 10^3$.	Dewpoint ° C.	Observed dewpoint ° C.
0·8	90	—
1·0	100	—
1·5	118	105
2·0	132	117
2·5	140	140
3·0	148	148

dewpoint of the sulphuric acid. The addition of 0·25 per cent. by weight of ZnO to coal has been shown to remove the acid dewpoint altogether from a previous value of 155° C., the only dewpoint observed being that of water. This is a promising observation and may lead to something even more effective. The known lesser tendency of pulverized firing to corrosion and blockage may be a combination of both effects; it has been shown that auxiliary pulverized fuel firing of a grate-fired boiler reduces markedly the rate of accumulation of acid deposits on tubes.

COAL AS PULVERIZED FUEL

In 1952 the amount of coal consumed in Britain for the production of power in large power stations was as much as 14 million tons, but owing to the advances made in the technique of power-station practice, very considerable expansion of this is forecast. It is planned that, by 1960, the quantity consumed on grates will be exceeded and a total reached of 34 million tons per annum. This may absorb completely the supplies of coal of small particle size and even lead to the breakage of large coal and coal grades. This remarkable advance has been brought about by the high rates of burning, and high levels of efficiency, which have been reached in the use of pulverized fuel equipment.

The advances in usage are mainly for electric-power stations as may be seen from the figures for 1948 and 1950, in millions of tons.

	Collieries.	Firms.	Electricity.	Metallurgy.	Cement.	Tota
1948	0·8	1·2	6·0	0·6	2·2	11·1
1950	0·8	1·2	7·8	0·6	2·8	13·3

By the reduction of coal to a fine state of division and carrying the powder forward into a furnace by an air blast, it is possible to obtain perfect combustion with entire absence of smoke when using the least excess of air, thereby obtaining a high efficiency. This method of using coal was first introduced to any extent for the firing of rotary cement kilns in which a flame of great intensity and length is necessary. The first successful application was made in 1895 and by 1905 this system of firing had been widely adopted. It was not until considerably later, however, that any appreciable amount of pulverized coal became used for other purposes. The greatest developments took place in the United States in connection with boiler firing for power purposes and a 100-fold increase in the amount of coal consumed occurred in the period 1918–25. In 1925 its use was increasing at the rate of 200 per cent. per annum. The increases were largely due to developments in steam raising and the growth of large central power stations. Advances in this country were slower and did not become of importance until after 1919 when an account by L. C. Harvey of the American work was published by the Fuel Research Board. By 1931 pulverized fuel had been applied widely at collieries to consume slacks which were sometimes of high ash content and difficult to sell, and also in factories to which cheap slacks were a monetary inducement. The advantages to large power stations became recognized, and by 1934 some 1·8 million tons of coal were being consumed there. In addition, 1·5 million tons were being consumed in cement and other kilns and perhaps 50,000 tons for metallurgical purposes. It is interesting to note that most of the pulverized fuel installations on land were made in conjunction with water-tube boilers, whereas the applications to ships were to horizontal boilers. The large combustion space of a water-tube boiler theoretically allows of a much longer flame and of more complete combustion of the coal particles.

The advantages of pulverized fuel systems of firing are similar to those of oil or gas firing and are :

1. Greater flexibility of control is possible and banking and stand-by losses are reduced to a minimum.

2. A wide variety of fuels can be used from coal of low volatile matter in large combustion spaces to high volatile bituminous coals. Low-grade fuels of high ash content can be used provided special precautions are taken to handle the clinker and ash formed and to avoid the carrying of fine dust into the atmosphere.

3. Combustion is complete with a low percentage of excess air ; this with high flame temperatures means high thermal efficiency. In large power stations thermal efficiencies of over 90 per cent. have been realized.

4. Maximum fuel economy can be ensured by close regulation of the rate of feed, etc.

5. Labour charges are low and certain repairs can be effected to mechanical stokers without waiting for cooling.

6. For metallurgical purposes high flame temperatures are possible and the character of the flame, whether oxidizing or reducing, is under easy control.

Pulverized fuel had at first a number of disadvantages but these have been completely overcome ; the chief of these was the relatively high cost of grinding the coal to the necessary degree of fineness. Others were the tendency for slagging of refractory walls and furnace linings, the excessive discharge of fine dust into the atmosphere and the necessity for large combustion spaces to complete the combustion of the coal and avoid deposition of carbon among boiler tubes or in flues.

Suitable Fuels. Practically any dry fuel, whether high or low in ash content or volatile matter, can be burned successfully in pulverized form, but, so far as coal itself is concerned, the most suitable is that which contains over 20 per cent. of volatile matter and is of not more than medium caking power. As the volatile matter in the coal decreases below 20 per cent. the coal becomes rather more difficult to burn completely ; low-volatile coals require large combustion spaces if incomplete combustion is to be avoided. With this precaution even anthracite can be burned successfully.

Opinions vary as to the degree of fineness to which coal must be ground, but for satisfactory combustion it is generally accepted that 70 per cent. of the coal should pass a 240 B.S. sieve and that none of the oversize should remain on a 72 B.S. sieve. When coal is reduced to this degree of fineness it means that a large proportion of the particles are very much smaller than those upper specified limits. The size of a 240-mesh particle is approximately 63 μ (1 μ = 0·001 mm.) and in coal pulverized so that 85 per cent. passes a 240 sieve it has been shown that 20 per cent. is less in size than 10 μ. The distribution of the different sizes is much the same for all types of coal. Similarly, the shape of the particles does not vary greatly ; from air-swept mills they are of irregular shape and have rounded edges, and from other mills they are of similar shape but have sharp edges. Although the above specification as regards size is a general one for bituminous coal, it is also true that the correct size for efficient combustion will depend upon the nature of the coal, e.g. coal of low volatile matter should have low particle size, and upon practical considerations such as the size of the combustion space and the behaviour of the coal ash. Where the combustion space is large excessively fine grinding is unnecessary. The ash particles tend to be carried in the gas stream and only 15 to 25 per cent. of them are retained in the combustion chamber. Of the remainder, some are retained in the flues but the greater part must be separated in cyclone extractors to avoid atmospheric pollution.

Pulverized fuel installations at first conformed to two classes : (1) using unit pulverizers and (2) central pulverization and distribution of the material in an air-borne stream to each furnace. The latter was at first applied in all power stations but now, owing to advances in the design of unit mills, it has been superseded almost entirely by the unit system.

An installation of the " bin and feeder " type is shown in diagram in Figure 24. It involves a crusher, dryer, pulverizer, storage bins, and a feeder system.

The coal is first crushed to $\frac{3}{4}$-in. size and passed over a magnetic separator to remove accidental inclusions of metal. The coal then passes to the dryer and to the mill. The powdered coal is air-borne to a cyclone separator placed in a convenient position and conveyed to a hopper from which it is taken in the primary-air stream to the burner.

In the unit system each furnace is fired by one or more unit pulverizers, each connected to its own burner. The apparent advantages are lower first cost, greater simplicity of construction and saving of space, and better control of the amount of coal to each burner. Additional drying plant may be necessary if the coal supplied is visibly wet, but the modern mill will take air-dry coals without difficulty. The pulverizer is placed near the boiler and under the coal feed hopper and driven by a shaft which also drives the fan. The coal is dried in the mill by means of heated primary air drawn by means of the fan through the hollow walls of the furnace.

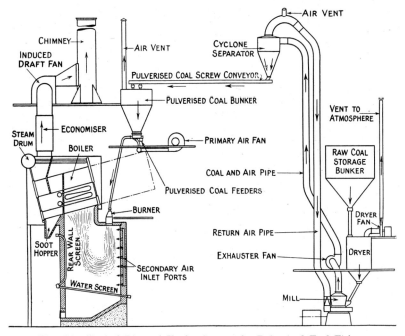

FIG. 24.—Typical Bin and Feeder System for Pulverized Fuel Firing.

This heated air carries the finely divided coal from the mill to the burner, leaving the coarser coal behind for further grinding. At the burner the secondary air required for combustion is supplied at openings round the burner and/or into the combustion space. The amount of primary air must be strictly limited since too much air would make ignition of the air-borne coal difficult. A suitable proportion is 25 per cent. of the total air required for combustion.

A modern large boiler installation fitted with unit pulverizers is shown in Figure 25. In this plant the pulverizers are shown on the left but can be replaced or augmented by oil or gas firing (integral system). The relatively large combustion space is seen and the positions of the superheater tubes, the feed-water heater or economizer, and the air heater. The boiler is a Babcock "high-head" boiler designed to generate steam at 925° F. and 950 lb. per square inch at the rate of 265,000 lb. per hour. At this rate the consumption of pulverized coal is 10 to 12 tons per hour.

The heating surfaces of the furnace and boiler are 3290 and 4620 sq. ft. respectively and the combustion chamber volume of 16,500 cu. ft. is designed

FIG. 25.—Model of Boiler with Unit Pulverizers.
(Babcock & Wilcox Ltd.)

A, Surface type attemperator ; B, P.F. burners (also gas and oil firing) ; C, Coal weighers ; D, Burner piping ; E, Coal pulverizing mills ; F, Primary air fans ; G, Saturated steam pipes ; H, Steam and water drains ; J, F.D. fans ; K, Primary superheater ; L, Economizer ; M, Air heater ; N, Secondary superheater ; O, Boiler generating tubes ; P, Bailey wall furnace ; Q, Hot-air duct.

for a heat release of 21,500 B.Th.U. per cubic foot per hour. The feed water is heated from 390° to 500° F. ; the air is preheated by gas to 480° F. The boiler is fired by six horizontal burners fed by three mills of which two are sufficient if the coal is adequately dry ; the mills are of the type described later and shown in Figure 26. The required fineness of grinding is 70 per cent. through a 200 B.S. sieve and 99 per cent. through a 52 B.S. sieve.

Preparation of the Fuel. In the early days of pulverized fuel all the coal was dried before grinding, but this has been largely superseded by the use of the air-swept unit mill in which any necessary drying is done by hot air in the mill. The driers may be of several types : (1) rotary drums fired by hot gases, (2) cell-type hot-gas driers, and (3) steam-heated driers. The hot-gas drier is now universal.

FIG. 26.—Babcock Type Unit Pulverizers.

For the grinding of the coal a number of types of mill are available. The most favoured for large plants has been the air-swept ball mill and for unit mills the high speed beater type or the ring-roll type, but unit ball mills are now taking the place of the latter by showing more reliability and lower maintenance costs. The mill used in the installation of Figure 25 is of the Babcock E type which is shown in section in Figure 26. It is in the form of a large, horizontal ball-bearing (seen through 9), the top or grinding ring (16) being stationary while the bottom ring is rotated by the drive at (18). The coal is fed centrally (arrows) and warm air from trunking (2) to the air ports (17) carries the ground coal through the gap between the rings, into the classifier (44) where any larger particles are struck out and returned to the feed. The fine particles are carried in the air stream via (11) and (12) to the burner. The hinges of the classifier and coal-feed chamber covers are shown at (H). Only clean air is supplied to the mill in order to reduce fan wear. The power consumption of this mill is about 24 kWh per ton of coal and the fineness of product is based on 70 per cent. passing a 200 mesh sieve, from coal having a grindability index of 50 (p. 113).

Burners. The important factor in any burner is the achievement of complete combustion of the coal particles before they reach the furnace walls or boiler tubes. The type of burner chosen is therefore dependent upon this factor and to a less extent upon the type of coal, particularly upon its content of volatile matter since this determines the length of the flame. The latter can be corrected however by adjustment of the degree of fineness, i.e. postulating 60–70 per cent. through a 200 B.S. sieve for high-volatile coals, 70–80 per cent. for medium-volatile coals and 80–90 per cent. for low-volatile coals and anthracite.

The types of burner used in Great Britain fall into three groups similarly :

High-volatile coals . . .	Short flame with self-induced turbulence.
Medium-volatile coals . .	Short flame with externally-induced turbulence.
Low-volatile coal and anthracite	Long flame or U type.

The principle of the short-flame burner is that relative motion is induced between the coal particles borne in the primary air stream and the secondary air. Both streams may be given rotary motion so that the coal particles are thrown outwards and dispersed in the fresh supply of oxygen. This rapid and continuous contact of coal with the air is achieved in one burner by applying resonant vibrations to it and in another (the Multijet) by dividing the burner area into a large number of adjacent streams, Fig. 27 (f).

Short-flame burners are usually arranged on one furnace wall so that the flame pattern fills the chamber but does not impinge on water-cooled walls.

Medium-flame burners are in use in many pulverized fuel boilers where the coal is of medium-volatile matter. The nozzles carrying the air-borne coal are set centrally within rectangular secondary-air ports so that a rather long annular jet is obtained surrounded by heated secondary air. The necessary turbulence is achieved by the arrangement of the burners so that an intense swirl is set up. The burners may be arranged in opposite walls or tangentially to an imaginary circle centred on the middle of the combustion space. The walls of the furnace are normally composed of water-cooled bare tubes to absorb heat by radiation as well as convection. It is usually necessary to operate such a system on unit mills in order to make certain of uniform distribution.

The long-flame burner was the first form to be used and was arranged to fire downwards into the combustion chamber as illustrated in Figure 24. The secondary air, and tertiary if required, is introduced through the furnace wall at right angles to the flame ; the arrangement of the ports is such as to give good control of the flame shape and to achieve complete combustion. The U-shape of the flame has given the name U-flame to these burners. They are most suitable for coal of low-volatile matter since complete combustion can be achieved in the long time of travel; the velocity of flow is however slow and involves the disadvantage of large combustion spaces. They are, however, suitable for furnace work in which a number of units are fired from a bin-and-feeder system.

The number of patented burners of these types is very large, but the following five are considered by Messrs. Babcock and Wilcox, who have wide experience in this field, to cover the normal requirements for boiler firing. Diagrams of these are included in Figure 27 by courtesy of the Firm.

The Circular Pulverized Fuel burner, Figure 27a, is designed to give a short, highly turbulent flame by the arrangement of adjustable vanes in the secondary air stream surrounding the coal-primary air stream. The entry of the secondary air by centrifugal motion accelerates the rate of combustion to a controllable extent. Mixing is assisted by the adjustable impeller shown at the mouth of the air-coal inlet. This burner can also be used for oil or gas firing.

The Horizontal Intertube burner, Figure 27b, is also turbulent in action and is intended for placing in the water-cooled front wall of the combustion chamber. The coal-primary air stream passes through narrow ports arranged vertically and the secondary air is directed into the stream from either side through similar ports. The turbulence so caused is increased by deflector blocks set in the primary stream.

The Cross-Tube burner, Figure 27c, has two inlet ports arranged one above the other which are fan-shaped to give a flame splayed out on the horizontal plane. Secondary air streams are directed into the stream from above and below to create turbulence.

The Multitip burner, Figure 27d, is designed for downward firing from the roof. It is similar in action to burner B but contains as many as sixteen ports arranged in groups to fire between pairs of boiler tubes. The secondary air is admitted between each group.

The Vertical Intertube burner, Figure 27e, differs from the above in meeting the requirements of a long flame burning in a large combustion space. It is therefore suitable for low-volatile coals. The burner is arranged in the roof of the furnace (as shown in Figure 24) to fire downwards with a long U-shaped flame. The secondary air is introduced round the burner ports and also through the furnace wall into the path of the flame.

The Removal of Dust and Oxides of Sulphur from Flue Gases. The use of pulverized firing in boilers or furnaces now implies the use of means for the removal of the fine dust and grits from the waste gases before

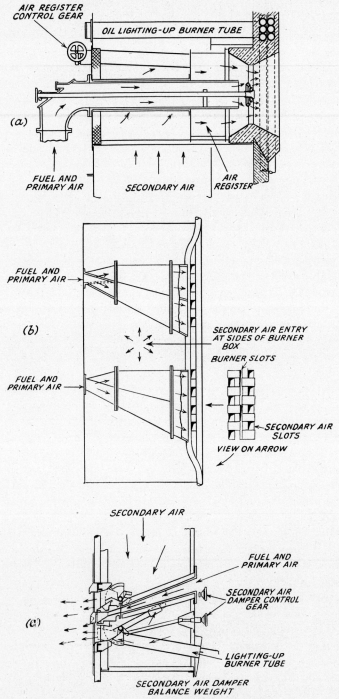

AIR REGISTER CONTROL GEAR

OIL LIGHTING-UP BURNER TUBE

(a)

FUEL AND PRIMARY AIR

SECONDARY AIR

AIR REGISTER

FUEL AND PRIMARY AIR

(b)

FUEL AND PRIMARY AIR

SECONDARY AIR ENTRY AT SIDES OF BURNER BOX

BURNER SLOTS

SECONDARY AIR SLOTS

VIEW ON ARROW

SECONDARY AIR

FUEL AND PRIMARY AIR

SECONDARY AIR DAMPER CONTROL GEAR

(c)

LIGHTING-UP BURNER TUBE

SECONDARY AIR DAMPER BALANCE WEIGHT

FIG. 27.—Types of Pulverized Fuel Burner.

(a) " Circular " burner.
(b) Horizontal inter-tube burner.
(c) Cross-tube burner.
(d) Multitip burner.

By courtesy of Messrs. Babcock & Wilcox Ltd.

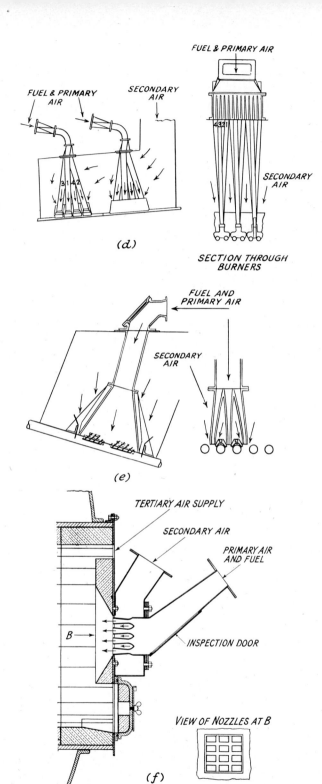

FUEL & PRIMARY AIR

FUEL & PRIMARY AIR

SECONDARY AIR

SECONDARY AIR

(d)

SECTION THROUGH BURNERS

FUEL AND PRIMARY AIR

SECONDARY AIR

(e)

TERTIARY AIR SUPPLY

SECONDARY AIR

PRIMARY AIR AND FUEL

B

INSPECTION DOOR

VIEW OF NOZZLES AT B

(f)

(e) " U " Flame burner. By courtesy of Messrs. Babcock & Wilcox Ltd.
(f) Multijet burner. By courtesy of Mr. T. F. Hurley, Fuel Research Station.

they are discharged from the chimney. The most successful means are special forms of cyclone separator situated near the base of the chimney. The design and principle of these are outside the scope of this book, but it is clear that a cyclone will remove the larger particles preferentially and allow the smallest ones to escape. With a chimney of suitable height, however, the fine dust will be dissipated at negligible density. Cyclones for this purpose are now applied also to grate-fired furnaces in large installations. One design which is well known is the Buell Van Tongeren ; for each boiler of the size shown in Figure 25 two rows of four cyclones are used to deal with a gas volume of 130,000 cu. ft. of gas per minute at 270° F. Under conditions of full load 99 per cent. of the dust particles over 20 μ in size are removed : below this size efficiency decreases to about 60 per cent. at 3 μ. In districts where even this fine dust may constitute a nuisance the cyclones may be followed by electrostatic precipitators which remove a further fraction.

The question of dust removal and atmospheric pollution is complicated by the need to remove also the oxides of sulphur, particularly in towns. According to the 17th Report on atmospheric pollution of the D.S.I.R. the amount of SO_2 collected in the London area is equivalent to over 35 tons per square mile per annum. A 1950 measurement of the deposition of SO_2 from the atmosphere of south-west London has indicated that this varies as follows in the summer and winter months. The readings were taken in the neighbourhood of the Battersea, Fulham, and Lots Road power stations, which in 1950 burned 19,000 tons of coal per day during the summer and 29,000 tons during the winter.

	SO_2 expressed as mg. SO_3/day/100 sq. cm		
	Max.	Min.	Average.
Summer	2·62	0·64	1·3
Winter	4·79	1·59	3·0

The winter figure is equivalent to 220 tons of SO_2 per annum per square mile, which is appreciably higher than the London yearly average.

Water sprays were tried in the first instance to wash out the oxides of sulphur, but SO_2 is not readily taken up by water and SO_3 is not easily wetted and may escape unabsorbed. The next step was to catalyse the oxidation of the SO_2 in solution by oxides of manganese or iron and a large installation using the latter was tried at the Battersea power station during 1934–40. The gases were sprayed with water in the presence of metallic iron and finally washed with chalk slurry of 0·25 per cent. concentration. The ferric iron is reduced but is in turn oxidized by the excess air so that its action is continuous. The time of contact of the gases was 35 sec. and 90 to 95 per cent. of the oxides were removed for a consumption of 20 tons of water and 10 lb. of chalk per ton of coal burned. The water was aerated to oxidize sulphites, diluted with the return condensing water, and returned to the river.

After the 1939–45 war the scrubbers were redesigned and the process brought up to date so that the whole of the washing process could be done in one continuous counter-flow absorption. A second plant of this type will be installed on the Thames, but others will not be possible because the limit of river pollution will then have been reached.

Continued agitation for a purer atmosphere, and the urgent need for the full recovery of sulphur from industrial processes, have kept the need for a cheaper process before the technician. Of those attempted only one shows promise of low cost and fairly complete recovery of the sulphur in a usable form. If 90 per cent. of the S is oxidized and 95 per cent. of this is recovered, a coal containing 1·5 per cent. S would yield the equivalent of 28·7 lb. S per ton burned.

The most promising of the new processes is that developed jointly by the Fulham power station and Messrs. Simon Carves Ltd. in that it has a product of commercial value. In the Battersea process it is estimated that the cost is about (1952) 7s. per ton of coal burned since it has no product of monetary value. In the Fulham/Simon-Carves process the product is ammonium sulphate and it would seem that, granted the supply of ammonia liquor from the gas industry at a fair price, the gases could be washed for zero cost, the sulphate being sold at current prices. In 1952 these were 4s. per unit ($\frac{1}{100}$ ton NH_3) for crude ammonia liquor and £17 per ton for the finished sulphate. The capital cost of a plant to deal with the effluent from one million tons of coal per annum was calculated to be £2–3 million.

The flue gases are washed at about 50° C. with a solution consisting of ammonium salts, sulphate 28 to 34, bisulphate 1 to 5, sulphite 0 to 6, and thiosulphate 4 to 11 per cent., which is made up constantly by the addition of concentrated gas liquor. A special electrical recorder is used to record the vapour pressures of SO_2 and NH_3 in equilibrium with the solution so that neither SO_2 nor NH_3 is allowed to escape in the scrubbed gas. Manganese sulphate is used as the oxidation catalyst. Solid ammonium sulphate is recoverable by the Katasulph process. Preliminary trials at the Fuel Research Station have been successful and a full-scale trial will be made at a power station.

The Direct Use of Pulverized Fuel for Power : The Gas Turbine

As long ago as 1891 an attempt was made to obtain power directly from coal by the combustion of coal powder in an internal combustion engine. MacCallum actually had an engine on show at the Glasgow Exhibition of 1911. The proposal to use coal was also implicit in the early patents of Diesel in 1892. During the period 1918–28 Pawlikowski, an associate of Diesel, demonstrated engines at Gorlitz and later experimental engines were built by the I.G. Company and others in Germany, reaching 600 h.p. No work was done after 1938.

In Great Britain the Fuel Research Station made contact with Pawlikowski during 1937 and started research work on the examination of the important factor of erosion by inorganic matter (ash). It was realized at this time that the basic difficulties were erosion by ash, measurement and feeding of the coal, and ignition. The latter had been overcome to some extent in Germany by the use of an ante-chamber for preheating.

The Fuel Research Station experimental work was done by injecting ash in the right proportion into the cylinder of a petrol engine and measuring the wear on a series of different liners, rings, etc. It was established that there was some promise of reducing wear to a practical level. The combination of a chromium-plated cast-iron liner with cast-iron pistons and rings reduced wear to one-seventieth on the liner, one-thirtieth on the piston and one-sixteenth on the rings, in comparison with steel.

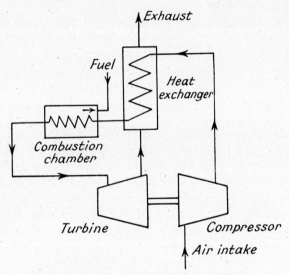

FIG. 28.—Diagram of Open-cycle Gas Turbine.

An attempt to run an experimental diesel engine on bituminous coal was not successful even at a compression ration of 17·5 and using a variety of ante-chambers. The engine did run on brown coal, however, although the thermal efficiency reached was only 32 per cent. in comparison with 40 per cent. for oil. The engine was a slow-speed type running at 230 r.p.m. The experimental work was discontinued at the outbreak of the last war.

A more promising development is now found in the " gas " turbine. This name has been given to the production of power by a turbine driven by hot gases under pressure. The gases can be heated air or the products of combustion of fuel gas, oil or oil fractions, or coal. The outstanding application is to aircraft, where one important consideration is a high power/ weight ratio (Chapter XII), but successful land applications have been made to the use of clean gas or petroleum fractions. Owing to the relatively high cost of oil fuel in Britain, however, it is clear that the most economic application can come about if the system can be adapted to burn coal. It is for this reason that the gas turbine is discussed in this context. The work is still in the experimental stage, although perhaps an advanced stage, and several power-station applications are in hand using a petroleum fraction.

In its simplest form the gas turbine operates as shown in Figure 28.

Air is compressed to, say, 75 lb. per square inch, heated by interchange with the exhaust gases, and used to burn fuel in a combustion chamber. The hot products of combustion drive the turbine to produce power. This simple form represents the open-cycle system, but it is evident that its

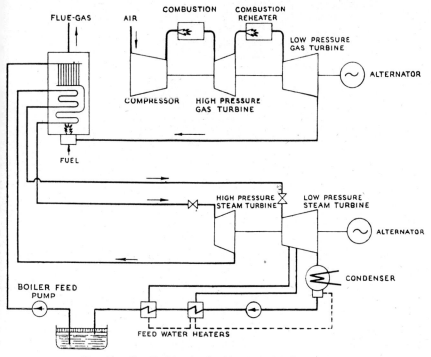

Fig. 29.—Gas Turbine in Combination with Steam Cycle.
By permission of Sir J. Hacking and the Junior Institution of Engineers (*J. Jr. Inst. Eng.*, 1954, **64,** 188).

efficiency can be increased by improved utilization of the heat of the exhaust, using a compressor in which the stages are compounded with intermediate air-cooling, and compounding the expansion of the turbine with extra heat addition between the stages.

At present the process is limited by the working temperature which the metal used will stand, particularly the blades of the turbine. This is now of the order of 700° C. Without a waste-gas heat-exchanger the temperature of the discharged gases would be about 330° C. and the thermal efficiency only 16 to 20 per cent. In an improved cycle such as is shown in Figure 29 the efficiency would be increased to 38 per cent. and the power output

F.—H

increased by 90 per cent. It is evident that these involve additional plant and are not applicable to the case of aircraft.

An alternative system is the "closed" cycle in which the working substance passes round a closed circuit and the heat is supplied by conduction

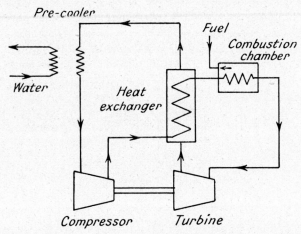

FIG. 30.—Diagram of Closed-cycle Gas Turbine.

in a heat exchanger. Apart from the external application of heat the principle of operation is the same as in the open cycle. The important advantages lie in the use of a clean fuel and the exclusion of any solid matter which might damage the turbine blades. Any disadvantage is contained in the temperature and efficiency limitations of metal preheaters. A simple form of closed cycle is shown in Figure 30.

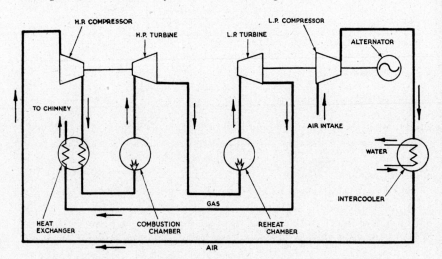

FIG. 31.—Diagram of 15-MW. Open-cycle Gas Turbine Set for Electricity Generation.

Modern plants of large size have been designed for electricity generation from oil fuel using both cycles, and an example of the circuit of one is shown in Figure 31. The output of this plant is to be 15 megawatts, which is equivalent to the combustion of about 260 tons of coal per day.

The compression ratio of this unit is 10/1, the intake of air at atmospheric pressure, and the working pressure 150 lb. per square inch. In a closed cycle the working pressure could be increased to 750 lb. and the output increased to 75 MW.

The Use of Coal in the Gas Turbine. The main problem in the application of coal to the gas turbine is the fact that it contains inorganic matter which, if it is not removed after combustion, would have an injurious effect on the blades of the turbine. A second problem is the need to burn the coal in a fine state of division so that its rate of combustion can respond with sufficient rapidity to changes of load and its combustion can be complete enough to prevent the forward passage of carbon particles.

The use of the closed cycle has advantages in avoiding the ash problem so far as the turbine itself is concerned and is regarded by some as the logical method of applying coal. It has a serious disadvantage, however, in that the heat exchanger or " air-boiler " must be of large size to be efficient. Messrs. Escher-Wyss (Switzerland) have designed a combustion chamber with annular walls through which the air for combustion passes and cools the walls sufficiently to allow them to be heated safely by radiation from the flame. The limitation is again the working temperature of the metal (700° C.), but by suitable design of the burner there need be no accumulation of ash or clinker on the burner or air-heater tubes, and no problem of damage to the turbine blades.

In the open cycle the obvious difficulty is to achieve sufficiently the separation of the inorganic constituents of the coal before they reach the cyclone. Rapid ignition is also necessary and it must be arranged that the air/coal ratio at injection is such that the maximum velocity of flame propagation is attained. After this the " ash " must be removed either as dust or, in slagging furnaces, as a molten stream.

One advantage of the cycle is that the combustion-gases must be cooled to the working temperature and the air used for this purpose can be utilized for cooling the walls of the combustion chamber. Since both air and products are under pressure the stresses on the hot walls are negligible, an important consideration at these high temperatures. There is as yet no means of fully separating fine dust particles, but there is reason to believe that the turbine may stand up to particles if they are not larger than 5 to 10 μ, and if so, it may be possible to design separators which will remove all particles larger than this and also not allow scale particles to become detached by thermal expansion or contraction of the metal. Deposits of

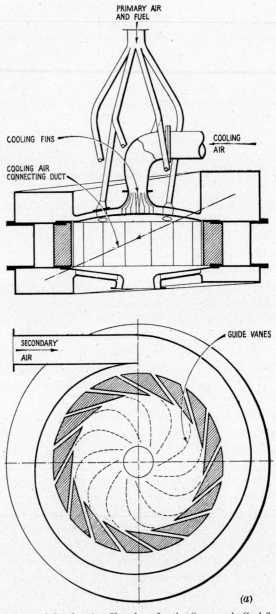

PRIMARY AIR
AND FUEL

COOLING FINS

COOLING
AIR

COOLING AIR
CONNECTING DUCT

GUIDE VANES

SECONDARY
AIR

(a)

FIG. 32.—Experimental Combustion Chambers for the Open-cycle Coal-fired Gas Turbine.
(a) Fuel Research Station, " Vortex ".

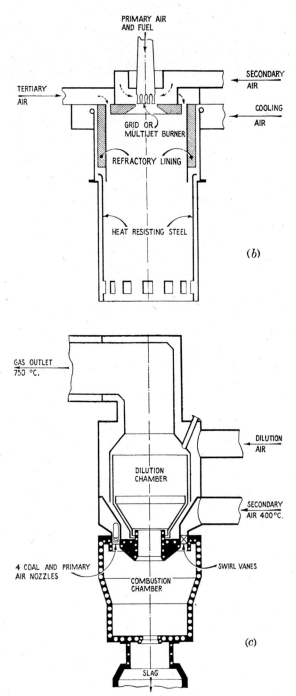

PRIMARY AIR
AND FUEL

TERTIARY
AIR

SECONDARY
AIR

COOLING
AIR

GRID OR
MULTIJET BURNER

REFRACTORY LINING

HEAT RESISTING STEEL

(b)

GAS OUTLET
750 °C.

DILUTION
AIR

DILUTION
CHAMBER

SECONDARY
AIR 400°C.

4 COAL AND PRIMARY
AIR NOZZLES

SWIRL VANES

COMBUSTION
CHAMBER

(c)

SLAG

FIG. 32 (continued).—Experimental Combustion Chambers for the Open-cycle Coal-fired
Gas Turbine.
(b) Fuel Research Station, Straight-through.
(c) British Coal Utilisation Research Association, " Cyclone " chamber.

carbon can also be dangerous and it is necessary to ensure fairly complete combustion, say not more than 20 per cent. of carbon in the ash. Another difficulty in the use of the open cycle is that of feeding coal into a system under pressure.

The problem of the design of the combustion chamber is being examined by a number of research groups. Coal or coke particles moving in a stream of combustion products require a long time for combustion, but this cannot be allowed because of the need to keep a pressurized chamber small. Turbulence is therefore necessary and, in consequence, suitably-cooled walls. The most advanced work is that of the Locomotive Development Committee of Bituminous Coal Research Inc. (U.S.A.). The combustion chamber developed is of the straight-through type with film cooling of the metal surfaces ; it burns 2000 lb. of coal (90 per cent. $<$ 200 B.S. mesh) at a pressure of 60 lb. The burner is of multijet type (Figure 27f), giving a completeness of combustion of 90 to 95 per cent. It is understood that the best run on the prototype machine has been 1000 hours. Ash is separated by multicyclones aided by a special " Dunlab " separator so that the gases do not contain over 19 per cent. of particles larger than 10 μ or 2 per cent. over 20 μ ; this has given a degree of blade erosion which was satisfactory after 1000 hours. Units are also being designed for power-station plant.

In Great Britain, experimental work is being carried out by the Fuel Research Station for the Ministry of Fuel and Power, and, by the British Coal Utilisation Research Association. The former is working on a study of ash deposition in a straight-through chamber with partly refractory and partly metal walls, using a multijet burner, and on a new " vortex " combustion chamber. The latter are working on an adaptation of the Babcock cyclone burner (Figure 23). The three burners are shown in diagram in the sketches of Figure 32.

It is clear that the gas turbine can have important applications to power production, using petroleum fractions at present where these are available at low cost, but later heavy oils as soon as a satisfactory burner is evolved. In Great Britain its future lies in coal and would seem to be not too far off, given a good burner design for the open-cycle turbine.

DOMESTIC HEATING

The importance of domestic heating in the consumption of fuel in Great Britain is evidenced by the following figures, which, though not entirely discriminating, show that the consumption represents in thermal value about 30 per cent. of the coal mined annually. Since the statistics quoted do not distinguish exactly between consumption in dwelling-houses on the one hand and offices and public buildings on the other, it is necessary to take the total figure. A very approximate split would be :

	Million tons
Coal	35
Miners' coal	5
Coke, gas industry	4
Gas, coal equivalent	9
Electricity, coal equivalent	11
Total	64

It should be obvious from the size of this total that the efficiency of house heating should be made as high as possible since inefficiency in the usage of so large a proportion of coal production can represent a large factor in the problems of coal production and distribution. Unfortunately this is not the case so far as truly domestic heating is concerned because of the high proportion of coal burned in the open fire, the prevalence of intermittent heating, and the construction of many houses in which the elementary principles of thermal insulation are not applied as they should be. It is generally considered that the lack of uniform severity in our winters is the reason, but it is true to say that a high proportion of our domestic coal is burned at low efficiency and that, in times of severe weather, the standard of comfort falls far below that of many other civilized countries. Many proposals have been made to amend this, particularly those of the Egerton Committee which advocated in particular better insulation in buildings, a form of background heating, and the use of more efficient appliances. Appliances are indeed being developed to meet the latter recommendation, but practically no move has been made to implement the others, so that the higher efficiency of new appliances has been discounted by lack of provision for their proper installation, and by undue heat losses.

These strictures do not apply to special cases, or to office heating where properly designed hot-water or warm-air systems are generally installed.

In the heating of dwelling-houses the position is complicated by the necessity to observe a reasonable economy to the householder, and the difficulty of applying new methods effectively to old houses. What does seem essential is that all new houses should be built with more attention to the need for attaining a reasonable standard of comfort at *all* times.

An example of the annual fuel requirements of a well-insulated, small (three-bedroom) house heated throughout to the Egerton requirements of a background temperature of 60° F. is available in the Stanmore experiments of Messrs. Radiation Ltd.

The fuel consumed included background heating to 60° F., the heating up of the living- and dining-rooms to 67° F. for 8 hours per day and the bedrooms for 4 hours per day. Water supply was 250 gal. per week in winter and 150 gal. in the summer and power for a washing machine and a refrigerator are included.

Coke	80 cwt.
Gas	125 therms
Electricity	500 units

If the cost of this is taken at 132s. per ton for coke, 1·6s. per therm for gas, and 1·5 pence per unit for electricity, the total cost per annum becomes £35 10s.

If a second example is taken from the experiments of the Building Research Station a different case is found in which there is no real background heating except from one radiator in the hall. The living-room is con-tinuous-heated from an openable fire, the dining-room from a domestic boiler, and the bedrooms have only occasional heating from electric fires. The boiler, with a 40-gal. tank, supplies the hot water, a towel rail in the bathroom and the airing cupboard.

Coal	46·2 cwt.
Anthracite	63·2 ,,
Gas for cooking	53 therms
Electricity	361 units

Taking the units at the same values, the overall cost was £44·2, provid-ing 250 gal. of hot water per week in the winter and 150 gal. in the summer.

In a third example in which the comfort level is low, but which is very common in Britain, we have evening heating in the living-room, occa-sional gas heating in the dining-room and electric radiants in bedrooms, with an independent coke boiler for hot water and bath-room radiator, and gas for cooking. The electric power charge includes radio, iron, and refrigerator.

Coal	20 cwt.
Coke	50 ,,
Gas	162 therms
Electricity	750 units

Taking the units at the same value, the overall cost of this is about £42 per annum ; this is of the same order as the two above examples but, in a four-bedroom house, does not provide a reasonable standard of comfort in the winter months.

If better standards of comfort are to be achieved without unduly raising the cost it follows that better insulation of houses must be provided with possibly some changes in room arrangement. It has been calculated that for an internal temperature of 60° F. in a three-bedroom house the fuel requirement, based on a 33-week " winter ", is not more than 550 therms per annum. One of the most important factors in achieving this is the control of the width of flues to reduce chimney draught and regulate the number of air-changes to 2 to 3 per hour. In many houses the rate of air change may be several times as much and lead to uncomfortable draughts. Further stoking is only an aggravation of the fault and the only remedy is restriction of chimney throat in old houses and the limitation of size in new ones. In stream-lined construction the throat may be as small as 5 sq. in. for an average room, but normally 12 sq. in. will not give more than one air-change too much.

Having reduced loss by conduction and convection the next step is to consider temperature. The classic experiments of Fishenden have shown that, in Great Britain at least, an air temperature of 65° F. is sufficient without radiation warmth to provide a feeling of comfort. At lower air temperatures radiation is increasingly required or, with a fixed amount of radiation, the zone of comfort round the source decreases in area. The latter effect is shown in the following diagrams for a coal consumption of 2 lb. per hour in a room of 14 ft. depth.

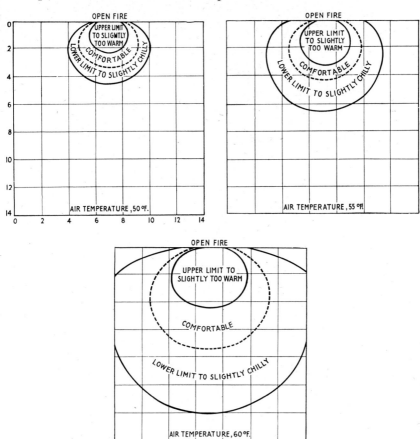

Fig. 33.—Zones of Comfort at Different Air Temperatures with Constant Rate of Radiation.
(Fuel Research Technical Paper 12, 1925, H.M.S.O.)

Radiation can, however, be greatly assisted by the convection of warm air since this air can remove the feeling of chill which is caused by the body radiating to the cold wall behind. This effect can be brought about by a convection heater which is independent of the source of radiation but in certain new appliances (see p. 204) can be part of it.

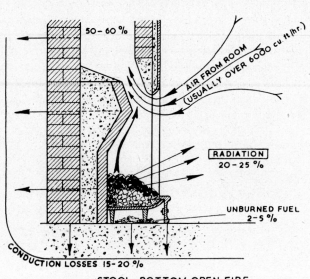

STOOL BOTTOM OPEN FIRE
(BURNING COAL)
(a)

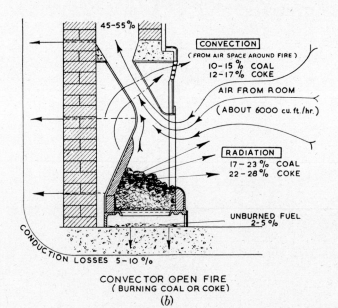

CONVECTOR OPEN FIRE
(BURNING COAL OR COKE)
(b)

FIG. 34.—Efficiency of Thermal Emission from Room-heating Appliances.

(By courtesy of Mr. J. S. Hales and the Director of the British Coal Utilisation Research Association.)

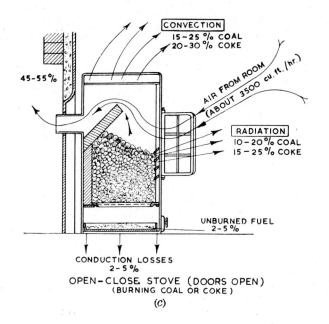

CONVECTION
15-25 % COAL
20-30 % COKE

45-55%

AIR FROM ROOM
(ABOUT 3500 cu.ft./hr.)

RADIATION
10-20 % COAL
15-25 % COKE

UNBURNED FUEL
2-5 %

CONDUCTION LOSSES
2-5%

OPEN-CLOSE STOVE (DOORS OPEN)
(BURNING COAL OR COKE)

(c)

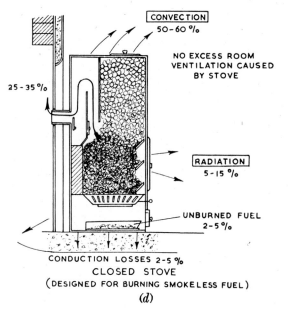

CONVECTION
50-60 %

NO EXCESS ROOM
VENTILATION CAUSED
BY STOVE

25-35%

RADIATION
5-15 %

UNBURNED FUEL
2-5 %

CONDUCTION LOSSES 2-5 %
CLOSED STOVE
(DESIGNED FOR BURNING SMOKELESS FUEL)

(d)

FIG. 34 (continued).—Efficiency of Thermal Emission from Room-heating Appliances.

The efficiencies of room-heating appliances are illustrated in Figure 34. The open-fire examples relate to the overlarge chimney apertures which are so common to-day; the excess air does not affect the radiation from the fire but does cool the room to an unnecessary extent. In the simplest case of the stool-bottom fire (Figure 34a), the approximate fuel cost of overcoming the effect of the undue ventilation is about 25 per cent., but even this is not effective since it would further increase draught.

A bright " open " coal fire radiates about 20 to 25 per cent. of its thermal value into the room (for coke 30 to 32), but its average performance over the period from fuelling to refuelling is probably not more than 15 per cent. Chimney losses are 50–60 per cent., but some of this is recoverable in wall heating and even in upper rooms (say 10 per cent.). If it is arranged as in Figure 34b for air to be drawn below the fire, heated against the fire-back and returned to the room, the flue loss is reduced to 45 to 55 per cent., conduction losses are decreased, and some 10 to 15 per cent. of the thermal value of the fuel is added to the radiation. This gain is real but seems to contribute in even greater degree to the feeling of comfort in that the movement of the warm air defeats the effects of cold draughts. In old houses an adapted convector grate with a restricted chimney throat can approach this desired condition.

The advantages of room-heating stoves are shown in Figure 34c and d. The closed type will give almost continuously, if kept free from ash accumulations, an emission of 65 per cent. with valuable convective heating and reduced flue losses of 30 per cent. If the doors are opened to give more radiation the increased draught increases flue losses and reduces the overall emission to 35 per cent. for coal or 45 per cent. for coke.

The radiant gas fire has a radiant efficiency of about 45 per cent.

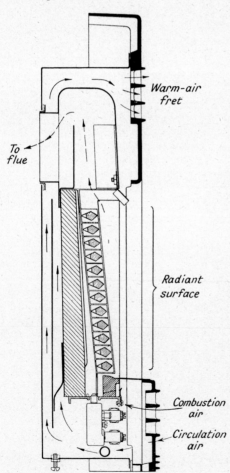

FIG. 35.—Radiant Gas Fire for Space Heating, with Convected Warm Air.

but its comfort condition can be improved and its efficiency raised by about 15 per cent., i.e. to 60 to 65 per cent., by convective heating arranged in a similar manner to that of Figure 34b as shown in the diagram Figure 35, and discussed later in Chapter XV.

The space heating of rooms can also be achieved by electric radiators and gas or electric space-heaters. The efficiency of these is generally assumed to be 100 per cent. since all the heat is passed into the room. In the case of the gas convector the products of combustion are a complication in that they contain traces of sulphur which in time cause corrosion, and moisture which condenses on cold surfaces and can have considerable nuisance value in certain circumstances. They are, however, efficient and comfortable in halls or rooms where the ventilation is adequate. A new form of gas convector heater is the " balanced-flue " heater which draws fresh air from outside and heats it by conduction, discharging the combustion gases to atmosphere. An example of this is shown in Figure 90 (Chapter XV). It requires to be fitted to an outside wall, but the aperture necessary is only one brick in area. The thermal efficiency of this form is about 75 per cent.

Central Heating. For the heating of buildings and offices a thermostatically controlled boiler with hot-water circulation is convenient and efficient if operated with an automatic stoker, but for small buildings and homes hot-water circulation is not so efficient except as an adjunct to other heat requirements, as shown above. In modern times, where the saving of labour has become important, it is possible that central heating by gas will become

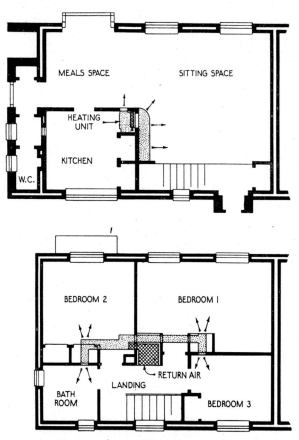

FIG. 36.—Central Heating by Warm Air Ducts.

more popular, making use of devices of the type which have proved successful in the United States using natural gas. Two methods of heating are possible ; the first requires special building in that warm air is carried by ducting as shown in Figure 36 to the lower part of each room, while other ducts leading from grilles in the upper parts conduct back to

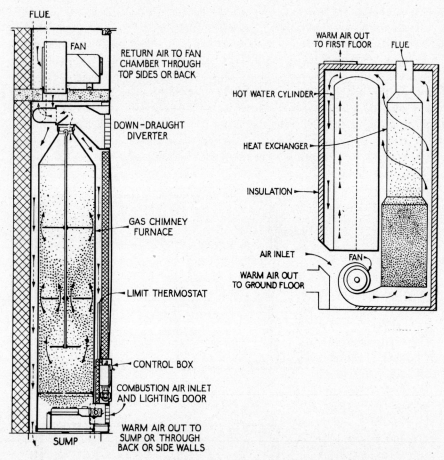

FIG. 37.—Central Heating Appliances for Small Houses.

(A. Forshaw, *Coke and Gas*, 1953, **15**, 209.)

the circulating fan. Messrs. Radiation Ltd. have developed a gas heater to provide 40,000 B.Th.U. per hour to a small house of 1000 sq. ft. floor space which can give background temperatures of 55° F. and room temperatures of 65 to 70° F. An alternative heater for hall heating but without ducting is also designed. Alternatively the same technique can be served by coke. The heating units are illustrated in Figure 37 and the annual consumption of fuel in the small house stated is as follows :

Gas heating   .   .   .   .   850 therms
or Solid fuel .   .   .   .   .   4 tons plus gas = 90 therms = 1290 therms

Both include also 250 gal. of hot water per week in winter and 150 gal. in summer.

Fuel requirements for larger houses would be greater but not so great as to be in proportion to the greater floor space.

District Heating. One form of domestic heating consists in the utilization of waste heat from the electric power station in the form of hot-water circulation to a building estate in proximity to the station. In Great Britain the heat available from this source is of the order of 587×10^{12} B.Th.U. in 1952, or the equivalent of 80 million tons of coal burned at 25 per cent. efficiency, i.e. more than the amount of house coal now consumed.

An example of what can be done is available in the Pimlico scheme, which is served by the Battersea power station on the other side of the Thames. A population of 11,000 flat dwellers will be served from an insulated hot-water storage tank of about 78,000 cu. ft. capacity, the water in which is maintained at a temperature of 135° F., or 70° to 80° F. above the house background temperature of 55° to 65° F. The heat-electric generating plant at the power station will generate 10×10^6 kWh. annually and supply waste heat at a maximum rate of 3150 therms per hour. The overall thermal efficiency of generation of heat and electricity will be 80 per cent. and the amount of house coal saved will be 11,000 tons annually.

In order to achieve this result it is necessary to balance the heat and power loads, which vary independently. Several methods have been proposed for this, including the operation of back-pressure sets and low-pressure condensing sets in parallel, the use of pass-out steam turbines, and the above method of hot-water storage with heat-electric generation. The thermal capacity of Pimlico reservoir is 4000 therms.

The Heat Pump. The high cost of modern fuels has redirected attention to a long-known method of obtaining " low-grade " heat from natural sources, with the expenditure of only a fraction of the heat energy which would otherwise be required. The proposal dates back to Lord Kelvin, who pointed out in 1852 that the refrigerator cycle which abstracts heat from a body also returns this heat in another place. Consideration of the " reversed " cycles showed that, with a reservoir of heat above 0° C., such as a lake or river or the atmosphere, the expenditure of some energy as work could obtain heat at a substantially higher temperature which would be equal to several times the energy expended. A demonstration of this was made in 1929 by T. Haldane, but it was not until 1940 that practical applications were made in Switzerland and in the U.S.A. Experiments have been made in Great Britain by the Ministry of Fuel and Power.

The basic components of a heat pump are a compressor, an expansion valve, and two heat exchangers as shown in diagram in Figure 38.

The low-temperature heat source may be an underground tank which draws heat from the earth, or the atmosphere. It is easy to achieve a circulating temperature of 95° F. which can serve for space-heating through radiant panels or, with more efficient compressors, to raise the temperature to 140° F. which is high enough for any domestic requirements of heat.

In an example quoted by J. A. Sumner of a 1500 sq. ft. bungalow, a

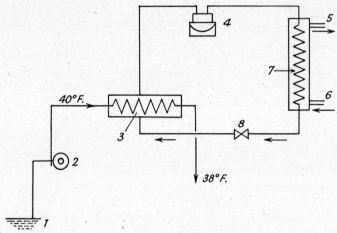

FIG. 38.—Heat Pump Installation using Water as Source of Low-grade Heat.

1, River, well or lake ; 2, Circulating water pump ; 3, Evaporator (cooler) ; 4, Compressor ; 5, Warm water to building at 120° F. ; 6, Return water 100° F. ; 7, Condenser (heater) ; 8, Expansion valve.

heat pump provided, with the expenditure of energy of 32 kWh. per day, the same comfort as 90 kWh. expended as thermal energy, i.e. a saving of two-thirds of the fuel bill.

The ratio of energy supplied (E) to work done (W) is proportional to $T_1/(T_1 - T_2)$, where T_1 and T_2 are respectively the absolute values of the upper and lower temperatures. This ratio has been termed the reciprocal thermal efficiency (R.Th.E.)[1] or the performance energy ratio (P.E.R.) and may range from 3·5 in the winter to 6·0 in the summer.

In the above house example it is 6 and, if associated with an efficiency of generation of electric power of 26 per cent., gives an overall efficiency of 0·73 when calculated back to the original coal. This is a very high efficiency of utilization in comparison with conventional methods of using fuel, but can be increased still further by the use of the oil engine operating at an efficiency of 40%. The overall efficiency may then be as high as 112%.

[1] The theoretical thermal efficiency of a heat cycle is $(T_1 - T_2)/T_1$.

Industrial applications are also possible when the industry requires heat in quantity at a fairly low temperature for such operations as drying. The " low " temperature heat source may then be the heat rejected from power plant, or cooling water in general. The use of these could give a R.Th.E. as high as 4·0 and a very high overall efficiency. In any factory this could take at least the heating load of the buildings.

A large-scale experiment on the heating of the Festival Hall (London) with a heating load of 30 therms per hour, using the Thames as the low-temperature heat source, has achieved a thermal ratio of 1·28 (Coefficient of Performance = 2·8). In obtaining this the river water was reduced in temperature by 4·5° F. in providing heat equivalent to 48 per cent. of the thermal value of the gas burned in a gas engine to produce the necessary power. The result was lower than the ratio of 1·40 expected, mainly because the installation was designed on too large a scale. The capital cost proved much too high but no doubt further development will bring this system into a cost focus which will allow in certain circumstances the savings of " stored " fuel which it obviously promises.

The Fuel Cell

A fuel cell is an electrochemical cell in which the free energy of combustion may be converted directly into electrical energy. Since this energy is obtainable theoretically at 100 per cent. efficiency, a practical cell would have a considerable advantage in thermal efficiency over the normal heat-engine method of producing electrical power, which presently has a limiting theoretical efficiency of 65 per cent. and a realized power-station efficiency of about 30 per cent.

A practical cell has not yet been realized but research work suggests that a method is in sight of utilizing the reaction between hydrogen or H_2-containing gases, and oxygen or air. This is, of course, only a partial stage since the use of solid fuel must be the aim if natural fuel is to be utilized. Carbon can be used as one of the reactants if the temperature of the cell is raised to over 500° C., but no practical method of operation has yet been suggested.

Most of the experimental work has been done with hydrogen and oxygen and one method can be taken to explain the technique. In the Bacon high-pressure hydrogen cell developed at Cambridge University the electrodes are of sintered (and activated) nickel and the electrolyte is a 27 per cent. solution of potassium hydrate. The former are 4-in. dia. discs, $\frac{5}{32}$ in. in thickness, with 30 μ pores, but having a skin of material of 16 μ pore size. The discs face one another, with the finely-porous side inwards, at a distance of only $\frac{1}{16}$ in., and the electrolyte is arranged to circulate through this space to prevent polarization. Heavy steel covers surround the electrodes and provide the gas spaces for the supply of hydrogen and oxygen to the negative and positive electrodes respectively. The pressure of the gases is about 45 atm. and the temperature of the electrolyte is about 200° C. A pressure difference of 1·5 lb. per sq. in. is maintained across the electrodes to prevent penetration of the electrolyte. The present output of such a cell is 1·08 amperes per sq. cm. at a potential of 0·6 V., 0·72 A. at 0·7 V., or 0·4 A. at 0·8 V.; these high current densities are maintained by the recirculation of the electrolyte and a life of the order of 500 hours has already been reached. There are still problems to be solved to attain longer life but it is understood that the solution is now in sight.

The practical application of the cell would consist in the construction of large batteries of thin cells constantly supplied with hydrogen and oxygen (or air) from pressure cylinders. The working temperature would be maintained by utilizing the heat developed in the cells. At 0·4 A. and 0·8 V. per sq. cm. the voltage efficiency would be about 68 per cent. of the theoretical. The cheapest combination would be a high-hydrogen water gas and air but this is not yet fully demonstrated.

Several systems are being explored for the hydrogen-oxygen fuel cell but practical application must obviously be limited to special cases where the higher cost of raw materials is offset by high thermal efficiency absence of noise, vibration, and effluent. The only effluent of the H_2-cell is the water formed at the hydrogen electrode. Application to solid fuel would seem still to have a long way to go.

REFERENCE BOOKS

Modern Gas Turbines. Judge. Chapman and Hall. 1950.
The Pulverized Fuel Conference. Inst. Fuel. 1947.
The Heat Pump and Thermal Compressors. Davies. Constable. 1950.
Ash and Clinker in Industry. Inst. Fuel Conference. 1953.
Fuels, Combustion and Furnaces. Griswold. McGraw-Hill. 1946.
Heating Ventilating and Air-Conditioning. Harding. John Wiley. 1935.
Heating Ventilating and Air-Conditioning. Severns and Fellows. Wiley. 1949.
Electric Power Stations. Carr. Chapman & Hall. 1948.
Boiler House and Power Station Chemistry. Francis. Edward Arnold (Publishers) Ltd., London. 1955.
Boiler House Practice. Williams. Allen and Unwin. 1953.
Combustion Engineering. de Lorenzi, New York. 1951.
Steam Turbine Theory and Practice. Kearton. Pitman. 1951.
Principles of Combustion in the Steam Boiler Furnace. Pratt. . 1950.
Waste Heat Recovery. Inst. Fuel Conference. Chapman and Hall. 1950.
Kempe's Engineering Handbook. Morgan Bros. Yearly.
Electrochemical Generation of Electricity. R. G. H. Watson. *Research*, 1954, **7**, 34.
A. M. Adams. *J. Inst. Fuel*, 1954, **27**, 366.
Chemistry of Coal Utilisation (Ed. H. H. Lowry). H. C. Howard. Wiley. 1945.

CHAPTER IX

CARBONIZATION AND CARBONIZED FUELS
FROM COAL

In this context the term carbonization means the heat treatment or distillation of coal out of contact with the air so as to produce a solid residue—coke—and liquid and gaseous products of distillation. The nature of the solid product, with which this chapter is concerned, depends upon the nature of the coal treated, the temperature of the treatment, and the rate of heating. It has been explained in Chapter V that the caking power of coal, i.e. its ability to form a hard, coherent mass on heating, varies from zero with lignitous coals to a maximum with coal of about 88 per cent. carbon, and then decreases sharply to zero again at about 92 per cent. carbon. It follows, therefore, that coals required for the manufacture of hard cokes must be chosen from that range in which caking power is well developed, i.e. in the range 83 to 90 per cent. carbon (see Figure 14).

A second consideration is the proportion of volatile matter associated with caking coals. If the primary consideration is the making of a hard coke with certain optimum properties the choice of coal must fall on those which achieve this and the yield of volatile products must be a secondary consideration. If the main objective is gas, with coke as a secondary product, as in the town-gas industry, the choice must fall in the high-volatile range of caking coals. If the objective is a coke of high reactivity, then the choice must fall in the first place on those coals which give the most scope for the production of reactive coke, whatever the process.

In Great Britain the carbonizing industries are principally those of the manufacture of town gas, and of metallurgical coke, with a comparatively smaller production of specially-reactive coke described in general as " smokeless fuel ". In 1951 the amounts of coal carbonized by these industries, and the amounts of their main products, were as follows :

	Coal, million tons.	Coke, million tons.	Gas, million therms.	Tar, million tons.	Benzole, million gallons.
Gas industry	27·1	12·3	2000⎫		
Coke industry	23·6	16·0	1300⎬	2·7	97
Smokeless fuel	0·8	0·5	—	—	—

Although the purpose of this chapter is to consider the properties of different types of coke, it is necessary, for a proper appreciation of this subject to deal briefly with the industrial methods of production and to show how these methods influence the behaviour of coal on heating and the properties of the cokes made.

211

When coal is submitted to the action of heat it loses volatile matter in the forms of gas and tar and leaves the coke as a solid residue. With non-caking coal this residue is either pulverulent or friable, depending on the size of the original material. As caking power increases the coal passes through the stage of plasticity and intumescence in which the original structure disappears and is replaced by a cellular structure which hardens to the characteristic appearance of coke. The degree of devolatilization of the coal depends upon the temperature reached but the process is almost complete at 1000° C.

The sulphur of coal is only partly driven off and the sulphur content of coke is normally about 80 per cent. of that of the coal. Since the yield of coke is about 75 per cent. this means that some 40 per cent. has been driven off. Part of the organic sulphur is converted to hydrogen sulphide, the pyrites is reduced to ferrous sulphide with the elimination of more H_2S, and still more H_2S is liberated on quenching with water by the partial oxidation of part of the FeS. If the coke is quenched out of contact with water the sulphur is distributed as organic S and FeS.

The nitrogen of coal is liberated partly as ammonia and cyanogen, partly as nitrogenous bodies in the tar, and only some 45 to 50 per cent. remains in the coke.

Manufacture of Metallurgical Coke

In the manufacture of metallurgical coke the objective is to obtain the highest possible yield of suitable coke from a given coal, i.e. to fix as much of the carbon of the coal as possible in the coke, regarding gas and tar as by-products.

The earliest methods of obtaining coke were similar to those in vogue for charcoal burning, the restricted combustion of the coal in piles, or in stacks with brick flues, this partial combustion furnishing sufficient heat to carbonize the remainder ; but such wasteful methods are practically obsolete. The natural development was combustion of the volatile constituents in a dome-shaped oven, arranged for suitable and easily-regulated air admission, above the surface of the coal, so that the heat slowly penetrated downwards and effectually coked the mass. These beehive ovens are still employed to the extent of about 0·5 per cent. (246 ovens) in Great Britain for the manufacture of particularly refractory coke for special purposes. In the U.S.A. the proportion is still 10 per cent.

The beehive ovens are from 12 to 13 ft. in diameter, 7 ft. high ; the coal is charged to a depth of about 3 ft. To economize heat the ovens are built in two rows, back to back, with a common flue arranged down the centre, the waste heat passing off under boilers.

For successful results in such ovens the coal must have strong caking properties, as the temperature at which coking commences is low, and the rise of temperature not rapid, since the previous charge has been cooled in the oven by water, and the oven has usually been standing two or three hours before recharging.

The slow initial rate of heating promotes the formation of well-developed cell structure, and the final high temperature attained ensures a dense hard character to the product. Low temperatures lead to irregularity in coking, lack of coherence and inflated cell development.

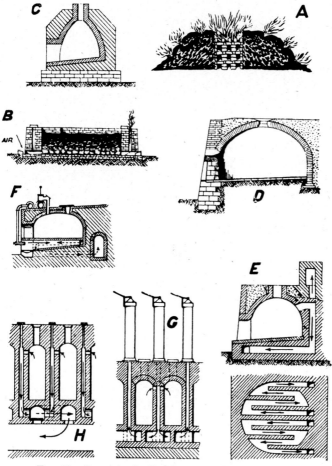

FIG. 39.—Stages in the Development of the Coke Oven.

The natural development to avoid the loss of coke substance was the introduction of ovens from which the combustion products could distil through suitable orifices in the walls, and meet the air necessary for combustion only in an exterior space. Stages in development are shown in Figure 39, starting with coal heaps before 1740 ; B, covered heaps ; C, first oven 1759 ; E, externally-heated sole-flue oven, 1860 ; G, H, vertical flue ovens, 1860. By the use of long horizontal rectangular ovens, closed by doors at the ends (Coppée), the coal could be charged conveniently and the coke pushed out by mechanical means ; or in vertical ovens with a slight taper (Appolt) the coke could be dropped when the lower doors were opened. With the beehive ovens, or ovens of the above pattern, far more gas was utilized for heating than necessary, and although the waste heat was to some extent recovered by passing the gases through boilers, the losses were great, and further all the valuable by-products were lost.

The average yield of a retort oven as compared with a beehive oven working on the same coal will be approximately 10 per cent. higher.

The modern oven consists of long rectangular chambers, 35 to 42 ft. long, 9 to 14 ft. high, and 14 to 22 in. wide, closed by doors at both ends, so that charging is performed at one end, the coke being pushed out by suitable discharging machinery and quenched at the other end. A section through a Becker oven is shown in Figure 40. A number of ovens are built up side by side to form a battery.

In Figure 40 the captions explain the different parts of the plant. The coal-charging car is shown in position for charging, the regenerators for preheating the air are shown in section and the coke from a completed charge is shown in process of discharge into the coke car. The car containing the hot coke is run under a tower (not shown) in which it is quenched with water. After quenching it is spread over the coke wharf to drain and to allow the combined process of drying by residual heat and cooling of the larger pieces to be completed. It is then safe for removal by the belt conveyor. This is a combination oven with arrangements as shown for the alternative use of coke-oven gas on the one hand and lean gas (blast-furnace or producer gas).

The main differences between the numerous forms of coking plant are to be found in the arrangement of the flues in order to secure the most effective and uniform heating ; on this the success of the operation is entirely dependent. The discussion of these various forms of construction is outside the scope of this volume. In the earlier forms the side flues were horizontal, the hot gases passing from end to end two or three times (Simon-Carvés, Semet-Solvay, Hüssener, etc.) ; but now these are not so favourably regarded, preference being given to vertical flues (Coppée, Otto-Hoffmann, Otto-Hilgenstock, Koppers, new Simon-Carvés, Collin, etc.), since it is more easy to obtain uniform heating by their use in the modern long oven. The types now in use in Great Britain are mainly Becker, Koppers, Otto, and Simon Carvés, with relatively few Coppée, Still, Kogag, and Willputte ovens.

Modern recovery plants are constructed for working on the " waste heat " or " regenerative " principle. In the waste-heat type the hot gaseous products of combustion pass through boilers where they meet any surplus gas, which undergoes combustion, so that steam is raised for works purposes. The temperature of the flue gases is from 920° C. to 1100° C., and with

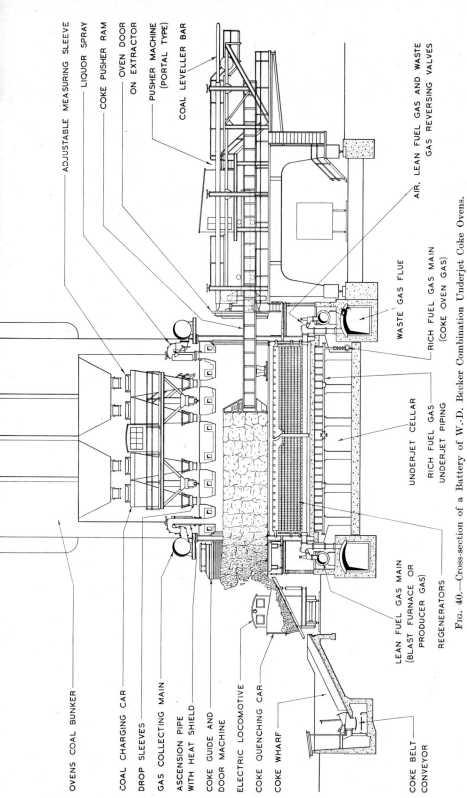

ADJUSTABLE MEASURING SLEEVE

LIQUOR SPRAY

COKE PUSHER RAM

OVEN DOOR ON EXTRACTOR

PUSHER MACHINE (PORTAL TYPE)

COAL LEVELLER BAR

OVENS COAL BUNKER

COAL CHARGING CAR

DROP SLEEVES

GAS COLLECTING MAIN

ASCENSION PIPE WITH HEAT SHIELD

COKE GUIDE AND DOOR MACHINE

ELECTRIC LOCOMOTIVE

COKE QUENCHING CAR

COKE WHARF

COKE BELT CONVEYOR

LEAN FUEL GAS MAIN (BLAST FURNACE OR PRODUCER GAS)

REGENERATORS

RICH FUEL GAS UNDERJET PIPING

UNDERJET CELLAR

WASTE GAS FLUE

RICH FUEL GAS MAIN (COKE OVEN GAS)

AIR, LEAN FUEL GAS AND WASTE GAS REVERSING VALVES

FIG. 40.—Cross-section of a Battery of W.-D. Becker Combination Underjet Coke Ovens.

(By courtesy of Woodall-Duckham Construction Co., Ltd.)

water-tube boilers 2 lb. of steam have been raised from and at 212° F. per lb. of coal carbonized ; with Lancashire and similar boilers from 1 to 1·25 lb. can be obtained.

The regenerative system has now replaced the continuous-recuperative system owing to the difficulty of maintaining a sufficiently long life with recuperators. In this system the arrangement is that sets of at least two chambers of firebrick chequers are used ; during the heating up of the one the other is imparting its heat to the incoming air or lean gas. This necessitates reversals at intervals of 20–30 minutes and it might be thought that this would adversely affect the brickwork, but this is not so since the fluctuations of temperature do not extend far into the walls and the oven temperature remains uniform and apparently unaffected by the reversals. This is no doubt due to the fact that the coefficient of expansion of silica brick is small above 1000° C. and the temperature does not fall below this level. When " rich " gas is used this is not preheated by regeneration but is fired directly ; the air for its combustion is preheated.

The temperature of carbonization as defined by the flue temperature is from 1200° to 1350° C. Higher temperatures can be used up to 1400° C. and will reduce the time of coking. They will not necessarily improve the coke, probably the reverse, but will reduce the life of the battery. The throughput of a modern battery is generally reckoned on a maximum flue temperature of 1350° C.

With regeneration only a portion of the distillation gases is required for heating the ovens, so that there is considerable surplus gas which is available for power purposes or for sale. Naturally this surplus entirely depends upon the character of the coal, but with most coking coals it amounts to 45–50 per cent. Part of this gas may be used in steel-works on the site but much of it is available for sale. Estimates of the quantities and details of composition are dealt with in Chapter XV. In integrated steel-works the ovens may be heated by blast-furnace gas, leaving all the coke-oven gas for steel process use, or sale.

The distinctive arrangement of by-product ovens using the waste-heat and regenerative systems will be made clear by the diagrams of Figure 41.

The efficiency of regeneration depends upon whether the battery is being fired with its own gas, blast-furnace gas or producer gas, since the proportion of air and gas heated is different. In the case of coal-gas firing only the air is heated and, if a 25 per cent. excess is assumed, the ratio air/ waste gas is 0·87 and the waste gases are cooled from 1100° C. to 260° C. and impart 78 per cent. of their heat to the air at 1050° C. In other words, 43 heat units are returned in the air for every 100 heat units burned as gas ; this indicates the large saving of fuel over a non-regenerative system. When firing with lean gas (blast-furnace or producer gas), both gas and air are heated in separate regenerators. 100 volumes of producer gas require, with 25 per cent. excess air, 160 volumes of air so that the ratio air plus fuel/waste gas is about 1·08 and heat recovery rather better. For blast-furnace gas the ratio is also about 1·08. If, as is sometimes the case with producer gas, only the secondary air were heated, the ratio air/waste gas would rise to 1·33 and the fuel consumption would be some 15 per cent. higher.

In coking, the best results are obtained with coal of small size ; in modern practice large coals are crushed to pass through a $\frac{1}{4}$-in. screen (80 per cent. below $\frac{1}{8}$ in.). This procedure is important in that it allows of the utilization of slacks provided they are clean. In some plants the coal is

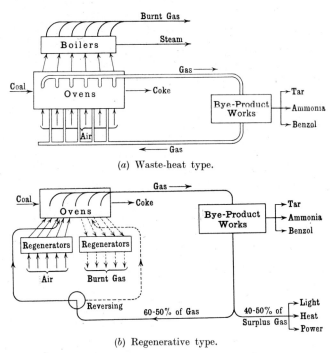

(a) Waste-heat type.

(b) Regenerative type.

FIG. 41.—Flow Diagrams of By-product Coke-oven Plant.

compressed in a stamper and charged into the oven in a solid mass slightly smaller than the inner dimensions of the ovens. From 10 to 12 per cent. of moisture is usual in the crushed coal, and this ensures sufficient binding for the mass to retain its proper shape when the retaining walls of the compressor are let down. The moisture also prevents the loss of fine coal dust in the gases evolved, which takes place with dry fine coal. By com-pression a charge some 25 per cent. heavier can be got into each oven, and the coke produced is firmer and more dense. The normal method is, however, to charge from the top without previous preparation.

The charges and time of carbonization vary greatly with the type of oven and to some extent with the nature of the coal. Beehive ovens take

10 tons, the period of carbonization being about seventy-two to ninety-six hours. By-product ovens vary in coking time with the width of the oven. A 14-in. oven takes 11 hours and an 18-in. oven 16–18 hours and their throughputs are 20–22 (max. 24) tons of coal per day. Modern practice favours the 16- to 18-in. oven as giving the best compromise between strength, rate of heating, size of coke and output.

Influence of Carbonizing Conditions on the Coke. The influences which are of importance with regard to coke properties are (1) the nature of the coal, (2) its size, (3) its moisture content, (4) the method of charging, (5) the rate of heating and (6) the method of quenching.

In general, the type of coal should be such that it has sufficient caking and swelling power to give on carbonization a well-developed porous structure which is retained during the hardening which follows. The very fusible caking coals which were necessary for the beehive oven have too high a caking power for the modern patent oven and tend to give a frothy and porous coke which is weak through excessive shrinkage and the formation of cracks. The blending of coals for coking purposes is now widely adopted not only for modifying the excessive caking power of some coals but improving others. The blends may be of different coals or of caking coal with anthracite, coke dust, etc., to give charging stocks having the correct properties for the type of oven to be used. Blending also serves as a means of modifying such properties in the coke as reactivity, density, hardness and porosity. One interesting blend constituent is fusain dust, and it is indicated that an optimum quantity of 3 per cent. added to caking coal gives large coke of increased hardness. Finely crushed coke is a good substitute for fusain. The most satisfactory size for coking coal is such that the coal contains no pieces larger than $\frac{1}{4}$ in. and that over 80 per cent. passes a $\frac{1}{8}$-in. screen. Finer grinding has no material advantage, the important point being exclusion of any coal larger than $\frac{1}{4}$ in.

It is generally accepted that the most satisfactory amount of moisture in coking coal is about 5 per cent. This fact is important in view of the increasing use of washed slacks which are normally charged at 10 per cent. moisture. Over-dry coals appear to give more fissured coke, whereas too wet coals require more heating and longer periods of carbonization. Mott and Wheeler indicate a decrease of coking time from thirty-six to twenty-six and a half hours for a reduction of moisture content from 13·0 to 1·0 per cent.

Rate of heating is probably the most important consideration in coking. In narrow ovens the rate of heating would be too great for highly-caking coals and blending is essential. If this is adopted the best results seem to be obtained at rates of coking of from 0·85 to 0·95 in. per hour. Narrow-oven coke, the result of a high rate of heating, has been found to be superior to wide-oven coke for blast-furnace purposes. The superiority appears to lie in hardness, uniformity made possible by blending and more even heating, and closer grading of size.

Quenching of oven coke is done by water spraying in a coke car or on an inclined bench, and is done so carefully that the finished coke should contain less than 1 per cent. of moisture. The coke car gives the most uniform result. Dry quenching by the circulation of inert gases with generation of steam by the heated gases has been adopted on the Continent, but there is only one plant in Britain ; the objections to it are high capital cost and maintenance charges caused by sulphuric acid corrosion.

Recovery of By-products. Two systems are employed for the recovery of the by-products—the Indirect and Semi-Direct, which terms refer particularly to the method of ammonia recovery. The Direct system of acid extraction has gone out of use.

The operating stages in the two systems now in use are :

Indirect	*Semi-Direct*
(i) Gas cooling with condensation of tar and ammoniacal liquor.	(i) Gas cooling with condensation of tar and ammoniacal liquor.
(ii) Extraction of the last traces of tar by some form of tar extractor.	(ii) Extraction of the last traces of tar by some form of tar extractor.
	(iii) Gas reheating.
(iii) Water washing to extract the remainder of the ammonia from the gas.	(iv) Acid washing to extract the ammonia from the gas.
	(v) Secondary cooling of the gas.
(iv) Oil washing to extract the benzole from the gas.	(vi) Oil washing to extract the benzole from the gas.
Note. Secondary cooling of the gas generally takes place before stages (iii) and (iv).	*Note.* The ammonia liquor produced in stage (i) is distilled, the steam and ammonia gases being passed back into the gas stream just before stage (iv).

If the debenzolized gas is to be sold to the gas industry, the oil-washing stages may be followed by oxide purifiers to remove H_2S, oil-washing to remove naphthalene, and washing with $CaCl_2$ solution to lower the dewpoint of the gas.

The adoption of the semi-direct system restricts the plant to the production of sulphate of ammonia. On the other hand, the indirect system can be arranged so that the ammoniacal liquor can be used to produce sulphate of ammonia or distilled to concentrated ammoniacal liquor. The overall steam consumption of the two systems need not be essentially different by proper arrangement of the plant. In both systems there is a considerable volume of spent liquor (somewhat more in the case of the indirect system than in the semi-direct system), the disposal of which presents a problem which has not yet been satisfactorily solved. Many specialized systems of gas treatment exist for the recovery of ammonia, sulphate, or sulphuric acid, but discussion of them is outside the scope of this book.

Economic Aspects of By-product Recovery. The recovery of by-products in coke manufacture is of the greatest importance since without the credits available from the sale of tar, benzole and gas, the process would be uneconomic. The recovery and sale of ammonia either in the form of sulphate or concentrated liquor is invariably practised since the subsequent recovery of benzole and the sale of gas depend on the removal of ammonia from the gas. In itself, the recovery of ammonia does not offer any net financial return and may constitute a debit on the coking process.

Practically all the coke-oven gas available after heating the ovens is utilized either by the gas or steel industries. Further quantities could be released by heating the ovens with producer gas either from coal or coke. At the present market values of coke and coal the monetary return from the released coke-oven gas would not repay the extra costs involved in making the producer gas.

The following gas grids are now in operation—Sheffield (crude gas), West Yorkshire (purified gas), South Wales (purified gas). These provide town gas through the gas industry. The total gas purchased in 1951 was 66×10^9 cu. ft., but represented only 26 per cent. of the gas made ; there is therefore considerable room for expansion.

Manufacture of Coke in the Gas Industry

The primary objective of the gas industry is to manufacture town gas for distribution but, since the early forms of gas-making plant produced this gas by carbonizing coal, the industry has grown up as a two-fuel industry making both gas and coke. With the introduction of carburetted water gas, which consumes coke in its manufacture (Chapter XVII), the amount of coke sold is becoming less and, if other oil gasification processes are introduced, and perhaps complete gasification, the industry may well revert to its original purpose of gas manufacture only. Whether it does so will probably be decided by economics.

William Murdoch was the first to distil coal for the production of gas (1754–1839) and the first steps in distribution were made in London in the early part of the nineteenth century ; by 1819 there were some 288 miles of gas mains in London and some 51,000 gas lights. The first retorts were of cast iron 6–7 ft. long and 20×15 in. in cross-section and the temperature of carbonization was about 800° C.

From then until 1890 efforts were made to produce gas of high luminosity, but with the advent of the Welsbach incandescent mantle (1885) luminosity became of no importance and the use of higher temperatures to obtain more gas led to the introduction of fireclay retorts. Eventually the carbonizing temperature was raised to the modern level of 1350° C., beyond which there would be little advantage to go and which is at present the ceiling temperature of modern refractory materials used in construction of retorts.

To-day in Great Britain the gas industry is nationalized and administered through twelve area boards. These work to declared calorific values varying from 350 to 560 B.Th.U. per cu. ft. This permits of the sale of the gas on a thermal basis, one therm being 100,000 B.Th.U.

Modern plants for the manufacture of coal gas belong to two types, static and continuous ; in the former the retorts may be horizontal or may take the form of rectangular chambers or ovens. The coke oven is also in use for gas manufacture since for large installations it can be operated at lower cost.

Figure 42 shows a modern battery of horizontal retorts in five tiers and Figure 43 an isometric drawing of a setting showing the heating flues.

FIG. 42.—Battery of 120 Horizontal Gas Retorts.

Each retort, of moulded fireclay or silica, is 20 ft. long and 23 in. in cross-section, the shape of the latter being oval ◯ or elliptical. The ends have metal mouthpieces and carry heavy cast-iron doors. From the mouthpieces ascension pipes carry the distillation products to the hydraulic main and thence to the condensing and gas-washing system. The description of this system is outside the scope of this book.

The method of heating is shown in Figure 43, using a built-in coke producer, the secondary air being preheated by the waste gas. The latter enters the recuperator at 1000° C. and leaves at 600° C., while the air is preheated to 800° C. With a waste gas/air ratio of 2·05 the recovery of heat is about 37 per cent. Total fuel consumption using hot coke as the fuel is about 42 therms per ton of coal. The residual heat in the waste gas can be partly recovered by a waste-heat boiler down to a final temperature

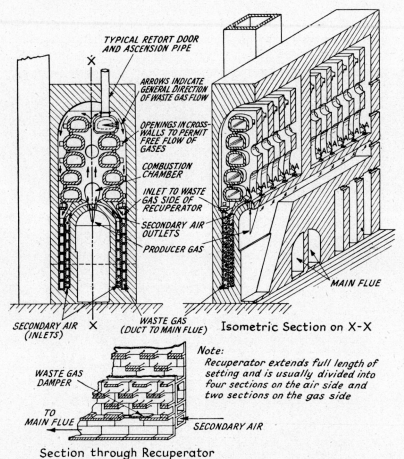

TYPICAL RETORT DOOR
AND ASCENSION PIPE

ARROWS INDICATE
GENERAL DIRECTION
OF WASTE GAS FLOW

OPENINGS IN CROSS-
WALLS TO PERMIT
FREE FLOW OF
GASES

COMBUSTION
CHAMBER

INLET TO WASTE
GAS SIDE OF
RECUPERATOR

SECONDARY AIR
OUTLETS

PRODUCER GAS

MAIN FLUE

SECONDARY AIR   X   WASTE GAS   Isometric Section on X-X
(INLETS)   (DUCT TO MAIN FLUE)

WASTE GAS
DAMPER

TO
MAIN FLUE   SECONDARY AIR

Note:
Recuperator extends full length of
setting and is usually divided into
four sections on the air side and
two sections on the gas side

Section through Recuperator

FIG. 43.—Isometric Drawing of Horizontal Retort Battery.

of 240° C., raising 850 lb. of steam per ton of coal or 2·8 lb. per lb. of coke to the producer.

The process is intermittent ; 12–13 cwt. of coal are carbonized in each retort every 12 hours. The hot coke is pushed out by a ram and quenched by water.

Intermittent Vertical Chambers. The intermittent vertical chamber may be a vertical oven 21 ft. high, 10 ft. across and tapering from 8 in. at the top to 12½ in. at the bottom, heated by gas from a built-in producer. The process is intermittent, a static charge of coal being carbonized in about

12 hours.   Steam is passed upwards through the charge during the last two hours to complete the carbonization of the charge and reduce the calorific value of the average gas.   The coke is dropped into a car and quenched by water under a tower to disperse the steam.   A bench consists of a number of settings of six chambers ; each setting is fired by a gas producer of the same height and placed centrally to provide gas to heating walls on both sides of each chamber.   The waste gases return through two recuperators, one on each side of the producer, which preheat the secondary air for combustion of the producer gas.   The temperature of carbonization can be modified to suit the coal, but a usual distribution is 1330° C. at the bottom and 1050° C. at the top and the normal fuel consumption is about 38 therms per ton of coal.   This could be improved by a more efficient form of recuperator, but this form does return about 6 therms per ton of coal or 15 per cent. of the thermal value of the coke fired.   A waste-heat boiler recovers 550 lb. of steam from the waste gas or 1·9 lb. per lb. of coke fired.

Continuous Vertical Retorts.   The principle of the continuous vertical retort is the regulated continuous descent of coal through a narrow vertical oven heated from both sides.   The speed of descent is regulated so that the coal is fully carbonized as it leaves the heated zone and enters the sealed coke chamber at the bottom.   Figure 44 shows a section of a retort with its heating flues.   The rate of movement of the coal is regulated by the speed of the coke extractor.   Steam is introduced into the coke below the extractor and serves the double purpose of cooling the coke and forming water gas which passes up the retort and dilutes the coal gas.   The final calorific value of the mixed gas depends upon the amount of steam added and the reactivity of the coke, but for Yorkshire coal the range is from 520 B.Th.U. at 5 per cent. steam to 460 B.Th.U. at 20 per cent. steam, and at the latter level 65 per cent. of the steam would be decomposed.   The coke cools further in the bottom coke chamber and can be discharged at intervals in the dry state and does not have to be quenched.

Figure 45 illustrates a setting of retorts in section through the major axis.   The latter may vary from 44 to 103 in., but the minor axis is constant at 10 in. at the top tapering to 18 in. at the bottom.   Heating is by producer gas from horizontal flues in the side walls and heat is recovered by means of a waste-heat boiler.   In the Glover-West system the secondary air is preheated in horizontal flues at the bottom and in the Woodall-Duckham system by arranging a special duct to cool the floor joists and one chamber.   This lower standard of recuperation is deliberate in order to simplify the settings and to raise works steam.

Fuel consumption at 10 per cent. steam is about 36 therms per ton of coal, which would be 15 per cent. higher without the return of about 7 per cent. of sensible heat in the secondary air.   The amount of steam raised is about 1600 lb. per ton of coal or 6·3 lb. per lb. of coke fired.   The continuous vertical retort is therefore a flexible instrument so far as throughput of coal, output of gas and gas calorific value are concerned. It is also capable of carbonizing a wide variety of coals from highly-caking Durham gas coal to sized weakly-caking coals.

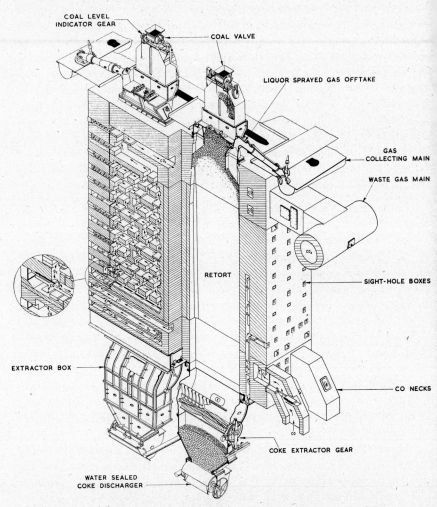

Fig. 44.—Cut-away Diagram of Woodall-Duckham Continuous Vertical Retort.
(*By courtesy of the Woodall-Duckham Construction Co., Ltd.*)

Variation in Gas-retort Cokes. The properties of cokes are dealt with in detail below but it is desirable at this stage to draw attention to certain general differences between gas-retort cokes. There are two major factors to consider, first the nature of the coal, and secondly the process. The reactivity of coke or its combustibility tends to increase with reduction of caking power. Highly-caking coal such as that of Durham gives the least reactive coke and the weakly-caking coals of the Midlands and Scotland,

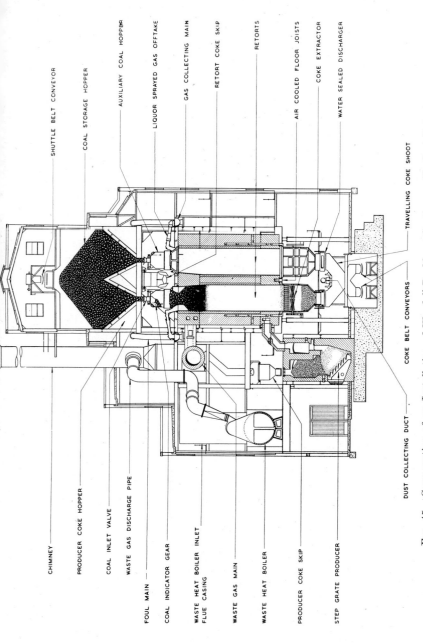

CHIMNEY

PRODUCER COKE HOPPER

COAL INLET VALVE

WASTE GAS DISCHARGE PIPE

FOUL MAIN

COAL INDICATOR GEAR

WASTE HEAT BOILER INLET
FLUE CASING

WASTE GAS MAIN

WASTE HEAT BOILER

PRODUCER COKE SKIP

STEP GRATE PRODUCER

SHUTTLE BELT CONVEYOR

COAL STORAGE HOPPER

AUXILIARY COAL HOPPER

LIQUOR SPRAYED GAS OFFTAKE

GAS COLLECTING MAIN

RETORT COKE SKIP

RETORTS

AIR COOLED FLOOR JOISTS

COKE EXTRACTOR

WATER SEALED DISCHARGER

DUST COLLECTING DUCT

COKE BELT CONVEYORS

TRAVELLING COKE SHOOT

Fig. 45.—Cross-section of an Installation of Woodall-Duckham Continuous Vertical Retorts.

(*By courtesy of the Woodall-Duckham Construction Co., Ltd.*)

which have to be carbonized in graded sizes to give a sized coke, the most reactive. The horizontal retort and the coke oven, in which a relatively thick layer of coal has to be carbonized by conduction, reduces the reactivity to the greatest extent, and the continuous vertical retort with partial internal heating and a thinner layer, the least. The intermittent vertical retort with a less thickness of charge than the other static retorts is intermediate in its effect. Both factors therefore contribute to this property of the coke and can be additive.

LOW-TEMPERATURE CARBONIZATION

In the early days of gas manufacture coal was carbonized in metal retorts at temperatures in the neighbourhood of 800° C. The gas yield was low and the coke was more combustible than modern coke. In modern processes of gas manufacture, the high temperature used in order to obtain a high yield of gas produces unavoidably a coke which is much less reactive and is unsuitable for combustion in domestic appliances in which a strong draught is not available, or in which the heat losses are not reduced to a minimum by insulation with brickwork.

The damage caused by smoke from domestic and factory chimneys created early in the twentieth century aroused interest in the manufacture of smokeless fuels which would mitigate the nuisance. Attention was naturally directed towards the manufacture of the more combustible cokes produced in the early days of gas manufacture, and T. Parker appears to have been the first to demonstrate the practicability of this by carbonizing coals between 500° and 600° C. in iron retorts.

Since then many processes have been tried with varying degrees of success and considerable sums of money have been spent in endeavouring to carry to a successful issue the commercial carbonization of coal on these lines. The advantages of low-temperature carbonization were, at that time, considered to be :

1. The production of a smokeless fuel suitable for burning in an open grate of the type normally used for coal, and without modification thereof.

2. The production of a high yield of tar of low viscosity, differing from ordinary coal tar and more suited for conversion into liquid fuels, thereby providing a home source of fuel oil.

3. The abatement of the smoke nuisance in cities.

The advantage of replacing by a smokeless fuel the raw coal burned in open fires is still real, but the production of a liquid fuel in this way is no longer of interest since the amount could never be significant. Despite this fact, only two processes have survived the test of commercial success in Britain, namely, the Coalite Process of Low Temperature Carbonization Ltd., and the Rexco Process of the National Carbonizing Co.

An important practical difficulty in carrying out low-temperature carbonization has been the transmission of heat through the coal. With externally-heated retorts too high a retort-wall temperature has meant excessive carbonization of the outer portions of the charge by the time the interior has been satisfactorily carbonized. This has enforced low flue temperatures, and consequently a low rate of thermal transmission. To counter this and obtain a reasonable time of carbonization it has been assumed that the coal must be treated in thin layers, or kept in motion in a stream of hot gas, and that the retort material must be a good thermal conductor, i.e. metal. Experience with metal retorts, chiefly cast iron, has not been happy, castings having a very short life if the temperature exceeded 600° C. New cast irons have become available since and the Coalite Co. are using retorts of this material successfully to-day. The Fuel Research Station, after experimenting for many years with metal retorts, changed over to brick retorts, making these of narrow section to avoid overheating of the surface layers. This process showed great promise but has not been tried commercially.

The various processes which have been put forward can be classified in terms of the method of heating the coal, as follows : The names of the best-known processes only of each type are quoted :—

1. External heating of static charges in thin layers : Parker (Coalite), Beilby, Tozer, Hird, Illingworth.

2. External heating of moving thin layers in metal or brick retorts : Beilby, Fuel Research, Crozier.

3. External heating in retorts with mechanical devices for moving or stirring the coal : Fusion, Freeman, Salermo.

4. Internal heating by combustion of part of the coke, i.e. semi-producers giving low-grade gas : Midland Coal Products, MacLaurin, Bussy.

5. Internal heating with superheated steam : Turner.

6. Internal heating with sensible heat of hot gases in rotating cylinders : L. & N., K.S.G., Thyssen.

7. Internal heating with sensible heat of hot gases of large static charges of weakly-caking coal : National Carbonizing Co. (Rexco).

To these should also be added, although the process is strictly high-temperature carbonization, the gasification of weakly-caking sized coal in continuous-vertical retorts at a temperature of 1050 − 850° C. or 250° C. below that normal to gas manufacture.

As is to be expected, the products from such diverse methods of treatment must vary very widely. It would be impossible to discuss the variations here and the reader is directed to a review of the situation in 1928 by Sinnatt (*Fuel*, 1928, **7**, 305). One important difference is in the type of solid fuel produced : in certain processes, where the solid product from the retort is necessarily of small size briquetting has to be resorted to, to produce a lump fuel. Where the briquettes are made with pitch subsequent stoving is necessary if the fuel is to be smokeless.

A considerable number of the processes have been the subject of test by the staff of the Fuel Research Station and detailed reports are available. From these tests it is possible to indicate a range of yields of products which would include all the processes indicated above, which produce a gas of high calorific value.

Coke	14–15 cwt.	
Tar	18–22 gal.	
Motor spirit from gas . . .	1–2 ,,	
Liquor	10–30 ,,	(incl. cond. steam)
Gas	2000–7000 cu. ft.	
,, ...	30–50 therms	

Table XXXIX shows the separate yields from certain of these tests.

Of the processes examined only those of Parker (Coalite) and National Carbonizing Co. (Rexco) have reached the stage of commercial success.[1] The Fuel Research process is the result of a long period of research under the D.S.I.R. ; it is technically sound but has not been taken up for commercial production. The production of Coalite smokeless fuel at one time reached 450,000 tons per annum and is now about 330,000 tons. Rexco has reached 30,000 tons and Phurnacite 216,000 tons.

Tar.—Low-temperature tar is a somewhat variable product owing to the many processes involved, but in general its characteristic properties are rather a function of the temperature than of the type of process. The maximum yield of tar is obtained with a carbonizing temperature of 550–600° C. Generally low-temperature tars have a lower specific gravity than gas tars (1·02–1·06 against 1·10) and are of lower viscosity. They contain little free carbon, 0·2 per cent., and little naphthalene and anthracene (< 1 per cent.) although substitution products of these are present in fair quantity. Their most striking feature is their high content of tar acids (up to 35%). These are normally of higher molecular weight than the tar acids of gas-retort or coke-oven tar, the lowest member, phenol, being present to the extent of only 1%. The greatest production of tar acids corresponds approximately to a carbonizing temperature of 550° C.

Low-temperature tar contains aromatic hydrocarbons, but the proportion is definitely less than in high-temperature carbons. The same hydrocarbons are present, even including benzene (about 0·5% of the tar), but generally those of low-temperature tar are of higher molecular weight. In addition the tar contains saturated, unsaturated and polymethylene (naphthenic) hydrocarbons. The saturated hydrocarbons amount to less than 6% and consist to a fair extent of solid paraffins, as much as 2% being found in one tar.

Morgan has described the properties of the " resinoids " of tar, i.e.

---

[1] To these may be added the carbonization of pitch-bound briquettes of carbonaceous coal at 900° C. to give a smokeless fuel, Phurnacite.

those amorphous or resinous constituents of high molecular weight which are insoluble in light petroleum but soluble in many organic solvents. On evaporation from solution they yield the resins as hard transparent films. The resinoids constitute as much as 15 per cent. of the tar and contain mainly neutral (resinene) and phenolic (resinoid) bodies with small quantities of resinamines and resinoic acids.

The utilization of low-temperature tars was at first delayed because the quantity produced did not justify separate treatment. This was overcome when the Coalite Co. set up their own refinery and were able to separate a number of valuable chemicals, particularly the higher phenols. The tar is also a suitable raw material for catalytic hydrogenation to motor spirit and diesel oil (p. 277).

Gas.—The gas produced by external heating at about 600° C. differs widely from town gas in that it contains a much higher proportion of hydrocarbons and less hydrogen. It has a higher calorific value and a high density. It can be used for heating the retorts, but its most obvious outlet would be for enriching coal gas for town purposes. The gas from certain processes such as the MacLaurin, where internal heating is used, is of low calorific value owing to dilution of the rich gas with producer gas.

The compositions of three gases are shown below in comparison with a town gas.

	Fuel Research.	Parker (Coalite).	MacLaurin.	Town gas.
CO_2	4·0	4·0	9·5	3·0
C_nH_m	3·4	4·3	0·9	3·0
CO	6·7	6·2	14·0	13·0
H_2	31·8	37·6	26·2	50·8
C_nH_{2n+2}	43·5	40·0	8·1	25·0
N_2	10·6	7·9	41·3	5·2
" n " (in C_nH_{2n+2}) . .	1·27	1·25	1·27	1·08
B.Th.U. per cu. ft. . .	725	710	233	540
Sp. gr. (air = 1) . . .	0·65	0·56	0·74	0·44

When stripped, low-temperature gas yields about 1·5 gallons of motor spirit per ton of coal. Although this type of spirit is high in unsaturated hydrocarbons (up to 35 per cent.) it is easily refined by washing with sulphuric acid and caustic soda, and forms, after mixing with the spirit obtained by distilling the tar, a motor spirit with the reasonably higher octane number of 70.

The Coalite Process. The process is based on the original Parker process and consists in the carbonization of selected coals in cast-iron retorts of small cross-section, externally heated by gas to give a carbonization temperature of about 600° C. The first plant was completed in 1927 to carbonize 100,000 tons of coal per annum. In 1929 and 1936 two other plants of double and treble this capacity were completed.

TABLE XXXIX
YIELDS OF PRODUCTS FROM CERTAIN LOW-TEMPERATURE CARBONIZATION PROCESSES
From the results of Tests by the Director of Fuel Research

Name of retort.	Fuel Re-search.*	Parker (Coal-ite).	Free-man.	Crozier.	Mac-Laurin.	Bussy.	L. & N.
Coal	Dalton Main.	Dalton Main.	Kirkby Top Hard.	Tully-garth Hawk-hill Seam.	Virgin.	Both-well.	New Lount.
Yields per ton of dry, ash-free coal :							
Coke, cwt. . . .	13·93	14·70	} 16·75	14·46	11·27	9·96	3·35
Breeze, cwt. . . .	1·87	0·72		3·04	1·20	2·04	10·70
Gas, cu. ft. . . .	7,050	6,220	2,150	8,390	34,150	47,890	102,200
Gas, therms . . .	49·4	43·9	19·3	27·1	79·6	90·3	37·8
Tar, gals.	20·1	20·1	22·3	18·6	18·3	20·9	15·7
Spirit, gals. . . .	—	1·2	—	0·9	0·3	0·1	Nil
Liquor, gals. . . .	27·6	11·0	11·8	—	49·5	29·1	—
S./ammonia, lb. . . .	10·5	15·0	3·9	10·3	43·1	22·7	—

* Fuel Research Tech. Pap. 35, 1933.

The carbonizing plant is built in batteries of 40 retorts, each of which is a " monobloc " casting, 9 ft. high, containing 12 tubes which taper from $4\frac{1}{2}$ in. at the top to $5\frac{3}{4}$ in. at the bottom. A horizontal section of the retort casting is shown in Figure 46, which is a diagram showing the arrangement of the retorts and heating system, captioned to be self-explanatory. The heating flues are arranged between the retorts as shown so that there is no flame contact and any overheating which might lead to distortion is avoided. The plant was designed in this form on the assumption that a metal retort and a narrow cross-section were essential to the transfer of heat into coal at the " low " temperature of 600° C. It has since been demonstrated that metal is not necessary and that adequate heat transfer can be attained in brick retorts through a coal section of 7 to 11 in. (see Fuel Research Station retort below).

With such a narrow retort there could be danger of sticking of the coke on discharge, but this is overcome by careful choice of the coal so that its caking power is in the region of F to G_1 of the Gray-King scale. From such coal the " coalite " breaks conveniently into pieces of good appearance with very little formation of breeze.

Recently quoted yields are Coalite 15 cwt., tar 16·5 gal., spirit 3·5 gal., liquor 30 gal., and gas 4000 cu. ft. or 28 therms. A feature of the process is the success that has been achieved in the production of special chemicals, particularly a wide range of phenols from the tar and liquor, in addition to the usual tar fractions.   This recovery contributes considerably to the commercial success of the process.

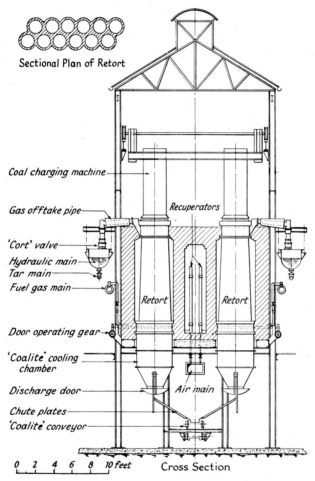

Sectional Plan of Retort

Coal charging machine

Gas offtake pipe

Recuperators

'Cort' valve
Hydraulic main
Tar main
Fuel gas main

Retort   Retort

Door operating gear

'Coalite' cooling
  chamber

Discharge door   Air main

Chute plates
'Coalite' conveyor

0 2 4 6 8 10 feet   Cross Section

FIG. 46.—" Coalite " Carbonization Process.
(By courtesy of Low-Temperature Carbonization.)

The Rexco Process.   As an example of the type of low-temperature process which achieves carbonization of coal at a " low " temperature by internal heating with a stream of hot gas the best is the Rexco process. The National Carbonizing Co. have brought this process to the commercial stage of 30,000 tons of smokeless fuel per annum and are proposing expansion to 150,000 tons.

The retort is a brick-lined cylinder of 10 ft. dia. × 25 ft. high with a

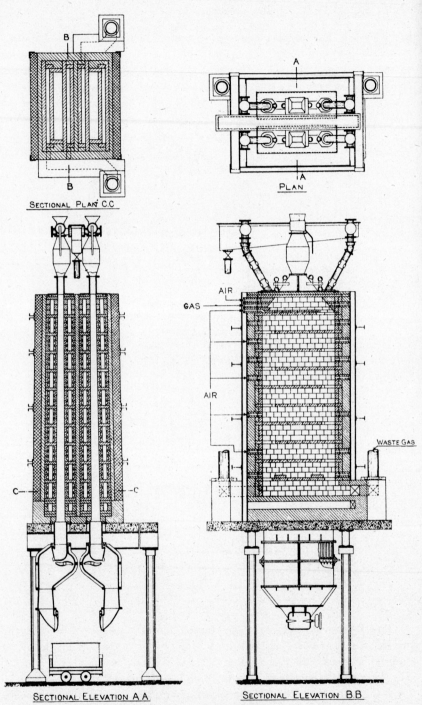

B

SECTIONAL PLAN C.C

A

A

PLAN

GAS

AIR

AIR

WASTE GAS

C — C

SECTIONAL ELEVATION A.A.

SECTIONAL ELEVATION B.B.

Fig. 47.—Fuel Research Process of Low-temperature Carbonization.
(Fuel Research Tech. Paper 50, 1939.)

232

hemispherical dome carrying a telescopic coal-charging chute. In this retort a charge of 34 tons of coal is carbonized by burning gas in the top and passing the products downwards through the charge. Carbonization is achieved in about 6 hours, when the air supply is shut off and the coked residue cooled by the continued recirculation of gas for about 7 hours. The process is simple and capital cost low in comparison with other low-temperature processes, but it has one important limitation, namely, that it can operate only on sized coal of low caking power. The size should be 33 per cent. of 2 × 1 in. with 67 per cent. of 4 × 2 in. material, and the caking power should be in the range B/C to E of the Gray-King assay. The

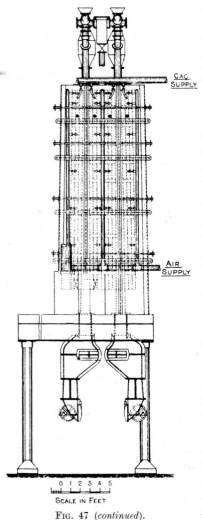

reason is that the charge must remain open to the passage of the gas without throwing an undue back pressure (not more than 6 in. water). Non-caking coal will operate satisfactorily, but the proportion of breeze tends to be too high, say 20 per cent.

The yields of products are coke (dry) 12·1 cwt., tar 14·8 gal., spirit 1·0 gal., surplus gas 24,500 cu. ft. at 140 B.Th.U. or 35 therms. The large coke is very suitable for the open domestic grate but the smaller sizes are particularly suitable for the stoves and heat-storage cookers.

The process is therefore suitable for localities in which sized weakly-caking coals are available, i.e. Notts and Derby, Northumberland and Scotland. The tar would no doubt sell to the coal tar market but the surplus gas would require a market for furnace heating or, via the gas turbine, for the production of electric power.

The Fuel Research Process. The Fuel Research process is, strictly speaking, a narrow, continuous vertical retort in which heating is by conduction through the side walls. Originally the retorts were made of cast iron, but these gave trouble by growth and distortion and were eventually replaced successfully by firebrick retorts of similar design. A section of a retort is shown in Figure 47. The top dimensions are

0 1 2 3 4 5

SCALE IN FEET

FIG. 47 (*continued*).

7 × 78 in. and the bottom dimensions 11 × 78 in. and the height is about 21 ft. Using a temperature of 650° C. on the inner face of the brickwork, a wide variety of coals can be carbonized successfully at the rate of about 6 tons per day. To achieve this temperature the combustion chambers are operated at 1100° C. at the top to 900° C. at the fifth horizontal flue and 500° C. at the bottom. Fuel consumption is about 20 therms per ton or 7 per cent. of the coal carbonized.

The yields from this process are given in Table XXXIX. The sized coke is reactive and suitable for the open domestic grate, the $\frac{1}{2}$–$\frac{1}{4}$ in. material

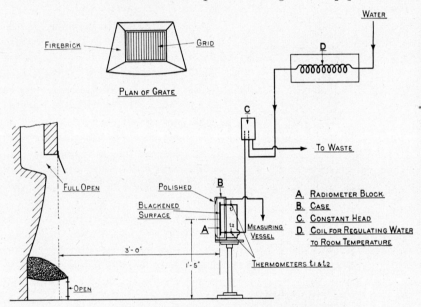

FIG. 48.—Diagram of Apparatus for Measuring Radiation.

is suitable for water-heating stoves. The proportion of smalls is very little, only about 5 per cent. from the most suitable coals. It has a low bulk-density of 18–22 lb. per cubic foot as compared with 24–28 lb. for gas-retort coke, and 50–55 lb. for domestic coal.

As a domestic fuel it is clean, easy to ignite, smokeless and free burning even with the minimum of primary air. It shows a high rate of thermal radiation in comparison with coal and, if examined by the simple radiation test shown in Figure 48, it gives an overall value of 30 per cent. of the heat of the fuel, compared with 22 per cent. for coal. In certain grates the absence of long flames is a drawback, as in the case of oven and water heating, but suitable grates can be constructed.

The Properties and Uses of Cokes

From the above processes of carbonization, and excluding the small amounts of low-temperature and special cokes made, there are two main types of coke, metallurgical coke made in ovens and retort coke made in the gas industry. The relative amounts of these made in 1951 are given above as 16·0 and 12·3 million tons per annum, but in order to understand the position regarding coke fuels it is necessary to analyse how coke is utilized. This is particularly important in metallurgical processes where the coke is a raw material in the process as well as the source of the thermal energy. The uses of coke are therefore analysed for 1951 as a pattern, and are shown in Table XL.

TABLE XL

THE PRODUCTION AND UTILIZATION OF COKE (1951)

(Quantities are given in millions of tons)

	Gas industry.	Coke industry.
Coal carbonized	27·2	23·6
Coke made	16·5	16·0
Coke breeze made	2·7	1·1
Used to heat retorts . . .	4·2	—
Used for works purposes . . .	0·5	—
Breeze for works purposes . .	1·4	—
Used to make water gas . . .	1·4	—
Available for sale :		
Coke	10·4	16·0
Breeze	1·3	1·1
Iron (blast-furnace)	—	10·54
Iron and steel	0·26	1·17
Engineering and industry . .	6·68	2·09
Railways	0·11	0·05
Domestic	2·84	1·01
Miscellaneous	0·51	1·15

Gas-retort coke is therefore sold mainly in the domestic market while oven coke is consumed mainly in the blast-furnace. A proportion of the oven coke is used for metallurgical purposes, e.g. in the foundry, and requires special properties above those of blast-furnace coke, but apart from these main uses, the remainder of both supplies are used as fuel and require to have only the general properties of solid fuel.

In general, it can be said that a desideratum in coke is a low ash content, but this is dependent upon the coal available and cannot be modified in lump coke after manufacture. A low moisture content is also desirable and normally this can readily be achieved by suitable control of the water supply during quenching. Failure to achieve this has suggested dry quenching, but this has not been applied because of high capital costs and corrosion troubles in the plant : in addition, dry coke is very dusty and can create a nuisance in certain circumstances. A further important factor is that, for most of its applications, coke is most efficient if broken and sized within fairly narrow limits.

Breakage and Sizing of Coke. The breakage of coke by mechanical means and its separation into size grades necessarily involves the production of fine material of lower commercial value, and it is important to carry out these operations under the conditions which produce the minimum of undersize material. The problem is more pressing in the gas industry where a higher proportion of the coke is sold in the domestic market and for water heating where sized material is more efficient than " large " coke. The effect of different forms of mechanical screening on breakdown has not been critically examined, but it is clear that the inclined shaker screen is the most suitable in that the coke is subjected to the least amount of shock in the process. It is important that the sized material should not be allowed to drop a long distance into a bunker but should slide down spiral or other suitable chutes ; this is unfortunately not always the practice.

The gas industry coke committee has examined the question of breakage and the Gas Research Board has carried out experiments which have given a lead to the main factors which can lead to better efficiency of breakage and minimum formation of fines. Coke breakers normally contain two parallel steel rollers of 8–10 in. diameter which are armed with conical teeth about 2 in. in height, and spaced 2–5 in. apart at the centre ; as these rotate inwards the larger pieces of coke are broken and the pieces fall through after theoretically one impact. Some breakers have only one roller operating against a steel plate, but the principle is the same. The rolls rotate at about 120 r.p.m. and their distance apart is adjustable from 2 to 5 in. Their teeth mesh together at closer settings and the points are just in line at a setting of twice the tooth depth or $3\frac{1}{2}$ to 4 in. A breaker with rolls about 22 in. long will deal with about 15 tons of normal coke per hour.

The results of the experiments of the Gas Research Board can be summed up as follows :

(1) The extent of formation of fines (breeze) increases with the degree of breakage as determined by the setting, or distance apart, D, of the rolls. At 6 in., for example, the proportion of breeze ($< \frac{3}{4}$ in.) may be 6 per cent., at 3 in. it will be about 12 per cent. and at 2·5 in. it will be about 20 per cent. The differences between types of coke are not large as shown by the curves of Figure 49. The mean size of the broken material varies with breeze as follows :

Mean size, in.	Breeze, $\frac{3}{4}$ in., per cent.
1·4	9
1·2	11
1·0	17
0·8	27

(2) The yield of any grade varies with D and within a small range the breaker can be set to give the optimum yield of any grade.

(3) The optimum yield in (2) is not achieved at minimum breeze formation and it is more economical to break a larger amount of coke at a wider

setting provided the demand for large coke allows of this. The saving in breeze formation may be as great as 6 tons per 100 tons of the grade.

(4) Variation of roll speed by ± 20 per cent. has little effect.

(5) Increase of rate of feed increases the formation of breeze and reduces the mean size of the product. The probable reason for this is that the choking of the feed on the rolls causes the large pieces to be " nipped " several times before the product can escape. The effect can be corrected by the use of a wider setting.

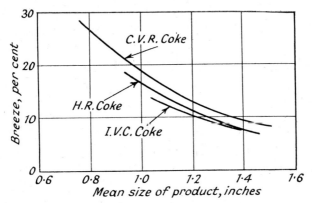

FIG. 49.—Relation between Mean Size of Breaker Product
and Breeze Container.

(6) The larger the size of the coke fed the smaller is the mean size of the product and the larger is the proportion of breeze. This is no doubt for the same reason as that given in (5) above, namely, more severe crushing.

(7) Breakage in two stages does avoid some breeze formation, as shown in the following example of the treatment of 100 tons of original coke.

(a) Scalp at 2 in., break at $2\frac{5}{8}$ in., screen scalpings and broken coke.
(b) Scalp at 2 in., break at $3\frac{7}{8}$ in., scalp at $1\frac{1}{4}$ in., break at $3\frac{5}{16}$ in. and screen all products.
(c) Repeat (b) with second breaker at $3\frac{3}{8}$ and $3\frac{7}{16}$ in.

Total breeze.	Breeze from breaker.	Over 2 in.	2–1¼ in.	1¼–½ in.
(a) 21·2	9·2	—	39·4	39·4
(b) 19·0	7·0	—	40·5	40·5
(c) 16·4	4·4	20	31·8	31·8
14·0	2·0	40	23·0	23·0

In (b), breaker breeze is reduced by 2·2 per cent. In (c), where the oversize left is 20 per cent., the formation of breeze is 4·4 for the production of 63·6 of graded material, which is a considerable improvement on 7·0 breeze on 80 of graded material. At 40 per cent. oversize a further improvement to 2 of breeze on 46 graded is seen.

These are general rules for the management of breaking and grading of coke ; the figures quoted may not be representative of all cokes but the principle remains. In practice it must always happen that the extent to which breakage is done will depend upon the market and no more breakage will be done than is essential. The above data, however, show that the overall result of two-stage breaking of a larger quantity may be beneficial in reducing losses of revenue by undue breeze formation.

The grades of coke recommended by the gas industry are shown below in comparison with those made in the coke-oven industry.

Coke-oven Coke. The position regarding the utilization of oven coke is different in that so high a proportion is used for the blast-furnace ; practically all the large coke over 3 in. in size is used and amounts to about 60 per cent. of production. This may contain pieces up to 5 in. in size, but breakage on the way to the furnace generally means that when charged there is very little material larger than 3 in., and some material below $\frac{3}{4}$ in. At some blast-furnaces a debreezing screen is operated at the furnace.

The material below 3 in. is screened into five standard grades :

No.	Mean size, in.	Sieve limits, in.	Gas industry, in.
1	$2\frac{1}{4}$	$3\frac{1}{8}$–$1\frac{3}{8}$	$3\frac{1}{2}$–$1\frac{3}{4}$
2	$1\frac{3}{8}$	2–$\frac{7}{8}$	2–1
3	$\frac{7}{8}$	$1\frac{1}{4}$–$\frac{1}{2}$	$1\frac{1}{4}$–$\frac{1}{2}$
4	$\frac{5}{8}$	$\frac{13}{16}$–$\frac{3}{8}$	$\frac{3}{4}$–$\frac{3}{8}$
5	$\frac{3}{8}$	$\frac{1}{2}$–$\frac{3}{16}$	$\frac{3}{4}$–$\frac{1}{8}$

These are considered to be the best series of grades from the points of view of the duties of the grades, the limitation of size range (ratio of upper to lower size) and existing plant ; they have been suggested as a result of the theoretical examination of screen sizes. In the operation of any screening plant it is necessary to make a careful check of the size range of material produced in order to adjust conditions so that only standard grades are made.

At some plants all the output is graded for furnace work in industry while at others harder coke is made for foundry purposes by the selection of coal and the use of a higher temperature of carbonization.

The larger sizes of oven coke are used for steam raising, for central-heating boilers and water heaters. Grade 3 is suitable for the smaller sizes of domestic boiler, while grades 4 and 5 are best suited for small water heaters and storage cookers.

Physical Properties of Cokes

The physical properties which are desirable in cokes vary with the purpose for which they are utilized, from the extreme hardness of blast-furnace coke to the high reactivity of the smokeless fuel used in the open domestic fire. In general, low moisture and ash contents are desirable, but for special purposes certain other components must not be present in more than a small proportion ; for example, the proportion of phosphorus in coke used in steel works must not exceed 0·03 per cent.

Gas-retort cokes are variable in water content, but metallurgical coke should not contain more than 1·5 to 2 per cent. It is estimated that each additional 1 per cent. of moisture in blast-furnace coke increases the consumption of fuel by 1·2 per cent. Similarly it is held that an increase of 1 per cent. of ash will increase the fuel consumption by 2 per cent. but, in addition, high-ash content can be a very undesirable factor if the ash is of the type which causes trouble in fusion.

Density and Porosity. In the carbonization of a caking coal, coke formation is the result of intumescence followed by devolatilization and the formation of a porous structure which increases in density by shrinkage during further heating at a high temperature. It is apparent that the more completely the coal is devolatilized the more closely will the density of the coke approach that of graphite at 2·3. This value is never quite reached since all cokes retain traces of hydrogen and also contain the mineral matter of the coal. Density is determined by grinding the coke to pass a 72 B.S. sieve to break down all the cells and dispersing it in water to displace air. An organic liquid cannot be used for this purpose because the formation of a condensed layer gives rise to a high value.

The higher the rank of coal the higher is the density of the coke made by one method.

Carbon per cent. dry, ash-free coal.	Density, g./ml. ash-free.
89	1·95
87	1·87
85	1·83
83	1·71
81	1·70

Taking the specific gravity of coke ash as 2·5, the above figures are calculated from the observed values using the formula :

$$\text{True density} = 100d - 2\text{·}5a/100 - a,$$

where d is the observed value and a is the ash percentage.

Generally speaking, density is a function of reactivity, this property increasing with decreasing density.

The *apparent density* of coke depends upon the development of its porous structure and varies from 0·95 to 0·85 for oven coke to 0·75 for low-temperature coke. It is determined by immersing entire pieces of coke in boiling water to displace the air from open pores, and allowing it to cool, and weighing the weight of water displaced per gramme. In making a determination it is necessary to take a number of large pieces or a larger weight of broken coke, the average deviation from 5 pieces may be 0·3 when the maximum deviation is 0·10.

The *porosity* of coke is calculated from the values for true and apparent density and is expressed as a percentage.

$$\text{Porosity per cent.} = 100\left(\frac{\text{Difference between density values}}{\text{True density}}\right)$$

The range of values for the porosity of high-temperature coke is small, between 50 and 55 per cent., but may increase to 60 per cent. in some low-temperature cokes. High porosity has been considered desirable in furnace cokes because of the greater accessibility of air to the surface, but this does not seem to be true except that, in the general sense, coke of low porosity does not burn satisfactorily and it is evident that a well-developed pore structure with interconnecting channels must give better access to the reacting gases. In the blast-furnace, charcoal of high porosity (70 per cent.) at one time gave very low fuel consumptions, but in the modern furnace high resistance to breakdown of size is more important than high porosity.

Bulk density is the weight of unit volume of material and depends upon several factors such as size grading, size of measuring vessel, shape of pieces and method of packing, and moisture content. It is evident that some of these can easily be standardized such as moisture content and size grading, but that a considerable personal factor may apply to the others. In the first place it is important that the container must be large in relation to the size of one piece and that the highest values will emerge from close packing. It has been established that a box of 2 cu. ft. capacity ($15\frac{1}{8}$ in. edge) will, with coke sized below 1 in., give results which show a variance up to ± 2 lb. per cu. ft. The variability of the results obtained with larger coke make the method unpractical in demanding boxes of impossibly large size to give this degree of accuracy.

Values for the bulk density of coke types cover the following ranges.

| | Lb. per cu. ft., dry. | |
Type of coke.	Unsized.	$1-\frac{1}{8}$ inch.
Coke oven	29–32	27–33
Horizontal retort	25–28	24–27
Continuous vertical retort	22–24	21–22
Low-temperature retort	19–23	18–22

Hardness and Strength of Coke. Hardness and strength are normally defined as the power of resistance of the material to breakage by impact when handled, dropped into bunkers, or submitted to heavy burden as in the blast-furnace. The " Shatter Test " has been applied for the measurement of resistance to shatter by impact and is intended for the examination of metallurgical coke, although it has been applied to others. Surface hardness, or resistance to abrasion, is measured by the Cochrane Test.

In the shatter test a representative sample of coke over 2 in. in particle size is prepared and 50 lb. of this is dropped from a box 28 in. long, 18 in. wide and 15 in. deep on to a steel plate and the amount of breakage measured by screening the product. The bottom of the box consists of hinged doors to allow of a sudden drop and is arranged at exactly 6 ft. from the base-plate, which is not less than $\frac{1}{2}$ in. thick. The sieves are of square stamped sheet with standard openings and sieving is done first by shaking and then by hand-placing.

The percentages of material remaining on the 2, $1\frac{1}{2}$, 1 and $\frac{1}{2}$-in. sieves are recorded. Typical figures for the shatter indices of coke types are given in Table XLI.

TABLE XLI

SHATTER INDICES OF INDUSTRIAL COKES

| | Metallurgical coke. | | | Gas retort coke. | | Low-temperature coke. |
	South Wales.	Durham.	York-shire.	Yorkshire coal. Horizontal.	Vertical.	F.R.S.
Over 2 in. . . .	83	75	66	60	55	65
„ $1\frac{1}{2}$ in. . . .	92	88	80	74	76	80
„ 1 in.⎱ . . .	98	98	96	88	85	88
„ $\frac{1}{2}$ in.⎰						
Through $\frac{1}{2}$ in. . .	2	2	4	5	8	7

A good blast-furnace coke should show 75 per cent. over 2 in., 85 per cent. over $1\frac{1}{2}$ in., and 97 per cent. over $\frac{1}{2}$ in. A foundry coke, where higher resistance to shatter is required, should show not less than 85 per cent. on 2 in. and may reach 96. The shatter index of gas cokes is not specified and is included only for comparison. Low-temperature coke shows a surprisingly high resistance despite its higher porosity and abradability, apparently due to a quality of toughness which softens shock.

The *abradability* of oven coke was one of the earliest properties to be measured (Lowthian Bell, 1904). As modified by Cochrane in 1919 and since modernized, the method consists in the rotation of a 28-lb. sample of $+3$-in. coke in a welded steel drum of 18 in. internal diameter fitted with $2\frac{1}{2}$-in. angle-iron lifting plates welded inside at an angle of 17° to the axis. The drum is rotated at 18 r.p.m. for 1000 revolutions and the abraded sample withdrawn and screened on a $\frac{1}{8}$-in. sieve. The *abrasion index* is the amount of material remaining on this sieve so that a high index means a high resistance to abrasion.

It was originally observed that the driving of a blast-furnace deteriorated if the abrasion index fell below 74 and was only 80 per cent. if the index fell to 70. Modern cokes have values of the order of 77 to 82. Abradability is increased by increase of ash content or the use of coal of low swelling power. In two examples, reduction of ash content from 15 to 9 and 15 to 7·5 per cent. respectively (in the coke) increased the index from (*a*) 69 to 74 and (*b*) 69 to 78. Values for gas-retort coke are from 60 to 65 and of low-temperature coke 50 per cent.

There is a rough correlation between the results of shatter and abrasion tests in the case of oven coke which may be taken as an increase of 1·0 in the abrasion index for every 0·2 increase in the $\frac{1}{2}$-in. shatter index.

Reactivity of Coke. The word reactivity in relation to coke is broadly defined as its ability to react with oxygen, carbon dioxide or steam, depending upon the purpose for which it is to be used. If used as a fuel its reactivity to air or oxygen only is of importance except that in the case of domestic fuels ease of ignition becomes a second factor. Where the coke plays a part in gas/solid reactions as in the blast-furnace or the gas producer, reactivity may or may not be important, depending upon whether only one or more than one reaction is involved. In the former the formation of carbon monoxide is promoted at the hearth so that high reactivity is desirable. In the cupola the high-temperature oxidation zone is large and unreactive coke in large pieces is preferred. In the gas producer high reactivity is favoured as a means of increasing the formation of carbon monoxide in the reduction zone. In making water gas high reactivity would be desirable in the " run " but undesirable in the " blow ", and on balance an unreactive coke is preferred. For the domestic market the accent is on high reactivity, partly because of the ease of ignition which accompanies it, and partly because of the need for a rapid pick-up of fire temperature when required and after refuelling, and also to allow combustion to be maintained in a small fire.

The Fuel Research Station have devised a method of measuring reactivity in terms of the extent of completion of the reaction $CO_2 + C = 2CO$ under standardized conditions at 950° C., when the equilibrium concentration of CO is 98·7 per cent. A standard volume of graded coke (7 ml. 10–20 I.M.M.) is maintained at 950° C. and a current of pure CO_2 passed through it at the rate of 5 ml. per minute. The CO formed is then measured. Three values are recognized.

R. I is the number of millimetres of CO formed per 100 ml. of CO_2 as nearly as possible to the start of the reaction. It is therefore the initial reactivity and has a limit at the equilibrium concentration of 197·4 ml.

R. II is an apparently constant value which is reached after the expulsion of the volatile matter.

R. III is a lower constant value reached after the continued action of the CO_2 on the sample of coke.

Characteristic curves are shown in Figure 50 for certain industrial cokes, and the values taken from the curves are shown in Table XLII.

TABLE XLII

REACTIVITY VALUES OF INDUSTRIAL COKES

	Reactivity value.		
	I.	II.	III.
Maximum	197·4	—	—
1. Charcoal, beech	180	—	160
2. Gas-retort coke	120	72	59
3. By-product oven coke . . .	98	72	57
4. S. Wales metallurgical coke . .	73	67	42
5. Beehive coke	43	40	42

It has been shown that the reactivity value is greatly affected by the presence of easily-reducible iron compounds. The Reactivity I value is that at which the ash exerts its full effect, the iron being in the metallic state, while R. III represents the value when the iron is present as ferrous oxide and almost inactive, i.e. the R. III value represents a close approximation to the ash-free reactivity of the coke. Metallurgical cokes contain very little reducible iron and therefore give flat reactivity curves. In cokes containing a high amount of reducible iron, as for example the vertical retort coke giving the curve shown in Figure 50 (0·2 per cent.), an approximation to the R. III can be obtained without prolonged passage of carbon

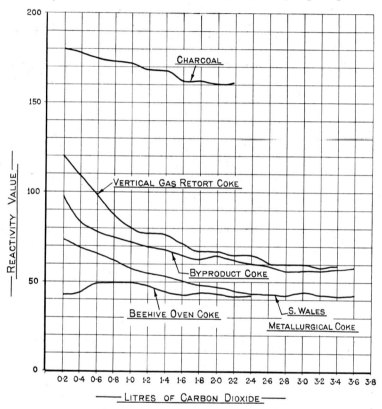

FIG. 50.—Reactivity Curves of Typical Cokes.

dioxide either by extracting the soluble iron with mineral acids or by adding to the coke the requisite amounts of hydrogen sulphide, silica, alumina or titania to combine with the iron and render it inert.

For metallurgical purposes Mott and Wheeler (*The Quality of Coke*) prefer to measure combustibility by a method based upon that of the U.S. Bureau of Mines. They use a fuel bed (1–1½ in. coke) of 14 in. depth in a laboratory furnace of 1 sq. ft. area and, under controlled conditions of air blast, determine the composition of the gases at a series of 8 points in the fuel bed at 1½-in. intervals from the grate. Temperatures are also read opposite these points by means of an optical pyrometer. The results are expressed as "reactivity with oxygen" of the coke expressed as the distance above the grate at which oxygen is no longer present in the gases ; "reactivity with carbon dioxide" as the distance at which the gases contain 20 per cent. or more carbon monoxide ; and the maximum temperature of the fuel bed. In the corresponding U.S. method reactivities are compared according to the ratios $(CO_2 + CO)/(2CO_2 + CO + O_2)$; values for bee-hive coke, oven coke and charcoal are, respectively, 72, 67 and 95.

Selected values from Mott and Wheeler's work on a $13\frac{1}{2}$-in. furnace are given in Table XLIII.

TABLE XLIII
REACTIVITIES OF METALLURGICAL COKES

Type of coke.	Oxygen disappears at, in.	20 per cent. CO at, in.	Max. temp. of fuel bed. ° C.
Charcoal	3	5	1560
Beehive	6	> 12	1800
Blend of coking and non-coking coal	4	7	1685
Yorkshire coking coal . . .	4	11	1700

The size of the furnace has since been increased to 2 ft. diameter and the bed to 24 in. depth in order to treat different grades of coke. The effect of size grading is seen in the following example. It is claimed that the values can be correlated approximately with temperature.

Size, inches	$3\frac{1}{2}$–3	$2\frac{1}{2}$–2	$1\frac{1}{2}$–1
Rate of combustion, lb./sq. ft. .	15·0	14·0	18·0
Oxygen disappears, in. above grate .	7·5	6·0	4·0
CO per cent. at 12 in. above grate .	10·5	21	30
Max. temperature, ° C. . . .	1620	1590	1610
at height above grate, in. . .	4	6	3

Cokes of high reactivity with oxygen are produced from non-caking coals or by blending coking coals with weakly-caking materials. Cokes made from strongly-caking coals alone have low values. Reactivity values with carbon dioxide generally follow the same order. The maximum tempera-tures developed follow only in a general sense since this depends also on other properties, such as porosity.

So far as blast-furnace conditions are concerned, it is concluded by Mott and Wheeler that a satisfactory hearth temperature is most economically maintained with unreactive coke containing little breeze, and that size and hardness are more important factors than high reactivity.

For the assessment of foundry cokes Sarjant interprets reactivity as the capacity of the coke to burn to CO_2 rather than CO at a high tem-perature. Preheated air is passed through a small bed of coke maintained at a constant temperature (1300° C.) and the issuing gas analysed. The reactivity is taken as the ratio of the weight of carbon in the gas $(CO_2 + CO)$ produced from unit volume of air to the weight at complete conversion to CO, i.e. $CO_2 + CO/2CO_2 + CO$. In the range 1200–1400° C. there is a correlation between reactivity and coke bed temperature (T_c) which can be expressed as $R = T_c - 719\cdot4/1000$. Values vary from 0·5 to 0·75 for cokes to 0·85 for charcoal, and can be used in the interpretation of cupola conditions and the economic attainment of the required melting temperatures.

The Critical Air Blast Method. This method of determining the reactivity of coke is of more general application and has been correlated to

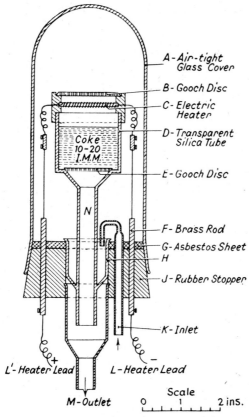

A - *Air-tight Glass Cover*

B - *Gooch Disc*

C - *Electric Heater*

D - *Transparent Silica Tube*

E - *Gooch Disc*

N

F - *Brass Rod*

G - *Asbestos Sheet*

H

J - *Rubber Stopper*

K - *Inlet*

L'- *Heater Lead*   L - *Heater Lead*

M - *Outlet*

Scale
0   1   2 ins.

FIG. 51.—Reactivity of Coke. Critical Air Blast Apparatus.

boiler firing and to domestic stoves and open fires. The C.A.B. value is measured as the minimum rate of flow of air, measured in cubic feet per minute, which will maintain combustion in a bed of closely-graded material (14–25 B.S.) which is 25 mm. deep and 40 mm. in diameter. The method is illustrated in the diagram Figure 51, and typical values are as follows :

	C.A.B. value.
Wood charcoal	0·005
Low-temperature coke	0·015
Anthracite	0·035
Gas retort coke, static	0·060
,, ,, ,, continuous vertical . .	0·050
Oven coke	0·065

Sulphur and Phosphorus

Both of these constituents are deleterious in the manufacture of steel since they find their way into the metal, with injurious result, unless precautions are taken. No satisfactory method has been found for removing, or even reducing, the sulphur in coke or during the carbonization of the coal. Good metallurgical coke should therefore contain the minimum of sulphur; British cokes range from 0·8 to 1·3 per cent.

Sulphur. The extent of removal of this element during carbonization and quenching has been referred to already. In the production of steel, a sulphur content of under 0·05 per cent. is usually desired and to ensure this it is desirable that the sulphur in the pig iron used should be of the same order. In the blast furnace (where most of the sulphur present is in the coke) the sulphur is removed in the slag as calcium sulphate and sufficient lime is required to ensure this as well as to remove silica from the burden as calcium silicate. With lean ores (or high-ash cokes) the lime requirements for silica removal give a large slag volume which is usually adequate for removal of up to say 1·5 per cent. sulphur in the coke but, with rich ores and low-ash cokes, low sulphur in coke (under 1 per cent.) is desirable. Still lower sulphur contents (under 0·8 per cent.) are desirable in foundry cokes used in an iron cupola where the slag volume is small and the blast is cold.

It is difficult to estimate the economic effect of sulphur; sometimes it is assumed that the slag cannot contain more than 1·5 per cent. sulphur and increased slag volume (and more coke to melt the slag) is required should this limit be exceeded; there is also an effect due to rate of drive, and in the basic Bessemer process faster rates of blast-furnace drive are obtained by discharging high-sulphur pig iron into a mixer where desulphurization is effected by treatment with sodium carbonate or lime.

Phosphorus. When making basic steel (i.e. in furnaces with basic brick linings) phosphorus can be removed from pig iron by the lining, the basic slag so produced being a valuable fertilizer; for such a process the phosphorus content of the coke need not be limited. When making acid steel (i.e. in furnaces with an acid (silica) lining), phosphorus cannot be removed and the coke used for making acid pig iron must not contain more than 0·012 per cent. of phosphorus; but for haematite pig iron, 0·03 per cent. phosphorus in the coke can be tolerated in South Wales.

REFERENCES

Coke for Blast Furnaces. R. A. Mott and R. V. Wheeler. Chapman and Hall.
The Quality of Coke. R. A. Mott and R. V. Wheeler. Chapman and Hall. 1939.
Analysis and Testing of Coal and Coke. British Standards Instn. B.S. 1016 (revised).
British Coke Research Association. Technical Reports. Coke Reviews, Conf. Paper.
Fuel and Metal. R. J. Sarjant. *Coke and Gas*, 1953, **15**, 89, 129.
King's Manual of Gas Manufacture. Walter King Ltd., London. 1951.

Modern Methods of Coke and Gas Manufacture. Arrow Press Ltd., Watford. 1948.
History of Coke Making. Heffer and Sons Ltd., Cambridge. 1936.
British Standards Institution. Test Codes for Carbonization Plant. Nos. 819, 899, 1034.
Tests by the Fuel Research Station of Low Carbonization Plant. H.M.S.O.
By-Product Coking Industry. Gluud. Ernest Benn. 1932.
Modern Coking Practice. Christopher and Byrom. Tech. Press, London. 1952.
Brennstoffschwelung. Thau. Halle, Knapp. Vol. I, 1950 ; Vol. 2, 1952.
Coal, Coke and Coal Chemistry. Wilson and Wells. McGraw-Hill. 1950.

CHAPTER X

PRODUCTION AND CHARACTER OF OIL FUELS

PETROLEUM

In the early days of petroleum its sole use was as a crude fuel for steam raising or furnace heating. This fuel was the residue of simple distillation to produce the naphthas and illuminating oils which were then in demand. The advent of the internal combustion engine changed this and motor gasoline became the desired product, followed later by heavier oil for the diesel engine. The residue was fuel oil, but in due time its advantages over solid fuel raised it to the status of a main product. In competition with coal, certain advantages were recognizable which caused it to displace coal for shipping and in some industries. These advantages were briefly :

(i) A higher calorific value than coal in the ratio 19,500/12,500 B.Th.U. per lb. and an absence of ash.

(ii) A higher stowage value in the ratio 38 to 43 cu. ft. per ton or 1·13/1 by volume. On a thermal basis the ratio is higher at 1·7/1.

(iii) Greater ease of control of combustion and considerable economy of staff ; high intensity of combustion.

(iv) Greater cleanliness in use and in refuelling, particularly on ships.

Later, with increasing demands for motor and aviation gasoline the emphasis in oil refining became more and more on the greater production of spirit or " gasoline " and the improvement of its quality and, after the recovery of kerosine and diesel oil, the fuel oil became in fact the heavy residue of refining rather than a prepared product.

The main source of fuel oils to-day is petroleum, of which some 620 million tons are produced annually (1952), as shown in Table III. A relatively small amount of oil shale is distilled, but the reserves of this material are large and it will become worked for oil when the reserves of petroleum begin to decrease. Still smaller amounts of liquid fuels are made from coal tars.

Of the world reserves, Table III, 50 per cent. are in the western hemisphere and 30 per cent. in the area of the Persian Gulf. To-day (1952) these represent twenty-five times the annual rate of consumption, but new reserves are still being found at a faster rate than that of consumption, and the probable date of exhaustion is quite obscure. Production is decreasing in the United States and increasing in the Middle East ; in 1952 the proportions were : U.S.A. 52, Middle East 18, South America 15, Russia 9, and others 6 per cent. Of the imports of crude oil into Great Britain 53 per cent. were from Kuwait and 22 per cent. from Iraq.

An impression of the form in which the petroleum is utilized is obtained by a study of the figures for past consumption in the United States and Great Britain and in the world as a whole. Industrial developments have changed the proportions in the past and will no doubt do so again, though not perhaps to the same extent. To-day, for example, the diesel is replacing the petrol engine and the jet-propelled aircraft is demanding a kerosine or special fraction rather than aviation spirit.

	Gasoline and spirits.	Kerosine.	Gas and diesel.	Fuel.	Lub. oil grease.	Wax.	Bitumen.	Others. Loss.
United States .	45·0	5·0	16·3	24·5	1·6	0·1	2·4	5·1
Great Britain .	31·5	7·3	15·7	20·0	4·2	0·2	3·9	9·2
World . . .	26·7	6·6	18·5	40·1	1·7	—	3·3	3·0

The relatively lower demand for fuel oil in the United States is due to the wide availability of natural gas. In Great Britain this is to some extent covered by manufactured town gas.

Crude oils are separated into fractions by methods outlined below and also provide the raw materials for a wide variety of industrial chemicals. It is estimated that in the United States already half the requirements for organic chemicals are met by petroleum products. The fuels that are produced are, in order of increasing boiling range : aviation and motor spirit, kerosine, gas and diesel oil, furnace or heavy fuel oils. The proportions in which these are produced from a given crude depend upon markets since, as explained below, the process of refining can be modified very considerably in terms of the yield and properties of the fractions made.

The origin of petroleum has been the subject of considerable controversy, but it is now accepted that it is organic in origin and that the raw material was the bodies of marine animal organisms with some water-deposited plant life. The oil may have been distilled from these by the action of heat and pressure or decomposed under anaerobic conditions by some living organism which acted as a catalyst, or the immensity of the time involved may have been an important factor. No wholly acceptable reason has, however, yet been put forward, possibly because oil is mobile and may not have been formed in the environment in which it is now found.

The rocks which form an oilfield are sedimentary, including that containing the organic material, the source rock. As the oil was formed it displaced the heavier water in the rock interstices and collected under the first impervious stratum which it reached. This is termed the reservoir or cap rock and can be some distance away if the intervening strata are pervious. If the cap rock is horizontal the oil formation is a thin horizontal layer beneath it ; if it is folded the oil moves to the highest part of the anticline and a large accumulation may occur over a small area, possibly with hydrocarbon gas trapped above it, as shown in Figure 52.   Other forms of rock strata can act as oil traps ; the stratigraphic trap is formed by the later deposition of impermeable material across the eroded uplift of oil-bearing strata ; the fault trap is formed by the downward or upward movement of strata at a fault so that a seal is formed by the impervious rock of another stratum ; a salt-dome trap is formed by the forcing of rock-salt formations upwards through the strata ; the salt is plastic under pressure and forms a good seal.

The occurrence of oil is recognized by the visual study of earth formation, by aerial photography, by boring and the mapping of the results, and by geophysical survey.   In the latter the method may be gravimetric, in which small changes in the force of gravity are measured ; an increase may indicate a dome of heavy rock while a decrease may indicate a salt dome.   It may be seismic, in which the rate of travel of a sound wave through the strata is measured on reflection or refraction ; in the former case a few pounds of

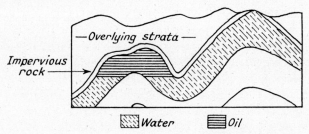

FIG. 52.—Collection of Petroleum in Arch of Folded Stratum.

high explosive are fired some 50 ft. below the surface and the impulses are reflected from heavy strata and picked up on geophones.   From the rate of travel and the relative positions of the shot and the geophone the out-lines of heavy strata can be mapped.   The refraction method requires several tons of explosive per shot and depends upon the fact that likely formations show a high speed of travel of the impulse.   Any impulse striking at the critical angle will travel along at higher velocity before reflection and can be distinguished at a suitable position of the geophone.

The oil is tapped for production by drilling, and the insertion of a pipe-line protected in the upper sections by steel casings whose diameters decrease with depth.   The greatest depth reached so far is about 18,000 ft. and this would be protected by a 15-in. diameter casing for the first 500 ft., an 11-inch casing to 4000 ft., an 8-inch casing to 7000 ft. and the pipe to the oil horizon would be of 6 in. diameter.   The technique of the methods used is beyond the scope of this volume and the reader is directed to the *Science of Petroleum*.   It is sufficient to say at this stage that the petroleum in the reservoir contains a high proportion of hydrocarbon gas in solution

(40–200 Vols. at N.T.P. per volume of oil) and that this gas must be separated from the oil without losing valuable low-boiling constituents. The first separation is made on partial reduction of pressure at the well-head in a large drum. The oil is then safe to process, when the remaining gas is separated. The " wet " gas first separated at the well-head is treated by oil or charcoal absorption, or by compression, for the recovery of " casing-head " gasoline. In wells where only gas is produced this is termed in the U.S.A. " natural gasoline ".

Chemical Composition of Petroleum

In all its forms petroleum consists of hydrocarbons associated with very small amounts of nitrogenous substances and variable amounts of organic sulphur compounds. These hydrocarbons may be paraffinic, olefinic, naphthenic, or aromatic in character, and the proportions in which they are present define the character of the petroleum.

The elementary composition varies only over a small range.

Carbon	.	.	.	.	.	79·5–87·1, average 84·5
Hydrogen	.	.	.	.	.	11·5–14·8 „ 12·5
Sulphur	.	.	.	.	.	0·1– 3·5
Nitrogen, oxygen	.	.	.	.	0·1– 0·5

The organic sulphur compounds present a serious problem to-day. U.S. petroleum contains only about 0·5 per cent. S, but the oils of the Near East contain much more ; Iranian oil contains over 1 per cent., while those of Kuwait and Iraq may reach 3 per cent.

Petroleum in general conforms to one of three types, (i) paraffin-base, in which the residue of distillation is solid paraffin wax, (2) asphalt-base, in which the residue is bitumen or asphalt, and (3) mixed-base, in which wax appears in the distillates but the residue is asphaltic. Some oils such as Pennsylvanian are paraffinic with a high proportion of low-boiling constituents, while others such as Mexican are asphaltic and of much higher boiling range. These variations are indicated in Table XLIV.

TABLE XLIV

CHARACTERISTICS OF CRUDE PETROLEUMS

	Pennsyl-vania.	Iran.	Venezuela.	California.	Mexico.	Kuwait.
Specific gravity .	0·811	0·845	0·850	0·975	0·988	0·86
Initial B.Pt., ° C. .	45	30	58	60	125	75
Vol. to 150° C., %	45	18	17	4	2	16
Vol. 150–300° C., %	28	31	36	36	13	28
Sulphur	0·1	1·08	1·42	0·78	5·18	2·2
Type	Paraffinic	Inter-mediate paraffinic	Inter-mediate asphaltic	Naph-thenic	Naph-thenic, very asphaltic	Inter-mediate paraffinic

By a combination of chemical treatment and accurate methods of fractional distillation a large number of hydrocarbons have been isolated from crude oils, and it has been established that all natural oils consist of mixtures of numerous hydrocarbons belonging to various well-recognized series, and members of at least eight such series have been identified. By a "series" is meant a succession of definite compounds, the individual members, as one ascends in molecular weight, showing a regular difference in the number of carbon and hydrogen atoms present, and it is therefore possible to write a general formula for the members.

Of these eight series of hydrocarbons the following are the principal:

Paraffins.	Olefines.	Naphthenes or polymethylenes.	Benzene or aromatic.
C_nH_{2n+2}	C_nH_{2n}	$n(CH_2)$	C_nH_{2n-6}

The lower members of a series are frequently gases, soon passing into easily condensable liquids, and finally through more and more stable liquids until solid substances are reached. Increase in molecular complexity is then accompanied by rise in boiling-point in the case of liquids, or of melting-point in the case of solids, and the rise in these properties is also associated with a rise in specific gravity and viscosity. Thus, in the case of the paraffin hydrocarbons, the first four members are gases; at C_5H_{12} pentane is a very volatile liquid; the subsequent liquid members increase in boiling-point and density until about $C_{18}H_{38}$ (octadecane) jelly-like hydrocarbons (mineral jelly) are reached, and these finally are succeeded, about $C_{21}H_{44}$, by solids, which in various mixtures constitute paraffin wax.

The presence of much asphaltum makes the oils dark coloured, increases their viscosity, and this concurrently renders it more difficult for water, dirt, etc., to separate out. Generally also asphaltic oils contain more sulphur than paraffin base oils. The latter may be free or almost free from asphaltum, but contain more or less paraffin wax. This wax distils in the refining process; asphalt, on the other hand, is left in the stills and much comes on the market as petroleum pitch. The character of an oil is, therefore, more strongly represented by its ring analysis.

The paraffinic types occur mainly in the U.S.A., and naphthenic oils in California and the Near East (Baku). The paraffinic-naphthenic type is widely distributed and the asphaltic type is found in Mexico and Venezuela.

A classification has been attempted on this basis as follows:

Paraffinic if side chains are over 75 per cent.

Naphthenic if naphthenic rings are over 70 per cent.

Asphaltic if asphaltenes exceed 60 per cent.

Paraffinic-naphthenic if side chains are 60–70 per cent. and naphthenic rings over 20 per cent.

Naphthenic-aromatic if naphthenic rings and aromatics exceed 30 per cent.

Certain general physical properties of petroleum and its products are of importance in its utilization.

Since oil is measured by volume, its *coefficient of thermal expansion* must be known. The value of this normally increases with decreasing specific gravity over the range 0·0007 to 0·0010 per deg. C. For oil fractions the variation is wider, as follows :

"Spirits" {Below specific gravity 0·740	.	.	0·00086
{Above „ „ 0·740	.	.	0·00081
Kerosine	.	.	0·00072
Gas oils	.	.	0·00064
Diesel engine fuels . . .	.	.	0·00063
Heavy fuel oils	.	.	0·00061

The *viscosity* of petroleum oils varies greatly even with oils from the same district. It increases with rise of specific gravity, the higher value for both being dependent mainly upon the presence of heavier hydrocarbons, possibly solid paraffins held in solution by the higher liquid paraffins, but no connection can be traced between viscosity and specific gravity, oils of the same specific gravity varying widely in viscosity. Increase of temperature causes a rapid decrease in the viscosity, and a rise of a few degrees will often cause a sluggish oil to flow freely.

The *specific heat* is frequently important, since it is often necessary to heat fuel oils before use. The specific heat decreases almost *pro rata* with a rise in specific gravity. The following are values for crude oils :

	Specific gravity.	Specific heat. cal./° C./gram.
Pennsylvania	0·810	0·500
California	0·960	0·398
Russia	0·908	0·435
Burma	0·924	0·406
Scottish shale	0·880	0·460

Refining of Petroleum

Crude petroleum is not marketable in its raw state and must undergo a number of distillation and other stages, and purification from sulphur compounds, before it is saleable.

In the early days of " refining " the procedure consisted simply of distillation from batch stills into kerosine, gasoline and fuel oil. The batch developed into the continuous shell still in 1885, and the pipe still in 1911, and the bubble-cap distillation column appeared about 1920. From this time onwards advances in methods of treatment were rapid, so that to-day the subject covers a vast field quite beyond the scope of this book.

With the advance of the use of the internal combustion engine the refiner was first called upon to increase the yield of motor spirit and later to increase its knock rating. This he did by thermal cracking, avoiding undue loss as gas by catalytic polymerization. Since 1940 a large number of catalytic conversion methods have been introduced, chief among which is that of catalytic cracking, but all have combined to make oil-treatment a complicated and variable procedure, as explained below, aimed at the preparation of products required by the markets, with the desired properties, and produced in balanced quantities to suit the market. It is clear, therefore, that the procedure in any refinery at any time is not standard and can be explained only by indicating the processes available and offering examples of alternative schemes.

The first step is the primary distillation of the crude oil, after removal of dirt and water, into primary fractions consisting of gasoline, light and heavy benzine, gas and diesel oil, and fuel oil, a separate vacuum stage producing lubricating oils from the fuel oil fraction. The approximate ranges of these are :

	Deg. C.	Specific gravity.
Motor spirit	40–180	0·70–0·76
Naphtha	110–180	0·80–0·82
Kerosine	140–250	0·78–0·83
Gas/diesel oil	250–340	0·85–0·88
Fuel oil, light	200–320	0·88–0·92
Fuel oil, heavy . . .	320 +	0·92–1·00 +

These fractions are re-treated as required, and as explained below. The straight-run or " distillate gasoline " is not normally re-treated, although it is freed from impurities, and represents about 40 per cent. of the gasoline sold.

The distillation scheme may be presented in the following outlines for the two cases of paraffin-base and asphalt-base crude oils.

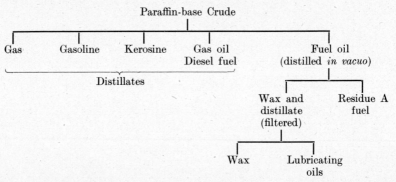

A may also be suitable for cylinder lubricating oil or improved lubricating oil and petroleum jelly.

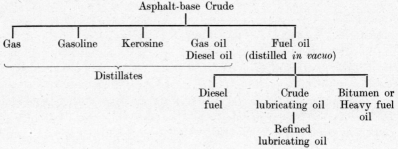

Separation of the crude oil into marketable products depends first upon the nature of the oil and secondly upon the extent upon which secondary treatments follow straight distillation. A refinery has a high degree of flexibility in meeting market requirements by the extent to which the secondary processes are applied and may operate anywhere between the limits of low gasoline and high fuel oil, and high gasoline and low fuel oil. The closer maximum gasoline production is approached the greater are the losses and the amount of fuel consumed in the refinery.

In recent years the main change has been the growing demand for high quality gasoline, which has been met first by thermal cracking and later by catalytic cracking, reforming, and other processes outlined below. The amount of straight-run gasoline has tended to decrease by decrease of the final boiling-point to increase the naphtha fraction, which in turn is treated to give a spirit of higher knock rating. The plant capacity in the U.S.A. is an indication of trends and shows in 1954 vacuum distillation 14 per cent., catalytic cracking 34, catalytic reforming 3, thermal processes 31, polymerization 1·2 and alkylation 1·2 per cent., the remainder straight-run gasoline.

Thermal Cracking. The purpose of cracking is to augment the yield of gasoline, but the reactions which occur differ with the type of oil treated.

Aromatic hydrocarbons retain their basic ring structure but the more complex bodies lose their side chains and give unsaturated hydrocarbons, and a little carbon is formed.

Paraffin hydrocarbons show simple C—C bond rupture, but this is accompanied by isomerization to *iso*-paraffins, cyclization to naphthenes and dehydrogenation to olefines and aromatics.

Naphthenes crack more readily than paraffins of the same molecular weight, C—C rupture occurs in both ring and side chain, but some of the former is retained. Some dehydrogenation to aromatics occurs with liberation of hydrogen which reduces the formation of olefines as compared with paraffins.

Cracking was formerly done by thermal treatment alone, but this is now superseded by thermal-catalytic cracking. Thermal cracking used pipe stills, a temperature of about 500° C. and a time of contact of a few seconds. The process suffered from heavy loss by the formation of carbon and the average yield of spirit was only of the order of 70–80 per cent., depending upon the type of cracking stock. The knock-rating of the spirit was 75, which is appreciably higher than that of straight-run gasoline.

Catalytic Cracking. By carrying out the cracking process in the presence of a catalyst (certain types of clay) much improved yields and quality of products are obtained under less severe conditions of cracking than obtain in the thermal-cracking process. In addition, the process is adaptable to quite high-sulphur oils and, by the use of higher temperatures and pressures, to oils of high boiling range.

Chemically, the use of a catalyst promotes C—C bond rupture, polymerization of olefines and hydrogen transfer, and is effective in the production of *iso*-paraffins of high knock-rating. The gasoline is therefore characterized by high knock-rating, low sulphur and "gum" content.

The catalysts used were at first acid-extracted bentonite clays but are now synthetic silica-alumina granules of the right size grading.

The application of catalysis to the thermal cracking of oil started about 1931, using hydrogenation under pressure. Later, however, this technique was displaced by cracking in the absence of hydrogen. Since cracking involves reduction of molecular weight, a proportion of the carbon of the oil molecule is deposited on the catalyst, and this carbon must be burned off at intervals under conditions which do not destroy catalytic activity. In the early stages of development, therefore, a unit plant embodied a number of cracking chambers which were treated in turn for the removal of carbon in order to obtain continuity of operation. These static beds of catalyst ("fixed beds") were of granulated or "beaded" material through which pre-heated oil was passed downwards under pressure (80 lb. per sq. in.) and at about 900° F. The Houdry and Hydroforming systems are examples of this technique.

The first step towards a fluid system was a process involving the movement of a coarse-granulated catalyst countercurrent to the preheated oil, and withdrawal of the fouled catalyst continuously for "burning off". The spent catalyst, fouled with carbon, is elevated mechanically to the feed hopper of a vessel down which it passes countercurrent to an air stream which removes the carbon by combustion. The revivified catalyst is then mechanically elevated to the feed hopper of the reaction vessel, and the cycle is complete.

When true fluid-flow catalysis was first introduced, about 1939, it represented a method of handling powdered solids in bulk which was new in the industry. The essential principle in the method of movement was the maintaining of the powder in a fluid, free-flowing condition, and circulating it by the air-lift method was well known in the movement of liquids. The motive power for the circulation of the fluid was obtained from the static head of gas–solid columns and by the introduction under pressure of oil vapours to the oil-cracking "reactor", and of air to the catalyst revivifier.

In the up-flow system the heated catalyst (20–40 μ) flows from a standpipe into a stream of preheated vaporized oil and is carried upwards into a reaction chamber. Since this chamber is of much greater diameter, the velocity of movement falls and a more dense turbulent bed is formed in which the solid particles are in violent motion. The entire stream is then carried over into a three-stage cyclone separator from which the oil vapours pass to a fractionating column and the solid catalyst, containing carbon, passes in a stream carried by injected air to a chamber ("regenerator") in which the carbon is burned off. The hot catalyst then returns via the standpipe leading to the oil inlet.

This procedure has now been largely replaced by a "down-flow" technique ; of the 36 fluid units in the United States in 1945, 32 were using "down-flow". The principle of this method is shown in the diagram in Figure 53. Revivified catalyst leaves the so-called "regenerator", by the standpipe, and enters the inlet pipe to the cracking chamber, its rate of flow being regulated by slide valves. Heated oil vapours from the feed-heater enter just behind this point and carry the catalyst upwards into a cracking chamber ("reactor") of large diameter, in which the velocity of flow is

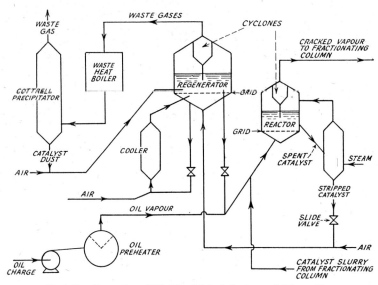

FIG. 53.—Down-flow " Fluidized "-bed System of Oil-cracking.

reduced to 1 to 2 ft. per sec. At this rate of flow the solid particles form a dense, turbulent bed with a definite boundary or surface at a certain level in the "reactor". From this surface cracked vapours escape with some entrained catalyst dust. Most of this dust is returned by the internal cyclone, and clean vapours pass to the fractionating column.

The cracking reactions take place in the "reactor", the temperature being regulated by the respective temperatures and proportions of heated catalyst and oil, and the time of treatment by the rate of flow.

The cracking reactions cause the catalyst to become coated with carbon, and it is withdrawn continuously, from the bottom of the dense zone, through a vessel in which it is swept with steam to remove entrained oil, into a standpipe from which it flows by gravity at a controlled rate (slide valve) into the inlet line to the "regenerator". It is then carried upwards into the "regenerator" by an air stream, which also provides the oxygen

F.—K

for burning off the carbon.   In the " regenerator " a dense, turbulent bed
develops which is similar to that formed in the "reactor".   The products
of combustion from the " regenerator " are cycloned to return entrained
solids, and pass through a waste-heat boiler and a Cottrell precipitator
before leaving to atmosphere with less than 15 gr. of entrained solid per
100 cu. ft.   The revivified catalyst (0·5 per cent. carbon) is withdrawn
through a standpipe to the oil-vapour injection point leading to the " reactor ".   A second standpipe with air entrainment (air 15 lb. per sq. in.)
circulates catalyst to and from the " regenerator " bed through a cooler,
and provides a control over the temperature to which the catalyst is heated
in the burning-off process.

Some finely divided catalyst inevitably reaches the heavy-oil distillates
from which it is recovered as a concentrated sludge by using a centrifuge.
This sludge is returned to the feed line.

The operating conditions vary widely, but the temperatures and
pressures used are approximately :   Oil-preheat temperature, 400° F. ;
" regenerated "-catalyst temperature, 1050° F. ;   cracking-zone temperature,
800° to 1000° F. ;   pressure at top of " reactor ", 8 to 12 lb., pressure at
top of " regenerator ", 2 to 4 lb., per sq. in.

Down-flow cracking plants are now of large size, treating from 500,000
to one million imp. gallons of oil per day.   Working conditions vary with
raw material and product, and the catalyst : oil ratio may vary from 5 : 1
to 30 : 1, so that up to 50 tons of solids per hour may be circulated in a
plant processing 1 million gallons of oil per day.   The " reactor " and the
" regenerator " are very large vessels.   The former, 50 ft. high × 25 ft.
diameter, operates with 75 to 100 tons of catalyst in the " fluidized " bed,
and the latter with 150 to 300 tons.   Continuity of operation for periods
of eight months has been achieved.

Loss of catalyst is not more than 0·4 lb. per 100 gal. of oil.

In the " fluidized " beds of the " reactor " and " regenerator " the
density varies from 25 to 30 lb. per cu. ft., and is referred to as a " dense-
phase " condition.   Flow of catalyst down the " regenerator " standpipe
(Figure 53) is also a " dense-phase " condition.   It is the height of this
standpipe which provides the static head for the circulation of the catalyst.
The rate of flow is controlled by the slide valves at the bottom, but aeration
is necessary to maintain the necessary fluidity.   This is done by supplying
air at points spaced about 15 ft. apart.   The air supply is regulated to
maintain a high phase density since the erosion varies inversely with phase
density.   At 25 to 30 lb. per cu. ft. the rate of flow is from 5 to 7 ft. per
sec.   Below the slide valve, the stream enters the " reactor " inlet line,
which is carrying the preheated oil and vapours which form the feed.   The
pressure at this point is equal to the total catalyst head to the surface of
the fluid bed in the " regenerator ", plus the small gas pressure (1 to 2 lb.)
in the latter.

Catalytic cracking is now the preferred form of treatment of the middle oils of the primary distillation and is being installed in new refineries. Its use infers the production of a different gasoline, a more aromatic diesel oil and a less-cracked fuel oil.

The gasoline produced has a higher octane number than straight-run spirit and may exceed 90. It normally contains a less proportion of olefines and has less tendency to gum formation in the internal combustion engine, and more response to the addition of lead tetra-ethyl.

Tertiary Methods of Preparation. Following the primary distillation of petroleum and the secondary cracking of the heavy distillate we have a number of available processes which are all aimed at the chemical reforming of hydrocarbons to augment the yield and improve the properties of the gasoline made. These hydrocarbons may be in the gas from primary distillation, cracking, or both, in the naphtha or kerosine fractions, or in the straight-run gasoline itself. The methods are too complicated to be described in detail here but some brief description of their principles is necessary and is given below.

Reforming. One process is designated by this term although all of them are reforming processes in the sense that they are designed to alter the nature of the hydrocarbons in distillate oils in order to increase their knock-rating. Reforming is used for the improvement of straight-run gasoline and for the conversion of naphtha into gasoline. Usually only the higher-boiling half of the former is treated, but the whole of the latter may be treated. The temperature of treatment is 550° C. and the pressure from 800° to 1200° C., and the time of treatment is of the order of 15 sec. In the treatment of gasoline the mean boiling-point is reduced and knock-rating increased. In the case of naphtha the product is fractionated into gas, gasoline, and light gas oil and any residue added to the fuel-oil fraction.

Thermal reforming is rather a drastic treatment and relies to a large extent on cracking with its attendant reduction of mean molecular weight.

If the reforming is carried out over a catalyst both temperature and pressure may be reduced with appreciable improvement of yield of gasoline. The product is also more aromatic, contains no olefines and has a better lead susceptibility.

A variety of catalysts have been used starting with chromium or aluminium oxides, but a great advance has been made recently by the application of platinum catalysts, which will probably lead to the expansion of this process. In 1954 the total of reforming plants in the U.S.A. has an output equivalent to about three per cent. of the crude oil handled, but it is stated that this will be trebled in 12 months' time. The processes are known under a number of names such as *Platforming, Cat-forming, Houdriforming*—all using platinum—*Cycloversion* using bauxite, and *Hydroversion* using MoO_3/Al_2O_3, *Thermofor* using Cr_2O_3/Al_2O_3, and several others.

The reactions which occur are dehydrogenation, isomerization, and aromatization, all associated with mild cracking. The conditions all vary to an extent depending on the catalyst. The U.O.P. Platforming process operates at 480° C. and 750 p.s.i., and hydrogen-rich gas is recycled to remove any carbon from the catalyst by hydrogenation to methane. A typical result from a Middle East naphtha boiling between 120° and 205° C. and having an octane number of 34 (motor) is :

Gas, including C_4	.	.	.	.	.	9·8 wt. per cent.
Butanes	.	.	.	.	.	5·5 ,, ,,
C_5 to 205° C.	.	.	.	.	.	84·7 ,, ,,

The butane is blended back to give 90 per cent. gasoline at 76 octane number (motor).

Hydroforming. If the catalytic reforming is carried out in the presence of hydrogen the process has been termed hydroforming. The main reaction which occurs is the dehydrogenation of naphthenes to aromatics, and the process was used during the 1939–45 war to produce nitration-grade toluene along with high-octane gasoline. The catalyst may be Cr_2O_3 or Al_2O_3 or MoO_3 on Al_2O_3, and reaction conditions are 500° C. and 150–300 lb./in.^{2}. The recycle gas contains not less than 70 per cent. hydrogen and the procedure is regenerative with two pairs of reactors in order to overcome the endothermicity of the reactions. During regeneration carbon is burned off the catalyst and sulphur retained by the molybdenum is eliminated.

Hydroformed gasolines have a low vapour pressure and can take more butane than usual : they have a good lead susceptibility.

The fluo-solids technique has been applied to hydroforming with improved yield of gasoline.

Catalytic Polymerization. Polymerization in this context involves the union of two or more olefine molecules to form olefines of higher molecular weight. Conditions are usually chosen to give the maximum yield of the dimer, but it is not possible to prevent the formation of 10–15 per cent. of trimer, and a small amount of higher polymers. The special value of the process lies in its use for the conversion back to the gasoline boiling range of the olefinic gases which are unavoidably formed in thermal- or catalytic-cracking, or in the reforming processes. These gases are rich in olefines, particularly propylene and the butylenes, and their conversion raises the total gasoline yield and its average knock-rating.

Two processes of polymerization are used, depending upon whether sulphuric or phosphoric acid is used. In the former the acid may be of 55–65 per cent. strength, or 75 per cent. strength. In the first case butylenes are treated in the cold and there is a preferential solution of *iso*-butylene in the acid ; this can then be isolated from the *n*-butylene as the dimer and hydrogenated to *iso*-octane. In the second case the acid is used at about 90° C. and the product is a mixed dimer of the two butylenes.

In the phosphoric acid process the acid is calcined with kieselguhr and the product pelleted. Two levels of pressure are used ; at 250 p.s.i. the system is regenerative to burn off carbon ; at 900 p.s.i. the catalyst life is sufficiently long to obviate burning-off. The temperature used may be 150–180° C. for selective polymerization or 190–250° C. for non-selective polymerization to give a high gasoline yield. The hydrogenation stage may be omitted and the dimer used directly as a blend component of gasoline.

The two processes of reforming and polymerization are combined in *polyforming* when the naphtha, or light gas oil fraction, is given a mild cracking treatment in the presence of C_3 and C_4 hydrocarbons. The charge, enriched with light gases produced in the process, is heated to about 580° C. at a pressure of 1000–2000 p.s.i. and flashed in an evaporator and fractionating system working at 360° C. and 350 p.s.i. The product is stabilized and the light hydrocarbons absorbed for use in the process. The process is not very widely used.

Alkylation. The term alkylation is used to describe the combination of an olefine with a cyclic, paraffinic or aromatic hydrocarbon to give a branched-chain hydrocarbon having a molecular weight equal to the sum of those of the reactants. In practice it is mainly confined to the combination of olefines and low-boiling *iso*-paraffins to give high-octane *iso*-paraffins boiling in the gasoline range ; *iso*-butane, for example, is combined with butylenes to give branched octanes. Normal paraffins are not readily alkylated.

The process has been used without catalyst and with boron trifluoride or aluminium chloride, but the latest catalyst is sulphuric acid. The *iso*-paraffin is mixed with sulphuric acid (98 per cent.) in equal proportions and C_4 olefines injected into the emulsion at 150 p.s.i. to keep them in the liquid phase. Contact is maintained for 20 minutes at a temperature of below 15° C., the mixture settled and the hydrocarbon layer separated, washed with alkali, and distilled to separate unchanged *iso*-paraffin for recycling. The reactions are exothermic and cooling is necessary ; the strength of the acid is maintained by small additions.

Alkylation can be achieved also by the use of hydrofluoric acid. In this case the process is continuous and the feed rates controlled to give a residence time of 15–20 minutes. The product is refined and fractionated ; it consists mainly of light alkylate of 90 octane number for aviation purposes, and 5–7 per cent. of heavier material which may be added to the gasoline fraction.

During the 1939–45 war aromatic hydrocarbons were alkylated to make blend components of high knock-rating for aviation purposes, e.g. Cumene or *iso*-propyl benzene, and Victane or *iso*-butyl benzene.

Refining of Oil Fractions. Any gasoline for use in an internal combustion engine is freed from impurities by washing with reagents ;

sulphuric acid removes unsaturated or gum-forming hydrocarbons, residual sulphur compounds are removed by washing with a solution of lead dioxide in caustic soda solution. Other fractions are treated similarly, the refining of lubricating oil being particularly meticulous, but the processes are too complicated to be described in this volume and the reader is referred to *The Science of Petroleum.*

Certain treatments of the residual fuel should, however, be described briefly as they can be of importance in reducing the proportion of fuel oil made if the market should demand this.

The most important of these is *vacuum distillation* of fuel oil, which has become customary in all new refineries. The oil is heated at 400° C. and 40–50 mm. Hg pressure, and the products are gas, gas-oil suitable for catalytic cracking stock, and a heavy residue. Intermediate fractions may be taken for lubricating oils and wax.

A second process is mild cracking at 480° C. and 200–500 p.s.i. to give some gasoline, gas-oil, and a heavy residue. This is termed *viscosity breaking* or *Visbreaking*. Alternatively the oil may be fully coked to give light distillates and a residue of coke only. The production of petroleum coke in the U.S.A. to-day is about 3·5 million tons, which represents 25–40 per cent. of the material treated. The other products may be gas 8, naphtha 25, and gas-oil 35 per cent.

Solvent extraction is being employed to an increasing extent, using liquid C_3 and C_4 hydrocarbons at 600 p.s.i. and 80° C. in a counter-current stream. The soluble oil is used as cracking stock and the asphaltic residue either sold as such, or coked.

Refinery Cycle. The refinery cycle at any time is decided by the manner in which the above procedures are combined. There must be many variations of this and the position is best explained by taking one example. This is illustrated in the diagram of Figure 54. The primary distillation of the crude oil (mixed base) is shown to give hydrocarbon gases, propane, butane, etc., gasoline, naphtha, kerosine, diesel oil, heavy fuel distillate, and asphalt.

The gasoline fraction will be of medium octane rating and may be purified and passed for blending as shown. The naphtha may be separated or reformed. The kerosine fraction may be prepared as an illuminating or heating oil or thermally reformed by dehydrogenation of the naphthenes to aromatics, hydrogenation-cracking of higher-boiling fractions and/or isomerization of the paraffins. These combined reactions give a gasoline of high knock-rating for blending with the straight-run gasoline. The higher the naphthene content of the stock the higher is the octane number of the product. The Diesel fraction is shown as suitable for sale direct, but could require desulphurization. The heavy distillate could be the cracking stock for the catalyst cracker which yields hydrocarbon gas, gasoline, diesel oil and recycle oil. The gasoline is blended with the other gasoline fractions and the recycle stock is continuously bled off for gas and diesel oil if required and for thinning the fuel oil for sale. The hydro-carbon gas is mixed with the gas from the primary distillation stage, poly-merized to gasoline and the latter blended away.

This is an essentially simple example of manufacturing procedure, but in view of the variations of type of oil and of use of secondary processes of treatment to meet markets there can be no typical scheme. One effect of type of oil could be preparation from paraffinic stock of kerosine and wax; one effect of procedure could be the preferential production of aviation

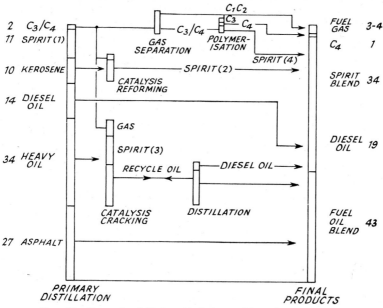

FIG. 54.—Example of Modern Technique of Petroleum Refining.

gasoline by the separation of the *iso*-paraffins, by alkylation, and other means. There are many variations which are too complicated for dis-cussion here, but all affect the yield and properties of saleable oils. These properties are discussed later in relation to their uses; the yields depend upon markets and some idea of these has already been given (p. 254).

In Figure 54 the actual quantities shown are not significant as this is only an example from which there can be wide variations as stated, but as an example, they are worth considering.

	Per cent.
Straight-run spirit	12
Reformed spirit	22
or total spirit	(34)
Kerosine	10 or nil
Gas or diesel oil	19
Fuel oil	43
Butanes	1
C_1, C_2, C_3 gases	3–4

This shows the sacrifice of kerosine to the gasoline fraction. Lubricating oil could have been obtained by the vacuum distillation of the heavy oil distillate from the primary distillation.

It is interesting to compare this example with the requirements of oil products in this country. If it were assumed that we were a self-contained country, i.e. that we bought crude petroleum and converted it into the fractions which we required ourselves, the proportions of these fractions would be:

		Per cent.	
Aviation spirit	. . . . . .	6 }	Total 25
Motor spirit .	. . . . .	19 }	
Other spirit .	. . . . . .	1	
Kerosine	. . . . . .	7	
Gas oil	. . . . . .	2 }	Total 19
Diesel oil .	. . . . . .	17 }	
Fuel oil sold	. . . . . .	36 }	Total 39
„ „ used	. . . . . .	3 }	
Lubricating oil	. . . . .	1·5	—
Bitumen	. . . . . .	3	83
Paraffin wax	. . . . . .	0·5	=
Butane and gases	. . . . .	4	

It is clear that some kerosine would be required as stated in Chapter XI but that all of it could be sacrificed to spirit as shown in Figure 54. No doubt the move towards the use of the Diesel engine for the private car will further reduce the spirit requirement in due course.

A further comparison is available when the same crude oil is treated by different procedures, as shown in Table XLV:

TABLE XLV

PERCENTAGE YIELDS FROM A MIDDLE EAST CRUDE OIL

(M. A. L. Banks, *Inst. Petrol. Rev.*, 1950, **4**, 59)

	Distillation.	Distillation and Reforming.	Distillation and Hydroforming.	Distillation, Reforming, Thermal cracking.	Distillation, Reforming, Catalyst cracking.	Distillation, Hydroforming, Catalyst cracking.
Gasoline	23	26	27	29	37	38
Kerosine/gas oil .	20	14	15	35	25	26
Fuel oil	52	53	51	25	28	26
Gas, fuel, loss . .	5	7	7	11	10	10

This table also demonstrates the important effect of catalyst-cracking on gasoline and fuel-oil yields.

Petroleum in Great Britain. A great deal of prospecting for oil has been done in Great Britain in places where the geological formations have appeared to hold promise, but in only three places, Eakring, Kelham Hills, and Caunton, has it been struck in sufficient quantity for commercial recovery. The quantity now being produced (1952) is about 55,000 tons per annum.

The crude oil is mainly of the paraffinic, wax-bearing type, and varies in sulphur content from 0·1 to 0·5 per cent. The wax content varies from 4 to as high as 12 per cent. The range of properties is approximately as follows :

Specific gravity	0·850–0·890
Pour point ° F.	50–40
Viscosity	60–190 sec. Redwood I at 70° F.
Wax per cent.	4–12
Asphalt per cent.	< 0·4
Sulphur per cent.	0·1–0·5

Distillate to ° C. . . .	75	100	150	200	300	Residue.
	1	3	18	358	61	39

An approximate separation into commercial products is as follows :

Spirit.	White spirit.	Kerosine.	Diesel oil.	Lubricating oils.	Residue.	Loss.
5–12	4–8	9–14	10–14	31–34	20–30	2

The spirit has the low octane number of 60, but the diesel oil is of very high grade with a cetane number of 55.

At Eakring in South Staffordshire the oil is of particularly good quality with 0·1 per cent. sulphur, no asphalt, 8·5 per cent. of wax and a lubricating oil of high viscosity index.

Bituminous (Tar) Sands

Petroleum, or material similar to it, is sometimes found impregnated into sand or clay relatively near the earth's surface. The exact mode of formation of such " sands " is not clear, but they are certainly similar to the first stage of petroleum collection in mineral matter before separation of the oil by water occurs under impervious strata.

The outstanding example of this material is found in Canada in the region of the River Athabaska of north Alberta. The area covered is certainly 1500 sq. miles and possibly 30,000 sq. miles. The deposits vary from 150 to 170 ft. in thickness and are covered by an overburden varying from several feet to several hundred feet. They outcrop, however, along the river, where their formation can be seen to consist of sand, silt and clay impregnated with very viscous asphaltic oil and water. The proportions of oil and water vary from 12 to 16 oil and 3 to 15 water per cent. and the density of the mass is 125 lb. per cu. ft.

The separation of oil from finely divided solids is a difficult matter, but a considerable amount of experimental work has been done which indicates that a practical method can be found. The recent discovery of large reserves of petroleum in Alberta, however, will probably delay the exploitation of the sands for many years. If a conservative figure is taken for the extent of the deposit, however, it is apparent that there is here a reserve of over 5×10^9 million tons of oil.

Oil samples separated in exploration work show considerable variation of properties, but all the oil is of the asphaltic type. Its specific gravity varies from 1·002 to 1·027, its sulphur content from 4 to 5 per cent., and its calorific value is about 18,000 B.Th.U. per lb. It is a heavy oil with only 5 per cent. boiling below 180° C.

Three methods have been tried for the separation of the oil ; these are separation with hot water, cold water, and distillation.

(1) The sand is milled with 10 per cent. by weight of hot water at 185° F., flooded with more hot water and settled. A froth of oil rises and is skimmed off. Recovery is 80 per cent. efficient and the recovered material contains 5 per cent. of mineral matter and 30 per cent. of water.

(2) The sand is milled with cold water one-third of its weight and an amount of kerosine equal to its oil content, with the addition of alkali and a wetting agent. The oil floats off, is skimmed and settled. Recovery is about 95 per cent., but the dry oil still contains 3 per cent. of mineral matter.

(3) Either product has been further treated in a fluo-solids process in which the hot distillation bed consists of tailings from the process. The reject material is blown with air in a separate vessel to provide the heat necessary. The oil yield is 13 lb. per cu. ft. of sand.

Technically, the process of recovery is assured at an assessed cost of 72 cents per barrel, but no large-scale development has been attempted.

The distilled oil has a specific gravity of 0·955 and has the following properties :

Water 0·2, ash 0·7, sulphur 4·2, Conradson carbon 6·0 per cent.
Viscosity, 157 centistokes at 70° F.
Distillation : 5 per cent. at 180, 10 per cent. at 230, 50 per cent. at 340, 80 per cent. at 360° C.
Analysis : carbon 83·6, hydrogen 10·4. Ratio = 8/1.

By straight distillation the oil would yield 15 per cent. of naphtha and 85 per cent. of fuel oil, but it is quite susceptible to cracking at 650° F. and would respond more favourably to modern methods of refining.

SHALE OIL

The reserves of shale in the world are considerable, amounting in oil equivalent to over 20,000 million tons, but, in view of the greater availability of petroleum, its utilization at present is comparatively negligible. The highest reserves are in the United States and Russia, but workable deposits are to be found in many parts of the world. In Great Britain the production of shale oil is of interest as the largest source of natural fuel oil. Suitable shale is found in the narrow belt between the Forth and Clyde in Scotland. Considerable deposits also occur in Dorset (Kimmeridge), but this shale is too high in sulphur content (4–6 per cent.) to justify working.

The distillation of shale in Scotland really began in 1851 at Bathgate with the treatment of torbanite by James Young. This gave a high yield of oil which was refined by distillation and washing with acid and alkali to give burning oils, and paraffin wax for candles. This torbanite was soon worked out and by 1861 a change over to shale was made to produce similar oil in smaller yield. By 1872 production of oil had reached 1·85 million gallons. Comparable yields from different materials available were :

	Ash per cent.	Oil, gal./ton.	Ash-free yield.
Boghead cannel	31	124	180
Cannel	4	64	67
Shale, Lothian	76	220	83

The difference of these yields on the ash-free basis shows the variation in the oil-bearing material. Oil shale is a dark brown to black rock, weathering to a dull grey. It is strong and hard and retains its shape on retorting, although its laminated structure is then more apparent.

Retorting of shale was first done in horizontal gas retorts, but now the only method in Scotland is the continuous vertical retort (Westwood) developed from the original retort of Young and Beilby. The use of a high proportion of steam in distillation was at one stage the saving of the industry in giving higher yields of oil and very high yields of ammonia. The output of shale reached a maximum in 1913 at 3¼ million tons, but is now about 1½ million tons. The retorts are 34 ft. high with considerable taper from 33 in. at the top to 56 in. at the bottom. They are heated externally by the process gas, the upper 14 ft. of the retort being of cast iron to facilitate heat transfer. The temperature varies from 480° C. in the upper section to 700° C. below. Operation is continuous at 10 tons per retort per day, using 40 per cent. by weight of steam. A small proportion of air (5000 cu./ft./ton) is added to the steam to burn out residual carbon and augment the fuel.

The crude shale oil is distilled to coke in pipe stills operated with final coking stills in order to give a more stable and saturated product. This gives crude spirit, wax-free oil, and wax-bearing oil. The wax is recovered by pressing at 20° F. The two wax-free products are refined by acid/alkali treatment and distilled to diesel oil and a 20 per cent. residue which is cracked at 400° C. and 75 lb. pressure to give spirit 30, diesel oil 40 and pitch 15 per cent. Being essentially paraffinic, the diesel oil is of excellent quality and high cetane number. For the same reason the spirit is not so suitable as a motor spirit in having a low octane value of about 58, but is satisfactory as a blending stock. The wax is refined and bleached and is sold in industry for candle-making, grease-proofing, etc., but is not used as a fuel.

Ammonium sulphate recovery gives 30 lb. $(NH_4)_2SO_4$ per ton of shale and the residue of spent shale is used for brick-making.

The average yield of oil and spirit to-day is about 23·5 gal. per ton ; its specific gravity is about 0·87 and its setting point 90° F. Yields of refined products are :

Sp. gr.

Spirit, gal.	3·2	Octane 58	0·723
Diesel oil, gal.	10·9	Cetane 53	0·843
Wax, lb.	13·1	M.Pt., 120° F.	
Coke, lb.	4·6		
Loss, vol. per cent.	4·3		

The production of shale oil in Scotland is about 106,500 tons per annum and is more than half of the world production at present.

COAL TAR AND COAL-TAR FUELS

In Great Britain coal tar is mainly the product of the high-temperature carbonization of coal in gas retorts or coke ovens ; the amount of low-temperature tar is relatively very small. In the gas industry the yield is from 12 to 14 gal. per ton of coal, and in the coke industry about 8·5 gal. The annual production is about 2·7 million tons and almost the whole of this is distilled for the production of refined products. The residual product of distillation is pitch, and if carried to this stage the distillates are :

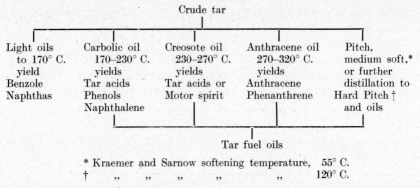

Crude tar

| Light oils to 170° C. yield Benzole Naphthas | Carbolic oil 170–230° C. yields Tar acids Phenols Naphthalene | Creosote oil 230–270° C. yields Tar acids or Motor spirit | Anthracene oil 270–320° C. yields Anthracene Phenanthrene | Pitch, medium soft,* or further distillation to Hard Pitch † and oils |

Tar fuel oils

* Kraemer and Sarnow softening temperature, 55° C.
†   „   „   „   „   „   120° C.

The motor spirit under creosote oil is obtained by secondary treatment by hydrogenation as described below. The tar fuels are prepared to specification as given in B.S. 1469.

In 1951 the annual production of 2·7 million tons of tar was converted into the following products :

Road tar	608,000 tons	Creosote oil	103 million gal.
Tar fuels	632,000 „	Total benzole	97 million gal.
Phenol	11,000 „	Motor benzole	50 „ „
Cresylic acid	11,000 „	Hydrogenation spirit	35 „ „
Anthracene	2,600 „		

The benzole was obtained only partly from the tar ; the higher proportion was obtained by the stripping of coal gas. The hydrogenation spirit was obtained by the treatment of creosote oil.

Certain properties of typical tars are shown in Table XLVI which also shows the natural variations in distillation range.

TABLE XLVI

COMPOSITION OF TYPICAL DRY COAL TARS

Percentages by weight

Origin.	Specific gravity.	Free carbon.	Tar acids.	Distillation range.				Pitch.	Naphthalene. Per cent.
				0–170° C.	170–230° C.	230–270.	270–pitch.		
Horizontal retorts . . .	1·18	12	3·5	4	8	11	17	60	5
Vertical retorts (20 per cent. steam) . . .	1·10	4	9	3	16	10	19	52	1
Coke ovens, narrow	1·15	6	3	2	7	12	14	65	7
Coke ovens, wide	1·20	15	4	2	3	7	17	71	5
Chamber ovens	1·15	3	5	2	9	12	15	62	1
Low temperature (Fuel Research)	1·06	1	12	6	16	12	31	35	trace
Blast furnaces Producers	1·10	—	3	1	2	9	25	63	trace
Water gas . .	1·04	1	nil	10	17	27	21	25	2

Tars contain polynuclear hydrocarbons which are thrown out of solution by dilution with benzole and have been termed free carbon : the proportion depends upon the severity of the temperature conditions of distillation of the coal.

Tar.	Free carbon per cent.
Low-temperature	0 to 1
Continuous vertical gas retort	5 to 10
Horizontal gas retort	8 to 15
Coke ovens, narrow	5 to 8
Coke ovens, wide	12 to 16

Unlike the petroleum oils, coal tars contain a proportion of oxygenated (phenolic) and nitrogenous (basic) bodies. The following analyses are of tars from the same coal.

	Horizontal retort.	Vertical retort.	Low-temperature.
Carbon	85·9	85·7	83·5
Hydrogen	6·3	6·3	8·5
Sulphur	1·2	1·6	0·8
Nitrogen	2·0	1·0	1·0
Oxygen, etc. . . .	4·6	5·4	6·2

Low-temperature tars are appreciably different from high-temperature tars in being of lower specific gravity, more fluid, free from naphthalene and free carbon.

Other properties of tars are :

Calorific value varies within comparatively small limits about 16,500 B.Th.U. per lb.

The coefficient of expansion per degree F. varies a little, the mean figure being 0·00035.

The specific heat of tar varies from 0·30 to 0·40 calories per gram per degree C. (B.Th.U. per lb./° F.) at 40° C., and that of tar oils from 0·30 to 0·38 at 15–90° C.

Commercial Fuels from Tar

Tar or tar fuel oil is not of universal application since it may not be admixed with petroleum fuel oil in tanks or pipe-lines. The reason is that admixture causes deposition of the pitch from solution in a heavy mass which would be impossible to handle. It is freely usable, however, where separate tanks and lines are available.

A range of fuels are now made in this country designated as C.T.F. 50, 100, 200, 250, and 300, these being the temperatures in deg. F. to which they must be heated to reach a condition suitable for atomization, i.e. a maximum viscosity of 0·25 stoke.[1]

Fuels 50 and 100 are blends of distillate oils, creosote or anthracene oils, blended with light creosote from which tar acids or other chemicals have been extracted. The distillate oil from the making of hard pitch may also be included.

Fuel 400 is the solid residue of distillation to the point at which it shows a softening temperature of 73–80° C., i.e. " medium-soft " pitch.

Fuels 200, 250 and 300 are combinations of fuel 400 with the creosote and anthracene oil fractions. They may be made directly by arresting the distillation of tar at the point where the residue would have the right viscosity or by dilution or " oiling back ", which consists in blending pitch with distillate oils. Fuel 200, which is the most popular, is a 50/50 pitch-creosote blend.

All these fuels are supplied to specifications which need not be repeated here, but certain of the important properties are as follows. The water content must be less than 0·5 and ash content less than 0·3 per cent. Their calorific values vary from 16,200 for fuel 400 to 17,000 B.Th.U. per lb. for fuel 100. Their specific heats vary from 0·40 to 0·34 in the same order. Thermal conductivity is of the order of 0·085 B.Th.U. per sq. ft. per hr.

The change of viscosity of coal-tar fuels with temperature is greater than with petroleum fuels, but the slope of the temperature-viscosity curve is much the same for all tar fuels. The logarithmic relationship between kinematic viscosity (stokes) and temperature (° F.) is :

Fuel 250	.	.	.	.	3·8 at $\log_t = 1·8$ to 0 at $\log_t = 2·25$
Fuel 300	.	.	.	.	4 „ 2 „ 0 „ 2·35
Fuel 400	.	.	.	.	4 „ 2·2 „ 0 „ 2·5

[1] The stoke is the c.g.s. unit of kinematic viscosity.

It is apparent that the heavier fuels have to be transported and stored in the warm condition.[1] In addition, heaters are necessary before the burners to attain the proper temperature for atomization. Atomization may be achieved by feeding under pressure or by the use of high-pressure steam or air, as in the case of heavy petroleum fuel oil, and a number of special burners are available. In most of these it is possible to make rapid replacement in the case of blockage. The need for these precautions imposes careful planning of distribution lines and heat requirements upon any factory wishing to utilize such fuels. Nevertheless, their application has become quite widespread and in 1952 some 650,000 tons were burned in Great Britain. The uses include steam raising, distillation and metallurgy ; in the latter the luminosity of the flame assures a high rate of heat transfer. Burners have been developed to burn up to 1200 lb. per hour. In addition to the usual applications of steam raising and furnace heating, hard pitch has proved of special value in heating large annealing furnaces, and metal-heating furnaces in general because of the uniform temperature attained and the low amount of ash in the fuel in comparison with coal.

Hard Pitch. If coal tar is distilled further than is indicated above, to the extent of taking off a further 15–20 per cent. of distillate, the final pitch becomes so hard that it can be pulverized in the air-swept swing-hammer type of mill (p. 185). Ball or ring-roll mills which work by grinding

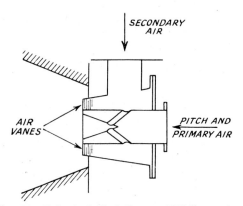

Fig. 55.—Pulverized Pitch Burner, 1200 lb. per hour.

are not applicable as the pitch softens under the temperature developed. The large masses of pitch are broken in a spike breaker to about one inch before pulverizing.

The burner used must be of a simple type and preferably water-cooled ; spreader devices cannot be used and the shape of the flame is modified by the mode of introduction of the secondary air as shown in Figure 55.

[1] Pumping is satisfactory at 3–10 stokes viscosity.

THE PRODUCTION OF FUEL OILS BY HYDROGENATION

Fuel oils and motor spirit can be produced by the treatment of coal and its products at high temperature and pressure in the presence of hydrogen (hydrogenation). When coal is carbonized it gives a yield of tar amounting to only 8 to 10 per cent. of the coal. When treated by the hydrogenation process, however, a crude oil amounting to about 75 per cent. by weight of the coal treated is obtainable. The hydrogenation of coal therefore offers a means of producing supplies of oil from coal in countries where natural sources of oil are not available.

The pioneering work in the treatment of coal was that of Bergius, who erected in 1924 an experimental plant at Mannheim, Germany. In 1926 a duplicate plant was installed at the Fuel Research Station, London, in order to determine how applicable the process was to British coals. Developments took place in Germany, particularly in the treatment of brown coal and brown coal tar, and it is reported that during 1932 as much as 350,000 tons of motor spirit were produced in this way. During the same period a programme of work was started by Imperial Chemical Industries, Ltd., which resulted in the construction and operation first of a unit plant of 15 tons per day capacity and eventually of a full-scale plant for the conversion of 400 tons of bituminous coal per day. This plant was operated for some time prior to 1939 but did not prove to be an economic proposition and was modified to treat creosote instead of coal. Working data were collected, however, for the successful technical treatment of coal. It was in Germany, however, that the process was put to greatest use. In 1944 twelve factories were in use, producing over $3\frac{1}{2}$ million tons of oil fuel, of which $2\frac{1}{4}$ were petrol. In this case the raw material used was not only a more readily-converted coal—brown coal—but included brown coal tar, tar oils and petroleum residues. The technique of hydrogenation has also been applied to the treatment of petroleum fractions, particularly for the production of aviation spirit of high anti-knock value.

The principle of hydrogenation is the reduction of the C/H ratio by the action of hydrogen on the material. In the case of coal where the C/H ratio is about 15 : 1 the amount of hydrogen necessary to bring the ratio down to the 8/1 of petroleum is obviously large, but the reward is in the high yield of liquid product of about 75 per cent.

Bergius Process. In the Bergius process 20 parts of coal (less than 2 mm. in size) were mixed with 8 parts of heavy tar and 1 part of " luxmasse " (to fix the sulphur as iron sulphide) and the pasty mixture was pumped through three horizontal converters in series, $6\frac{1}{2}$ ft. long by 8 in. internal diameter with $2\frac{1}{2}$ in. walls and fitted with stirrers. The temperature was kept at 450–480° C. under a hydrogen pressure of 200 atmospheres. The product leaving the last converter was a thick tarry liquid containing as a stable emulsion water, iron oxide and residual solid matter from the coal. The products obtained from a Yorkshire coal containing 7·2 per cent. of ash and 0·9 per cent. moisture were :

TABLE XLVII

YIELDS FROM BERGIUS PROCESS PER TON OF PURE COAL

Hydrogen consumed = 114 lb.

Fraction	0°–175°	= 83 lb.
,,	175°–230°	= 208 ,,
,,	230°–270°	= 197 ,,
,,	270°–310°	= 105 ,,
,,	310°–360°	= 208 ,,
Pitch		= 329 ,,
Gas benzine		= 42 ,,
Residual gas		= 325 ,,
Unconverted coal		= 363 ,,
Water		= 179 ,,
Coal ash		= 161 ,,
Loss		= 154 ,,
		2354 ,,

The modern process is operated in two main stages of liquid and vapour-phase treatment. In the first the coal is pulverized, mixed or " pasted " with heavy oil and catalyst (0·1 per cent. of a tin salt) and pumped with hydrogen at a pressure of 250 atmospheres through a preheater into the bottom of the liquid-phase converter and maintained there at 400–480° C. The average time of this treatment is about two hours.

The reaction products which vaporize are carried with the excess hydrogen and hydrocarbon gases through a condenser, a separator and a gas-washing tower.

The reactions involved are exothermic (450 cal. per kg. of coal), but additional heat is required to reach the necessary reaction temperature ; this is supplied to the preheater. In the converter, cooling is achieved where necessary by introducing cold hydrogen at different levels. Improved conversion to oil is obtained by the addition of halogen compounds to the feed, but this involves the addition of anti-corrosion measures during the condensation of the product. The crude condensate is separated into three fractions :

(1) Spirit		to 170° C.
(2) Middle oil		170° to 230° C.
(3) Heavy oil		over 230° C.

The materials which resist the action of the hydrogen—fusain, inorganic matter and catalyst—are run off continuously as a heavy sludge with some oil. The sludge is distilled for the recovery of some of the oil and this is used for pasting. The second stage determines the character of the final product, which is motor spirit. The middle oil from stage 1 is passed with hydrogen through a similar converter containing a static bed of catalyst again at a

pressure of 250 atm. or more.   The heat of reaction is exothermic and is
sufficient to maintain the reaction temperature of 400–480° C.   The vapours
are condensed, the oils distilled and the heavier fractions recycled ; the

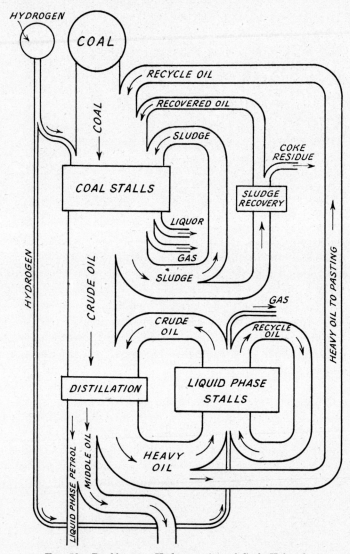

FIG. 56.—Double-stage Hydrogenation of Coal (Holroyd).

gases, which consist of residual hydrogen and gaseous hydrocarbons, are
processed for the production of hydrogen.   The time of treatment in this
phase is about one minute.   Partial condensation may alternatively be used
for separation in both phases, when a separated middle oil can be passed
directly from stage 1 to stage 2.

Figure 56 illustrates the stages of the process. The pressure vessels are very large, e.g. 30 ft. high by 48 in. dia., and treat some 20 tons of material per hour.

Yields. The following quantities may be regarded as typical of British coal and are calculated to ash-free material :

Stage 1 :

Hydrogen consumed . . . . 30,000 cu. ft.
Oils boiling below 170° C. . . . 40 gal.
Oils boiling over 170° C. . . . 130 gal.

Stage 2 :

Hydrogen consumed . . . . 18,000 cu. ft.
Spirit, b.pt. 170° C. . . . . 170 gal. or 57 per cent. by weight

The overall result is that 170 gal. are produced for a net consumption of one ton of pure coal and 48,000 cu. ft. of hydrogen, of which 22,000 cu. ft. enters into combination with the coal to form oil and water. The remaining hydrogen forms hydrocarbon gases, mainly methane. Some excess of hydrogen is required and the total compressed hydrogen requirement is 53,000 cu. ft.

Hydrogen. The hydrogen for the process may be produced directly from coke, or by liquefaction from coke-oven gas, or by the catalytic cracking of gaseous hydrocarbons. It can be calculated that, if 15 of the 85 per cent. of carbon in the coal were converted in the process to methane, and this cracked with steam, the process would become virtually self-contained as regards hydrogen and the yield of spirit would attain 72 per cent. by weight of the coal. The operation of the process requires fuel and power, and it is estimated that this amounts to $1\frac{1}{2}$ tons of coal per ton of coal treated ; this means that the total requirement of coal per ton of spirit would be from 3 to 4 tons when the hydrogen was made by the methane-steam reaction from by-product gas.

The process used by I.C.I. Ltd. for the manufacture of hydrogen was no doubt selected because of the prior existence of the synthetic ammonia plant ; it has the following stages :

1. Carbonization of coal in ovens.
2. Conversion of coke to water gas.
3. Catalysis by the water-gas shift reaction with steam to CO_2 and H_2.
4. Removal of the CO_2 by washing with water under pressure and of the residual CO by washing with an ammoniacal copper solution. The water may with advantage be replaced by ethanolamine solution which has a higher solubility for CO_2.

The thermal efficiencies of the steps of the process are coal to coke 85, coke to water gas 69, water gas to hydrogen 93, and overall coal to hydrogen 55 per cent.

The hydrocarbon/steam process was originally introduced for the manufacture of hydrogen from natural gas and can be expressed as :

(1) $CH_4 + H_2O \longrightarrow 3H_2 + CO$ over Ni at $550°$ C.
(2) $3H_3 + CO + H_2O \longrightarrow 4H_2 + CO_2$ over Fe/Cr at $450°$ C.

Both reactions are endothermic, but an overall efficiency of 74 per cent. is attainable. Since the catalyst used in the first stage is Ni, it is necessary either to remove sulphur compounds or to work at a higher temperature of $825°$ C. In practice, sulphur compounds can be removed by passage over activated bauxite at $700°$ C.

The process hydrogen need not be pure ; for the first stage it need not be richer than 85 per cent. H. On leaving this stage it is about 70 per cent. H. For the second stage the concentration entering the converter should not be less than 90 per cent.

Hydrogenation Catalysts. The catalyst used in the liquid phase may comprise any of the elements of the fourth group of the periodic classification, but the most active is tin or a compound of tin ; the amount required is less than 0·1 per cent. of the coal treated. The effect of the catalyst is to accelerate the rate of combination of hydrogen to such an extent that a reaction temperature can be used at which thermal effects such as coking become negligible ; the " pasting " of the coal with oil has also an important effect.

The conversion of the middle oil in the second stage is substantially the same in principle as the treatment of the paste in the liquid phase. The first stage of the reaction is hydrogenation ; this is followed by cracking, with simultaneous hydrogenation of the unsaturated products. The temperature used (between $400°$ and $500°$ C.) is carefully controlled to suit the catalyst chosen and the type of product required, but the result is necessarily a compromise between cracking and hydrogenation to obtain the best yields ; these vary between 82 and 90 per cent. by weight of the middle oil.

The catalyst is used in a static form, i.e. the reaction vessel is packed with a granulated material which does not impede the passage of the vapours. The most active are compounds of molybdenum and tungsten, particularly the sulphides, and halogens, particularly iodine. The reactions are strongly exothermic and a metallic catalyst of high thermal conductivity would be useful. The control of this heat of reaction is readily achieved in practice by arranging the catalyst in layers and introducing controlled quantities of cold hydrogen between the layers.

Products. The main product of the hydrogenation of coal is motor spirit. As stated above, the nature of this spirit depends upon the type of vapour-phase catalyst used. The range is defined by Holroyd in describing three types :

(*a*) Those which operate at high temperature (500° C.) have high cracking power and give a rather lower yield of spirit rich in aromatic hydrocarbons.

(*b*) Those with a high saturating power and which operate at a low reaction temperature (400° C.).

(*c*) Those which operate at an intermediate temperature and which favour isomerization and, therefore, increase of octane number.

The composition of three spirits representing (*a*), (*b*) and (*c*) are shown in the following table as percentages by volume :

VAPOUR-PHASE SPIRITS

	(*a*)	(*b*)	(*c*)
Butane	5	5	5
Paraffins	11	14	4
iso-Paraffins	5	28	30
Aromatics	43	3	7
Unsaturateds	3	—	—
Naphthenes	18	25	28
Octane number (motor)	80	68	76
„ with 4 c.c. of tetra-ethyl-lead	86	86	90

The lead susceptibility of spirits (*b*) and (*c*) is marked. The recycle middle oil, using catalyst (*b*), could provide a fair diesel oil as it is naphthenic and highly saturated. It has a specific gravity of 0·836 and a spontaneous ignition temperature of 265° C.

Attempts to make lubricating oils from coal by hydrogenation have not been successful.

A wide range of coals are suitable for hydrogenation up to a carbon content of 84 per cent., but the best range is from 80 to 84 C, and 5·0 to 5·8 H. Coal of higher carbon content requires a higher working temperature and a longer time of treatment. Coals of lower carbon content are more amenable but give lower yields of oil. Comparative data for British coals treated under identical conditions are :

	1	2	3	4	5
Carbon	87·5	85·1	83·5	82·0	78·7
Hydrogen	5·3	5·6	5·5	5·4	5·6
Solid residue	18·2	10·4	9·4	5·6	7·7
Soluble oil	71·0	74·6	73·4	72·4	70·3

The high figure for solid residue in 1 shows the greater resistance of this coal to reaction ; the yield of soluble oil decreases with decreasing carbon content below 85 per cent.

German Brown Coal. During the 1939–45 war very considerable quantities of lignite were hydrogenated in Germany for the production of motor spirit. The wet coal containing 50 per cent. of water and 5 per cent. of ash is mixed (pasted) with 4 per cent. of alkaline iron oxide to act as a catalyst, dried to 5 per cent. water, and pasted with its own weight of heavy oil from the process. The paste was treated in four converters in series at a pressure of 230 atm. and a temperature of 430–490° C., with circulation of hydrogen at the rate of 1000 vols. per volume of paste. The liquid product separated at 400° C. is reduced to atmospheric pressure, diluted with distillate oil, centrifuged to remove mineral matter, and used as recycle oil ; the sludge is carbonized for oil recovery. The vapour separated at 400° C. is cooled, the product distilled to 325° C. and the heavy oil returned for treatment. Conditions are controlled to provide just enough pasting oil for the process. At Leuna the coal stall of four converters treated the equivalent of four tons of dry, ash-free coal per day.

The yield of petrol and middle oil was 50 per cent. of the dry, ash-free coal, for a hydrogen sorption of 6–7 per cent. and a hydrocarbon gas formation of 15 per cent. The middle oil is retreated by vapour-phase hydrogenation and the overall yield was :

	Motor spirit.	Aviation spirit.
Motor spirit	46·2	40·2
Hydrocarbon gas	19·3	25·7
H_2 consumed	9·1	9·3

Vapour-Phase Hydrogenation of Middle Oils. The above middle oils, recycle oil, tar fractions and heavy petroleum oils were converted to petrol in the German war effort. The general principle was the addition of sufficient hydrogen to keep the oils in the vapour phase and to pass these through static catalysts at 250–300 atm. pressure at a temperature of not more than 450° C. The catalyst was tungsten sulphide and the product was rather oversaturated and not of very high octane number. This can now be overcome by operation in two stages, the first being a mild hydrogenation and the second a molecule-splitting stage which is the main source of material of low boiling-point. The modern technique is explained below with reference to the treatment of creosote.

In Germany each stage was arranged in stalls capable of treating 400–600 tons of middle oil per day. The yield of spirit was 92–95 per cent. or 80 per cent. of aviation gasoline.

Hydrogenation of Creosote

Hydrogenation can also play an important part in the treatment of tars and tar oils for the production of either chemicals or fuels.

Creosote, a fraction of high-temperature tar, is already being treated in large quantities for the production of motor spirit. Unlike coal, it does not necessarily require liquid-phase treatment, although this is advantageous in order to remove a small proportion of intractable material. Crude tars can also be hydrogenated, but require the liquid-phase stage for fairly complete conversion. Their ease of treatment increases with reduction of the carbonizing temperature of the coal, and low-temperature tar is an excellent raw material for the process. The temperature of treatment is about 480° C. at 200 to 250 atm. pressure. The product from the first stage is fractionally distilled (or condensed), the heavy ends rejected and the middle oil recycled. The oil from this stage is recycled to complete conversion in the vapour-phase.

Typical conversion data are :

	Low-temp. tar.	Vertical-retort tar.
Hydrogen absorbed per cent.	5·5	6·4
(1) Spirit to 170° C. per cent. by weight .	15	12
Oil over 170° C. ,, ,, .	68	70
Residue ,, ,, .	4	4
(2) Spirit to 170° C. ,, ,, ..	71	73
Yield per cent. by volume . . .	95	99
Properties of Spirit.		
Specific gravity at 150° C. . . .	0·810	0·830
Aromatics	7	4
Unsaturateds	1	1
Saturateds	92	95
Per cent. above 100° C.	33	40
Octane number (motor)	67	67

These results show that all the tar made could be hydrogenated to spirit, if plant were available, with a loss of only 3 to 4 per cent. of untreatable residue. One ton of tar yields about 0·6 ton of spirit.

I.C.I. Process. The two-stage treatment of distillable oils boiling below 330° C. can be explained in relation to creosote, and is illustrated in the diagram Figure 57. The catalyst in both phases was tungsten sulphide ; in the first the pure substance is used ; in the second it is dispersed on activated earth. To avoid over-hydrogenation in the saturation stage the amount of hydrogen reacting is limited and to increase the life of the second-stage catalyst ammonia is removed from the feed-stock. In order to reduce still further the hydrogenation in the splitting stage the tungsten sulphide catalyst is now replaced by one based on iron and a higher average octane number is attained. The effect of the two-stage process is shown in Table XLVIII in comparison with the result of a single-phase treatment in which over tungsten sulphide there is undue hydrogenation. The pressure used is 256 atm., the concentration of the inlet

TABLE XLVIII

The Conversion of Creosote to Motor Spirit by Hydrogenation

(K. Gordon, *J. Inst. Fuel*, 1946/7, **20**, 42)

	One stage.	Saturation stage.	Splitting stage. (a)	Splitting stage. (b)
Tons feed/m³ cat./hr. . . .	1·1	1·2	1·3	1·0
H₂, m³/ton feed	2000	2800	1600	1700
Cooling gas, m³/ton feed . . .	1700	1900	900	850
Temperature, °C.	420	385	400	370
Spirit yield, weight per cent. . .	86·5	—	88·5	75·0
H/C gas yield, weight per cent. . .	16·8	1·5	13·0	27·5
H₂ consumed, weight per cent. . .	8·4	5·1	3·0	3·5
Octane, number, C.F.R. motor . .	68	—	75	77

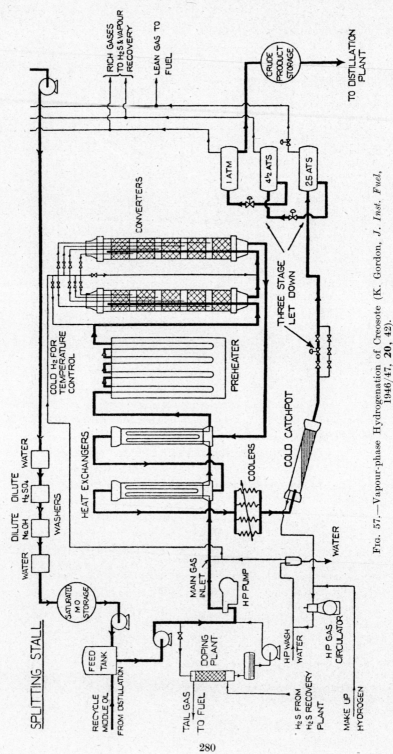

Fig. 57.—Vapour-phase Hydrogenation of Creosote (K. Gordon, *J. Inst. Fuel*, 1946/47, **20**, 42).

(By permission of the Institute of Fuel.)

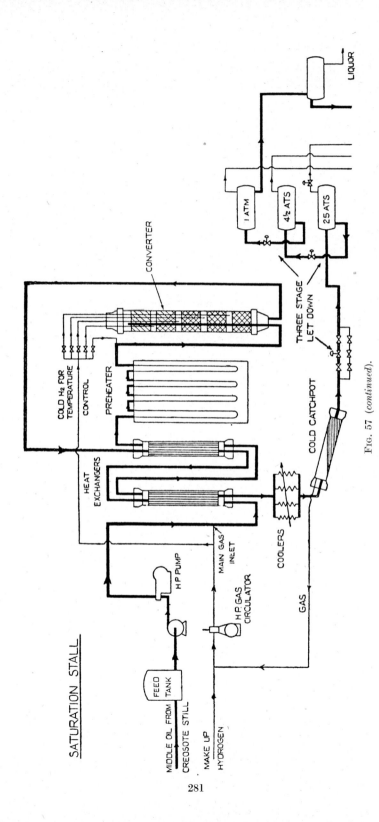

SATURATION STALL

MIDDLE OIL FROM CREOSOTE STILL

FEED TANK

MAKE UP HYDROGEN

H.P. PUMP

H.P. GAS CIRCULATOR

MAIN GAS INLET

HEAT EXCHANGERS

COLD H₂ FOR TEMPERATURE CONTROL

PREHEATER

CONVERTER

COOLERS

GAS

COLD CATCHPOT

THREE STAGE LET DOWN

25 ATS

4½ ATS

1 ATM

LIQUOR

Fig. 57 (*continued*).

281

hydrogen is 85 per cent., and hydrogen is also introduced at stages in the catalyst bed to prevent rise of temperature by the exothermic heat of reaction.

One ton of creosote, with 0·08 ton of hydrogen, can, therefore, yield 0·88 ton of high-grade gasoline and 0·03 ton of butane.

This means that 100 volumes of creosote can yield from 115 to 125 volumes of high-grade motor spirit.

Treatment of Hydrogenation Products. The butane fraction, recovered to the extent of 3–4 per cent. by weight, contains *iso*-butane and is a good raw material for the making of aviation spirit. The butane is dehydrogenated by a Cr/Al catalyst at 560° C. and atmospheric pressure to the *iso*- form with liberation of heat. The C_4 fraction is separated, polymerized by a phosphoric acid catalyst, the dimer and trimer separated and hydrogenated over a nickel catalyst to *iso*-octane. The process is complicated but gives a yield of 78 per cent. by weight of *iso*-octane of great value as an aviation spirit blending stock. One volume of the product with 3 volumes of hydrogenated spirit has a knock-rating of 110.

The new techniques of the petroleum industry are all available now for the further treatment of distillates of all kinds and there is no technical limit to the chemical reforming of hydrocarbons into fuels or chemicals.

Methanol. Methanol is a valuable component of special motor spirit (p. 342) ; it can be made by the passage of synthesis gas ($2H_2 + CO$) over a ZnO/Cr_2O_3 catalyst at 400° C. The plant must be protected by copper lining or by the use of stainless steel from the action of the carbon monoxide which under these conditions produces iron carbonyls. The product is a mixture of 75 per cent. methanol, with very little ethanol, and 25 per cent. higher alcohols ; the latter are recirculated though with appreciable gas loss. Their formation cannot yet be avoided.

Indirect Production of Oil from Coal

Indirect processes involve first the complete gasification of coal or coke, and the conversion of the gas to oils. The first indications of the existence of the reactions were due to Sabatier (1905), but the development of a process was due first to the Bädische Anilin A.G. and Fischer in Germany, and to Patart in France. In the first form of the process, mixtures of carbon monoxide and hydrogen were passed over catalysts (e.g. zinc and chromium oxides) at pressures varying from 70 to 250 atm. and at temperatures varying from 300° to 410° C. This work has now developed into a process for the manufacture of methyl and higher alcohols, consuming 2 tons of coal per ton of methyl alcohol or 3 tons per ton of higher alcohols.

A remarkable variation of the process was advanced by Fischer and Tropsch in 1925. Using a catalyst such as nickel or cobalt oxides, they produced liquid hydrocarbons from mixtures of hydrogen and carbon monoxide at atmospheric pressure and at about 200° C. Since then the process developed to a remarkable extent in Germany and during the war produced half a million tons of fuels per annum. Since the war technical-scale research has been carried out on the process in the United States, by the Bureau of Mines ; in Great Britain continuous research at the Fuel Research Station has kept abreast of scientific knowledge.

The process consists in gasifying coal or coke, adjusting the H_2/CO ratio to 2/1, purifying this from sulphur compounds, and passing the synthesis gas over a granular cobalt catalyst at 190–200° C. In the U.S. work synthesis gas is also made from natural gas and the possibility of using a fluid-bed catalyst has been explored.

$$nCO + 2nH_2 \rightarrow C_nH_{2n} + nH_2O$$
$$nCO + (2n + 1)H_2 \rightarrow C_nH_{2n+2} + nH_2O$$

The gas must be rigorously purified down to 1/10th grain of sulphur per 100 cu. ft. and a new process had to be evolved by the development company in Germany before they could proceed. The process found consisted in the passage of the gas over alkaline iron oxide at a temperature of 200° C., when the organic sulphur compounds were destroyed and absorbed.

The synthesis reactions are not easy to control, since they are strongly exothermic (7200 B.Th.U. per lb. of liquid products) and the heat must be removed rapidly ; an undue rise of temperature of the catalyst would cause rapid deterioration of its activity. In the German plants this was achieved by circulating water through horizontal steel tubes of small diameter, arranged in a nest, around which the catalyst is packed. The pressure of steam raised was used as a means of temperature control. This method of catalyst control depends upon thermal conduction across small spaces and may be superseded by one of the new methods of control developed in the oil industry.

The catalyst chambers (Figure 58) are large, each having a through-put of about 1000 cu. m. of gas per hour, or a normal productivity of 1000 tons of liquid product per annum. They are operated on a cycle (1) to allow of catalyst replacement (normal life, six months), and (2) to divide the synthesis into two or more stages, the second stage taking spent gas from the first, and so on. In the first stage, 70 to 80 per cent. of the CO is converted, and with the second stage, about 90 per cent.

The products are recovered by direct cooling with water, followed by scrubbing with active carbon. Since they are practically free from sulphur, a light wash with alkali is sufficient refining treatment. Chemically, the products are all straight-chain hydrocarbons, so that the motor spirit is of low octane number (52) and the diesel oil fraction of high cetane number (105).

The condensable oils and gases are usually referred to as " total primary product ", and include heavy hydrocarbon gases (C_3 and C_4), and oils covering the whole range up to wax (over C_{35}). The theoretical yield is about 208 gm. per cu. m., but the average yield in practice is about 140 to 160 gm. The conversion of some of the carbon monoxide to methane is unavoidable. The following table illustrates yields at (a) atmospheric, and (b) 15 atm. pressure.

	Yields of Primary Products, per cent. by wt.	
	(a)	(b)
Methane	18	14
C₃–C₄ hydrocarbons	11	6
Spirit to 200° C.	43	33
Oils to 300° C.	20	26
Paraffin wax	8	21
Gm. per cu. m. of synthetic gas . .	120	135

Catalytic cracking and polymerization of the total crude oil gives an 85 per cent. yield of 68-octane motor spirit, of which 50 per cent. could, after *leading*, be aviation spirit and 35 per cent. motor spirit.

Fig. 58.—Catalyst Chambers for Fischer-Tropsch Synthesis at Atmospheric Pressure.

The diesel oil fraction is probably the best known, having a cetane value of over 105, and has particular merit as a blending stock.

The hydrocarbon gases are condensable into cylinders and can be used for transport power or for chemical processes.

The general process has been modified by the introduction of new catalysts which allow of operation at pressures up to 15 atm. The modification has the main advantage of greater yield, but the product moves, with increasing pressure, in the direction of wax. In the German pressure plants, the catalyst is placed inside the tubes and the water, or other thermal fluid, flows outside ; this modification is occasioned by considerations of strength as well as of heat transfer. Also, the condensation of the primary product is by indirect cooling.

	Gas.	Liquid.	Solid.	Catalyst.	P atm.	T ° C.
Paraffins and olefines .	little	much	little	NiCo	1	190
Paraffins and little olefines .	,,	,,	much	Co	5–20	190
Paraffins and much olefines .	,,	,,	little	Fe	5–20	240
Mainly solid paraffins .	,,	little	much	Ru	>100	200
iso-Paraffins	much	much	—	—	>100	>200
Naphthenes and aromatics .	,,	,,	—	—	>100	>200

At medium pressures the highest wax yield is obtained at 10 atm., using cobalt. With ruthenium, striking new waxes are being made and iso-synthesis (high octane) is claimed.

There are strong indications in this work that plant on Fischer-Tropsch lines would be a considerable asset to Great Britain, partly as a source of fuel, but mainly to provide liquid products from town gas plant during periods of low gas demand (summer).

Efficiency and Yields. The Fischer-Tropsch process has been adversely criticized because of alleged low thermal efficiency. As a source of chemicals rather than of fuels, high thermal efficiency is not so essential, but the true value is not so low as the 25 per cent. usually quoted.

In Germany the brown coal lends itself to a process of complete gasification to make synthesis gas, but it has not yet been shown that this can be done with British coals other than Welsh steam coal. In Britain, therefore, the only logical procedure at present in erecting a pilot plant would be to associate it with the carbonizing industries, particularly as they already know the technique of gas production and purification necessary. The joining of a Fischer-Tropsch plant into a unit already producing gas and/or coke might well lead to an overall efficiency not realizable in an independent plant. Assuming both coke and gas available, and cracking some gas to raise the $H_2 : CO$ ratio of water gas (made from coke) to 2 : 1, it can be calculated that 3·45 tons of coal only are required to produce 1 ton of primary product. The calculation assumes synthesis in three stages, the spent gas after each stage being cracked with steam to make additional synthesis gas, and the heat of reaction being utilized in the form of steam to operate the entire plant, including the manufacture of catalyst. This figure of 3·45 tons is equivalent to a thermal efficiency of 42 per cent., which will not be improved until the yield of 160 gm. of primary product per cubic metre can be made to approach more closely the theoretical figures of about 208 gm. The thermal efficiencies of the hydrogenation and synthesis processes, therefore, are of the same order.

Developments. During the post-war years considerable advances have been made in the original German process. The fixed-bed system of catalyst control has been improved by the Ruhrchemie Co. so that the catalyst capacity of a unit reactor is increased fourfold and, by increase of linear velocity of the reacting gases, the space-time yield is increased fivefold. These changes increase the output of a unit from 2·5 tons to 50 tons per day.

In the Hydrocol plant at Brownsville, Texas, the gases pass upwards through a fluidized iron catalyst at 320° C. and 400 lb. pressure. This plant was built to make 300,000 tons of motor spirit per day, and other products, but never more than one-third of the designed output was achieved.

The original cobalt catalyst is now replaced by catalysts based on iron as these are of lower cost and greater range. The cobalt catalyst was restricted to a synthesis gas of $H_2/CO = 2$ and a temperature of 170–230° C. whereas iron can be used over the range 200–350° C. and $H_2/CO = 2 : 1$ to 0·5 : 1. This cheapens the cost of process gas and offers a wider range of products, which include olefines, and alcohols. The iron catalysts are made by precipitation from solutions of iron salts but may be made from fused magnetite or mill-scale. The only common promoter is potassium oxide in the proportion of 0·5 to one part per 100 parts of iron.

The pressure can also be raised from a maximum of 220 lb. to 750 lb. per sq. in.

The product can be made to vary widely so far as the production of chemicals is concerned, e.g. it may contain as much as 50 per cent. of hard wax, but so far as fuel is concerned it is important that high octane spirit can be made in high yield. At 300° C. the product may be wholly olefinic ; by polymerizing the propylene and butylene, and reforming the naphtha, the yield may reach 80 per cent. at an octane number of 80.

It may be concluded that the process is not attractive for the purpose of producing fuels only, except in circumstances where the source of fuel for making the synthesis gas is cheap. This is not likely to recur in the western hemisphere but is a Dominion possibility, e.g. in South Africa, where a major development is taking place. The process remains of interest, however, as a means of making partly chemicals and partly fuels, and as a means of integrating material requirements in the carbonizing industries at times of peak load.

REFERENCE BOOKS

Our Industry. Anglo-Iranian Oil Co., Ltd., London. 1947.
Coal Tar Fuels. Assoc. of Tar Distillers, London. 1944.
Fuel Oil and Oil Firing. G. J. Gollin. *The Heating and Ventilating Eng.*, 1947.
The Science of Petroleum. Dunstan. Oxford Univ. Press. 1938.
Oil Shale and Cannel Coal. The Inst. of Petroleum. 1938.
Progress in the Hydrogenation of Coal and Tar. K. Gordon. *J. Inst. Fuel*, 1947, **20, 42.**

Hydrogenation in the Fuel and Chemical Industries. K. Gordon. *Ibid.*, **21**, 53.
American Petroleum Refining. Bell. van Nostrand. 1945.
Chemical Constituents of Petroleum. Sachanan. Rheinhold Publ. Corp. 1934–8.
Fischer-Tropsch and Related Syntheses. Storch, Golumbic, and Anderson. John
    Wiley. 1951.
Petroleum Technology. Gurwitsch and Moore. Chapman and Hall. 1932.
Liquid Fuels. Moore. 1935.
The World's Oilfields: Eastern Hemisphere. Illing. 1953.
World Geology of Petroleum. Pratt and Good. Princeton Univ. Press. 1950.

CHAPTER XI

PETROLEUM FUEL OILS

As explained in Chapter X, petroleum fuel oil is essentially the high-boiling residue of the processing of petroleum oils.; it may be the straight-run residue of the primary distillation, or the heavy, uncrackable material from thermal or catalytic cracking, or any mixture of these depending upon the refinery programme at the moment. It will also vary with the type of crude petroleum from which it is the residue. Further, it may contain the residues of any of the stages or secondary processes of refining and purification. In spite of this apparently non-standard composition its calorific value remains in the range 18,200 to 19,500 B.Th.U. per lb. and, with suitable technique, it finds many applications as the fuel for steam raising and furnace work in general. Quantitatively it is of great importance to the economics of petroleum processing since it may represent as much as 40 per cent. by weight of the crude oil.

The chemical characteristics of fuel oils must therefore vary considerably, but not all of these affect their utilization as fuels and a generalized technique can achieve their use with high efficiency. Certain properties, however, remain of importance and are the subject of specifications to which the oils must conform. The most important of these is viscosity, which is referred to a specific temperature ; in Great Britain the standard is 100° F., in the U.S.A. it is 122° F., while in Europe there are two levels of 50° and 20° C. In general the terms " light " and " heavy " are used to describe fuels of low and high viscosity respectively. The upper limit of viscosity to-day is about 7000 sec. in the Redwood I viscometer at 100° F., but a number of other grades are recognized down to 250 sec. Residue oils of viscosity higher than 7000 sec. are normally subjected to mild cracking to break down the heavier bodies and so reduce viscosity ; this process occasions some loss of oil as gas and is called *viscosity breaking*. The second factor of importance is flash-point, but for reasons of safety not of utilization ; the minimum flash-point of all grades is 150° F. The third factor is water content. Since really heavy oils approach the density of water it is a matter of importance to keep them free from water during preparation and handling since the small difference in density would make later separation very difficult. Finally, the oil should be free from sediment since this would gradually collect in tank bottoms. Certain British specifications are given at the end of the chapter. These may seem simple but it is necessary to remember that the purpose of the oils is combustion only and that combustion conditions can be set up to burn with efficiency a wide

288

range of materials. At one time it was thought that the residues from cracking would be less efficient as a fuel but this is not so. Their free-carbon content is below 0·1 per cent. but they may have a tendency to sludge; this is overcome by attention to blending and the use of " deposit " tanks at the refineries.

The essential factor, therefore, in the utilization of fuel oils is the control of their combustion and the selection of a grade for any particular purpose is governed technically by the size of the combustion chamber, the nature of the equipment (pumps, etc.), and the type and size of burner and the method of atomization. Price is of course a factor since the use of the cheaper, high-viscosity oils means the provision of heating pipes in storage tanks and heated service piping.

General Arrangement of Oil Supply to Burners. The oil should be almost free from suspended water and solids, but most installations provide for the contingency of this not being wholly the case. When the oil is supplied by gravity from tanks it is usual to employ a pair of supply tanks into which the oil is pumped ; here it is heated by a steam coil to promote the separation of water and increase the fluidity of the oil.

At ordinary temperatures the separation of finely divided water is very sluggish, since the difference of gravity is but slight, and with the high viscosity of the oil these globules remain suspended almost indefinitely. On heating the oil two distinct changes occur—first, its viscosity is reduced very rapidly, and secondly, the oil expands at a greater rate than water, so that the difference in specific gravity is considerably increased. The relative coefficients of expansion of heavy oils and water are approximately per degree Centigrade 0·00070 and 0·000476 ; or, per degree Fahrenheit, 0·00039 and 0·000264.

Oil may be preheated above its flash-point, but only under pressure, and it is very essential to the attainment of smooth working, with the least necessity for alteration of the oil or atomizing agent valves, that the temperature shall be fairly uniform and the pressure of the oil supply constant.

When steam or air atomization is employed the supply of oil may be from a feed tank or tanks at a sufficient height to give the necessary flow. Since very viscous oils cannot be effectively atomized heating is necessary and where steam is available a suitable heater may be arranged in the supply line. For actual pumping the temperature required may be 100–250° F. and for atomization at the burner 150–300° F.

Oil is normally pumpable at a viscosity of 3000 sec. and for this value the temperature varies.

	Sec. at 100° F.	Pumping temp. ° F.
Oil	200	45
Oil	600	60
Oil	1500	80

In pressure-spraying systems filters are provided in duplicate on both the suction and pressure sides of the oil pump, the gauze in the filters in the suction side being of larger mesh than that in the pressure side, the actual mesh of the gauze being determined by the fluidity of the oil used.

Instead of these simple gauze filters other and more efficient methods of removing solid matter are available, such as the well-known " Stream-line " filters or the " Auto-Klean " filters. In the latter the oil passes from outwards between a number of perforated thin steel plates, with fine clear-ances between them. Between the plates are a number of thin fixed steel knives. On giving the filtering cartridge a half-turn the accumulated dirt is cleared away and falls into a sump from which it is readily removed. To provide for the proper regulation of the oil pressure a loaded valve on a connection between the pressure side and the suction side of the pump is fitted, and lifts when the maximum is reached. For the oil to attain the necessary working temperature it is circulated through suitable heaters by piping leading from the oil supply pipe to the burners (which are shut off) back to the suction side of the pump.

The general arrangement in the different systems is very similar, and is illustrated in Figure 59.

Oil Atomization and Oil Burners

For the complete combustion of the oil it is essential that as perfect a mixture as possible with air shall be attained. On theoretical grounds this is accomplished most easily with the oil vapour, but it is not practicable to vaporize properly the heavier fuel oils, since the temperature requisite leads to " cracking " of the oil and the formation of carbonaceous deposits in the vaporizer and burning of the metal. The system however is applic-able with low boiling oils, such as kerosine and intermediate oils, and little trouble is experienced if the vaporization takes place in presence of an adequate proportion of air.

With the heavier oils which are usually employed as fuel oil, con-version into as fine a mist of oil globules as possible enables proper admixture of air to be attained, and various forms of sprayers or atomizers are em-ployed, which increase the oil/air interface by forming droplets of a maximum size of 4 to 6 thousandths of an inch. The burner has other duties which may include any of the following :

Lift the fuel from a lower level.

Introduce some or all of the atomizing medium at such a speed that its momentum will entrain the amount of the secondary air required for a given flame length.

Maintain a stable flame front and a flame suited in shape to the furnace.

Complete the combustion of the oil droplets before the flame is chilled to the extent that smoke is formed.

Where the burner gives a narrow-angled, high-velocity flame the com-bustion air is sucked into the flame by its injector action. The design of

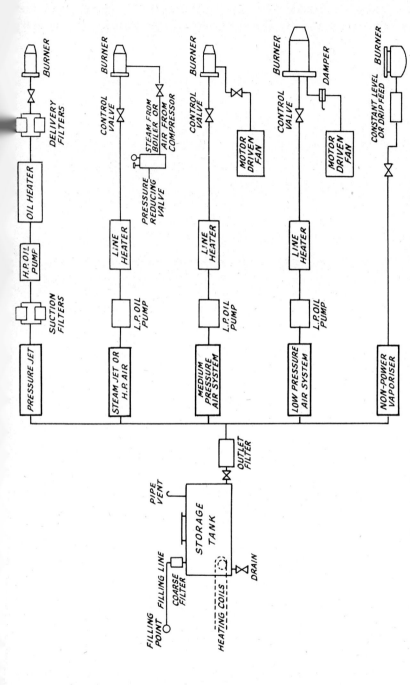

Fig. 59.—General Form of Oil-burning Installations for Different Forms of Burner
(G. J. Gollin, *Heating and Ventilating Engineer*, 1947).

the air intake is not important in this case but with a wide-angle flame the design of the air intake or " register " is of great importance and is really an integral part of the burner.

In order to ensure that a burner will continue to work at the desired output three factors must be satisfied :

1. The oil must arrive at the metering point at a constant viscosity.
2. The pressure at the same point must remain constant.
3. The metering device must remain unchoked.

Constant viscosity implies constant temperature and thermostatic control to within about $\pm 10°$ F. In small installations any drop of temperature between heater and burner is reduced by the use of a ring main round which hot oil is circulated. The amount circulated may be $1\frac{1}{2}$ times the maximum load on the burners. A constant pressure is difficult to maintain in any gravity-fed system, and is achieved by the use of a ring main of relatively high capacity, or by a special type of spring-loaded valve.

Two methods are available for maintaining a constant rate of supply of oil, (a) the use of a pump of fixed output delivering to a distributor box with two orifices (i) to burner and (ii) back to suction, so that the burner receives a constant proportion, and (b) the use of a piston pump with variable speed or stroke.

The control of the air for combustion is probably more important than the control of the oil since on its proper distribution depends the complete combustion of the oil ; this is dealt with below under type of burner.

Oil burners fall into two main groups depending upon the method of atomization of the oil but both depend upon the heating of the oil to a temperature at which the viscosity of the oil is between 80 and 100 seconds (Redwood 1) :

(1) Blast burners : atomization of the oil by air or steam blast—
  (a) At " low " pressures of 4 to 30 in. water gauge.
  (b) At medium pressures of 3 to 10 lb. per sq. in. gauge.
  (c) At high pressures of 10 lb. and upwards.
        The Rotary burner may be regarded as a variation of the low-pressure air burner.
(2) Pressure-jet burners : atomization of the oil by ejection under pressure through a special orifice.

A third form is a practical combination of these which gives better atomization of the oil than is possible with the pressure-jet alone.

Blast Burners. In this type of burner a high-velocity stream of air or steam impinges upon an issuing stream of oil in such a manner that it is torn into thin filaments and these dispersed in the form of a fine spray. The class is really divided into two groups, in addition to the pressure classification above, depending upon whether the atomizing medium and the oil meet mainly outside or within the burner ; in the latter case it may be added in several stages. The proportion of the atomizing medium depends mainly upon its pressure.

The low-pressure burner usually operates on a minimum of 20–30 per cent. of the air required for combustion but, for furnace work, can be supplied with the full quantity of air in order to make it independent of

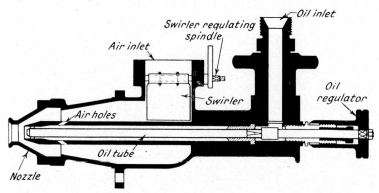

FIG. 60.—Low-pressure Oil Blast Burner (Wallsend Slipway and Engineering Co., Ltd.).

chimney pull or forced draught for the secondary air. Such a burner is shown in Figure 60, in which the air supply surrounds a central oil pipe, and both issue at a forward nozzle. With forced air the pressure may be 8–20 in. w.g. and the initial velocity 230–360 ft./sec. Adjustment of the radial velocity will give the desired flame-length and spread. At this low pressure the air aperture is large in relation to the oil nozzle. The burner will operate down to one-fifth of full load.

The medium-pressure burner atomizes the oil with 3 to 5 per cent. of the air for combustion, i.e. 5–10 cu. ft. per lb. of oil, or an equivalent amount of steam. The secondary air is supplied round the issuing stream. A typical

FIG. 61.—Medium-pressure Oil Blast Burner. Urquhart S.F.F. 2. 2/3 full size.

burner is shown in Figure 61 in which, under natural-draught conditions, the output is increased by increase of pressure of the air fraction used for atomization.

Air at lb. per sq. in	2	4	7	10
Oil burned, lb. per hour	35	50	75	90

The secondary air may be preheated to as high a temperature as possible by interchange with the waste gases. This type of burner is effective down to a size of a few pints per hour and has the good turn-down ratio of 4 or 5 : 1.

The high-pressure burner uses from 0·2 to 1 lb. of air or steam per lb. of oil, depending upon the particular design. Figure 62 illustrates a burner in which steam at 80–10-lb. pressure is used with a turn-down ratio of 8 : 1. The consumption of steam is about 0·5 per cent. of the boiler output. This particular burner has a wide range of output and will burn inferior oil with high efficiency.

The flame from a high-pressure burner is usually of narrow angle ($< 20°$) and its initial velocity about 1000 ft. per sec. The secondary air is sucked in by this injector action. The flame is difficult to ignite in a cold chamber because it is too rich, but in a heated chamber a stable flame

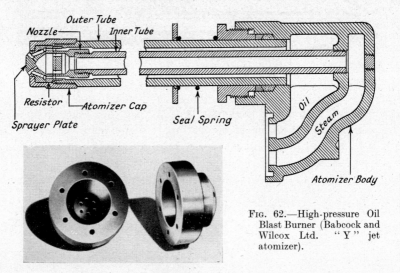

FIG. 62.—High-pressure Oil Blast Burner (Babcock and Wilcox Ltd. " Y " jet atomizer).

front is established about 18 in. from the burner nose. It has been shown that the flame length varies inversely with the initial momentum so that, for example, at the same fuel supply and same oil/air ratio, an air pressure of 100 lb. would give half the flame length obtained at a pressure of 10 lb.

Atomization. For efficient atomization of the oil stream it is evident that this must be uniformly distributed into the air stream as indicated above. The simplest form of atomizer is the " scent-spray ", in which the air is simply blown across a stream of oil as shown in Figure 63(a). This gives only a coarse spray and is not in common use. A simple method which is in use, particularly in locomotives, is to cause the oil to flow in a thin sheet downwards into a thin stream of the same width of high-pressure steam ; the secondary air being drawn in by natural draught. This is also shown in Figure 63(b) where A and B are air-nozzle and oil-inlet in the scent-spray and C and D are oil-feed and injector of the weir type.

Another method of thinning the oil stream without a nozzle is implicit in the rotary burner, where the oil is fed into a cup rotating at the high speed of 5000–7000 r.p.m. The motion of the cup thins out the oil which spills over the lip into the air stream. Some 15 per cent. of the air is passed round the cup in order to control the angle of delivery of the oil film.

The cup is rotated either by means of a small turbine or driven by an electric motor. The arrangement of such a burner is shown in the diagram Figure 64. The oil enters at low velocity and emerges into the air stream as a thin film. The thickness of this film is proportional to the weight of oil, W, taken per hour divided by Dv, where D is the diameter of the cup and v is the velocity of the oil in the plane of the axis of the cup. For commercial burners W/D varies between 125 and 250 lb. per hour per inch of cup diameter. The axial velocity attained

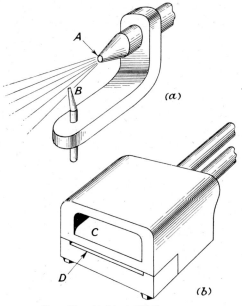

FIG. 63.—Air-blast Oil Burners.
(*a*) " Scent-spray " type. (*b*) Weir type.

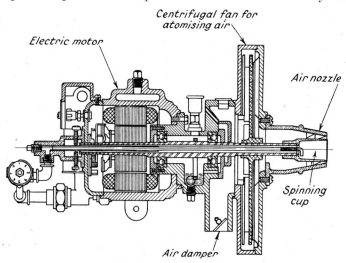

FIG. 64.—Rotary-cup Oil Burner.

depends upon the degree of taper of the cup and its speed of rotation. Air-driven cups use a speed of 5000 to 7000 r.p.m. and motor-driven cups 3000 to 3500 r.p.m.

Finally, a positive method of ensuring good atomization with a means of measurement of the rate of flow of the oil is to incorporate a pressure jet (below) in a blast burner. This is, however, a specialized application and is not common.

Steam Atomization. Steam is used in essentially the same way as air is used in the medium- or high-pressure burners. It is obviously desirable to limit the amount of steam used to a minimum since it does not take part in the combustion, and this is done by the use of a fairly high pressure. If the system in question is an oil-fired steam boiler the amount of steam consumed may be from 3 to 5 per cent. of that raised in the boiler. In other applications a self-generating steam atomizer is available which, after starting on air, provides the necessary steam from a flash-boiler arranged around the flame.

Secondary Air. The proper distribution of the secondary air around the flame is just as important as that of the oil ; this applies to all types of burners. The amount of total air is 18–20 lb. per lb. of fuel and it is apparent that this relatively large mass can have a large effect on flame stability and completeness of combustion. It has been shown above that, for air-blast burners, the proportion of the air for combustion which must be supplied around the flame varies from 60 per cent. in a low-pressure burner to 95 per cent. in medium- and high-pressure burners. In the case of the pressure-jet burner the proportion is 100 per cent.

Assuming that atomization is satisfactory, the air must be admitted around the cloud of oil vapour in the correct amount, at the right place, and with the right direction of flow. Too much air or too high a velocity at the flame can cause over-cooling of the flame or even its projection from the nozzle. In practice the air is introduced through an air-director or " register " which gives it a velocity of 40–50 ft. per sec. and a degree of tangential flow. Too high an axial velocity is not desirable as it causes instability of the flame. With air-blast burners the atomizing air has so much effect on the flame that the register really only delivers the right amount of air round it. This register may be in the form of a slotted plate round the burner with adjustable area of air inlet, or it may be in the form of a box with side-air intakes to give a degree of swirl. In the case of the pressure-jet burner considerable care is necessary if good combustion is to be achieved at 12–13 per cent. CO_2 content without smoke. Originally the air was supplied through a plain pipe round the burner, but now the pipe contains deflectors to give tangential flow. In other registers the air may be divided by annular flow, the inner stream being deflected into the oil vapour, and the outer being given radial flow. Both streams are controllable in

A. Insulation.
B. Air door.
C. Impeller plate.
D. Burner throat cone.
E. Sprayer plate.
F. Distance tube.
G. Air-door links.
H. Air-door adjustment.
J. Air-door lock.
K. Atomizer guides.
L. Distance-tube plug.
M. Atomizer.
N. Lighting door.
O. Oil supply.

FIG. 65.—The Decagon Air Register (Babcock and Wilcox Ltd.).

quantity.   The complicated character of an efficient air register is indicated
in Figure 65.

The Decagon register is designed for high air turbulence in order to
have a short flame length.   It has six curved air doors which overlap and
can be completely closed.   Turbulence is achieved by curved blades at the
entrance to the conical throat.   In order to avoid flame instability the
atomizer is shielded by an impeller which forms an eddy, and ensures
the start of combustion close to the burner tip.

Viscosity of Oil.   The maintenance of a suitable oil temperature,
and therefore viscosity, is an important factor in ensuring good atomization.
Viscosity ranges for different types of burner are as follows, taken at jet
temperature :

	Seconds Redwood I
Low-pressure air blast	100–150
Medium-pressure air blast	150–200
Rotary-cup air blast	up to 350
Pressure jet, large	100–120
„ „ small	70

Uses of Blast Burners.   The blast burner is the mainstay of furnace
work and the type chosen depends upon the design of the furnace, the
nature of flame required, whether operation is continuous or intermittent,
the temperature of operation and whether the materials being heated are
sensitive to the effect of temperature.

In the continuous furnace heat is recovered in the form of hot combustion air either from the waste gases in the case where the product is
discharged hot, or also from the product if this is required cold.   In either
case the burner is chosen to give a flame of the right size and shape and to
operate with the minimum amount of air.

Where a medium to high temperature is required (1200–1700° C.) very
fine atomization is not essential nor a flame which is essentially stable in a
cold enviroment.   In a tunnel kiln, for example, the burner is designed
to give a long narrow flame which is not stable in the cold and separate
means of heating from cold are required.   Burners for high-temperature
work, therefore, are either medium- or high-pressure air burners in which
the secondary air may be preheated up to about 1000° C.   Should the
furnace have to work at a pressure above atmospheric a medium-pressure
burner is mounted in a forced-draught casing, or a low-pressure air burner
is used and all the air passed through the burner.   Where too high a
degree of radiant heating is not desirable the internal-mixing type of
burner is used since it gives flame radiation more of the order of a gas
flame.

For steam raising in Economic boilers there is now a move towards
replacing the pressure-jet burner by blast burners of the rotary-cup type
for which the turn-down ratio can be 4 : 1 if the secondary air is correctly

applied. A high-pressure blast burner will serve the same purpose if an independent means of ignition is available.

Practical examples of the applications of air-blast burners can be taken from bakeries, grain etc. driers, metal-forging heaters, crucible and heat treatment furnaces of all kinds.

Baking ovens with side flues (Figure 66) require a long flame and may use any air-blast burner provided it is mounted in a proper air register to give the right distribution of secondary air for a slightly-hazy flame. Ovens heated from side and top flues require low-pressure burners in which all the combustion air passes through the burner, fine atomization, and high-speed circulation of the combustion gases to carry heat over the whole surface.

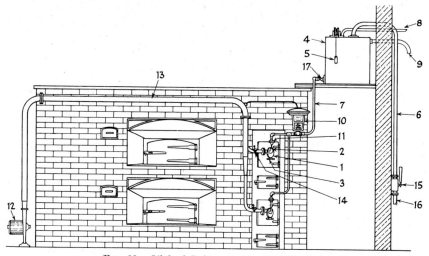

FIG. 66.—Oil-fired Baking Oven with Side Flues.

1, Burner; 2, Oil control valve; 3, Burner carrier gear; 4, Oil service tank; 5, Oil level indicator; 6, Filling pipe; 7, Oil supply pipe; 8, Air vent; 9, Overflow; 10, Automatic safety valve; 11, Oil pipe coupling; 12, Air blowing fan and motor; 13, Air supply pipe; 14, Butterfly damper; 15, Semi-rotary hand pump; 16, Oil pipe from oil storage; 17, Stop valve.

Insulation in the primary combustion zone may be necessary to avoid over-heating here and to release combustion gases hot enough to reach the end of the flues.

Grain driers are a special case since there must be no overheating and the amount of water to be evaporated is large. In the belt-type drier the burner is operated independently and the products of combustion diluted till they have a temperature of 300° F.; any efficient burner will suffice provided the diluting air is not allowed to chill the flame. In the pneu-matic drier the time of exposure of the grain is short—a few seconds—and the temperature may be 900° F. The medium-pressure burner is the most effective since it is less sensitive to flame chilling by the secondary air; such chilling could deposit soot on the grain.

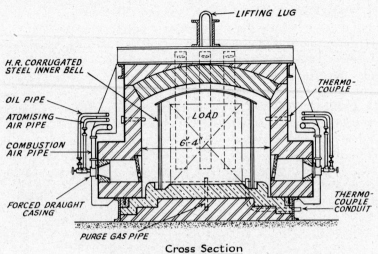

Cross Section

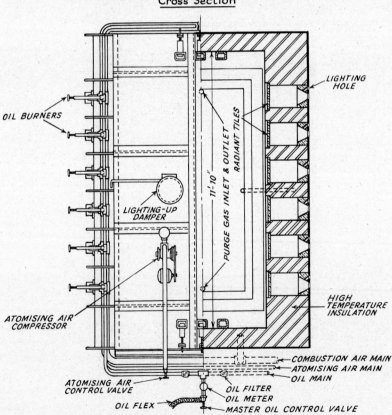

Fig. 67.—Oil-fired Bell-type Sheet Annealing Furnace.

300

In metallurgical work, air control is important in order to avoid scaling effects. The medium-pressure burner is supplied with 5 per cent. air for atomization while the secondary air is preheated and is under a pressure of a few inches w.g.   The preheat for the air is obtained by recuperation from the waste gases,   Crucible furnaces use a low-pressure burner inserted tangentially to give a rotary motion of gases round the crucible and increase the rate of heat transfer.   In this case the atmosphere is not important and regeneration of heat almost impossible.   In annealing or heat-treatment furnaces, or in carburizing steel, the atmosphere is again important as well as the temperature of the operation.   Figure 67 illustrates a bell-type furnace for the annealing of sheet steel at 650° C.   It is fired by medium-pressure air burners using forced-draught secondary air.   Adequate control is obtained by adjustment of the master valves of oil and air supply.   In

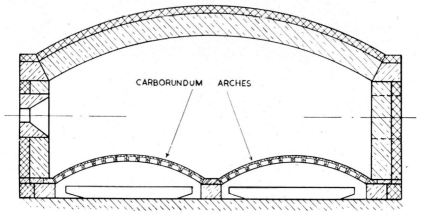

FIG. 68.—Copper-billet Heating Furnace.

a furnace of this type the combustion takes place out of contact with the materials being treated.   The fuel consumption for this purpose is about 5·5 gal. of oil per ton of steel.

A second example (Figure 68) may be taken from a billet-heating furnace designed to heat copper billets to 920° C. for rolling into wire. Low-pressure burners are used in order to operate under a slight pressure by passing all the combustion air through the burner.   The burners fire into a combustion chamber with a carborundum arch, extending 13 ft. towards the feed end, to protect the metal from flame radiation.   Recuperation provides air for combustion at 350° F.   At a throughput of 15 tons of copper per hour the consumption of oil is 14·4 lb. per ton.

A third example, in which the attainment of a high temperature may be necessary, is the crucible furnace.   The easy attainment with oil of this high temperature, the ease of control of this, the constant character of the combustion, all combine to ensure high efficiency.   An example of a

In the figure: CARBORUNDUM   ARCHES

metallurgical crucible furnace is given in Figure 69; in this type the furnace is arranged to tilt for discharge of molten metal.

Fig. 69.—Morgan Oil-fired Crucible Furnace.

An indication of the amount of oil consumed is given below. The amounts are relatively high since such furnaces cannot be arranged for recuperation from the waste-gases to the combustion air.

METAL MELTING IN OIL-FIRED TILTING FURNACES

	Brass.		Bronze.		Aluminium.	
Weight of charge (lb.) . . .	250	1120	250	1120	80	375
Average time of melt (min.)						
First heat	55	100	60	110	35	60
Other heats	35	70	40	75	20	35
Total weight of metal melted in						
eight hours (lb.)	2250	6720	2000	5600	1040	3375
Oil used per 100 lb. of metal (lb.)	12	8	13	9	16	12

A fourth example is the regenerative glass tank (Figure 70). Using medium-pressure air burners, two are arranged on each side of a tank of

22 tons glass capacity and used alternately with half-hour reversals. The burners are operated with 5 per cent. of combustion air and the secondary air is heated to 1050° C. by regeneration. No less than 11 tons of glass are melted per 24 hours.

Oil firing has also been applied to the open-hearth furnace, which was usually operated with gas. The high-pressure burner is used with steam injection (0·5 lb. per lb. oil) to give a long, narrow-angled flame directed on the slag furnace. For the melting of a 200-ton charge 2 tons of oil are burned per hour and the overall consumption is about 20 gal. per ton when

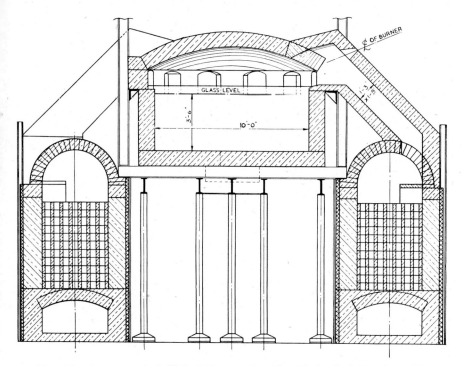

Fig. 70.—Arrangement of Oil-fired Regenerative Glass Tank (Shell Petroleum Co., Fuel and Light Oils Department).

working with 15–20 per cent. of excess air. The interest in using oil for this purpose is that a high proportion of the heat is used simply to keep the furnace at a high temperature, and it should be possible to achieve high heat-transfer rates to the steel from the very high emissivity of the flame ; the first few feet of this is known to approach perfect black-body conditions.

The need for economy of usage of fuel is causing a strong trend towards the elimination of batch furnaces and the general use of continuous operation and heat recuperation. The latter is also essential to the easy obtaining of high temperatures if that is necessary.

The Pressure-jet Burner. This type is the most common and probably burns a larger tonnage of oil than all the other types put together ; it is universal for shipping boilers, and in oil-fired power stations. The principle of the burner is extremely simple ; oil at high temperature and pressure is pumped through tangential ducts into a swirl chamber of a conical shape and leaves through a final orifice at the apex of the cone. The oil is first heated till its viscosity is in the range 10–30 centistokes (50–100 sec. Redwood I, and raised in pressure to 100–300 lb. per sq. in.

The main feature of this burner is the conical swirl chamber from which the oil, fed through cylindrical ducts drilled tangential to the circumference,

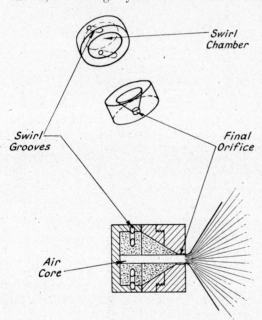

emerges at a velocity of about 30 ft. per sec. This angular velocity is increased as it approaches the orifice so that it forms a rapidly-rotating annulus about a central core of air. As this leaves the orifice it assumes a bubble shape within the distance of an inch and then spreads to a network of fine droplets which mix with the combustion air. The thickness of the oil annulus is from 7 to 10 per cent. of the diameter of the orifice. The droplet size is not uniform, but as a generalization it may be said that they vary from 20 to 200 μ.

Fig. 71.—Details of Simplex Pressure-jet Oil Burner (Shell Petroleum Co.).

The fundamentals of the design of a burner of this type are complicated and modern burners are more the result of repeated trial than exact calculation. Figure 71 shows the internal structure of one burner. The oil is fed through swirl-grooves to the inlet of tangential ducts which are cut in the spherical face which makes a joint with the inside of the cap.

The pressure-jet burner differs from the blast burner which not only atomizes the oil but plays a greater part in moulding the shape of the flame and stabilizing it. The pressure jet deals only with the first stage of the combustion and effective distribution of the secondary air is still essential to good performance. In modern practice this air is introduced through a high-speed-air director which operates on pressure air or demands a chimney pull of not less than 0·5 in w.g. The air director has already been discussed. The pressure drop across the air-intake is arranged to give an air-flow

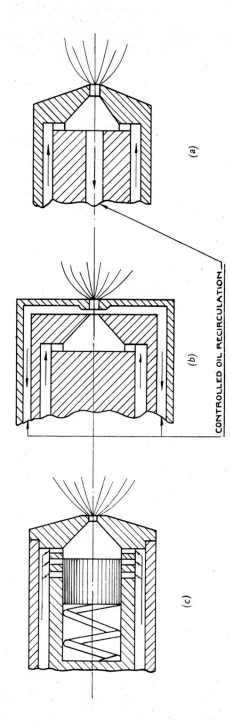

CONTROLLED OIL RECIRCULATION

(a)

(b)

(c)

Fig. 72.—Wide-range Pressure-jet Burners.

305

pattern which will penetrate the oil spray and give a stable flame front. The minimum drop is probably $\frac{3}{4}$ in. w.g., which corresponds to an air velocity of about 60 ft./sec.

The advantages of the pressure-jet system of burning oil lie mainly in simplicity and the ability to make the burner in all sizes of 5 lb. to more than 5 tons per hour. In addition, the burners have a wide range, and the throughput can be varied by variation of delivery pressure without making adjustments to the burner itself. Further modification can be made by removing the cap and changing the grooved disc and the final delivery plate.

Disadvantages are the high degree of oil-preheat necessary (200–300° F.) and the need for filters to prevent choking of the fine orifices used. In addition there is a tendency for degree of atomization to decrease with size of burner. Since output varies with $\sqrt{}$ pressure the output can only be doubled by increase of pressure from 50 to 200 lb. per sq. in. ; this is rather a severe limitation but which can be overcome in large applications by the use of a number of burner-units. In view of the higher output range of the blast burner (5 : 1) several designs have been made to improve the useful range of the pressure-jet. Three of these are illustrated in Figure 72.

In (a) part of the oil is returned from the swirl chamber to the pump. This allows the full velocity of swirl to be maintained at low outputs. In (b) the oil is returned from a point between two orifices after the swirl chamber. In (c) the swirl chamber has several sets of grooves for oil supply which can be covered or uncovered by the movement of a piston. The position of the piston can be automatically controlled by oil pressure or manually by a rod and wheel. Burners of this type can operate over the ranges of 10 : 1 or even 20 : 1 but obviously only if the air register is adjustable to suit.

The most important example of the use of the pressure-jet burner is in steam raising. Normally in large installations the increase of load is covered by the increase of the number of burners, not by increase of size. Figure 73 illustrates a Lamont water-tube boiler which has five burners, each with its own air register. This boiler is rated at 70,000 lb./hr. of steam at 500 lb./sq. in and 750° F. The atomizing pressure is high, 300 to 500 lb., in order to achieve good atomization (weight of droplet varies as 1/Pressure) and a high combustion intensity is achieved of 100,000 to 250,000 B.Th.U. per hour per cu. ft. of combustion space. In order to accommodate this a high-quality refractory lining is necessary in the combustion chamber, preferably high-alumina material of over 40 per cent. Al_2O_3. The consumption of oil is about 1170 lb. per burner.

Combustion of Oil Fuel. Special consideration has to be given to the furnace arrangements for the combustion of oil fuel for steam raising. Little difficulty is experienced in obtaining perfect combustion and high efficiency where the duty of the boiler is low, but it is otherwise when a high duty is demanded and a large quantity of oil has to be consumed.

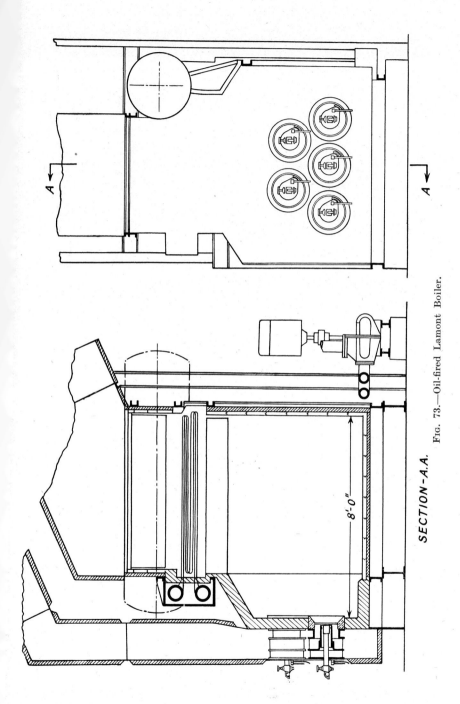

SECTION-A.A.

Fig. 73.—Oil-fired Lamont Boiler.

8'-0"

It is for this reason that the solution of the problem of the smokeless combustion of oil fuel was established at a much earlier date in the mercantile marine and in shore practice than under the conditions existing in a warship.

The conditions for perfect combustion differ radically from those existing in the case of solid fuel. When coal is burned beneath a boiler, by destructive distillation some 11,000 to 12,000 cu. ft. of gas, as measured at ordinary temperatures, and about 10 gallons of tar in the form of vapour are evolved per ton, whilst 75 per cent. of the coal is burnt as solid fuel on the grate, and the relationship between heating surface and grate area is of importance.

In the case of oil, practically the whole is burnt as gas or heavy vapour, and the essential factor is volume of combustion space.

The question of generous provision of combustion space is not only indicated by the above considerations, but also by reason of the greater amount of air theoretically demanded per lb. of oil fuel as compared with coal. It is, however, true that the air requirement for the same heat release is much the same for both coal and oil.

	Weight of air per lb.	Volume of air in cubic feet	
		at 0° C.	at 60° F.
Coal	11·5	140	147
Oil	14·0	172	181

In a series of American trials, in endurance tests of 116 hours' duration and a combustion space of 121 cu. ft., the following relative results for coal and oil (air-injection) were obtained :

	Natural draught.		Forced draught.		
	Lb. per cu. ft.	Evaporation from and at 212° F.	Pressure inches.	Lb. per cu. ft.	Evaporation from and at 212° F.
		lb.			lb.
Coal	8·3	10,000–11,000	3·00	30	30,150
Oil	7·6	15,000–16,000	3·75	27	35,560

The guiding principles for the ensuring of complete combustion and absence of smoke have been laid down already, namely, sufficient air, proper admixture and maintenance of temperature.

The air supply in the case of oil fuel may be divided into *primary air*, the injection air where this system is used, and secondary air drawn in by the injector action of the atomizer, i.e. air supplied to complete the combustion partly carried out by the primary air or of any oil spray or vapour not yet attacked.   For smokeless combustion not only must the air supply be sufficient, but it must be mingled as intimately as possible with the escaping spray, and there must be no local cooling.   Primary air does not need heating, as combustion in the region of its action will always be sufficiently vigorous to maintain a high temperature, but when special provision is made for secondary air to be introduced, such air is best supplied at as high a temperature as possible.   There is no tendency for smoke production during the first 18 in. or 2 ft. of the flame ; smoke is produced by the less rapidly moving portions constituting the farther end of the flame.   Here it is that the proper admixture of hot secondary air is best

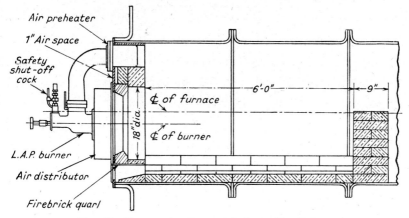

FIG. 74.—Furnace Arrangement in Lancashire Boiler.

arranged for.   A domestic example of this is found in the effect of an oil-lamp chimney in obviating smoke.

Large particles of soot need never be formed since the particle size of oil from an efficient burner is never more than 0·3 μ.

In a well-designed oil-burning system there should be no impingement of unburnt or partly-burnt material on the furnace walls, but a sutiable arrangement of other brickwork may, in some installations, play an important part in ensuring complete combustion.   It may assist combustion by re-radiating heat to the flame and maintaining the high temperature in the combustion zone : it may also protect those parts of the plant which might otherwise be over-heated.

The use of a refractory quarl or throat round the root of the oil spray assists the initial vaporization of the fuel and the maintenance of a stable flame front.   With a modern burner additional refractory is not required for flame stability, and refractory baffles in the flame zone are not to be recommended because of the risk of forming deposits of carbon.   Figure 74 shows the arrangement of the furnace of a Lancashire or Economic boiler : the furnace tube is unlined, but brickwork protects the front plate and carries a refractory throat which both reflects heat for vaporization and directs heat into the oil spray.

With water-tube boilers, especially for marine use, it is general practice to fit an extension to the furnace, at the outer face of which the sprayer is mounted, and the air supply is directed through an inner ring with a series of openings fitted with deflecting plates so that the air is given a powerful swirling motion, thus ensuring its proper mixing with the oil spray. One arrangement is illustrated in Figure 75 ; the air is first passed through the

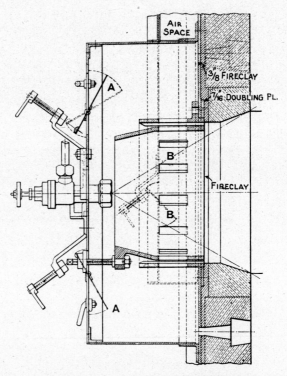

Fig. 75.—Furnace Front for Fuel-oil Firing.

adjustable openings (A) in the outer plate into the circular chamber when a portion passes through the inner ring of openings (B).

Automatic Burners, and Domestic Heating. Domestic heating by oil-fired boilers in central-heating systems is not common in Great Britain but has a wide application in the U.S.A. Self-contained units are now normally installed with automatic equipment for intermittent firing unless the installation is large enough for industrial-type boilers to be used.

A census by the U.S. National Oil-Burner Exhibition showed the following order of popularity in 1946 and 1955 (% of total demand) :

	1946	1955
(1) Pressure-jet	80	80
(2) Medium-pressure air	2	10
(3) Horizontal rotary	16	—
(4) Vertical rotary	2	9
(5) Vaporizing	—	1

The type of oil used in the pressure-jet unit is not heavy fuel oil but a light fuel oil with a viscosity of 40 sec. (Red. I at 100° F.). The basic control is the delivery pressure ; provided the oil is delivered to the burner at constant pressure and temperature the jet forms an adequate metering device. Ignition is by a suitably-placed, high-tension electric spark.

The regulating valve maintains a pressure of 70–100 lb. at the nozzle but has a special shut-off valve behind it which does not open until the pressure is 20 lb. below the operating pressure. This avoids " dribble " when starting and stopping. In this system the thermostat starts and stops the burner as required. The main advantage of intermittent operation in this way is the exact maintenance of the same air/fuel ratio which would not be so easy in a system in which the shut-down were gradual and the burner had to operate over a considerable range of input. A disadvantage is that the burner must be set to give smokeless combustion at all times and is generally adjusted to take care of the " starting " condition, which is not necessarily the best for the main time of operation.

An important consideration in assuring a reasonably-high level of efficiency is the relation between the makers' rating of the unit and the heating load. The latter should be a high percentage of the former, at least 70 per cent., in order that the boiler will not lose heat unduly during off-periods. The shorter the off-periods the higher will be the mean efficiency.

A pre-heating type of pressure-jet burner has now been developed which will operate with heavier oil of 1000 sec. viscosity (Red. I). It embodies a method of pre-heating which ensures that there is hot oil at the nozzle even after an idle period. For this burner the scale must be large, exceeding 400,000 B.Th.U. per hour.

Specifications for Fuel Oil. In the case of fuel oil the factor of prime importance is high calorific value, but a high flash-point (> 175° F.) is stipulated by law, and it is fair to demand reasonable freedom from water and solid matter. Apart from these, the real consideration is the choice of oil to suit the particular conditions of use and storage. If heated storage is not available the choice must fall on oil grades of low viscosity and pour-point ; if heating is available the heavier and cheaper types can be taken. The type of burner is also significant.

In Great Britain, British Standards Specifications exist for a number of grades of oil of which the heaviest is known as Bunker " C " since it is in universal use for ships' bunkers. The terms of these specifications are quoted below but it should be understood the specifications change with great frequency and also that special requirements can always be asked for and readily prepared from blending stocks.

	E	F	G	H
Flash-point (min.), ° F.	150	150	150	150
Viscosity, Redwood I at 100° F., sec. (max.)	250	950	2500	7000
Water (max.), per cent.	1	1	1·5	1·5
Sediment (max.), per cent. . . .	0·5	0·5	1·0	1·0
B.Th.U. per lb. (min.)	18,500	18,000	18,000	18,000

In the United States there are similar specifications laid down by the Bureau of Standards, of which No. 6 is much the same as Bunker " C " grade. The others range from a light distillate oil with an end-point of 330° C. to No. 5 which has a viscosity of Saybolt Furol of 40 sec., which corresponds to a Redwood I value of 750 at 100° F.

No good purpose would be served in quoting more such specifications since users have many, often contradictory, requirements and all are subject to change, but it is worth while to discuss a little further the purpose of the clauses.

Calorific value has little significance since the difference between the lightest and heaviest grades is only some 8 per cent. The value can be calculated roughly from specific gravity by the formula

$$C \ (B.Th.U. \ per \ lb.) = 22,320 - 3780d - 1 \ per \ cent.$$

The net value is taken as 1080 B.Th.U. lower, although it varies with the hydrogen content.

Viscosity is the factor of most importance as stated above. For example an oil may change viscosity with temperature from 6,000 sec. at 100° F. to 17,000 sec. at 80° F. and to 30,000 sec. at 70° F. when it has become unmanageable. The same oil may be burned at 250° F. when its viscosity has fallen to 100 sec. Low-temperature viscosity measurements of this type are more reliable than pour-point in deciding the storage quality of an oil.

Sulphur and ash content are not important in many applications but can be important if the usage is in metallurgical processes in which either could affect the material to be heated.

Finally an important factor is whether the fuel oil is a distillate oil or a residual oil since the latter will contain a high proportion of asphaltic material and the former will not. This may be important in drying foodstuffs ; distillates are essential for vaporizing burners.

REFERENCE BOOKS

The Science of Petroleum. Dunstan. Oxford Univ. Press. 1938.
Oil Heating Handbook. Kunitz. Constable. 1947.
Fuels, Combustion and Furnaces. Griswold. McGraw-Hill. 1946.
Oil Burners. Steiner. McGraw-Hill. 1950.

Industrial Furnaces. Trinks. John Wiley. 1951.
Science of Flames and Furnaces. Tring. Chapman and Hall. 1953.
Liquid Fuels. Moore. 1935.
Atomization of Liquid Fuels. Giffen and Muraszev. Chapman and Hall. 1954.
Petroleum Chemicals Industry. Goldstein. Spon. 1949.
See also Reference Books in Chapter X.

CHAPTER XII

MOTOR SPIRITS (PETROL, GASOLINE), KEROSINE

In the early days of the motor industry the fuel was obtained solely by the distillation of crude petroleum oils, the naphtha fraction being redistilled to give the desired boiling range in the final product. Refining by acid and soda washing removed small amounts of unsaturated hydrocarbons and improved the colour. As explained in Chapter X, straight distillation is still the first step in the treatment of the crude oil and part of the motor-spirit marketed is "straight-run" spirit which is a relatively unchanged fraction of the original crude oil.

As the demand for automotive and aviation spirits increased, the yield of suitable material, and its quality, were improved by the introduction of processes for the cracking of the higher distillates (gas oils, etc.), the chemical reforming of the heavy naphtha, and the polymerization of the lighter fractions. A further source of supply has been the removal of the condensable hydrocarbons carried in natural gas.

The yield of motor spirit from the crude oil has been greatly increased in this way and, depending upon the market demand, may be as high as 40 per cent. instead of a former 12 per cent. In addition, the chemical changes which occur in the secondary treatment make its composition appreciably different from that of straight-run distillate.

Because of these changes the nomenclature has become a little difficult The name petrol was originally a proprietary one but became so commonly used that it was applied to all motor spirit. Also, although the name spirit is used in the expression "aviation spirit", there are industrial spirits of different boiling range for which "spirit" is the only description. These uncertainties are causing the more common use of the American term gasoline or aviation-gasoline, leaving the term *spirit* to describe industrial spirits in general. These terms are used in the remainder of this chapter.

Natural Gasoline (Casing-head Spirit). The composition and properties of natural gases are dealt with in Chapter XV. So far as the recovery of condensable hydrocarbons from them is concerned they have been defined as follows :

Dry	.	.	.	containing up to 0·1 gal. of condensate per 1000 cu. ft.
Lean	.	.	.	containing from 0·1 to 0·3 gal.
Wet	.	.	.	containing over 0·3 gal.

It is only the last of these which can be economically treated for the recovery of natural gasoline.

Natural gas contains mainly the five lower members of the paraffin hydrocarbon series. In addition, there are smaller amounts of branched-chain and *cyclo*-paraffins boiling in the same general range. The physical properties of some of the hydrocarbons are given in Table XLIX.

TABLE XLIX

PROPERTIES OF THE PRINCIPAL HYDROCARBONS IN NATURAL GAS

	Boiling-point ° C.	Critical temp. ° C.	Critical press. atm.
Methane	−164	− 95·5	50
Ethane	−84	+ 34	50
Propane	−44	97	44
Butane (normal) . . .	+0·3	—	—
,, (tri-methyl-methane). .	−17	—	—
Pentane (normal) . . .	+36	197	33
,, (*iso*-) . . .	30	194	33
Hexane (normal) . . .	69	250	30

The first two members are not condensable in the practical sense but all the higher members are, and can be recovered. Normally only those higher than propane go to form natural gasoline ; *n*-hexane is unusual.

Three methods have been used for the recovery of the condensable hydrocarbons : (1) compression in stages and cooling, (2) absorption in oil, and (3) sorption in activated carbon. Processes (1) and (2) are the most common. The process of recovery is regulated to ensure the complete recovery of the pentanes and all higher hydrocarbons, but in doing so an appreciable proportion of the butanes are included and the product has a vapour pressure which may be too high for motor spirit. A natural gasoline which contains no butane will have a vapour pressure (Reid) of 12 lb. per sq. in. at 100° F., but the presence of 25 per cent. of butanes will raise this to 20 lb. In butane-free spirit the proportions of the hydrocarbons are generalized as : pentanes twice the hexanes, hexanes twice the heptanes, and octanes and over equal to the heptanes. This is at least true of U.S. spirits and agrees with theoretical calculation of vapour pressures. An example of the three stages of treatment to give a final spirit is as follows :

	Sp. gr.	Vapour pressure. lb.	C_2H_6	C_3H_8	C_4H_{10}		C_5H_{12}		Over C_5
					n	*iso*	*n*	*iso*	
Raw product .	0·63	60	1·5	14·7	30	10	15	5	23
Stabilized . .	0·68	17·5	—	—	15	2	21	7	55
Debutanized .	0·69	11·0	—	—	3	—	25	8	64

If the intention in manufacture is the blending of the natural gasoline with other gasoline which may have a low vapour pressure it is not necessary to reduce the vapour pressure so low as 11 lb.

The number of different hydrocarbons present is large and it is not necessary to define them all here. It is sufficient to say that the main usage is blending for the production of market spirit. For this purpose the vapour pressure should be as high as the blend stock will stand since there is a rough correlation between vapour pressure and octane number, for example from 65 octane at 10 lb. pressure to 68 octane at 15 lb. and 78 octane at 30 lb.

Straight-run Gasoline. The chemical composition of refined straight-run gasolines has been examined more thoroughly than any other petroleum fractions. They consist wholly of paraffin, naphthene and aromatic hydrocarbons and do not contain unsaturated bodies, or *cyclo-* derivatives of propane, butane or heptane. *Cyclo-* derivatives may be present of pentane and hexane, and even benzene and toluene. The proportions of the main classes vary widely according to the source of the oil as shown in the following examples :

	Sp. gr. 15° C.	End pt. ° C.	Aromatic.	Naphthene.	Paraffin.
			Wt. per cent.		
Pennsylvania . . .	0·732	207	7	18	75
Oklahoma	0·739	177	10	29	61
Texas	0·750	150	22	21	57
Mexico	0·727	200	10	35	55
Roumania	0·736	150	12	30	54

The naphthenes and paraffins, therefore, tend to be the main components Straight-run gasolines from paraffin-base crudes are rich in paraffins up to 70 per cent., mixed-base crudes show up to 50 per cent., and asphaltic crudes 3 per cent. Gasolines rich in naphthenes or aromatics are uncommon, but Borneo crude oil gives a gasoline rich in aromatics.

Normal straight-run gasoline distils between the limits of 40° and 200° C. and contains the hydrocarbons of the above series which boil in this range. The properties of the normal hydrocarbons in this range are shown in Table L, but in addition to these there are many isomeric compounds in the same boiling-range which vary in amount from one crude oil to another.

It will be noted that the hydrocarbons of the polymethylene series are of higher specific gravity than those of the paraffin series of about the same boiling-point, and that the specific gravity in each case increases with rise of boiling-point, whilst the specific heat and the latent heat decrease.

The specific gravity alone of a gasoline is therefore not a criterion of its volatility, and a distillation test is the most satisfactory basis of comparison. In such a test, comparison is made of the volume of fraction distilled at certain fixed temperature points. Since the boiling-point is dependent upon the vapour pressure, the higher the proportion of distillates obtained at a low temperature the greater is the degree of volatility as a whole.

TABLE L

" *Normal* " *Paraffin Hydrocarbons*

	Formula.	Boiling-point ° C.	Specific gravity D_4^{20}	Specific heat.	Latent heat of vaporization.
Pentane	C_5H_{12}	37	0·63	—	85·5
Hexane	C_6H_{14}	69	0·66	0·527	79·4
Heptane	C_7H_{16}	98	0·68	0·507	76·5
Octane	C_8H_{18}	125	0·7	0·505	71·0
Nonane	C_9H_{20}	150	0·72	0·503	—

" *Naphthene* " *Hydrocarbons*

	Formula.	Boiling-point ° C.	Specific gravity at 0° C.	Specific heat.	Latent heat of vaporization.
cyclo-Pentane . . .	C_5H_{10}	49·5	0·754	—	—
cyclo-Hexane . . .	C_8H_{12}	81·4	0·779	0·506	87
cyclo-Heptane . . .	C_6H_{14}	118	0·811	—	—
cyclo-Octane . . .	C_7H_{16}	150·6	0·839	—	—
cyclo-Nonane . . .	C_9H_{18}	172	0·770	—	—

The chemical composition of spirits is, therefore, in the main a matter of academic interest except in cases where there may be a higher than usual concentration of those which have a high octane number, or of special members such as toluene which it may be desired to separate for use in chemical industry. An indication of the extent of the variation of the main components is recorded from the analyses of some ten representative spirits. The quantities are given as volumes per cent.

C_5

n-Pentane . . . . . . 0·5–1·0
cyclo-Pentane 1–2

C_6

Dimethylbutanes 2–3
Methylpentanes 4–8
Hexane 5–12
cyclo-Hexane 5–15
Benzene 0–2

C_7

Dimethyl-pentanes 3–6
Dimethyl*cyclo*-pentanes . . . 3–12
Methylhexane 1–3
Toluene 0–16

C_8

Dimethyl-hexanes 1–4
Trimethyl*cyclo*-pentanes . . . 3–7

Cracked and Reformed Gasolines. The many manufacturing processes which are used for the conversion of the middle distillates into gasoline, the alteration of the composition of distillates by hydrogenation, reforming, etc., and the building-up of olefinic gases, all present a more complex picture of final composition than is the case with natural or straight-run gasolines and the subject is too complex for this volume. The reasons for the changes of composition have been dealt with in the process descriptions of Chapter X; for additional details the reader is directed to *The Science of Petroleum.*

Physical Properties of Gasolines. Consisting as they do of complex mixtures of the hydrocarbons which boil in a given range, petroleum gasolines cover only the range C_4 to C_8 and do not show wide differences in physical properties. In Great Britain to-day there are five main grades marketed, three aviation grades, and premium and regular automotive gasolines, which differ in the important characteristic of knock-rating. This implies that they contain different groupings of hydrocarbons but, in addition, the distillation range or volatility differs. Aviation gasoline has the narrower boiling-range, $40°$ to $170°$ C., and contains a higher proportion of low-boiling constituents, about 50 per cent. at $105°$ C. The corresponding figures for motor gasoline are $40°$ to $205°$ C., and 50 per cent. of distillate at $125°$ C. Some of the properties can, however, be generalized and this is attempted below as far as possible.

The ultimate analyses lie in the range of carbon 85·1–85·5, and hydrogen 14·4–14·9 per cent., with less than 0·1 per cent. sulphur. The specific gravity varies with distillation range from 0·700 to 0·745. The freezing-point is very low, about $-130°$ C., but the specification limit for this is only $-60°$ C.

The specific heat (mean 0–150° C.) varies from 0·53 to 0·54 cal./g./° C. Although it is not strictly proportional to the density it may be calculated from this as a first approximation by using the expression K/d, where K is 0·35. Specific heat varies with boiling-range as shown in the following example, the actual specific heat at $30°$ C. being given.

75–100° C.	0·463	150–175	0·458
100–125	0·461	175–200	0·452
125–150	0·460		

The latent heat of vaporization is about 70 cal. per g.

There is no specification for the flash-point of motor spirits, but it is interesting to record the variation of flash-point of the fractions into which a gasoline may be divided.

Fraction, ° C.	50–60	60–70	70–80	80–90	90–100	100–150
Flash-point, ° C.	-58	-38	-42	-30	-22	$+10$

Calorific Value. Very little difference is found in either the *gross* or *net* calorific value of petrol on a weight basis. The *net* calorific values recorded by Ricardo (*J. Soc. Auto. Eng.*, 1922, **10,** 305) are given in Table LI. It is to be noted that spirit of high specific gravity will have a much higher relative heat content per gallon than lighter spirit of about the same calorific value per lb.

TABLE LI

CALORIFIC VALUE (NET, B.TH.U.) AND LATENT HEAT OF VAPORIZATION OF
PETROLS (*H. R. Ricardo*)

Index No.	B.Th.U. including latent heat of vaporization.		B.Th.U. excluding latent heat of vaporization.		Vapour pressure at 0° C. mm. Hg.
	Per lb.	Per gal.	Per lb.	Per gal.	
1	19,020	137,500	18,890	136,600	86
2	19,250	135,500	19,130	134,700	68
3	19,090	137,100	18,970	136,400	70
4	19,120	137,000	19,000	138,100	54
6	18,890	143,500	18,770	142,600	18
7	18,580	145,200	18,450	144,300	28
8	18,920	145,000	18,790	144,100	17

The properties of 100-octane aviation gasoline are tabulated in Table LII in comparison with those of a motor gasoline and, since these can be used as blend components, those of motor benzole and methylated

TABLE LII

PROPERTIES OF GASOLINES, MOTOR BENZOLE AND METHYLATED ALCOHOL

	Aviation 100 octane.	Motor gasoline.	Motor benzole.	Ethyl alcohol.
Specific gravity	0·724	0·733	0·878	0·794
Composition :				
Carbon, per cent.	85·1	85·5	91·6	52·1
Hydrogen, per cent.	14·9	14·4	8·1	13·1
Sulphur, per cent.	0·01	0·1	0·3	nil
Boiling-range :				
Initial ° C.	42	37	79	—
50 per cent. at ° C.	97	112	86	—
Final	170	185	170	78·3
Reid vapour pressure, lb. per sq. in. at 100° F.	6·8	7·3	—	—
Mean specific heat, cal./g./° C. .	0·53	0·53	0·39	0·53
Latent heat, cal./g.	70	70	96	204
Coefficient of expansion/° C. × 10⁻⁴	8	8	7·7	6·2
Calorific value, cal./g. :				
Gross	11,300	11,200	10,025	7,093
Net	10,510	10,440	9,600	6,403
Theoretical air requirement at N.T.P. :				
Cu. metres dry air per kg. . .	11·5	11·4	10·3	6·9
CO_2 per cent. in dry waste gas .	14·9	15·0	17·4	15·0
Explosive range, per cent. . . .	1·5–5·3	1·4–5·2	2·7–6·3	4·0–13·6
Compression limit, lb./sq. in. . .	90	80	85	200 +

ethyl alcohol. The gasolines are taken from a mixed-base crude petroleum. The differences disclosed between the two grades of gasoline are slight except in boiling-range and in knock-rating.

The spontaneous ignition temperature of gasoline appears to increase with its knock-rating. Three values obtained in air by the same method have given 300° C. at octane 73, 390° C. at octane 92, and 430° C. at octane 100.

The Combustion of Gasoline. The first consideration in the combustion of gasoline is the vaporization of small increments and their injection into the cylinder of the engine. When air is bubbled through spirit or passes at normal temperature over a surface saturated with it, the more volatile components evaporate first. In the early days of the petrol engine, carburation was achieved in bubbling or surface-type carburettors and the fuel was of lower boiling-range and specific gravity. With the introduction of spray-type carburettors this was not necessary since the spray is carried forward as a mist into the hot induction pipe near the engine and vaporized there. It is still necessary, of course, for the spirit to contain sufficient material in the low-boiling range to achieve proper starting from the cold. From the point of view of the proportions boiling in different temperature ranges the essential properties of a good spirit may be summarized as :

> A fair proportion of low-boiling fraction to achieve good starting, but not so much that it might cause vapour lock in warm weather or cause undue loss in storage by evaporation.
>
> Not too high a final boiling-point (end-point) or too high a proportion of material boiling near the end-point since these " heavy ends " may not be completely burned and may cause excessive carbon formation or lead to dilution of the engine lubricating oil.
>
> Freedom from water, acid components which might cause corrosion, and any solid residue of evaporation.
>
> Freedom from objectionable odour and substances which tend to form a gummy deposit on valves or plug points.

Many attempts have been made to define the right degree of volatility, but now it is defined in terms of the initial boiling-point and the temperature at which 50 per cent. will distil over in a standard distillation test. The lower the temperature the more volatile is the gasoline, assuming a smooth distillation curve in both cases. Starting should not be difficult if the air temperature is not more than 55–60° C. below the point at which 10 per cent. will distil over in the same test. A typical distillation curve is shown in Figure 76. This gives 10 per cent. at 58° C. and 50 per cent. at 102° C. The curve is not a straight line but is approximately so, except at both ends.

At this volatility this gasoline would be satisfactory for starting, down to an air temperature of about −18° C. Suggested 10 per cent. yields for different levels of air temperature are as follows :

Atmospheric temp., ° C. . .	−30	−20	− 5	5
10 per cent. distillation at ° C.	35	50	70	80

These figures suggest that an increasing difference between the 10 per cent. point and the air temperature is permissible as the latter rises but it would not be practicable to sell gasoline except with a wide margin of safety to cover the usual variations of weather conditions. The 10 per cent. point for winter gasoline in Great Britain and the United States is therefore much the same at 50° C. despite the fact that the weather conditions in the latter country are liable to be more rigorous.

The vapour pressure of a gasoline is a function of the proportion of low-boiling constituents, but its definition as a maximum in gasoline specifications is made mainly from the point of view of avoiding vapour lock. If a spirit is overheated in its passage through the fuel system, gasification may occur which will prevent the flow of liquid; this is termed vapour lock. The standard method of determination of vapour pressure is the Reid method which gives values at a temperature of 100° F. when the vapour space is four times that of the liquid. Where

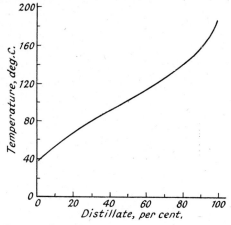

FIG. 76.—Typical Distillation Curve for Gasoline.

the amount of material evaporated is small the values approximate to the true vapour pressure of the mixture. Correlation between vapour-pressure values and tendency to vapour lock is not exact, but arbitrary limits to the Reid pressure are imposed on the safe side, i.e. the value shall not exceed 9 lb. at 100° F. ; if the gasoline is used at maximum temperatures of 85° and 75° F. the values may be 10 lb. and 12 lb. respectively. A research correlation suggests :

Atm. temp. ° F.	Max. Reid vapour pressure to avoid vapour lock. lb.
50	13
60	12
70	11
80	10
100	9

Since the imposition of a vapour-pressure limit may interfere with the volatility requirement the obvious remedy is to improve the cooling of the fuel system.

F.—M

The term " gum " in relation to gasoline relates to the formation of polymers of high molecular weight under the conditions of combustion. In straight-run and natural gasolines gum should be absent, but it can occur in gasolines produced from material which has been derived from thermal or catalytic cracking, owing to the presence of unsaturated hydrocarbons. Undue amounts of gum cause sticking of carburettors, inlet valves, etc., and are obviously undesirable.

Gum is referred to as " pre-formed " and " potential ". The former, or existent material already present in the gasoline, is measured as the residue on evaporation of a measured portion of gasoline. Potential gum is the additional gum which can be formed by an oxidation treatment of the gasoline. Except in some exceptional cases gum is a complex mixture of the oxidation products of reactive unsaturated hydrocarbons and the figure for gum is a rough measure of the amount of such bodies left in the gasoline. Exposure to light can promote the oxidization or polymerization of these unsaturated bodies, and gasoline exposed to light shows their presence by the development of a yellow colour. It has been stated that the gum-forming materials consist largely of peroxides, per-acids, aldehydes and ketones, and gum formation to be a process of auto-oxidation, the resinous substance remaining after evaporation being of ester or lactone structure.

Gum formation may be inhibited by a number of organic compounds, bodies themselves readily oxidized. Amongst these are alpha-naphthol, catechol, ortho-aminophenol, mono- and di-benzylpara-aminophenol, the latter said to be effective in concentration not exceeding 0·005 per cent. A recent addition is 2 : 4-methyl-6-benzyl phenol.

Rate of Flame Propagation in Gasoline/Air Mixtures. This is obviously an important consideration, determining as it does whether combustion has ceased before the end of the working stroke of the piston, and how soon after ignition the maximum pressure is reached, which determines incidentally the point in the cycle where ignition should take place. Obviously, with an engine running at, say, 5000 revolutions per minute, a slow-burning mixture could conceivably be alight when the inlet valve opens, with consequent firing back (" popping ") into the carburettor.

The degree of turbulence in the mixture has, however, an important modifying influence in practice, and to a large extent determines a far more rapid spreading of the flame throughout the mixture. Further, turbulence has an important effect in diminishing the liability of a charge to burn with excessive speed, setting up undue pressures and leading to the well-known trouble of detonation or " pinking ". The amount of turbulence will depend largely upon engine design. Flame speed increases to a maximum over the first 10 per cent. of travel across the combustion space, is then maintained up to about 90 per cent., and then decreases.

Fig. 77 shows the effect of fuel/air ratio on flame speed. A maximum is shown at 0·09, which is richer than the stoichiometric mixture but corresponds with the mixture giving the highest power output. Under other conditions the maximum may vary from 50 to 80 ft. per sec.

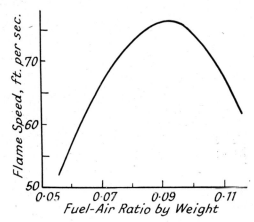

FIG. 77.—Rate of Flame Propagation in Gasoline/Air Mixtures (Neuman).

The Combustion of Gasoline in the Engine. If a gasoline were burned completely with the theoretical amount of air, the dry exhaust gases would consist of carbon dioxide and nitrogen only. Taking as an example an average gasoline, the quantities involved may be calculated as shown in Chapter II.

	lb.	Cubic feet at 0° C.	at 60° F.
Per pound	15·24	187	197
Per gallon	109·60	1346	1420

One volume of the liquid requires, therefore, 8400 (at 0° C.) to 8900 (at 60° F.) times its own volume of air for complete combustion. Similarly, the percentage of carbon dioxide in the *dry* exhaust gases for petrol of this composition will be 14·3 per cent. The dew-point of the wet gases will be 52° C.

Owing to the complex nature of gasoline, it is not possible to calculate accurately the actual volume in the state of vapour which a given volume of liquid gasoline would occupy, as, for example, when it is taken up as vapour in an air current. 1 lb. of hexane would occupy 4·2 cu. ft. in a state of vapour at 0° C. (4·4 at 60° F.), whereas 1 lb. of octane would occupy 3·15 cu. ft. at 0° C. (3·32 at 60° F.). Taking a round figure of 4 cu. ft. of vapour per pound of gasoline, it will be found that the theoretical air required is about 48 times the volume of the gasoline vapour, or the mixture contains practically 2 per cent. gasoline vapour.

The calorific value of 1 cu. ft. of the theoretical gasoline/air mixture may now be calculated.   The total volume of mixture per pound is 4 + 187 = 191, and the calorific value of gasoline per pound is approximately 20,000 B.Th.U., hence $\dfrac{20,000}{191} = 104 \cdot 5$ B.Th.U. per cu. ft.   Similarly, at 60° F. the value per cu. ft. is approximately 99·5 B.Th.U.

Air is able to take up a far greater amount of gasoline vapour than the above ; dry air will take up 17·5 per cent. by volume of 0·650 gasoline at 50° F. (= 1 vol. gasoline vapour to 5·7 vols. of air), whilst at 68° F. it will take up 27 per cent. (= 1 vol. vapour to 3·7 vols. of air).   It is evident, therefore, that a large excess of air must be employed in practice to bring such a mixture down to theoretical strength.

Further, above a certain percentage of vapour the mixture, although highly inflammable, is not explosive.   The range of composition between which mixtures of gasoline vapour and air are truly explosive is very limited. The figures given by Coward and Jones are : *minimum*, 1·4 per cent. by volume ; *maximum*, 6·0 ; explosive range, 4·6.   On the assumption that 1 lb. of gasoline gives 4 cu. ft. of vapour, the explosive mixture figures are approximately :

	lb. air.	Cubic feet at 0° C.	at 60° F.
At maximum for 1 lb. gasoline .	5·76	71·5	74·5
At minimum ,, ,, . .	29·0	360·0	375·0

The above data relate to combustion under perfect conditions but, in the engine, complete combustion may not be achieved for a number of reasons. When the engine is warming up the air/fuel ratio is reduced since ignition is more easily obtained under these conditions.   The result is the appearance of a higher proportion of carbon monoxide in the exhaust gases.   Some fuel may even escape combustion altogether during this period, and it is important that its duration should be as short as possible to avoid dilution of the lubricating oil.   Maximum thermal efficiency is attained, not at the theoretical air/fuel ratio but at a ratio about 10 per cent. higher, i.e. with a weaker mixture.   This is considered to be due to the reduction of the temperature of the cylinder wall and, therefore, less loss of heat to the cooling medium.   Also, maximum thermal efficiency is attained at slightly below full load, at which maximum mechanical efficiency is reached.

Under practical conditions, maximum power is attained at an air/fuel ratio 20 per cent. on the low side, and it is interesting to consider what the ratios are under other conditions and what is the effect of variation on efficiency of combustion.   For an average gasoline the theoretical amount of air required per lb. of fuel is about 14·5 lb.   At full load the thermal efficiency varies with compression ratio as follows :

Compression ratio . .	4·0	5·0	6·0	7·0	8·0
Thermal efficiency . .	25	28·2	30·0	32·0	33·0
Mechanical efficiency .	89	88·5	88	87	86

At the present usual level of compression ratio (7·5) the exhaust gas composition can vary with the air/fuel ratio as shown below, but for normal running the ratio is set at 10 per cent. weak and the amount of unburnt gases in the exhaust is quite low.

	A/F ratio	O_2	CO_2	CO	H_2	CH_4
Max. power . . .	14 : 1	0·4	13·3	0·4	0·6	0·4
Max. efficiency . .	17 : 1	4·3	11·5	0·2	0·1	0·3
Theoretical A/F ratio .	14·5 : 1	0·0	13·0	2·0	1·5	0·5

Under normal running conditions the loss of potential heat units in the exhaust is therefore small, of the order of 0·8 per cent. of the heat of the fuel. This is not so when starting, idling, or running at high speed as can be deduced from the air/fuel ratios under these conditions.

	A/F ratio.
Starting	about 4
Idling	10
High speed	12
Cruising	16

The conflicting considerations of high economy of fuel and high power have had a considerable influence on engine design and control, and the design of carburettors to give, by the use of a number of jets, the best conditions for starting, for economical running, and for maximum power when required for climbing or for acceleration.

A relatively simple carburettor with not too many jets is shown in Figure 78 to explain the principle of operation. The head of fuel is controlled by the float which governs the flow of fuel from the main tank. Fuel flows from the main (measuring) jet G into the well A, where it meets air drawn downwards through the calibrated air jet a and injected into the spirit, through the small holes ch, into the annulus. The mixed air and spirit rises to four spraying orifices of which two are shown, oo in the waist of the tube, whence it is carried in the main air stream through the throttle V (shown closed) to the induction manifold and to the engine.

Idling is effected by spirit drawn from the well v through a small channel leading to the pilot jet g and to the adjustable orifice io which is on the engine side of the throttle. Air is drawn in at bp to prevent over-richness when idling but goes out of action as soon as V is opened.

The starting jet is the auxiliary carburettor on the side of the main one. The air jet GA meters the air supply and Gs regulates the flow of spirit. Operation is from the dashboard through sl which causes rotation of a central shaft to open channels D and C. The engine suction operates through d and (with V closed) draws a rich mixture through Gs via Sb into the mixing chamber of the starter. After starting, a second position of the control gives a weaker mixture for warming up while the closed position puts it out of action.

All the jets are, of course, carefully calibrated during construction of the instrument.

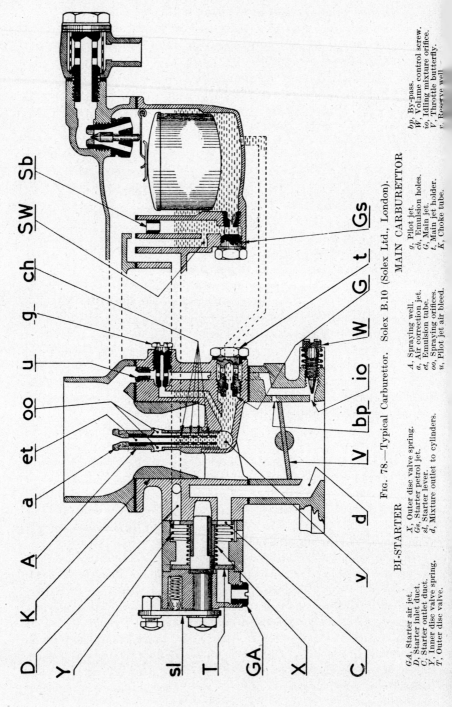

FIG. 78.—Typical Carburettor. Solex B.10 (Solex Ltd., London).

BI-STARTER

GA, Starter air jet.
D, Starter inlet duct.
C, Starter outlet duct.
Y, Inner disc valve spring.
T, Outer disc valve.

X, Outer disc valve spring.
Gs, Starter petrol jet.
sl, Starter lever.

d, Mixture outlet to cylinders.

MAIN CARBURETTOR

A, Spraying well.
a, Air correction jet.
et, Emulsion tube.
oo, Spraying orifices.
u, Pilot jet air bleed.

g, Pilot jet.
ch, Emulsion holes.
G, Main jet.
t, Main jet holder.
K, Choke tube.

bp, By-pass.
W, Volume control screw.
io, Idling mixture orifice.
V, Throttle butterfly.
v, Reserve well.

326

Chemical Composition and Engine Performance. The efficiency of an internal combustion engine is directly related to the degree of compression of the gases prior to ignition. For the highest efficiency it is desirable to have the highest practicable compression, but a limit is soon reached. Obviously with a fuel/air mixture over-compression would raise the temperature to that of spontaneous ignition (p. 20) and *pre-ignition* would occur before the timed spark functioned. In general, before this point is reached trouble is experienced, particularly with rich (and therefore rapid burning) mixtures, through a portion of the charge burning with exceptional rapidity *after* the usual ignition by the spark, giving rise to the well-known " pinking ", " knocking " or " detonation ". In the early days of the petrol engine it was known that some fuels were more liable to detonation than others and that the addition of benzole overcame or materially reduced the knocking.

H. R. Ricardo (*Eng.*, 1920, **110**, 325, 361 ; *The Automobile Eng.*, 1921, **11**, Feb.–Aug.), using a specially designed engine which enabled the compression of the mixture to be varied during running, made a series of valuable tests on petrols which enabled some correlation to be made between composition and performance. Briefly, Ricardo showed that whilst at moderate compression ratios (5/1) all hydrocarbon fuels give much the same efficiency, because it was possible to work at considerably higher compressions with those containing a high percentage of aromatic hydrocarbons, or naphthenes, considerable gain in efficiency was possible. The limit to higher compressions is directly or indirectly the spontaneous ignition temperature of the charge. For any fuel a practical limit to the degree of compression allowable could be arrived at—the " highest useful compression ratio " (H.U.C.R.). A few of Ricardo's results are given in Table LIII.

TABLE LIII

COMPOSITION OF PETROLS IN RELATION TO COMPRESSION AND CONSUMPTION
(*Ricardo*)

Index No.	Approximate composition.			Highest useful compression ratio.	Temperature at H.U.C.R. ° C.	Consumption at H.U.C.R. per B.H.P. hour	
	Paraffins.	Naphthenes.	Aromatics.			lb.	pints.
7	26	35	39	6·0	430	0·393	0·402
8	10	85	5	5·9	428	0·389	0·405
1	62	23	15	5·7	422	0·393	0·435
6	38	47	15	5·35	410	0·407	0·428
3	68	20	12	4·7	387	0·435	0·484
X.	63	35	1·7	4·85	392	0·422	0·471

X.—A petrol from which aromatic hydrocarbons had been removed.
The Index numbers refer to the fuels quoted in Table LI.
It may be noted that Petrols 1 and 3 are of almost identical composition, but exhibit a considerable difference in the highest useful compression ratio.

Ricardo suggested that this " anti-knock " quality might be expressed in terms of the equivalent " toluene value " of the fuel, this hydrocarbon having the greatest influence of the three—benzene, toluene and xylene. By a fairly simple analytical method an approximation of the amount of each aromatic hydrocarbon in the petrol can be determined and from the data the " toluene value " calculated.

Detonation of Liquid Fuels, Knock-rating. Following on Ricardo's work, which first showed the importance of the nature of the hydrocarbons in petrol in determining its combustion characteristics, there were developments in the direction of measuring the " anti-knock " value, using variable compression engines. This work has now been satisfactorily standardized and agreement reached between the principal standardizing bodies in the United States and in this country. Not only must the engine and procedure be standard, but a standard of reference for the different fuels agreed upon. This is the " octane number ".

Pure iso-octane (2 : 2 : 4—trimethylpentane) (C_8H_{18}) was first suggested as a standard of very high anti-knock character by Edgar (1931) ; the converse, a hydrocarbon of high knocking character, was n-heptane (C_7H_{16}). Their respective boiling-points are approximately the same (99° C.).

Assessing the anti-knock value of iso-octane as 100, and that of n-heptane as 0, the " octane number " is numerically the percentage by volume of iso-octane in an octane/n-heptane mixture which matches the petrol by its detonation characteristics in the engine test. Thus with a 70/30 octane/heptane mixture matching the fuel the " octane number " of that fuel is 70.

The engine standardized is the Co-operative Fuel Research engine (C.F.R.) ; its compression ratio can be varied between 3 and 30 to 1 and the onset of knocking is detected by audition or by an electronic detonation meter. The standard procedure of test has four variations of engine conditions and four values are recognized as shown in Table LIV.

TABLE LIV

C.F.R. ENGINE CONDITIONS FOR KNOCK-RATING OF GASOLINE

Method	Research	Motor.	Aviation.	Aviation 3C. Supercharge.
Designation	C.F.R.F1.	F2.	F3.	F4.
Engine, r.p.m.	600 ± 6	900 ± 9	1200 ± 12	1800 ± 45
Air intake, ° F.	125 ± 2	100 ± 25	125 ± 5	—
Mixture temp., ° F.	—	300 ± 2	220 ± 2	—
Ignition advance, deg.	13	*	35	45
Coolant temp., ° F.	212 ± 3	212 ± 3	374 ± 9	375 ± 5

* Varies with C.R.

The motor method is now used only for low-octane gasolines. It measures the incidence of knock under weak-mixture conditions when the knock is most pronounced. The Research method, F1, is used for high-octane automotive fuels, and methods F3 and F4 for aviation gasolines. These distinctions have not always been made and it is important to remember this when looking at older records ; new data should be marked with the method used.

At maximum power in the test engine the highest permissible compression ratio without knock varies from 7/1 at an octane number of 98, to 5/1 at 84 octane, and 4/1 at 67·5 octane.

The octane number of commercial gasolines has risen steadily through the years to keep pace with improvements in engine design and increase of compression ratio. Aviation fuels have achieved a rating of 100 plus. 1954 ratings in Great Britain are given below ; in 1928 they were 58, and in 1936, 70, for the Regular Grade.

Grade.	Test method.	Octane number.
Premium	F1	92
Regular	F2	70–72
Aviation	F1/F4	91/96
Aviation	F2/F4	100/130
Aviation	F3/F4	108/135

In view of the high cost of pure *iso*-octane and *n*-heptane the Institute of Petroleum have arranged for the preparation of sub-standards which are selected spirits of good storage quality whose characteristics have been determined by a number of laboratories.

The octane rating for aviation fuels has now extended beyond 100 and the higher ratings are obtained by reference to blends of *iso*-octane and tetraethyl lead which have been assessed by engine tests.

It has been made clear that the property of high knock-rating is associated with the structure of the hydrocarbons which comprise motor spirit and that the secondary processes of preparation of petroleum fractions aim at the preferential formation of substances of high rating. In view of the obvious interest to both refining and engine per ormance a great many of the likely hydrocarbons have been examined. A selection of them is given in Table LV.

The knock-rating of a hydrocarbon is reduced by the following changes of structure.

(1) Increase of length of carbon chain in paraffins and olefines.
(2) As the double bond becomes less central in isomeric straight-chain olefines.
(3) With decrease of compactness of structure in branched-chain olefines.
(4) With increase of the length of side-chain attached to an aromatic nucleus up to *n*-propyl but a decrease thereafter.
(5) With increase of ring-size of naphthenes and with increase of length of the longest side-chain. A naphthene has a higher rating than a paraffin with the same number of carbon atoms.

The rating of a blend of substances is not quite the arithmetic mean of the octane numbers except in the case of a wholly paraffinic blend. A blend of paraffin and aromatic shows a rating lower than the mean, and of paraffin and olefine higher.

TABLE LV

KNOCK-RATINGS OF PURE HYDROCARBONS

Paraffins.	F1.	F2.	Aromatics.	F1.	F2.
n-pentane	61·7	61·9	Benzene	100 +	2·75 ml.*
n-hexane	24·8	26·0	Toluene	100 +	0·27*
n-octane	—	− 17	Xylenes	100 +	100 +
2 : 3-di-me-pentane .	88·5	89·0	Ethyl benzene . .	0·8*	97·9
3 : 4-di-me-hexane . .	76·3	81·7	iso-Propyl benzene .	2·1*	99·3
3 : 3-di-me-hexane . .	75·5	83·4			
2 : 2 : 3-tri-me-pentane	100 +	99·9	Naphthenes.		
3-me : 3-et-pentane .	80·8	88·7	cyclo-pentane . .	100	85
2 : 2 : 4-tri-me-pentane			me-cyclo-pentane .	91·3	80
" iso-octane " . .	100	100	cyclo-hexane . . .	83	78·6
			et-cyclo-hexane . .	45·6	40·8
			1 : 1 : 3-tri-me-cyclo-		
			hexane	81·3	82·6
			n-bu-cyclo-hexane .	34	35
			iso-bu-cyclo-hexane .	32	31

Olefines.	F1.	F2.
2-pentene	98	80
2-hexene	89	78
2-heptene	70	62
1-octene	28·7	34·7
2-octene	56·3	56·6
2 : 3-di-me-1-hexene	96·3	83·6

* ml. T.E.L. in the iso-octane.

Rich Mixture Rating. Aircraft engines require to develop greatly increased power at the " take-off " and this is obtained by an increase of fuel supplied to give a rich mixture. The air/fuel ratio for complete combustion is about 15/1 by weight but, for maximum economy, the mixture usually contains about 20 per cent. of excess air. For maximum power the air/fuel ratio is about 10 to 20 per cent. on the rich side. Under these conditions the octane number is not a reliable indication of power output since fuels of the same octane number may behave differently. For testing, the same C.F.R. engine is used but with a modified procedure. The compression ratio and engine speed are kept constant and power output under light-knock conditions is compared with the maximum power output obtained from a reference fuel consisting of iso-octane to which has been added 1·28 ml. of tetraethyl lead per gallon. The result is reported as a Performance Number, but is of course the ratio of maximum power output test fuel/ reference fuel. The rating can be increased by the addition of certain organic substances.

An increase of octane number from 90 to 100 allows the compression ratio to be raised from 8·0 to 9·5. Since the efficiency of the engine cycle is given by

$$E = 1 - \left(\frac{1}{CR}\right)^{0.258}$$

this means an increase of efficiency of 10 per cent. from 0·40 to 0·44. In aircraft this means an increase of range or pay-load.

For a given aero-engine, the use of higher octane fuels increases the power available for take-off; the increase, for example, by changing from 90 octane fuel to 100 octane fuel might be as much as 30 per cent.

Anti-knock Agents. Certain organic compounds have been found to have the property of suppressing knocking; conversely, certain others induce it. Midgley and Boyd (*Ind. and Eng. Chem.*, 1922, **14,** 589; 894) found that aromatic amines, in general, belong to the former class, but that the most effective agents were organo-metallic compounds. Thus, compared with benzene, xylidine was 12·5 times as effective; di-ethyl telluride $[(C_2H_5)_2 \, Te]$, 250 times; lead tetraethyl $[(C_2H_5)_4 . Pb]$, 625 times. Carbonyls (e.g. iron) are also materials for which patents have been taken out.

The agent now commonly used is lead tetraethyl (T.E.L.) and amounts up to 3·6 ml. per imp. gal. have been added to motor spirits, and up to 5·5 ml. to aviation spirits. It has the disadvantage of being poisonous and, to avoid risk, fuels containing it are given a distinctive colour. The degree to which spirits respond to the addition of T.E.L. differs and the factor for response is termed " lead susceptibility ". In general terms the susceptibility is greater for saturated than for unsaturated hydrocarbons, and increases with increase of condensation of the molecule.

The colours of spirits containing lead identify the octane number as follows (1954):

Octane number.	Colour.	Octane number.	Colour.
92	red/orange	91–96	blue
100–130	green	118–135	brown

In order to prevent the deposition of metallic lead on engine valves, ethylene dibromide and dichloride are added to the T.E.L. to the extent of 60 per cent. In their presence a volatile lead halide is formed which is discharged in the exhaust gases.

Pure T.E.L. is a colourless liquid of specific gravity 1·65, which is easily decomposed by mineral acids. It is distributed in a coloured solution with ethylene halides in different proportions for automotive and aviation gasolines but both containing 61·4 per cent. by weight of T.E.L. In defining the addition of lead to a gasoline the number of millilitres per imperial gallon is stated, not the amount of lead solution.

The limiting addition at present for motor gasoline is 3·6 ml. per gal., and for aviation gasoline either 4·8 or 5·5 ml., depending on the current regulations.

Gasoline Specifications. Standard specifications are issued from time to time for gasoline grades, but it is not wise to quote these in a text-book since they are subject to frequent change. They contain clauses defining limits of purity such as sulphur and gum content, limits of volatility, vapour pressure, octane number, etc., which bear upon engine performance in the manner described above.

LIGHT OILS, KEROSINE, PARAFFIN OIL

The term " paraffin oil " is now obsolete as far as the petroleum industry is concerned. Light oil or kerosine is the second fraction of the primary distillation of crude oil and is the fraction collected between the straight-run naphtha and the beginning of the gas-oil or diesel-fuel fraction. There is a certain amount of overlap in boiling-range at both ends, depending upon markets, but the normal kerosine fraction boils in the range 140° to 280° C. A similar fraction is in common use for tractors for agricultural purposes and is called vaporizing oil.

The amount of these oils consumed represents some 6 per cent. of the crude oil distilled, and in Great Britain amounts to about 300 million gallons annually. The properties of typical oils are shown in Table LVI.

TABLE LVI

PROPERTIES OF TYPICAL LIGHT OILS FROM A MIXED-BASE CRUDE OIL

	Kerosine.	Vaporizing oil.
Specific gravity, 60/60° F.	0·79	0·82
Flash-point, ° F.	110	90
Initial boiling-point, ° C.	160	145
Final boiling-point, ° C.	280	266
50 per cent. at, ° C.	210	195
Octane number (motor)	—	50
Sulphur per cent.	0·08	0·35 max.
Smoke-point, mm.	25	—

Some of these properties are the subject of specification in relation to their uses. It is desirable that the sulphur content of lamp oils should be less than 0·1 per cent., the vaporizing oil should have an octane number of 50 or more, the flash-point must be over 73° F. for safety reasons. The carbon and hydrogen content of these oils is about 86·5 and 13·5 per cent. respectively and their calorific value about 20,000 B.Th.U. per lb. or 1·6 therms per imp. gal. at 60° F.

Illuminating Oils. If the oils are to be used for illuminating purposes or in oil stoves for house heating the tendency to smoke is an important factor. This is measured in a special lamp device as the height of flame at which the tip becomes smoky ; it is an empirical test which has value solely as the result of experience. The constitution of the oil is the important factor in smoking. Oil of a paraffinic character may burn clearly and without smoke, while naphthenic and aromatic oils, particularly the latter, form smoke readily. The best lamp oils are therefore those of a paraffinic character. Low sulphur content is necessary for two reasons ; sulphur forms a bloom on glass lamp-chimneys which impairs illuminating power, and promotes the deposition of carbon on wicks ; in heating stoves it forms oxides of sulphur which are corrosive. The proportion of material boiling over 300° C. must be small also to avoid carbon formation.

If the lamps are operated with incandescent mantles the composition of the oil is less important.

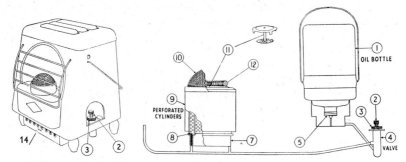

FIG. 79.—" Fyrside " Kerosine Stove (Rippingilles Ltd., Birmingham).

Blowlamps, primus stoves, and mantle lamps burn the oil as vapour. The oil is fed under a slight pressure through a vaporizing tube at the base of the flame and is vaporized there.

Figure 79 shows a " Fyrside " type of paraffin heater. The burner consists of an oil bowl (7) with a kindler or wick (8) and a series of perforated cylinders which lead to a gauze (10), an air diffuser (11) and a radiant coil (12). When first lit the flame is small and at the bottom of the cylinders ; it then grows until the gauze glows red. The flame is blue and should not appear above the gauze. The container (1) has a capacity of 0·5 gal. which is intended to last for 10 hours. The valve (4) has two controls, a shut-off needle valve (2) and a regulator (3).

Vaporizing Oil. The use of kerosine-type oils in the spark-ignition engine offers some advantages over gasoline for certain power purposes. Of higher density than gasoline, and of equal calorific value, they contain some 10 per cent. more heat units per gallon, and are normally lower in price.

Owing to their relatively low vapour pressure it is impossible to form an explosive mixture with air in the same manner as with a petrol carburettor ; heat has to be applied in order to vaporize the oil. Without special care this may lead to " cracking " of the oil, and this again to a considerable modification of the amount of air required, besides the almost certain appearance of sooty deposit. When a spray of paraffin oil is carried forward into the cylinder condensation of some portion is very likely to occur before complete combustion, and generally it is more difficult to attain that uniform composition of the mixture necessary in a high-speed engine. This uniformity is of far greater importance in a high-speed engine running on kerosine-range oils, because the range of explosion of the mixture is only about half that of the petrol/air mixture, which itself is a narrow one.

Petrol engines have been designed for use with tractor oils and work successfully at nearly constant speeds, but the difficulty of maintaining the constancy of the mixture with variable speeds has practically confined the general use of these higher distillates to slow-speed engines operating without the wide variations of load which occur with the motor vehicle. Useful application is found in farm tractors and in fishing boats. In these applications the engine is started on petrol and vaporization is achieved by the heat of the engine exhaust.

Kerosine as an Aviation Fuel. The advent in the war years of jet propulsion, and more recently of turbine-driven propellers, for aircraft has provided a new and important use for the kerosine fraction. In the year 1949 no less than 21 out of 41 new craft used turbines, 14 for jet propulsion and 7 for turbo-driven propellers. One important factor of such engines is the very low weight/power ratio in comparison with piston engines ; a second is the high thermal efficiency of the system at high altitudes. The engines have been designed to burn mainly " aviation kerosine ", but in recent years there have been fuel developments which may lead to the use of a fraction intermediate between gasoline and kerosine.

The normal engine consists of a number of combustion chambers grouped together and leading through one turbine to the jet, or to the propeller turbine. The jet engine gives its maximum duty at an air/fuel ratio of 50 or 60 : 1 as against the stoichiometric ratio of 14 : 1. It is still possible, therefore, to burn additional fuel in the hot gas stream, and this is being attempted to give more thrust as the plane takes off.

The unit combustion chamber is comparatively small but will burn kerosine at a very high rate per unit volume. An ordinary air-blast gas burner burns about 7 therms of gas per cubic foot of combustion space per hour at one atmospheric pressure ; the jet combustion chamber of 3 to 4 cu. ft. volume will burn 7000 lb. of kerosine per hour, the residence time being only about 10 milliseconds. The chamber operates at a pressure of about 5 atm. so that this rate means about 80 therms per atm. per cu. ft. per hour or eleven times the rate of the gas burner. The arrangement of the chamber is shown in the diagram, Figure 80 ; fuel is delivered under pressure to the special atomizer at one end, burned in the stream of compressed air at high velocity of 350 ft. per sec., delivered by swirl devices around the spray and forced as secondary—and tertiary—air through openings, or vents, in the sides of the chamber. The stream of hot gases pass straight through the turbine to the jet where their expulsion provides the thrust. The turbine provides the power for compressing the air for

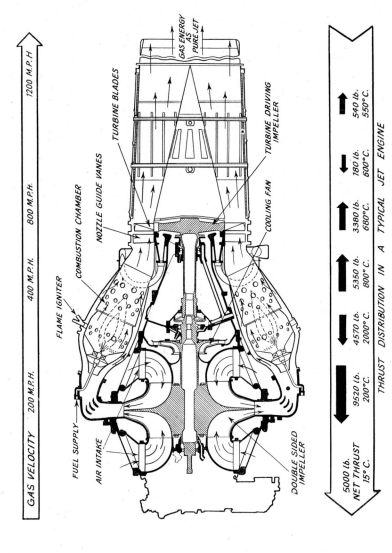

GAS VELOCITY 200 M.P.H. 400 M.P.H. 800 M.P.H. 1200 M.P.H.

GAS ENERGY AS PURE JET

TURBINE BLADES

COMBUSTION CHAMBER

NOZZLE GUIDE VANES

TURBINE DRIVING IMPELLER

FLAME IGNITER

COOLING FAN

FUEL SUPPLY

AIR INTAKE

DOUBLE SIDED IMPELLER

THRUST DISTRIBUTION IN A TYPICAL JET ENGINE

| 5000 lb. NET THRUST 15° C. | 9520 lb. 200°C. | 4570 lb. 2000° C. | 5350 lb. 800° C. | 3380 lb. 680° C. | 180 lb. 600° C. | 540 lb. 550° C. |

FIG. 80.—Section of Jet Aero-engine (Joseph Lucas Ltd.).

335

combustion ; its blades are made of special heat-resisting metal to take the highest blast temperature possible. At present this temperature is about 800° C. and is a limiting factor in the reduction of the air/fuel ratio. The air is delivered in the annulus around the chamber and is both preheated on its way to the burner and cools the chamber wall. The chambers are of light-gauge heat-resisting steel, so that the thrust/weight ratio is high. Comparative figures for the piston engine, turbo-prop, and turbo-jet are 1·6, 2·0, and 2·6 at take-off, and 0·22, 0·39, and 0·87 at 300 m.p.h. and 25,000 ft. altitude.

A great deal of experimental work was done on atomization of the fuel and method of supply of air to achieve combustion which cannot be dealt with here ; it is sufficient to say that it was essential to find conditions which would allow of intimate mixing of fuel and air, adequate cooling of the thin walls and avoidance of carbon formation. It was realized that it would be ideal to have atomization to particles of uniform size and this was attempted as closely as possible. A typical size distribution now follows the usual distribution curve between the limits of 200 and 10 μ with few particles smaller and a small number above 200 μ. This means that there are 5×10^6 droplets per ml. of spray. Ignition of these is by high-tension plug or by special torch, which is in effect a miniature combustion chamber burning a rich mixture.

Fuel Properties. It is apparent that rather special properties are called for in fuels for this purpose. A light fuel would be required if weight were the limiting factor and a heavy fuel if it were volume, so that the best must be a compromise.

Fluidity at a low temperature is important since a low viscosity is necessary for good atomization even at high altitudes. The upper limit is 7–10 centistokes at 0° C., but the oil must also have a low freezing-point ; in the U.S.A. this is −60° C. and in G.B. −40° C. Viscosities of this order are obtainable with petrol or kerosine but not with gas or diesel oils.

The fuel must not contain free water, but oils do have a distinct solubility for water which increases with decrease of temperature. Oil saturated with water at 20° C. can therefore deposit water when the fuel is cooled at high altitudes and could block the filters ; while it remains in solution or as liquid it is not a difficulty. The solubility of water in a paraffinic kerosine is about 0·005 per cent. at 20° C., and in benzene is 0·06 per cent. This difference is large in practice and is one argument in favour of paraffinic, and against aromatic, fuels. 1000 gal. of kerosine saturated at 20° C. and cooled to −10° C. would give 0·3 pint of water, but 1000 gal. of benzene would give ten times this, or 3 pints.

The deposition of carbon on combustion-chamber walls or on turbine blades was a serious difficulty in the development of the jet engine. It was overcome by the obvious method of obtaining the best possible atomization, the most uniform distribution of air, the use of scrubbing air directed along the walls, and by running at the weakest air/fuel ratio which would still give a high combustion efficiency. These are mechanical factors but it is apparent that chemical composition must play an important part. It is well known that aromatic hydrocarbons of high C/H ratio have a greater tendency to deposit carbon from flames than naphthenes, and these in turn than paraffins, but other factors also operate. Long-chain hydrocarbons have a greater tendency than those with short, branched chains and sulphur compounds tend to promote carbon formation. The choice is now therefore in favour of short-chain paraffins, but the real answer is to improve combustion conditions still further in order to use high-density fuels of greater heat value per unit volume.

The problem of combustion at the higher altitudes of 40,000 ft. or so is a matter for special study. At such a height the engine becomes unstable below 60 per cent. load because of the rarefication of the atmosphere, and flame extinction can occur at low loads or when accelerating or decelerating. Relighting the flame is then a difficult matter.

Fuel Specifications. The present specification for aviation kerosine really covers a " wide-cut " gasoline and is very meticulous in its clauses. In view of the frequency of the changes which are made by the issuing body, the Ministry of Supply, only a few of the more important clauses are quoted below.

	2482.	2486.
Specific gravity	—	0·739–0·825
Flash-point, ° F. (minimum)	100	100
Distillation range, ° C. :		
Initial boiling-point	—	—
Final ,, ,, ...	300	—
Distillate at 121° C. min.	—	10
,, ,, 204·4° C. min.	—	90
,, ,, 200° C. min.	20	—
Sulphur, per cent., max.	0·2	0·04
Freezing-point, max., ° F.	−40	−76
Water tolerance, max., ml.	0·2	0·2
Viscosity, max. cs. at 100° F.	6	—
Aromatics, vol. per cent., max.	20	25
Gum, mg., max.	6	20
Calorific value, B.Th.U./lb., min.	18,300	18,400
Vapour pressure (Reid), max., lb.	—	3

REFERENCE BOOKS

The Science of Petroleum. Dunstan. Oxford Univ. Press. 1938.
Motor Fuel Preparation. Nash and Howes. Chapman and Hall. 1945.
Aviation Gasoline Manufacture. Winkle. McGraw-Hill. 1944.
Carburation. Fisher. Chapman and Hall. 1951.
The High-Speed Internal Combustion Engine. Sir H. R. Ricardo. Blackie and Son. 1953.
The High-Speed Compression-Ignition Engine. Dicksee. Blackie and Son. 1946.
Physical Constants of Hydrocarbons. Egloff. Rheinhold Corp. 1939–47.
The Conversion of Petroleum. Sachanan. Rheinhold Corp. 1945.
Natural Gas and Gasoline. Huntingdon. McGraw-Hill. 1953.

CHAPTER XIII

MOTOR BENZOLE, ALCOHOLS AND MIXTURES

MOTOR BENZOLE

In the carbonization of one ton of coal by the gas and coke industries some three gallons of crude spirit are formed which are distributed between the gas and tar. On the recovery from these it is designated as crude benzole (gas) and naphtha (tar). In processes of high-temperature carbonization a high proportion of this spirit consists of benzene and the next members of the benzene series, toluene and the xylenes. In low-temperature processes the proportion of aromatic hydrocarbons is less, about 30 per cent., although the volume yield of crude spirit is about the same. Crude spirits have been termed 90's, 65's, etc., " benzoles ", indicating the percentage distilling below 100° C.

In Great Britain the greater part of the crude benzole is distilled to refined motor benzole, although some is separated to provide pure benzene, toluene and xylenes. In 1951 the production of total benzole was 97 million gal., from which was sold 50 million gal. of motor benzole. The quantity of low-temperature carbonization spirit was much less, about 1·2 million gal. Other industrial uses for benzole have now reduced the amount of motor benzole sold to about 20 million gal.

Refined motor benzole has the approximate composition of benzene 70–75, toluene 12–15, xylenes 5–10, and other hydrocarbons 0–12 per cent.

The average yield of total benzole from coal is about 3 gal. per ton, but the yield varies with the type of coal and the conditions of carbonization. In the coke-oven industry practically the whole of it is recovered, but in the gas industry the recovery is variable depending upon the required calorific value of the gas, and probably not more than 60 per cent. of what is available is recovered. Much the greater proportion of this yield is recovered by scrubbing the gas, the remainder is obtained by distillation from the tar. The proportions are of the order of 15 : 1 by volume.

Distillation of Tar. Crude coal tar yields, as a first fraction of distillation, light oils and naphtha to the extent of 5–8 per cent. These contain the benzole and this is recovered by refractionation ; the final temperature determines the proportion of benzole in the product. A 90's benzole from tar will contain benzene 84, toluene 13 and xylenes 3 per cent.

Recovery from Coal Gas. Benzole is recovered from gas by scrubbing with wash oil or by adsorption in activated carbon. The oil used may be a petroleum oil in the gas-oil range or a refined creosote oil. The scrubber-oil is steam distilled for the removal of the benzole and returned to the process. The sorptive capacity of these oils is about 3–5 per cent. by weight and the volume required to scrub 10,000 cu. ft. of gas is 80–100 gal., which is some 25 per cent. more than the theoretical amount.

The activated carbon is in granular form and absorbs some 30 per cent. by weight of benzole ; it is steamed to remove the benzole, cooled and used again. The cycle may be 20 minutes sorption, 30 minutes steaming, 20 minutes cooling.

Crude Benzole. If the benzole has been obtained by oil-washing it will contain a proportion of wash-oil depending in amount on the efficiency of the plant ; this is not so in recovery by active carbon.

Coke-oven benzole is fairly uniform in quality and contains after refining over 90 per cent. of aromatic hydrocarbons. Gas industry benzole varies with the process used ; horizontal retorts give a product similar to that from coke ovens, but the continuous vertical retort, and to a less extent the intermittent vertical chamber, give a benzole of much lower aromatic content. Table LVII illustrates this for Durham coal.

TABLE LVII

EFFECT OF TYPE OF GAS-RETORT ON THE COMPOSITION OF BENZOLE

Plant.	Yield gal./ton.	Arom. h/c.	Unsat. h/c.	Sat. h/c.
Horizontal retort . .	3·03	91·4	3·5	4·2
Intermittent vert. retort .	2·49	73·2	9·6	15·6
Continuous vert. retort .	2·90	69·0	10·2	17·9
C.W. gas	—	86	13	1
L.T. gas	3·5	32	29	39

Analyses of carburetted water gas and low-temperature carbonization gas " spirits " are included for comparison. The latter must be very variable since it is known that the proportion of aromatics tend to increase rapidly as the temperature of carbonization exceeds 550–600° C., and these processes tend to show wide variations of temperature near this range.

Refining of Benzole and Motor Benzole. The crude benzole is washed with alkali to remove tar acids, with 40 per cent. sulphuric acid to remove pyridine bases, and distilled to remove carbon disulphide and low-boiling hydrocarbons as first runnings and naphtha and possibly some wash oil as final runnings. The intermediate fraction of say 70–180° C. represents the benzole.

Saleable motor benzole must be free from gummy or resinous material, corrosive substances and objectionable odour ; its sulphur content must also be under 0·1 per cent. and it must not develop colour on storage.

Half of the organic sulphur in the crude benzole is carbon disulphide, which is removed in the first runnings of the primary distillation. Alternatively the CS_2 may be removed by washing with ammonium polysulphide solution. The remainder is in the form of thiophen and its homologues and this has to be removed by treatment with small amounts (2 per cent.) of strong (98 per cent.) sulphuric acid.

The tendency to form gum on storage is presumed to be due to the polymerization and oxidation of the small amounts of unsaturated bodies present. The proportion of these can be kept low by suitable acid-washing or the use of oxidation and polymerization methods, but it is difficult to achieve complete removal. An alternative is to add a small proportion of a substance which will prevent oxidation for a period. The most effective substances are the phenols and amino-phenols and the concentration necessary for inhibition is from 0·001 to 0·05 per cent. by weight.

Benzole as a Motor Fuel. Despite its high C/H ratio and initial boiling-point benzole will operate an internal-combustion engine quite satisfactorily, without alteration to the engine. For economic reasons, however, it is seldom used alone as fuel ; it is generally employed in admixture with gasoline as " benzole mixture ". Alone benzole has three disadvantages, a freezing-point which is too high ; the " first drop " temperature is not far below 80° C., whilst that of gasolines is about 40° C. ; and it is somewhat difficult to burn without soot.

Ease of starting an engine depends largely upon the proportion of low-boiling components, roughly indicated by the temperature at which the first drop falls from the condenser during a distillation test. In this respect benzole is at a disadvantage.

At the upper end of the distillation range, whilst most petrols have an " end-point " about 200° C., motor benzoles usually are completely distilled at about 145–150° C.

This upper limit cannot well be exceeded since it is very difficult to refine the hydrocarbons boiling at a higher temperature sufficiently to prevent the development of yellow colour and resinification on storage. Further, the exhaust gases have an objectionable smell.

An incidental advantage of benzole containing little boiling above 150° C. is that crank-case dilution of the lubricating oil in an engine is less liable than with gasoline.

The National Benzole Association's specification for motor benzole is given below :

Specific gravity, 15/15° C.		0·870–0·886
Distillation range—		
Not less than 60 per cent. at . . .		100° C.
Not less than 95 per cent. at . . .		155° C.
Crystallizing-point, not above		5° C.
Sulphur, not more than		0·4 per cent.

As stated previously, benzole is not normally used as a motor spirit alone but in admixture with gasoline ; alcohol is sometimes included in the blend. Since the quantity produced, or likely to be produced, is only about 3 per cent. of gasoline consumption, there is no need to consider its use except as a blend component. Its most important property as a blend component is its high anti-knock value. Benzole itself cannot be made to knock, but its blending octane number is about 90 by the motor method, and a 50 per cent. blend with gasoline of knock-rating 70 would have a value of about 80. It has, therefore, obvious value as a means of improving gasolines of low knock-rating.

Under non-knocking conditions motor fuels all give much the same thermal efficiency so that fuel consumption is proportional to net calorific value. Since the net calorific value of benzole is 8 per cent. less than that of petrol, its consumption on a weight basis is higher, but since fuels are sold on a volume basis the advantage is in favour of benzole since its higher specific gravity gives it 10 per cent. more therms per gallon.

Benzole has little effect in blends on starting quality, but it follows that the proportion of benzene itself in the benzole should be high. Normally no carburettor adjustments are necessary if the benzole does not exceed 30 per cent.

In certain circumstances such as aviation the high freezing-point of benzole can be a difficulty. If the freezing-point of the benzole is $-5°$ C., a 50 per cent. blend will freeze at $-20°$ C. and a 30 per cent. blend at $-35°$ C. The latter is quite safe in Great Britain for road vehicles but would not be for aviation, for which the upper limit is $-60°$ C.

Benzole can also be used in ternary blends with petrol and methyl- or ethyl-alcohol. In this case the position is complicated by the fact that there are definite limits of solubility which must be on the safe side for the most stringent conditions likely to occur ; in addition, the slightest contact with water can bring about dilution of the alcohol and immediate separation into layers.

ALCOHOL FUELS

Comparatively little alcohol is used to-day as a fuel for the internal combustion engine, but it deserves careful consideration as the only fuel for this purpose which does not come under the heading of " stored " fuel. Indeed, it may be regarded as one direct method of obtaining energy from the sun without the intermediary of storage in the earth for long periods of time. In addition, it has certain properties as an engine fuel which give it particular value as a blending agent with petroleum spirit and benzole. In view of the relatively very small quantities in which it can be made economically available, however, it can never be regarded as being of more than very secondary importance except perhaps in tropical countries where vegetation for its production is plentiful and supplies of petroleum products difficult to obtain at a reasonable price.

The use of alcohol in Great Britain or the United States was never more than a very small proportion of the fuel used for the internal combustion engine, but its use did gradually increase up to 1939. Since then its use was discontinued, but is now starting again (1954). The same situation developed in the United States, Germany and France, but at the present time only France makes use of it in any quantity (60,000 tons in 1952). In the U.S.A. the pre-war interest resulted in extensive engine trials in comparison with gasoline. The total consumption of motor-alcohol in the world in 1938 was about 600,000 tons and is still of the same order : this represents about 20 per cent. of total production of alcohol.

Alcohols. The alcohols which are of interest as motor fuels are, for reasons of boiling-range, only the first few members of the monohydric series : methyl- b.pt. 65°, ethyl- 78°, n-propyl- 97°, n-butyl- alcohol 117° C. Further, ethyl alcohol is the only one obtainable by fermentation ; methyl alcohol was obtained by distillation of wood and it is the one on which most of the engine experimental work was carried out during the period 1920–35. Synthetic methods now exist for the production of methyl and higher alcohols as well as ethyl alcohol, but it is not apparent that these could be operated cheaply enough to be used as fuels. For these reasons this discussion is limited to the consideration mainly of ethyl alcohol or ethanol, methyl alcohol, and methanol.

Ethyl alcohol is obtained by the fermentation of vegetable matter. The cost is high for starch-containing bodies such as potatoes or root crops, and collection costs are high for grasses, although both can give high yields of the order of 20 gal. of 95 per cent. alcohol per ton, or 120 gal. per acre.

Grain crops produce more and molasses a similar amount. Some comparison is made below :

	Gal./ton.	Gal./acre.
Mangolds	8	150
Artichokes	28	500
Potatoes	22	220
Grain	78	50
Sugar-beet	21	240
Molasses	66	—

Methods have also been put forward for the hydrolysis of hemi-cellulose in grasses to pentoses and the fermentation of the latter to alcohol ; these have been technically successful but have not been applied to any extent. Catalytic methods are also available for alcohols other than ethyl alcohol, but are too expensive for the production of fuel.

Methyl alcohol was formerly obtained by the distillation of wood for the manufacture of charcoal (Chapter II), but is now made by synthesis from carbon monoxide and hydrogen (water gas), present-day production being about 1·5 million gal. per annum in Britain and 15 million gal. in the United States.

The straight distillation of ethyl alcohol cannot produce a material richer in alcohol than 95·6 per cent. by weight (97·2 vol.), but the normal commercial product is 92·5 weight, or 95 per cent. volume spirit. In the early days of the use of alcohol this was a serious limitation since the presence of the water seriously limited the miscibility of the alcohol with hydrocarbon spirits. Also, the addition of further quantities of water, even in very small amount, could cause separation of components. This difficulty was overcome first by the use of drying agents such as quicklime, or an alcoholic solution of alkali acetates, but the application of methods of azeotropic distillation later produced 99·5 per cent. spirit at much the same cost as the old 95 per cent. spirit. The substance forming the azeotrope may be benzene or, preferably, trichlorethylene, added to the extent of ten times the amount of water present. On distillation, the ternary azeotrope distils first (67·2° C. for trichlorethylene) and the anhydrous alcohol is separated by close fractionation in a distillation column.

This was a very important development so far as the use of ethyl alcohol as a fuel was concerned, since the amount of 95 per cent. alcohol which would form a stable mixture at −10° C. with petroleum spirit had to be as much as 70–80 per cent. of the mixture, depending upon the petroleum spirit used. With 99·5 per cent. spirit, almost complete miscibility is obtained in any proportion, certainly well beyond limits of probable mixtures.

Advantages and Disadvantages of Alcohols. Ethyl alcohol as a fuel offers the advantages of great safety, by reason of its low degree of volatility and higher flash-point, about 17° C. (65° F.) ; its vapours are not quite half as heavy as those of petrol, so that it does not creep and accumulate in dangerous quantities on low levels, and a higher proportion is needed to form an explosive mixture ; it mixes in all proportions with water, and burning alcohol can be extinguished with water. Although of much lower thermal value than petrol and benzole, it shows a relatively good thermal efficiency, and the actual consumption for a given power is not much higher than with these other fuels. Its uniformity of composition is another point in its favour.

The higher degree of safety renders the storage, handling and transport of alcohol more free from those necessary restrictions which have to be imposed on petrol and benzole, and would appreciably affect insurance rates. Further, in many hot countries the use of the more volatile spirits is almost impossible, whilst in the hottest climate alcohol is perfectly safe.

On the other hand, there is the problem of cost and exemption from many of the restrictions at present imposed on its production to be overcome. Further, as minor objections, come the question of possible corrosion, the fact that some 5·5 per cent. of the total heat of its combustion is required for vaporization, and that some addition, such as benzole, or the prior running of the engine on either petrol or benzole to warm up is necessary before alcohol can be used directly. The corrosion trouble is not serious, neither is that of vaporization, once the engine is hot, for there is always the sensible heat of the exhaust gases available ; but that of difficulty in starting from the cold is inherent in a fuel of low vapour pressure.

Other apparent disadvantages can be listed as follows :

(1) Its calorific value is only two-thirds that of gasoline.
(2) It has a higher specific gravity and viscosity which make modifications of the carburettor necessary.
(3) It has a higher surface tension and is less easy to atomize.
(4) It will not mix with oil and causes lubrication difficulties in the upper parts of the cylinder.
(5) It has high solvent power which affects joints and can wash previously-deposited gum from tanks and transfer them to the engine.
(6) It must have a denaturant.

Taking these together, it is apparent that the most important factor is its high knock-rating since the disadvantages can be overcome in one way or another. This can be utilized in two ways, (1) as a blend constituent for improving straight-run or other spirit of low octane number, and (2) by its use in a special engine of high compression ratio of the order of 12/1. A third method is now proposed but has not yet been applied. It consists in using it as a duo-fuel by separate injection when required. The ordinary motor engine makes full use of high knock-rating of the fuel only during a small proportion of its service. If it were operated on a cheaper fuel of relatively low rating but with automatic means for alcohol injection under high loads, the combination might well make for greater economy under conditions in which most of the above disadvantages would disappear.

Composition of the Fuel Alcohols. As stated above, the only alcohols of practical interest as fuels are the first two members of the series. Their composition is given below.

Name.	Formula.	Percentage composition.			Specific gravity.	Boiling-point.
		Carbon.	Hydrogen.	Oxygen.		
Methyl alcohol .	CH_3OH	37·5	12·5	50·0	0·8102	64·7° C.
Ethyl alcohol . .	C_2H_5OH	52·2	13·0	34·8	0·7946	77·8° C.

The important difference from petrol is the high proportion of oxygen and the resulting low calorific value of 12,820 B.Th.U. per lb. in comparison

with 20,000 B.Th.U. for gasoline.   Other properties which are of importance
to the internal combustion engine are :

	Petrol.	Ethyl alcohol.	Methyl alcohol.
Specific heat	0·53	0·53	0·55
Latent heat, B.Th.U./lb.	135	367	475
Specific ignition temp. in O_2, °C. . . .	320	392	470
Reid vapour pressure, lb./sq. in. . . .	4–9	2·5	—
Flash-point, °F.	over 20° F. at − 40°	55	30
Limits of inflammation, per cent. . . .	2–6	4–13	7–30
Viscosity at 20° C., cs.	0·45	1·19	0·59

Calorific Value. The values determined by different observers differ
somewhat, possibly due chiefly to small variations in the strength of the
alcohols and admixtures, but the figures below are selected as being most
reliable.

Alcohol or mixture.	Specific gravity 15° C./15°.	B.Th.U. per lb.		B.Th.U. per gallon.	
		Gross.	Net.	Gross.	Net.
Methyl alcohol	0·796	9,605	8,515	76,456	67,780
Ethyl alcohol	0·794	12,820	11,690	101,800	92,820
Methylated spirit	0·816	11,815	10,690	96,410	87,230
Alcohol 77 per cent. ⎱ . . Benzole 22·5 per cent ⎰	0·832	14,010	12,900	116,560	107,330

The volume of air for the combustion of ethanol is 111 cu. ft. at N.T.P.
per lb. or 882 cu. ft. per gal., which is equivalent to 9 lb. of air per lb. on
ethanol.

Excise Restrictions. The use of alcohol for power purposes was
retarded for some years by the need for excise control, but this was overcome
in the 1921 Act which stipulated that the spirit sold should contain 2·5 per
cent. of wood naphtha, 0·5 per cent. of crude pyridine and 5 per cent. of
benzole and be coloured red by the addition of 0·75 oz. of eosin and 0·25
of " spirit red 3 " to every 1000 gal.   Before issue from bond it had to be
mixed with not less than 25 per cent. of benzole, petrol, or ether.

" Power alcohol " can be imported in bulk under Customs supervision
at certain specified ports and stored in approved tank warehouses.   When
the above additions have been made (also under Excise supervision) the
spirit may be distributed without further restriction.

In France the denatured alcohol is very similar in composition, but for
power alcohol a new denaturant was introduced in 1933 in which 0·6 gram
of anthracene dissolved in 1 litre of benzole with 0·2 gram of ethylboric
ether is added to the hectolitre of alcohol.   In Germany two classes of
denatured spirit are available ; for ordinary use, 2·5 vols. of methyl alcohol
in 100 of ethyl, together with a small quantity of the pyridine bases extracted

from coal tar ; for fuel purposes, half this quantity of methyl alcohol and not less than 2 per cent. of benzole, the mixture being given a distinctive colour by the addition of methyl violet—one of the coal-tar colours.

Ethyl Alcohol as an Engine Fuel. The first consideration in the use of ethyl-alcohol as an engine fuel is that it has a high knock-rating and could operate at a compression ratio of 12/1. This attracted attention at a time when high-octane gasolines were not available and the compression ratio of the ordinary " petrol " engine was limited to 4·5. It was more valuable even than tetra-ethyl lead since its effect, unlike that of lead, is proportional to the amount added. To-day, however, high-rating gasolines are available and the use of alcohol is reduced to an alternative which might in certain circumstances be more economic than the reforming of petroleum which is necessary for making high-octane fuel and which inevitably decreases the yield and reduces the quality of the other fuel oils.

In these early days Ricardo defined the advantages of the use of alcohol on thermal efficiency as follows :

Fuel.	Highest useful compression ratio.	Corresponding indicated thermal efficiency.	Minimum consumption at H.U.C.R. Pints per B.H.P. hour.
Gasolines.	4·55/1 to 6·0/1	30·2 to 34·9	0·402 to 0·484
Benzene (98 per cent.) .	6·9/1	37·2	0·355
Alcohol (98 per cent.) .	7·5/1 *	40·4	0·533
Methylated spirit . . .	6·5/1 *	38·5	0·609

* With alcohol fuels the limit was not actually reached, but Ricardo regarded these figures as the useful practical limit.

This advantage over " low " octane gasolines overcomes the relative disadvantage of lower calorific value in the ratio of 1·55 : 1, but would not, of course, do so now with gasoline of high octane rating. To-day the normal car engine has a compression ratio of 7 or 8 : 1 and operates at the higher efficiency at full load.

Thermal efficiency is not the only criterion of engine performance and one aspect of the degree of conversion of heat to useful work is the thermal value of one charge of air and fuel into the cylinder. Since the air requirements of petrol and alcohol are in the ratio of 15/9 lb. per lb. of fuel, and this is the same as the ratio of their net calorific values, it follows that the same heat is developed per cylinder charge. Ricardo gives the following figures for power development per cubic inch of cylinder volume : gasoline 46·2, methanol 45·5, ethanol 44·5 ft.-lb., which are very closely similar.

Volumetric efficiency, or the relation between the weight of the cylinder charge and its weight calculated to N.T.P., depends upon the charge density, and this is affected by completeness of filling and by temperature. Charge temperature is lowest with fuels of highest latent heat, and since alcohols have high latent heats they show high values for volumetric efficiency. At correct mixture strength volumetric efficiency for petrol is 76 and for ethanol 82 per cent. With very rich mixtures the difference is greater, a fact which has been applied in the use of alcoholic racing fuels.

Knock-rating. Methyl alcohol has a blending octane number by the C.F.R. Motor method of 108 and ethyl alcohol of 106. 50/50 alcohol/ gasoline blends with a gasoline of 70 would therefore have ratings of 89 and 88 respectively, increases which are considerably more than would be achieved by the addition of tetraethyl lead, to the extent of 3·5 ml., to the gasoline. These increases are valuable in themselves but unfortunately cannot be further increased by the addition of tetraethyl lead since alcohol blends have a low lead susceptibility, particularly ethanol blends.

The C.F.R. Motor method suggests a compression ratio of 7 : 1 for an octane number of 90, so that an engine of this compression ratio could use 70 octane petroleum spirit if alcohol were available as a blend component. Ricardo has shown that minimum fuel consumption at 7 : 1 compression ratio is petrol 0·35 and ethanol 0·55 pint per h.p./hr. This is in the same ratio as their calorific values.

If, however, the fuel is consumed at its highest useful compression ratio (H.U.C.R.) a much higher power output is obtained from methanol than from gasoline of knock-rating of the order of 70. The figure for ethanol is 0·535 pint per h.p./hr. as against 0·435 for 70-octane petrol, or 23 per cent. more ; but the power output is 20 per cent. higher.

These facts suggest the use of a special engine for ethanol, although there are obvious possibilities in its use as a duo-fuel with petrol of moderate octane number.

Incomplete Combustion. The other disadvantages of ethanol are all curable by modification of engine design and are outside the scope of this book, but one other factor is of importance in relation both to engine efficiency and to atmospheric cleanliness. It is that alcohol fuels tend to give less carbon monoxide in the exhaust gases than petroleum motor spirits. Lichty and Phelps have recorded the effect of adding 20 per cent. of ethanol to an unleaded petrol. Their general conclusion is that the percentage of CO is 1 to 2 per cent. less at all loads and speeds and that this means a lower thermal loss of 2 to 4 per cent. This is valuable in itself, but the gain in atmospheric purity is important since an engine under full load will give an exhaust gas which contains 2–3 per cent. CO, which may increase to three times this at half-speed.

Corrosion with Alcohol. One of the troubles which have arisen with alcohol in engines has been that of corrosion of valves, etc., due to the production of acid bodies. The partial oxidation of an alcohol takes place at a low temperature, and leads first to the formation of *aldehydes*, and these in turn become acids. Thus—

Methyl alcohol		Formaldehyde		Formic acid
$CH_3.OH$	$\rightarrow$	$H.COH$	$\rightarrow$	$H.COOH$
Ethyl alcohol		Acetaldehyde		Acetic acid
$C_2H_5.OH$	$\rightarrow$	$CH_3.COH$	$\rightarrow$	$CH_3.COOH$

Ethyl alcohol begins to show formation of aldehydes at 300° C., but methyl alcohol, which oxidizes more readily, at 160° C.

Aldehyde formation is due to incomplete combustion ; given an excess of air it should not occur. With even a small deficiency at a moderate temperature some acetaldehyde and acetic acid are certain to be formed from the ethyl alcohol, and the exhaust gases are always liable to contain traces of acids. Running a few revolutions on petrol or benzole before stopping the engine is found to overcome the trouble of corrosion, and this offers no great difficulty, for in many cases such fuels are necessary for starting up. It must be remembered that while the engine is hot these acid products will not affect the metal ; it is only on cooling, leading to their condensation on the surfaces, that action will be set up. For this reason the silencer generally is found to suffer most.

To neutralize the acid products which cause corrosion various basic volatile bodies, concentrated ammonia, nicotine, etc., are sometimes added in very small quantities.

Another type of corrosion is that set up by the fuel itself on tanks, piping, etc. In extensive trials of power alcohol and alcohol-benzole mixtures carried out by the London General Omnibus Company, copper and iron were found to be badly attacked. By " tinning " with lead, or a lead-tin alloy, this was prevented. The action appears to be due to esters in the wood naphtha, which, on hydrolysis, give rise to traces of organic acids. It should not occur therefore with the synthetic methanol.

The addition of a small quantity (0·2–0·3 per cent.) of sodium benzoate is stated to be a preventive. Oomandy claimed that corrosion did not take place if anhydrous alcohol were used.

Alcohol as a Blend Component. The value of alcohol as a blend component has been considered above in relation to engine performance, but another factor in its use is the stability of the blend against accidental inclusion of water and the effect of a drop in the temperature of storage.

The most widely used mixtures used were those of alcohol with petrol, and in some countries the use of a certain amount of alcohol with petrol is compulsory. In France three motor fuels are recognized which contain alcohol of 99·5 per cent. strength : (1) *carburant tourisme*—which may be either light petrol, or this with 11–20 per cent. of alcohol ; (2) *carburant poid lourd*—a heavy petrol or white spirit with less than 35 per cent. of alcohol ; (3) *super carburant*—Alcohol over 15 per cent., octane no. 75+.

The petrol/alcohol fuels were also extensively investigated in the United States of America, in view of proposals to penalize other fuels not containing alcohol in the interests of agriculture. In one series of tests extending over ninety days, using 28,000 gal. of the mixture containing 10 per cent. of alcohol, with car speeds of 30 m.p.h., the fuel showed about 10 per cent. less mileage ; one pint of commercial anti-knock petrol gave a mileage of 3·2 ; 60–62 U.S. petrol, 3·175 ; alcohol/petrol, 2·9 miles. Laboratory engine tests showed about 4 per cent. decrease in efficiency.

On the other hand, it was claimed that German " Monopolin ", 20 per cent. absolute alcohol, 80 per cent. petrol, showed a saving of 1·7 per cent. over petrol and 10 per cent. over a petrol/benzole mixture.

In tests made on the standard C.F.R. engine the 10 per cent. alcohol/petrol mixture gave 5 units higher octane value.

King and Manning state that alcohol/petrol mixture (25 per cent. alcohol, 75 per cent. petrol), (a) cannot be used satisfactorily in a standard petrol engine ; (b) is difficult to start from cold, although the engine can be changed over after starting on petrol ; (c) the range of mixture strengths over which smooth running is obtained is extremely limited, and also uneconomical ; (d) satisfactory results would probably be obtained by a " hot spot " or re-designing the induction manifold.

So far as stability against separation of water from petrol/alcohol blends is concerned it is established that there is an empirical relationship

$$\log w = a - b/\mathrm{T}$$

where w is the percentage of water in the blend, T the absolute temperature and a and b are constants depending upon the petrol and its concentration in the blend.

Other components have been suggested to improve stability but of these only benzene remains. In the proportion likely to be used in practice, i.e. up to ethanol 20 and benzene 20, the limiting proportion for separation of water at 60° F. is given by

$$\text{Water per cent.} = (1 \cdot 2\mathrm{A} - 3)(\mathrm{B} + 30)/1000$$

where A and B are the percentages of ethanol and benzene respectively. To give an example we have :—

	B.5.	B.10.	B.20.
A.20, water tolerance, per cent.	0·75	0·88	1·15
A.10, ,, ,, ,,	0·30	0·33	0·42

These figures illustrate the care which must be taken in handling blends to avoid the intrusion of water especially as the limits are much closer in winter when the temperature is lower. This temperature limitation is more important in the case of aviation fuels when temperature of −50° C. may be encountered. At this temperature a blend consisting of petrol 60, ethanol 20 and benzene 20 may have a water tolerance of only 0·3 per cent. as against 1·1 per cent. at 60° F. If the benzene were replaced by ethanol

making 40 per cent. of the latter the tolerance is increased to 0·52 at −50° C.
owing to the greater solubility of water in the ethanol. The proportion of
benzene cannot be increased in the absence of ethanol since crystals of
benzene would begin to separate at −17° C.

Generally speaking there is a prejudice against the use of ethanol for
aviation because of the separation danger and the lower calorific value,
but it would have some advantages such as reduction in boost temperature,
cooler engine temperature and the prevention of icing of carburettors owing
to lower volatility.

" TETRALIN "

Tetrahydronaphthalene, $C_{10}H_{12}$

This liquid hydrocarbon, produced by the hydrogenation of the naphthalene ($C_{10}H_8$) abundantly present in high-temperature tars, has been employed
to a small extent in blended fuels and remains of interest for special uses in
aviation. German " Reichskaftstoff " was a mixture of benzole, 50 parts ;
alcohol, 25 parts ; tetralin, 25 parts. The vapour pressure of tetralin is
only about 0·5 mm. at 20° C., so that alone it is incapable of carburetting air.

The specific gravity is 0·975 ; boiling-point, 205° C. ; freezing-point,
−35° C. ; flash-point, 79° C. (176° F.), and the gross calorific value is
20,880 B.Th.U. per lb.

Further information is available in a paper by Sir F. L. Nathan (*Fuel*,
1924, **3**, 346).

REFERENCE BOOKS

Motor Fuel. Nash and Howes. Chapman and Hall. 1938.
Motor Benzole. Hoffert and Claxton. The National Benzole Association. 1938.
Power Alcohol. Monier Williams. 1922.
Alcohol Fuels. Ribignac.
Alcohol for I.C. Engines. Pleeth. Chapman and Hall. 1949.

CHAPTER XIV

GAS OIL, DIESEL FUEL, THE COMPRESSION-IGNITION ENGINE

As explained in Chapter X, the fraction obtained in the primary distillation of petroleum, boiling between 200° and 320° C., is generally termed gas oil or diesel oil. Oil in this range is also obtained from the recycle oil from either thermal or catalytic cracking but has the important difference that its composition is changed by cracking ; its paraffin content is reduced by the formation of unsaturated and aromatic hydrocarbons and its ignition quality and cetane number are reduced.

The term gas oil was originally applied to oil used for the production of illuminating gas by cracking and, although this usage is no longer common, the term has remained, since considerable quantities are used for the carburetting of water gas. For this latter purpose it is important that the oil should be of a paraffinic character in order that a high yield of gas of high calorific value can be obtained by thermal cracking (see Chapter XVII). It is desirable, therefore, that gas oil should be a straight-run distillate from a paraffin-base oil, but other oils can be gasified at a sacrifice of enrichment value, even up to heavy fuel oils. It must be recognized, however, that gas oil prepared from cracked recycle stock is less satisfactory for this purpose.

Diesel fuel is by preference in the same distillation range as gas oil, and indeed may be the same material, but is literally any oil which can be burned in a compression-ignition engine, colloquially called a Diesel engine after the original inventor Rudolf Diesel. Diesel engines vary considerably in size and speed and cover a wide range of fuels from petroleum distillates to coal-tar fractions and to vegetable oils ; indeed, the original aim of the inventor was to use coal dust. The favoured oil is a petroleum oil of rather higher boiling range than gas oil and having suitable ignition characteristics for the type of engine used.

Gas Oil

As a distillation product, gas oil naturally varies in composition according to the nature of the crude oil, but certain properties are specified such as flash-point and distillation range. An idea of the range of variation is given in the Table LVIII.

The main usage of gas oil is the carburetting of water gas and the stripping of benzole from coal gas, but it can be used as a fuel for the Diesel engine depending upon its cetane number. If of high cetane number it is very suitable for small, high-speed engines.   It is less suitable for slow-speed industrial or marine Diesels owing to its low viscosity, which gives it a liability to leakage at the fuel pump.

TABLE LVIII
PROPERTIES OF GAS OILS

Specific gravity, 60/60° F. . .	0·84	0·88	0·86
Flash-point, ° F.	200	186	186
Viscosity, Redwood I at 100° F. .	35	33	37
Boiling-range, ° C. to . . .	220	200	210
x per cent. at 300° C. . . .	65	90	72
Cetane number	62	34	47
Conradson carbon, weight per cent. .	0·02	0·07	0·03
Pour-point, ° C.	−4	−9	−12

Diesel Fuel and the Diesel Engine

The properties of fuel for the Diesel engine are best explained after some consideration of the features of the compression-ignition engine.

The fundamental principle of this engine is that it relies upon the heat of compression to achieve ignition of the fuel.   The fuel is injected in an atomized spray at the end of the compression stroke when the air for combustion has been compressed to 450–650 lb. per sq. in. and has reached a temperature, due to its compression, of at least 500° C.   This temperature is sufficient to ignite suitable fuel and start the power stroke of the engine, and is attained by the use of a high compression ratio of 15/1.   In turn the pressure developed is high, of the order of 1000 lb. per sq. in., and the engine is heavier and more robust than the petrol engine.   As with the petrol engine, the Diesel engine may operate on the four-stroke or two-stroke cycle, but the two-stroke engine is mainly of the opposed-piston type while the four-stroke engine may be either this type or double-acting. The double-acting engine utilizes both ends of the cylinder as combustion chambers, it normally has a larger power output and its main field of application is marine.   The opposed-piston engine has two pistons in each cylinder moving inwards simultaneously on the compression stroke, the fuel being injected between these ; power is taken at a single point by coupling the pistons.

In the normal four-stroke engine the first stroke draws in air, the inlet valve closes, the second stroke compresses the air into the clearance volume when the atomized fuel is injected, the third is the power stroke with all valves closed, and the fourth is the exhaust stroke.   This completes one cycle and the next begins with the closing of the exhaust valve.   There are therefore one power stroke and three idle strokes for every two revolutions of the crank shaft.

In the two-stroke cycle the air is compressed as before, but near the end of the power stroke the exhaust valve opens and the cylinder is swept by scavenge air from a pump so that the return stroke compresses a fresh charge of air. It is arranged that part of the scavenge air follows the exhaust gases since complete scavenging is necessary to the attainment of high efficiency of combustion. In this case the four strokes take place in one revolution of the crankshaft and the engine develops more power and is more smooth-running than a four-stroke engine of the same size and speed.

In modern practice it is usual to supply the air under a pressure of about 5 lb. per sq. in. in order to give a higher power output. Super-charging reduces ignition delay by increasing the effective compression ratio and gives smoother running.

Fuel Injection and Combustion. In the early forms of the Diesel engine the fuel was injected by compressed air to achieve fine atomization and good distribution, but this is now limited to large, slow-speed engines because of the difficulty of providing compressors. To-day the normal method is so-called " solid injection " through a nozzle either from a pressure line or from separate plunger pumps for each cylinder. The injector may be of various types to give good mixing ; the operating pressure is of the order of 2000 lb. per sq. in.

Assuming satisfactory injection of the oil, it is apparent that the design of the combustion chamber must be such that the most intimate mixing possible is achieved with the air. This means vigorous movement of the latter either as a definite swirl, or turbulence, or both ; it is achieved in the case of direct injection by arranging the air-inlet ports to create a swirl which persists during compression, and by the shape of the cylinder head. It may also be attained by the use of pre-combustion chambers in which the fuel is incompletely burned with air and from which a rich mixture is injected through holes into the combustion chamber proper. This chamber may be quite large and its air intake designed to give a strong swirl to the air.

Advantages of the Diesel Engine. The main advantages of the Diesel engine lie in its compactness, cleanliness and high thermal efficiency, and may be listed as follows :

(1) For marine purposes it occupies less space for a given power output than steam plant.

(2) It does not consume water since cooling water can be circulated.

(3) For road purposes its fuel injection system is more efficient than that of the petrol engine and fuel consumption at full load is only about half.

(4) It may be started from cold and brought to full power almost at once, a very large advantage over any steam plant.

(5) Combined with electric generation it is more efficient than any other plant for the provision of power for intermittent use. The shunting locomotive and the tugboat are examples of this.

(6) It operates with the high thermal efficiency of 30–35 per cent.

F. —N

The Semi-Diesel Engine. This type of engine is becoming obsolete. It operates by using an auxiliary heating surface or " hot bulb " to assist compression ignition. The central part of the chamber may also be ribbed to give extra heating surface. Hot-bulb engines are usually built on the two-stroke principle, but the scavenge air does not come into contact with the hot bulb and the small amount of hot exhaust gas left in the chamber aids the ignition of the fuel. The compression ratio is lower than in the true Diesel (about 200 lb. pressure) and thermal efficiency is lower by about 5 per cent.

The semi-Diesel will operate satisfactorily on a heavier oil than the true Diesel, but is not efficient at slow speeds owing to cooling of the hot surface.

Properties of Diesel Fuels

It is apparent from the above account of the Diesel engine that, apart from the usual requirements of cleanliness, suitable boiling-range and high flash-point, the important property to be considered in a diesel fuel is its ignition quality. In the first place it must be capable of ready ignition sufficiently below the temperature of compression to ensure ignition even with a cold start. Secondly, the time which elapses between injection and firing must not be too long or too much oil will be in the cylinder when ignition does occur and unduly high pressures will result which will make the running of the engine rough. Ignition quality is therefore measured by its spontaneous ignition temperature and by engine tests specially designed to give a numerical value to ignition delay.

The spontaneous ignition temperature (S.I.T.) is broadly related to the hydrogen content of the oil and was at one time regarded as a rough measure of suitability. A standard method of test was developed by the British Air Ministry in which the flash-point in an atmosphere of oxygen was determined by dropping droplets of the oil into a heated metal cup. A low temperature of self-ignition in the oxygen was considered to be indicative of suitability, but there were so many exceptions to this that the test is now regarded as giving only a broad indication of suitability.

The S.I.T. of motor spirit (75 octane) is about 300° C., of diesel fuel (cetane number 50) is 260° C., and of cetane itself 235° C.

Ignition Quality. The best method of assessment of the quality of a diesel fuel is by test in an engine, but an approximate estimate can be obtained by measuring the proportion of paraffin hydrocarbons in the fuel. In the case of petroleum fuels the higher the paraffin content the higher the ignition quality, but this is not always true of other fuels such as shale oils and tar distillates, or doped fuels.

The method of test is known as the *Aniline Point*; it is based on the fact that aromatic hydrocarbons mix readily with aniline at room temperature, but paraffins must be heated to a relatively high temperature before they become miscible. For example, the aromatic hydrocarbon, hexyl benzene, has an aniline point [1] below $-12°$ C., while the reference paraffin, cetane, has a value of $95\cdot1°$ C. A high aniline point is therefore an indication of high paraffin content and of high suitability.

The aniline point is converted into a " *Diesel Index* " by the expression :

$$\text{Diesel index} = \text{Aniline point } °\text{F.} \times \text{A.P.I. sp. gr.}/100.$$

The index is not so reliable as the cetane number but is a useful guide in the absence of engine tests. Numerically it is usually about 3 units higher than the cetane number and can be converted to the latter by the formula devised by the Institute of Petroleum :

$$\text{Cetane number (calc.)} = \tfrac{2}{3} \text{ Diesel index} + 0\cdot068 \text{ mid-B.Pt. } °\text{F.} - 22.$$

The specific gravity of petroleum oils is also actually a fair indication of the rating of a diesel fuel but only in the middle of the range.

Specific gravity.							Cetane range.
0·85	.	.	.	.	.	.	59–63
0·875	.	.	.	.	.	.	50–56
0·90	.	.	.	.	.	.	47–52
0·925	.	.	.	.	.	.	44–47
0·95	.	.	.	.	.	.	36–38

These values can be correlated by the I.P. formula :

$$\text{Cetane number (calc.)} = 175\cdot4 \text{ log mid-b.pt. } °\text{F.} + 1\cdot98 \text{ A.P.I. sp. gr.} - 496$$

and are reported to be reliable to within ±5 units.

Cetane Number. When the ignition quality is tested in an engine the result is expressed in terms of the cetane number. Cetane is a paraffin hydrocarbon, hexadecane, of high ignition quality to which is given the value of 100. The zero of this scale is represented by the aromatic hydrocarbon α-methyl naphthalene, which has a lower value than any known petroleum fuel. The actual cetane number is the percentage by volume of cetane in a mixture of the two hydrocarbons which is equivalent in ignition quality to the fuel under test. For routine testing, because of the high cost of these pure hydrocarbons, secondary reference fuels may be used ; the British Institute of Petroleum have standardized a low-cetane fuel at 18 and a high-cetane fuel at 70·5, which can be blended to suit.

There are two methods of making the engine test. In an engine there is a definite time lag of 0·5 to 10 milliseconds between injection of the oil and its ignition, and this *ignition delay period* is constant for a given fuel when measured in terms of crank angle. The delay period of a fuel, or a function of it such as the compression ratio required to bring it to a standard value, is used as the measure of ignition quality and is quoted in terms of cetane number. Two methods of test have been standardized in Great Britain, and can be used on any engine having a pre-combustion chamber.

---

[1] Equal volumes of oil and aniline are used in the test method.

Method A consists in the direct measurement of the delay period under normal running conditions. Since this is measured as the number of degrees through which the crankshaft turns in this period it is necessary to employ an instrument which will record pressure variations and also the exact point at which the spray-valve opens. A cathode-ray indicator is often used which embodies a thermionic valve device which integrates pressure and rotation time and allows the delay angle to be measured.

Method B is more simple ; a surge chamber fitted with a throttle is attached to the engine intake port. When this valve is closed the surge-chamber pressure is reduced, compression pressure is less and the delay period is increased until a misfire occurs which is indicated by a puff of white smoke. The air pressure in the surge-chamber at this point is taken as a function of delay period and compared with similar pressures from blends of the reference fuels. The result is quoted in cetane number.

In the United States a C.F.R. test engine has been standardized to run under specified conditions of air temperature, speed, fuel rate and coolant temperature. The compression ratio is variable and is measured for a standardized delay period of 13°, which is taken as the measure of cetane number.

The general significance of ignition quality is therefore that a suitable fuel is one which has a suitable ignition delay in the modern engine. A high cetane number, exceeding 48, is necessary for the high-speed engine, but a slow-speed engine is not so demanding since there is more time for combustion. Other factors affect this conclusion ; a higher air temperature or greater intimacy of mixing of air and fuel will deal with fuel of lower cetane number at the same speed. The general statement is true, however, and the correlation between engine speed and cetane range is approximately as follows :

Engine speed r.p.m.	Suitable cetane range.
Over 1500	60–50
1500–800	55–45
800–400	50–35
400–100	40–30
Under 100	30–15

The effect of using too low a cetane value fuel is to collect too much fuel in the cylinder before ignition takes place ; a high pressure is developed which becomes audible as " diesel knock ". It is necessary to distinguish clearly between this and knock in a gasoline engine. If diesel fuel with its required tendency to ignite readily in a hot engine were to be used in a spark-ignition engine it would fire too readily and cause knocking in the petrol-engine sense. In other words, its knock-rating would be low. In the petrol engine the maximum power output is limited by the octane number of its fuel ; increase of compression ratio or supercharging would only aggravate this. In the Diesel, on the other hand, ignition delay is most pronounced at low loads and increase of compression ratio or air pressure reduces diesel knock. It is interesting to note that an engine requires a better fuel for high altitudes than it does at sea-level, the reason is of course the reduction of effective air pressure. The loss of power is about 4 per cent. per 1000 ft. of altitude.

Chemical and Physical Tests

Certain of the tests for diesel fuel may be termed purity tests and include ash content, sediment, water and asphalt. Low ash is important in reducing engine wear ; in a distillate oil it does not exceed 0·01 per cent. Sediment and water *should* be absent but the latter may be as high as 0·25 per cent. Asphalt or asphaltenes are materials of indefinite composition but of high molecular weight which tend to be incompletely burned and cause the deposition of carbon on the engine. Two main types are recognized ; " hard asphalt ", which is insoluble in petroleum spirit boiling between 60° and 80° C. ; " soft asphalt ", which is precipitated from an ether solution of the oil by the addition of alcohol. Soft asphalt is not nearly so objectionable as hard asphalt ; engines have been run successfully for considerable periods on oils containing a fairly high percentage of soft asphalt.

Large slow-speed engines may run happily on oils containing 4 to 8 per cent. of hard asphalt, but for small high-speed engines, with limited combustion-chamber volume, in which the time available for combustion is short, oils containing more than about 0·1 per cent. of hard asphalt are not to be recommended. In general, this means the use of distillate oils which are naturally free from all but traces of asphaltenes.

Residue oils, on the other hand, are more widely obtainable and less costly. Provided that they are not too viscous, not too high in asphalt and ash content, they form very serviceable fuels for slow-speed compression-ignition engines. It is a common practice to put such fuels through a high-speed centrifuge before injection, and this removes practically all water, sediment, and abrasive ash, so reducing cylinder wear.

Distillation tests are of little importance with heavier compression-ignition engine fuels, though for the lighter fuels for high-speed engines, such as aircraft, they are of value. Le Mesurier states that indicator diagrams are more erratic when the fuel has a wide distillation range, and further that high naphthenic oils are more liable to " shocks " in running. A general rule is that not less than 80 per cent. of the oil should distil below 350° C., for the high-speed engine.

The asphaltene content is not a complete measure of the tendency of an oil to form carbon or gum in the engine and this is usually determined empirically in a laboratory test (Conradson, Chapter XVIII) in which the oil is heated out of contact with air and the residue of carbon weighed. This test indicates fairly well the tendency to coke formation at the atomizer nozzle. For high-speed engines the value may not be much above 0·05 per cent., but for the slower and heavier diesel oil can be used up to over 8 per cent. A higher value would lead to severe cylinder wear. The Conradson coke value is usually twice the magnitude of the asphaltene value but is more reliable as a guide to engine performance ; tests should be made, however, as there is no real correlation.

Diesel Fuel Specifications

To reduce wear in the injection system diesel oil is usually filtered. For slow-speed engines up to 500 r.p.m. a fine wire gauze suffices, but high-speed engines usually have felt or fabric filters. Where the oils are of high viscosity, or contain paraffin wax which might settle, they are heated in special heaters to improve atomization and ease of starting.

Table LIX gives typical specifications for diesel fuel, but for exact British specifications reference should be made to B.S. 209, revised 1956.

TABLE LIX
TYPICAL SPECIFICATIONS FOR DIESEL ENGINE FUELS

Engine speed, r.p.m.	Below 300.	300–800.	Above 800.
Not more than, per cent. :			
Ash	0·1	0·03	0·01
Water	1·0	0·5	0·1
Asphaltenes	4·0	2·0	0·1
Sulphur	3·0	2·0	1·5
Carbon, Conradson	6·0	3·0	0·2
Pour-point, ° F.	—	30	20
Viscosity, Redwood I. sec. 100° F.	450	70	40
Not less than :			
B.Th.U. per lb.	18,250	18,750	19,000
Flash-point, ° F.	—	150	150
Cetane number	28	35	48

Improvement of Ignition Quality. The cetane number of oils of low cetane value can be raised by the addition of pro-ignition " dopes " which reduce the ignition delay period. Ethyl nitrate, iso-amyl nitrate and acetone peroxide have been used for this purpose ; the additions of small quantities of the order of 1–1·5 per cent. will, for example, increase the cetane number by 23–29 per cent. It is unfortunate that it is the fuel of high cetane number which is most responsive to dope ; it is obviously not necessary to dope fuel of already high cetane value. A further disadvantage is that dope does not improve ease of starting from cold. For these reasons the use of dopes is not common.

Tars and Tar Oils as Diesel Fuel

In general, crude coal tar is unsuitable for the internal combustion engine because of its considerable content of free carbon, pitch and ash. Low-temperature tars and particularly lignite tars are less unsuitable with some preparation. Tar distillates would be suitable from the point of view of freedom from coke-forming constituents but have other disabilities. In the first place they have low cetane values of the order of 18 and high ignition temperature of the order of 420° C. (petroleum fuel oil 260° C.) which limit their use to slow-speed engines. Secondly, they are rich in tar acids which reduce their calorific value, increase fuel consumption, and also cause rough running. The removal of the tar acids makes a considerable improvement and a " neutral " low-temperature tar oil has been made with a cetane value of 28, which has been raised to 35 by the addition of ethyl nitrate. Two per cent. of this substance reduces the spontaneous ignition temperature to 200° C. and the ignition delay to 0·1 sec.

In view of the small quantity of tar oil available in relation to the amount of diesel oil required, the best method of utilization is the blending of the neutral oil with good diesel oil. If the cetane number of the latter is as high as 60 the proportion of tar oil may be as high as 50 per cent., while ensuring a good performance in the high speed engine. One precaution must be taken since such a blend tends to deposit a sludge shortly after mixing ; the blend must be desludged some time after the blend is made.

Engine Tests

The Diesel engine has two main applications, one using engines of large size for electric power generation and the other using small high-speed engines for automotive purposes.

The Annual Report of the Diesel Engine Users Association provides data regarding fuel consumption, running costs, etc., which illustrate the high level of efficiency which can be obtained with the modern engine. The size of the engines used varies from 100 to over 1000 kW. and the mean load factor is of the order of 66 per cent. The mean consumption of fuel per kWh. is 0·587 lb. With air-blast plus mechanical injection of the fuel the consumption is lower at about 0·56 lb. and with mechanical injection only it is higher at about 0·67 lb.

Recent experiments with the high-speed engine have shown that a thermal efficiency of over 34 per cent. is readily attained and the highest figure so far recorded is 36·2 per cent.

The majority of modern engines have a compression ratio between 15/1 and 16/1 and the theoretical efficiency at this level is 55 per cent. Considerations of strength and weight limit the extent to which the ratio can be raised, but an increase to 20/1 would give 58 per cent. and 25/1 would give 60·7 per cent. efficiency.

The theoretical air requirement for the combustion of diesel oil is about 14·4 lb. per lb. of fuel. For starting purposes a rich mixture is used and the exhaust gas must contain a high proportion of carbon monoxide and fumes of partly-burned oil. Under steady running conditions the air/fuel ratio must be increased to about 20/1 so that the excess air is about 40 per cent.

Satisfactory running can be achieved at 20 per cent. excess air, but the exhaust gas may not be free from smoke. At 40 per cent. excess air the composition of the dry exhaust gas would be carbon dioxide 11, oxygen 4, carbon monoxide 0·12 per cent.

The carbon dioxide reaches a maximum at an air/fuel ratio of about 15/1 (13·9 per cent.). At less ratios the proportion of unburnt gas increases as follows :

Air/fuel.	CO_2.	O_2.	CO.	H_2.	CH_4.
18/1	12·0	4·0	0·1	—	—
16/1	13·4	2·2	0·2	—	—
14/1	13·6	1·2	1·2	0·2	—
12/1	11·8	0·6	3·4	1·3	0·2
11/1	10·6	0·5	5·4	2·6	0·5

Serious loss of thermal efficiency does, therefore, occur if the ratio falls below 14/1.

The thermal efficiency of the Diesel engine can be increased by super-charging, i.e. by increasing the pressure of the air supplied by means of a turbo-charger driven from the engine. So far, the pressures reached have not exceeded 10 lb. per sq. in., but at this level the thermal efficiency is increased by about one per cent. Judge quotes fuel consumption differences as follows :

Normal air pressure	0·40	lb./b.h.p./hr.
Mechanical compressor	0·38	„
Turbo-compressor	0·365	„

It is likely that further gains in efficiency will be attained in this way, particularly if the air is cooled after compression ; Ricardo quotes a gain from 0·43 to 0·39 lb./b.h.p./hr. by cooling.

REFERENCE BOOKS

The Science of Petroleum. Dunstan. Oxford Univ. Press. 1938.
Motor Fuel Preparation and Application. Nash and Howes. Chapman and Hall. 1945.
The High-Speed Internal Combustion Engine. Ricardo. Blackie and Son. 1953.
The High-Speed Diesel Engine. Judge. Chapman and Hall. 1943.
Diesel Engine Fuels and Lubricants. Wright and Purdey. Constable. 1950.
Heat Engines. Grundy. Longmans Green. 1948.

CHAPTER XV

GASEOUS FUELS : TOWN GASES

Gaseous fuels possess important advantages over solid fuels in that (1) the gas can be produced at a central point and clean gas distributed over a wide area, (2) the nuisance of smoke production and ash disposal can be eliminated, (3) greater control can be achieved of variations in demand, conditions of combustion, and nature of both flame and heating atmosphere, (4) greater economy by the use of heat-exchange methods and, in the case of town gas, (5) the avoidance of the need for storage space or fuel tanks. In a minor degree the use of gas of low calorific value also permits of the utilization as fuel of waste vegetable materials.

In Great Britain the chief source of gaseous fuel is the town-gas industry which annually converts some 27 million tons of coal and 0·5 million tons of oil into town gas and distributes some 2400 million therms for domestic and industrial purposes. For industrial purposes and furnace heating producer gas is manufactured from coal and coke to a very large extent as a cheaper gas than distributed town gas. Water gas is also made but to a less extent and only for special applications. Naturally-occurring gas has not been available until recently owing to the almost complete absence of petroleum or hydrocarbon gas. Now, however, gas rich in methane is being recovered from the coal measures in certain suitable areas and is being distributed with town gas by blending. The increase of the refining of petroleum in Great Britain from 0·5 million tons per year to 24 million tons will soon make available also waste refinery gas which must also be distributed for use as an economic measure ; this may in time amount to 400 million therms.

The types of gas available are set out in comparison in the following scheme, with the range of calorific value in terms of B.Th.U. per cu. ft. in each case.

	B.Th.U. per cu. ft.
Natural gas :	
Petroleum	1050
Coal measures	950
Petroleum refinery " tail " gas . . .	1750
Petroleum refinery butane (Calor gas) . . .	3200 (vaporized)
Coal gas :	
Gas retorts	420–520
Coke ovens	525
Carburetted water gas	420–500
Water gas (blue)	280–295
Producer gas, coal	162
Producer gas, coke	132
Blast-furnace gas	92

The properties and uses of these gases are discussed below, excepting water gas and producer gas, which are dealt with in Chapters XVII and XVI respectively.

TOWN GAS

The use of coal gas was confined for the great part of a century to purposes of illumination ; the development of the gas engine and its great increase in thermal efficiency subsequently rendered coal gas an important power-producing fuel, and with its extended use for domestic heating purposes, and still more recently, with cheaper rates and highly efficient methods of combustion, it has become an important fuel in many manufacturing operations, such as metal melting, annealing, etc., all contributing to the further and extended use of this efficient and convenient form of gaseous fuel.

The main important features which contribute to the successful commercial application of coal gas are—the constancy of supply of fuel of uniform composition, available at any moment, the avoidance of all stand-by costs and the high thermal value and high efficiency which can be obtained.

The standard of manufacture of town gas is now, by the Gas Regulation Act of 1920, its calorific value and gas is sold on a thermal basis. Each gas undertaking works to a declared calorific value, chosen by itself, and submits its accounts in units of " therms " of 100,000 B.Th.U. each. Consumption is still assessed by a volume measurement as before but the consumer is safeguarded by the accurate control of the mean calorific value of the gas sent out. The value of this system of charging is potential rather than actual since it enables the gas engineer to adopt the most economical process of production in his circumstances.

The quantity of coal carbonized for town gas and the volume of gas distributed has steadily increased through the years of this century at first owing to increasing demands for domestic use but recently also in the industrial field. The following figures show the increases from 1931 :

	1931.	1951.	
Coal carbonized	18,145,000	27,150,000	tons
Oil for carburetted water gas	53,124,000	130,745,000	gals.
Total gas made	315,570	496,582	million
Coal gas	254,350	400,425	cu. ft.
Water gas, carburetted	40,800	83,871	
Coke sold	7,672,000	10,400,000	tons
Coke breeze sold	528,000	1,280,000	tons
Tar	212,682,000	350,873,000	gals.
Ammonium sulphate	103,000	—	tons

To the 1951 figures should be added 65,760 million cu. ft. of gas purchased from the coke-oven industry. This represents only 26 per cent. of the coke-oven gas available and, as the balance becomes utilized to a wider extent, as it should, it will slow up production in the gas industry. Gas from the petroleum refineries and the coal measures will have an additive effect. The overall amount of gas distributed in 1951 was, therefore, 562,342 million cu. ft.

The methods of manufacture of coal gas and coke-oven gas have been described in Chapter IX and those of carburetted water gas follow in Chapter XVII. Carburetted water gas has always had an effect on the amount of coal carbonized since it is used as a balancing factor to control the production of coke for sale according to the market. Coke-oven gas, on the other hand, has become an increasing factor. These effects are shown in the percentage figures over the years 1921 to 1951, when the volume of coke-oven gas increased from 1.3×10^6 to 65.7×10^6 cu. ft.

	1921.	1930.	1940.	1950.	1951.
Coal gas, per cent.	77·7	81·6	77·9	70·3	71·2
Water gas, carburetted, per cent. .	20·0	12·6	8·9	15·5	14·9
Other gas, per cent.	1·8	1·6	2·1	2·6	2·2
Bought from coke ovens, per cent. .	0·5	4·2	11·1	11·6	11·7

In considering how production has increased it is interesting to observe that the yield per ton of coal carbonized increased between 1921 and 1951 from 12,300 to 15,460 cu. ft. or from 64 to 72·5 therms. In water gas production the increase is greater, from 40,000 to 59,000 cu. ft. per ton of coke.

So far as type of carbonizing plant is concerned the tendency has been towards continuous vertical retorts ; the proportion of gas made in the different types during the year 1940 was :

	% Coal carbonized.	% Therms.	Gas, C.V.
Horizontals	39·6	30·3	534
Continuous-vertical retorts . .	49·8	43·4	463
Intermittent-vertical chambers . .	6·8	5·8	523
Coke ovens	3·2	2·7	539
Water gas, carburetted . . .	—	16·3	442
		Average	493

Town gas is now used for many different industrial purposes in addition to the original ones of domestic uses and street lighting. A rough separation into classes of usage is as follows, as taken from the data available for 1950, when 494,860 therms were sold.

DISTRIBUTION OF TOWN GAS PER CENT., 1950

Domestic.	Industrial.	Offices.	Public administration.	Street lighting.
58·1	24·8	12·6	2·2	2·3

The discussion of lighting is outside the scope of this book, but the other uses are discussed below in relation to the properties of the gases as fuels. It is interesting to observe that gas still carries half of the street-lighting load and that nearly half of the gas sold is used for cooking and carries 75 per cent. of the total cooking load.

The Composition of Town Gas

The composition of town gas depends to an extent on the above declared calorific value but also on the process used. This is illustrated in the table of gas compositions below (Table LX). Since most large works, however, contain more than one type of plant, the gas distributed is a mixture which does vary in composition and, what is more important, as will be seen later, in its combustion characteristics. This is particularly true of carburetted water gas which has a specific gravity some 55 per cent. higher than coal gas and will not necessarily burn efficiently alone in an appliance adjusted to the normal density of 0·40 to 0·45.

In Table LX the outstanding differences between types, apart from specific gravity, lie in the proportions of hydrogen and carbon monoxide, and, with carburetted water gas, the higher proportion of unsaturated hydrocarbons.

The analyses of the vertical-retort gases are for Yorkshire coal; the horizontal-retort and coke-oven gases are for Durham coal; the oil gas is that of the new Onia-Gegi and Segas processes for the cracking of heavy fuel oil.

The unsaturated hydrocarbons in coal gas (C_xH_y) consist mainly of benzene, ethylene, propylene and butylene. The proportions vary with the type of process and whether benzole recovery is practised. The olefine total in high-temperature gases is about 2·0 per cent., of which ethylene may be 1·7, propylene 0·3, butylene 0·05. In unstripped gas the additional amount of benzole vapour is about 0·6 per cent. Coke-oven gas is fully stripped, but with town gas the extent of stripping varies very widely and on average is not more than 50 per cent. In calculation it is taken that the mean calorific value of the unsaturated hydrocarbons found in the gas analysis is 2300 B.Th.U. per cu. ft.

The carbon monoxide in town gas is, strictly speaking, an undesirable component owing to its poisonous character, but the proportion is not limited by law. A Board of Trade Committee of 1922 did not recommend its limitation but insisted upon careful supervision and inspection of gas appliances.

The saturated hydrocarbons in coal gas consist mainly of the first member of the series, methane, but small quantities of ethane and less of butane are usually present. Their presence is indicated by the "n" value being greater than 1·0.

Organic Sulphur Compounds in Town Gas. Before distribution town gas is purified with particular reference to hydrogen sulphide and hydrogen cyanide. Both are removed substantially completely, the statutory limit for H_2S being less than one part per million. The crude

TABLE LX

Compositions of Town Gases from Different Sources

Percentages by volume

Gas.	B.Th.U./ cu. ft.	CO_2.	C_xH_y.	O_2.	CO.	H_2.	C_nH_{2n+2}.	N_2.	x.	n.	Sp. gr. air = 1.
Gas retort :											
Horizontal	560	2·0	3·6	0·4	8·0	52·0	30·0	4·0	4	1·08	0·40
Cont. vertical, 5 per cent. steam	517	1·4	2·1	0·7	11·3	49·7	25·9	8·9	4	1·05	0·41
" 10 " "	477	3·5	1·7	0·6	15·5	50·8	21·0	6·7	4	1·05	0·43
Intermittent vertical (steam 5 per cent.) . . .	541	1·5	3·1	0·2	14·0	57·0	21·3	2·9	4	1·13	0·40
Coke oven	525	2·0	2·6	0·4	7·4	54·0	28·0	5·6	2·5	1·08	0·38
Water gas, carburetted . . .	500	5·6	7·0	0·4	30·5	37·0	14·0	5·5	2·5	1·10	0·63
	450	4·3	5·9	0·1	32·8	38·6	11·4	6·9	2·5	1·10	0·67
Oil gas, cat. cracked :											
Onia-Gegi	481	5·6	5·2	0·8	23·6	47·2	13·0	6·6	—	—	0·49
Segas	500	11·0	6·7	0·4	14·7	48·9	15·3	3·0	—	1·01	0·55
Horizontal retort gas :											
First hour	750	2·0	6·5	0·4	7·8	38·6	40·7	4·0	—	—	—
Fourth hour	580	1·4	1·0	0·4	6·4	58·8	27·3	4·1	—	—	—
Eighth hour	380	1·0	—	0·2	11·4	69·3	5·5	12·6	—	—	—

gas also contains organic sulphur compounds which are not removed in the H_2S purification-process although two constituents, thiophene and carbon disulphide, are partly removed by oil-washing for the recovery of benzole. The normal limit for this amount of residual sulphur is 20 grains per 100 cu. ft. of gas. Even these traces of sulphur compounds are not desirable in the gas since they form oxides of sulphur on combustion which are corrosive in domestic usage and limit the application of town gas in metallurgy.

A Gas Research Board survey of the variation of organic sulphur concentration over the country (1945) showed that quite wide variations existed in the amounts and in the distribution of the individual sulphur compounds. The following are approximations from the data, the quantities being grains S per 100 cu. ft. of gas.

	COS.	CS_2.	C_4H_4S.	Mercaptans.	Total.
Before benzole recovery :					
Horizontal retorts . .	6	23	8	3	40
Vertical retorts, continuous .	8	16	5	2	31
Water gas, carburetted .	7	1	2	1	11
Producer gas . . .	10	0·5	—	1	11·5
After benzole recovery :					
Horizontal retorts . .	6	12	1·5	1·5	21
Vertical retorts, continuous .	7	6	1·5	1·5	16

It is apparent that the further limitation of these organic sulphur compounds is desirable and processes have been designed to this end. In the Griffith method the gas is passed with a small proportion of air ($\equiv 1·2$ per cent. O_2) over a nickel sub-sulphide catalyst maintained at a temperature of 220–360° C. A high space velocity of about 1500 is attainable and the organic sulphur content of the gas is reducible to about 8 grains per 100 cu. ft. or 2 grains after oil-washing. Other catalysts, including hydrogenating ones, have been developed but neither these nor the nickel catalyst will break down thiophene so that the low figure of 2 grains is obtainable only after benzole recovery or oil-washing. The cost of the Griffith method in 1946, working on a scale of one million cu. ft. per day, was 0·135 penny per therm of gas.

The organic sulphur compounds before and after cleaning of the gas are, typically,

Gm. S per cu. metre.	CS_2.	COS.	C_4H_4S.	Mercaptans.	Total.
Before	0·39	0·14	0·25	0·03	0·81
After	0·02	0·02	0·03	Nil	0·07

In the steel industry small unit plants are used for the purification of the fuel gas when special steels are being heat-treated.

Coke-oven Gas

Coke-oven gas is sometimes considered separately from gas-retort gas, but since the treatment of the coal does not differ essentially from that in the horizontal retort and the intermittent-vertical chamber the composition of the gas is very similar.   The gas may be used for the firing of the ovens or for process work in associated steel-works but any gas to be distributed for " town " purposes must be taken by the gas industry and purified before such distribution.   The amount so taken has been steadily increasing and, in parts of the steel-making areas of Yorkshire and South Wales in particular, the gas industry has ceased to carbonize its own coal.   This trend will continue until all oven-heating possible will be done by blast-furnace gas and producer gas made from coke breeze, or low-grade coal.

The composition of coke-oven gas, since the process is intermittent, varies from the beginning to the end of the carbonizing period.   In a large battery the variation is smoothed out since the ovens are all at different stages of heating.   In the Claude synthetic ammonia process, however, the end gas has been utilized as a source of hydrogen.   The hydrogen content of this gas reaches 70 per cent. and separation of the hydrogen by liquefaction becomes an economic possibility.   It does seem that this method could also be used for the supply of hydrogen for hydrogenation processes relating to coal, coal oils and petroleum residues.

The applications of coke-oven gas in practice as a fuel evidently will be identical with those of coal gas, although the application in most cases clearly must be limited to special operations because of local conditions, so that the considerations relating to coal gas in the next section apply equally to coke-oven gas.   It is, of course, essential that the latter shall be freed from impurities in the same manner as coal gas to conform with recognized standards.

Town Gas from Heavy Fuel Oil

Several processes have been put forward for the production of town gas by the cracking of fuel oil in special plant other than water-gas generators. In the earlier days a difficulty was that the gas had a high specific gravity unsuited for distribution with normal town gas in Great Britain.   This disability has now been overcome and at least two processes are available, the Segas and Onia-Gegi processes.   In the United States where the alternative town gas is natural gas the procedure is different in order to obtain a gas of higher calorific value of the order of 1000 B.Th.U. per cu. ft.

The Onia-Gegi Process.   Oil is burned in a combustion chamber and the hot products passed downwards through a catalyst bed of alumina maintained at 860–900° C.   Fuel oil is cracked with steam in the bed by downward spraying.   The procedure is cyclic ; heating lasts for 4·5 minutes, oil-cracking for 3·5 minutes, purging, etc., takes 1·5 minutes, making a total cycle of 9·5 minutes.

One plant at Cahors (France) produces 280,000 cu. ft. per day, but no doubt larger units will be built.   The yield of gas is 55,000 cu. ft. per ton of total oil, of which 80 per cent. is gasified and 20 per cent. burned as fuel. Since the calorific value of this gas is 480 B.Th.U., this represents a thermal efficiency of about 60 per cent. excluding recovered steam from a waste-heat boiler. Other yields are 11 per cent. tar and 3·8 per cent. benzole with a crystallizing-point of $-3°$ C.

From a British plant at Stafford, making 52,000 cu. ft. of gas per ton of total oil, at 464 B.Th.U. and 0·60 sp. gr., a gas composition is reported of: CO_2 11, C_nH_m 2, CO 18, H_2 46, CH_4 16, and N_2 7 per cent.

The Segas Process. Fuel oil is sprayed with superheated steam over chequer work consisting of bauxite/bentonite forms, which serve as a cracking catalyst, at a temperature of 900–1000° C. The reactions are endothermic and are operated on a 3×3-minute cycle; the reaction temperature is maintained by the combustion of deposited carbon with air in the blow part of the cycle. The hot gases pass backwards through the steam superheater and raise its temperature to about 700° C. For an oil consumption of 130 gal. per hour, three vessels of approximately 20 ft. $\times$ 8 ft. diameter are required with a cracking surface of 800 sq. ft. Steam and air requirements are 2600 lb. and 9500 lb. respectively and the gas yield (27,000 cu. ft. per hr.) is 1·15 therms per gal. of heavy fuel oil, at a calorific value of 480–508 B.Th.U. per cu. ft. The process is now in the stage of full-scale development (1954). The overall efficiency is about 60 per cent.

The Hall High-B.Th.U. Process. This is essentially a modification of water-gas plant in which the carburettors of two units are connected together at the top to serve as oil-gas generators, and top connections made to each for burning oil and cracking oil. A three-way valve is placed at the top of each superheater. Air connections are made to the top of each shell and steam connections to the top of each superheater. The cycle of operations consist of:

Passing primary air into one superheater and generator to burn off carbon while burning oil with secondary air in the other two.
Passing cracking-oil into the second generator to make gas and taking this off from the top of the superheater.
Reversing these two operations.

Oil of Conradson value up to 13 per cent. is treated and gas of about 1000 B.Th.U. calorific value made at the rate of 1000 cu. ft. per 12 gal. of oil of which 0·8 is fuel oil. The tar yield is 20 per cent. of the oil and the overall efficiency is 80 per cent. The composition of the gas is CO_2, 5; C_nH_m, 25; CO, 3; H_2, 18; C_nH_{2n+2}, 33, and N_2, 16 per cent. One drawback is that the gas has a high specific gravity of 0·85, which rather limits its substitution for natural gas (0·56) as a town gas.

Methane from Coal Measures

Since the year 1943 there have been considerable developments in methods for the collection of the methane associated with coal in situ and which was formerly given the name of " firedamp ". As firedamp it has always been a menace to safety underground, particularly in " gassy " pits, and the first attempts to deal with it were safety measures to assist ventilation. It is now realized that the fuel value of the gas is considerable and that every attempt should be made to recover it from suitable seams. Altogether the thermal value of the methane available is from 1–2 per cent. of that of the coal.

It seems clear that the methane in coal measures was originally formed in the coal, but it is also clear that part of it is now trapped in the overlying strata. When the coal is mined any gas under pressure is released, but a considerable proportion remains in the coal. At atmospheric pressure the volume of methane which coal will adsorb increases from 5 ml. per g. for bituminous coal to 15 ml. for coal of high rank and anthracite. Pressure increases the amount by some 50 per cent. at 30 atm., which is the apparent maximum likely to occur in coal measures. Various estimates have been attempted of what this means ; if it were assumed that half the amount were retained by the coal and half liberated during mining it is calculable that the 200 million tons mined annually in Great Britain could yield 12×10^{10} cu. ft. or 12×10^8 therms. This amount is beyond the bounds of possibility but shows that the prospect is large. It has already been shown in the Ruhr area, where 12 mines are being drained of methane, that the yield is 90 cu. ft. per ton of coal mined ; this is quite a step towards the above theoretical 600 cu. ft. per ton.

The composition of coal methane is variable, but it is essentially a high-concentration methane. The many analyses quoted cover the range methane 93–99, ethane nil–3, carbon dioxide 0–4, nitrogen 2–6, and traces of hydrogen and rare gases.

The existing methods of extraction of methane or " methane drainage " are described in the Report of the Working Party set up by the Coal Board and the Ministry of Fuel and Power (1951) and are as shown in the Table overleaf.

In the first method $4\frac{1}{2}$-in. boreholes are driven from the approach road to the coal face at an angle of 45° for a distance of about 200 ft. The holes in long-wall mining are driven at an angle over the coal face. Collecting pipes are connected from the boreholes to the main which passes up the pit shaft. Gas is drawn from the holes until the flow falls off and the pipes are then moved forward to follow the advance of the face. Figures are quoted for Framerie (Belgium) which show from 4000 to 7000 cu. ft. of 92 per cent. methane per hour from each borehole. The highest yield has been obtained from the pipeline inserted 150 ft. from the face, the end of which is about 50 ft. from the face and above the goaf.

Name used in present communication.	Portion of strata drained.	Where employed.	Name in Working Party Report
1. Boreholes in roof	Rock above face	Ruhr, Belgium, Saar, S. Wales	Cross-measure hole method
2. Headings in over-lying seam	Rock above face	Ruhr and particu-larly Saar	Superjacent heading
3. Pack-cavity	Strata above goaf	Saar	Pack-cavity
4. Drainage of underlying virgin seam	Coal seam lying below workings	Point of Ayr, Wales	Cross-measure hole method
5. Drainage of old workings	Old workings (probably the roof)	Saar, Northern France	(Miscellaneous)
6. Collection from blowers	Usually from faults or blisters	Ruhr, Saar	(Miscellaneous)

In method 2 the holes are drilled from special roads parallel to the main seam but at a higher level. From this road, boreholes radiate all over the working area of the lower seam which may be 80–100 ft. below. After the holes are all cut the system is sealed off and methane withdrawn steadily as mining progresses below. In this procedure the method of mining need not be "long-wall"; it has been used with success in the Saar district of Germany, although it seems that the gas tends to contain rather more air. In method 3 corridors are left in the pack behind the workings of a long-wall face, sealed off, and gas withdrawn from the goaf by slight suction. The only difficulty is the maintenance of air-tight seals, but the method is not now used in the Saar.

Method 4 is of special interest as being that used at the Point of Ayr colliery in N. Wales where the pioneer work in Britain has been done. This must, however, be regarded as a special case in that the rock strata are of a very impervious type and the mine has always been a very gassy one. Holes are bored from the floor of the seam in production to tap the underlying seams which lie below at 35-yard intervals. The gas in this case is delivered under pressures up to 300 lb. per sq. in. and the collecting main is run at 15 lb. pressure. This is not necessarily a good feature as areas of lower pressure cannot be vented into this main. This scheme now yields about one million cu. ft. of very pure methane per day, the equivalent of 30 tons of coal.

It may be concluded from the above that methods are now available for the drainage of methane from several active boreholes at any active coal face and that the yield of methane will be from 50–80 cu. ft. per minute per hole. The utilization of this methane as a fuel is easy, first through the existing town-gas industry and secondly for the setting-up of special industries near the source of supply to manufacture chemicals and other by-products.

Refinery Gases

The considerable increase in petroleum refining in Great Britain (p. 16) raises the question of the efficient utilization of the C_2 to C_4 hydrocarbons which are available after the separation of part of the C_4 fractions for sale as bottled gas. Some of these gases are used as fuel in the refineries but are less suitable for this purpose than residual oil and a high proportion is being burned to waste (1954). The total amount produced when 24 million tons of petroleum are refined may be 350×10^6 therms per annum; this is the equivalent of 1·2 million tons of coal and obviously must be utilized.

The first utilization would seem to be as fuel gas or chemical process gas in the neighbourhood of the refineries. By the terms of the Gas Act of 1950 the utilization is in the hands of the Area Boards of the National Gas Council and it would seem logical for the gas industry to build pipelines to large centres of gas manufacture and to integrate the refinery gas into the scheme of production of town gas in the same manner as has been done in the case of coke-oven gas in Yorkshire and S. Wales.

Several methods of utilization are possible. The first is the simple one of blending as an enriching agent, but the proportion which can be added to town gas without adversely affecting its combustion characteristics is less than 8 per cent. and would not cover the amount available. A more satisfactory method is to " reform " the gas into a town gas of the same calorific value and characteristics as the gas normally made so that it can be blended in any proportion in which it should become available. Cost also enters into the problem since the total cost of the reformed gas must not be greater than that of the gas industry's own production.

The composition of the refinery gas will vary with the methods used in the refinery, the proportion of C_3 and C_4 hydrocarbons separated, and the amount used as fuel, but the following represents a possible range of composition.

$H_2S.$	$H_2.$	$CH_4.$	$C_2H_4,$ $C_2H_6.$	$C_3H_6,$ $C_3H_8.$	$C_4.$	B.Th.U./ cu. ft.	Empirical formula.	Sp. gr.
6–8	6–8	8–10	8–12	40–55	5–30 *	2150	$C_{2\cdot8}H_{6\cdot6}$	1·35

* The amount depends on the butane market.

At the above calorific value and specific gravity the thermal value of one ton is 440 therms.

Because of mains corrosion and catalyst poisoning the high proportion of sulphur is a serious disadvantage and it would be more satisfactory if the hydrogen sulphide were taken out at the refinery and recovered as elementary sulphur.

Reforming. This is the term given to the partial combustion of the gas with air over a catalyst consisting of alumina, according to the reaction :

$$2CH_4 + O_2 = 2CO + 4H_2 + 1480 \text{ cal.}$$

The Koppers-Hasche process, for example, has been applied to the reforming of natural gas substantially to the above reaction and then, by the mixing of the product with more natural gas, a mixed gas of any desired calorific value between 300 and 1000 B.Th.U. per cu. ft.   A reaction chamber 20 ft. long, 20 in. high and 9 in. wide is packed with alumina chequer tiles and separated into two chambers to be operated on the regenerative system.   Methane, with half its volume of oxygen (as air), passes into one half-chamber, which has been heated to the reaction temperature of 820–860° C., where the reaction takes place.   The heated gases pass through the second half-chamber and heat this to reaction temperature.   Reversal of gas flow takes place every minute and production is continuous at the rate of one million cu. ft. of gas per day.   The gas leaves the regenerator at the temperature of 300° C. and the process is self-sufficient in heat energy and operates at a thermal efficiency of about 96 per cent.

When the process is operated on higher hydrocarbons such as refinery gas the reaction need not be taken to completion but can be arranged to give directly the gas required.   For example, in the reforming of propane partial cracking may give a gas of 637 B.Th.U. per cu. ft. having the following composition :

CO_2	C_2H_2	C_2H_4	C_3H_6	O_2	H_2	CO	CH_4	C_3H_8	N_2
1·4	0·6	13·9	3·6	1·7	8·5	6·9	13·8	4·7	44·9

The proportion of air used in making this gas was 2·1 : 1 and the specific gravity of the gas made was 0·9.   This specific gravity is too high for direct use in Great Britain and would have to be used for blending with other gas of lower density.

Enrichment. The gas can be used to a limiting extent as an enrichment agent for water gas, or gas from continuous vertical retorts, but the amount which may be added is limited to about 8 per cent. because at higher concentrations the combustion characteristics of the mixture become too different from those of normal town gas and upset appliances set up to burn the latter.

LIQUID FUEL GASES

Condensable hydrocarbon gases, produced as a by-product of the refining of petroleum and the hydrogenation of creosote, are the basis of a thriving industry in Great Britain for the supply of gaseous fuel to country houses, caravans, etc., to which there is no public supply.   They are also finding a ready sale for certain industrial purposes, such as the heat treatment and oxy-flame cutting of metals, metal spraying and as a fuel for portable equipment. Domestic appliances are available for lighting, cooking and heating, which are modified forms of those commonly used for town gas.

The domestic supply is essentially commercial butane which is a mixture of C_4 hydrocarbons containing up to 20 moles per cent. of C_3 hydrocarbons and not more than 2 moles per cent. of C_2 hydrocarbons. It is provided in steel cylinders which contain 14, 32 or 83 lb. respectively. Distribution is by tank car up to 10 tons capacity.

The industrial supply is mainly C_3 hydrocarbons, propane and propylene, and tanks for factory storage may be cylindrical or spherical vessels tested to approx. 300 lb. per sq. in. pressure. The working pressure of these tanks is not likely to exceed 120 lb. per sq. in. Filling ratios of cylinders are based on a 95 per cent. capacity at 113° F.

The gases are supplied to specifications which limit, among other items, the vapour pressure, the proportion of heavy ends and the total sulphur. They must be free from hydrogen sulphide and entrained water. Organic sulphur compounds, mainly sulphides and disulphides, are added, in small amount, as a warning agent so that the smell will indicate the presence of gas down to concentrations in air of $\frac{1}{5}$ of the lower explosive limit.

Since the combustion characteristics of C_4 hydrocarbons differ very considerably from those of normal town gas, a whole range of burner equipment has been designed for its use. In mixtures of C_3 and C_4 hydrocarbons, the C_3 hydrocarbons evaporate at a faster rate, so that burner design has to take into account the satisfactory combustion of both types of gases. Since the gas is under high pressure by gas industry standards, a special governor is required between the cylinder and the house mains.

Important physical properties of pure normal butane and propane are as follows :

	Propane.	n-Butane.
Boiling-point, ° F.	−43·7	31·1
Vapour pressure in p.s.i.g. :		
(i) at 60° F.	92·4	11·6
(ii) at 100° F.	172	37·5
Liquid specific gravity, 60/60° F. .	0·5079	0·5844
Specific gravity of gas (air = 1) . .	1·550	2·084
Cu. ft. of gas per lb. of liquid . .	8·453	6·286
Calorific value, B.Th.U/cu. ft. . .	2,563	3,390
,, ,, B.Th.U/lb. . . .	21,663	21,308
Latent heat of vaporization at 60° F.,		
B.Th.U./lb.	152·6	162
Ignition temperature, ° F. . . .	932	896
Limits of inflammability in air :		
Lower limit, per cent. . . .	2·37	1·86
Upper limit, per cent. . . .	9·5	8·41
Maximum flame temperature in air		
(observed), ° F.	3497	3443
Air required for complete combustion		
(Ideal gas), cu. ft. air/cu. ft. gas .	23·9	31·1

In Great Britain the industry started in 1935 and is now supplying some 350,000 country houses with 45,000 tons of butane. The supply to industry has reached 8,000 tons per annum. Domestic supplies are sold under a variety of names of which the best known is Calor Gas.

Other applications in industry are in the field of town-gas manufacture and are either in the form of butane or propane/air or in the direct enrichment of producer gas and water gas.

Butane Enrichment. Commercial butane can also be used in the blending and enrichment of town gas to permit of higher steaming rates in the operation of continuous vertical retorts, or to permit of the greater use of producer gas, but again this procedure is limited by considerations of high density and unsuitable combustion characteristics. In the former case a retort may be steamed to a gas calorific value of 460 B.Th.U. and re-enriched to 520 B.Th.U. by the addition of 2·8 lb. of butane per 1000 cu. ft. of gas. The effect of this on the specific gravity (+0·04) would not be appreciable. There may be circumstances apart from the utilization of the butane in which this arrangement has economic advantages in the making of town gas. If the butane were added separately in dilution with producer gas the specific gravity would again be a limitation since the specific gravity of this gas at 520 B.Th.U. is about 1·0.

Butane-air Gas. In villages not connected with a gas distribution system it may be more economic, and is certainly more convenient, to utilize refinery butane by volatilizing it in an air stream after the established practice in the U.S.A. before the widespread distribution of natural gas.

The explosive limits of butane in air are from 1·8 to 8·4 per cent. at atmospheric pressure and it is necessary to make a mixture which is quite far from these limits from the point of view of safety. A convenient mixture is that which gives a calorific value of gas of 700–750 B.Th.U. per cu. ft. and consists of 23 per cent. butane vapour and 77 per cent. air. In Great Britain this gas is safe also from the point of view of condensation of the butane.

One method of production (Mallet, Gas Air Corporation, N.Y.) is to vaporize the liquid butane from storage at 22 lb. pressure in the annular space between two concentric tubes by supplying the heat necessary in the inner tube by burning about 4 per cent. of the gas made. The vapour is then issued through a jet in a venturi throat in such a manner that the right proportion of air is entrained.

At this calorific value, and at a specific gravity of 1·22, this gas cannot be used with the appliances normal to the British town gas, but with suitable jets in bunsen-type burners and Bray jets designed for the purpose the gas is as satisfactory in usage as normal carbonization gas.

NATURAL GAS

Very little natural gas is available in Great Britain, but search is being made for it, and it is wise to deal briefly with the position in the United States where it is now so widely distributed by pipeline that it has almost entirely (95 per cent.) replaced coal gas in the supply of town gas. To-day some 8·4 trillion cu. ft. are produced, which is 5 per cent. more than in 1952 and double the production of 1943. The gas is produced in the oil-bearing areas, but an immense network has been built to deliver it from some 150,000 miles of long-distance mains.

Two-thirds of the gas is obtained from gas wells and one-third from petroleum wells by separation from the oil. Efforts towards conservation are made by repumping unwanted gas into suitable geological formations in the earth and it is doubtful if the wastage is now over 10 per cent. The gas is available in 27 different States, but Texas accounts for about half and also has about half the estimated reserves. The composition of the gas varies in different parts of the field from 60 to 95 per cent. methane with decreasing amounts of C_2 and C_3 hydrocarbons and relatively small amounts of isomers, naphthenic and aromatic hydrocarbons, carbon dioxide and nitrogen; in some places small but recoverable amounts of helium are found. A typical analysis is:

CO_2.	CH_4.	C_2H_6.	C_3H_8.	C_4H_{10}.	N_2.	B.Th.U./ cu. ft.	Sp. gr.
0·8	91·0	3·1	1·7	0·7	2·7	1045	0·60

The gas is distributed in steel pipes of up to 30 in. diameter at a pressure of 55 atmospheres. On long-distance lines there are pressure-booster stations at intervals which can raise the pressure some 15 atm. The pipelines are protected against corrosion by layers of cellulose wrapper and asphalt and also by anodic protection. Internal protection is assured now by removal of water vapour, hydrogen sulphide and organic sulphur compounds before distribution. Large cities are detoured and are served by branch-lines of smaller diameter, also cathodically protected, working at a pressure of 13 atm. Public service is at a pressure of about 10 in. w.g.

The power necessary for the transmission of the gas is considerable, amounting to 25 h.p. per million cu. ft. of gas per day, but the overall cost is not large at 1–2 cents per million B.Th.U. per 100 miles. A good deal of work has been done on transmission calculations and formulæ have been developed for the calculation of pipe diameters in terms of pressure and rate of flow of gas. The original formula is due to Weymouth but a modified form may now be used. The Weymouth formula is:

$$Q_s = 433 \cdot 45 \frac{T_s}{P_s} \sqrt{\frac{d^{5\frac{1}{3}}(P_1{}^2 - P_2{}^2)}{LST_1}}$$

where $Q_s = $ cu. ft. per day at P_s and T_s

$P_1 = $ initial pressure in lb./sq. in abs.

$P_s = $ standard pressure

$L = $ distance in miles

$d = $ pipe diameter in inches

$P_2 = $ terminal pressure

$S = $ specific gravity (air $= 1$)

$T_1 = $ standard absolute temperature of flowing gas, $°\,F$.

If T_s is taken at $520°\,F$. abs., and P_s at $14 \cdot 73$ lb. per sq. in. the equation becomes :

$$Q_s = 15{,}302 \sqrt{\frac{d^{5\frac{1}{3}}(P_1{}^2 - P_2{}^2)}{LST_1}}$$

and, if the specific gravity be taken as $1 \cdot 00$ and the distance as one mile, it becomes for a pipe of one inch diameter :

$$Q^s = 671 \sqrt{P_1{}^2 - P_2{}^2}$$

Since natural gas does not contain carbon monoxide it is not poisonous and its distribution suffers less from leakage danger than manufactured gas, but it is odourless and leakage which might lead to the formation of an undetected explosive mixture must be guarded against. The addition of a number of organic sulphur compounds has been tried including ethyl mercaptan but the present choice is a cyclic sulphide called by the trade name of Calodorant C. ; the amount required is about 1 lb. per million cu. ft. of gas. It is important that the amount be sufficient to be detected at a dilution in air of 4 per cent. since the explosive range begins at this concentration. One difficulty is the absorption of odour in dust in the mains and in damp soil surrounding a pipe-line.

The physical properties of natural gas differ from those of manufactured gas and equipment changes must be made if a change-over is made from one to the other. The speed of flame propagation of natural gas is about one quarter, and its calorific value twice that of coal gas, so that changes of burner characteristics are made as described on p. 377. These are mainly increase of burner-port area, decrease of diameter of orifice jet, and adjustment of the air ports. For non-primary aerated burners a special range is required. For the same thermal output the natural gas flame is of greater volume and the burners are positioned further away from the object under heat.

THE COMBUSTION OF GASEOUS FUELS

Formerly, considerable importance attached to the gas engine as the source of power for electricity generation and for power production generally. This is no longer the case and the use of the gas engine, using either coal gas or producer gas, is limited to only a few special circumstances. The consumption of gas in a modern engine is about 15 to 17 cu. ft. at 520 B.Th.U., or 8300 B.Th.U. per b.h.p. hour, an efficiency of 30 per cent.

To-day the main applications of town gas are for cooking and heating in the home, for oven and furnace heating in industry, and only the small proportion of 2 per cent. is used for lighting. For water gas the main application is in the production of carburetted water gas ; for producer gas the only application now is furnace heating.

Coal gas, or other rich gas containing hydrocarbons, is normally burned with an aerated flame using a burner of which the classical example is the Bunsen burner. The general principle of the action of an aerated burner is that the gas, entering through a jet into a narrow passage, draws sufficient air round the flame to render it non-luminous. This primary air is not sufficient for complete combustion and the additional or secondary air necessary is obtained by entrainment through the flame envelope. Insufficient primary air will give a long flame with a smoky tip ; increase of the primary air shortens the flame until combustion becomes intense and eventually the flame blows off. The blowpipe flame is an example of the effect of a high rate of primary air. In practice the gas is usually at mains pressure, but the air may be at atmospheric or higher pressure. In the latter case there is greater control of rate of combustion and of flame length. Alternatively the flame may be aerated by entrainment by using a special jet which creates an entrainment stream of primary air at the base of the flame and a highly-turbulent spread-out flame above the burner to achieve access of the secondary air. For the larger industrial burners of this type a high pressure of gas supply is necessary with atmospheric air, and at high rates of consumption the flame is practically non-luminous. With smaller burners of the type of the Bray jet mains pressure is sufficient to give complete combustion ; although the flame is luminous it gives no smoke up to a calorific value of gas of 540 B.Th.U. per cu. ft.

In both types the burner is designed to make the most efficient use possible of the pressure of the gas. In the Bunsen type the expression

$$V = 40 \cdot 4 \sqrt{P/S} \quad \text{or} \quad 59 \sqrt{P/S}$$

for the rate of flow of gas through an orifice or nozzle is for sharp-edged and tubular orifices respectively, where V = velocity in ft. per sec., P = gas pressure at orifice in inches of water, and S — gas specific gravity (air = 1) and the coefficients of contraction being $0 \cdot 61$ and $0 \cdot 89$.

As much air as possible is drawn in with the gas, the limiting factor being the amount of air which will cause the flame to strike back from the end of the burner tube to the jet. The tube carrying the mixture of gas and primary air, and the ports of the burner itself, should be such as to offer the minimum resistance to the flow of gases. Also the former should be so arranged as to avoid turbulence. The burner orifice may be either sharp-edged or tubular, the former ensuring a higher gas velocity for the same gas volume and therefore a greater efficiency of air injection.

Generally speaking, the greater the amount of primary air injected, the shorter the flame produced, or in other words, the greater is the rate of combustion. When the degree of aeration approaches 100 per cent. the height of the inner cone is small and is independent of air-gas velocity.

In the town-gas industry, where the nozzles (injectors) are specially made, in order to attain a high coefficient of discharge, the expression can be written in terms of volume of gas, Q cu. ft. per hour.

$$Q = 1655 \; K.A. \sqrt{P/S}$$

where A is the area of the injector opening in square inches, and K is the coefficient of discharge. The latter varies with design but is usually between 0·8 and 0·9. The higher value can be attained, for example, with an injector having an internal taper of 30° to the axis and an external taper of 60° and a tube length of 1–1·5 times the diameter of the orifice.

The area of the flame ports should increase with decreasing calorific value of the gas; with 500 B.Th.U. coal gas it is between 30,000 and 40,000

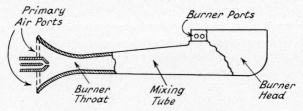

Fig. 81.—Domestic Town Gas Burner.

B.Th.U. per hour per sq. in. at a supply pressure of 2·5 in. w.g. The cross-section of the tube itself should be twice this and that of the burner throat two-thirds.

The area of the air ports should be larger than necessary, say one to two times the area of the flame ports, and adjustment should then be made by means of an air shutter or a screw throttle.

In the case of natural gas having a calorific value of the order of 1000 B.Th.U. per cu. ft. the same rules apply, but the diameter of the gas orifice is less and, for smooth mixing the throat area is less, i.e. about 0·4 times the area of the burner ports.

An illustration of a domestic gas burner is shown in Figure 81.

In domestic heating or cooking the emphasis is on complete combustion and therefore on short, well-aerated flames. In industry there are so many different requirements that no generalization is possible. It may be necessary to obtain intimate mixing for the development of a high temperature in a confined space or delayed mixing for the heating of large surfaces or spaces, or any intermediate condition. Industrial burners therefore cover the whole range from the simple type of a gas jet introduced into a combustion flue to that of a thermostatically controlled high-pressure air-blast burner.

Figure 82 illustrates certain of the common types of burner used for different industrial purposes.

Types (*a*) and (*b*) are used where the gas is burned in combustion flues. Type (*c*) may also be used in this way, but high temperatures can be developed in restricted spaces. Type (*c*), where the gas and air are led in separately without any attempt at mixing, can be used only for heating large

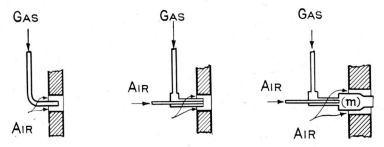

(*a*) Simplest Form with Induced Air Supply.

(*b*) Forced Primary Air and Induced Secondary Air or with Mixing Chamber (*m*).

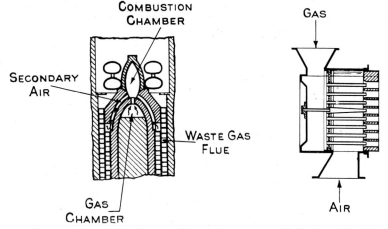

(*c*) Separate Air and Gas Ports to Combustion Chamber, Low-grade Gas delaying Mixing for Heating Large Spaces.

(*d*) Producer Gas Burner using Compressed Air.

FIG. 82.—Types of Industrial Gas Burner.

spaces or extended flues. This type of burner has innumerable forms, in the simplest of which the air and gas enter the combustion chamber at a series of ports, the distribution of the gases being controlled by dampers over the ports. Type (*d*) is used where the gas is at a low pressure and injection in the form of a definite flame is desired.

In heating large surfaces it is frequently necessary to liberate the heat from the gas in stages along heating flues. This can be done either by

burning a limited quantity of gas with an excess of air at the point of introduction and introducing additional gas, without air, at suitable points, or
by introducing all the gas with a limited primary air and completing the
combustion by introducing secondary air at the necessary positions. A
burner of the latter type is shown in Figure 83, designed at the Fuel Research
Station for use with any type of fuel gas.

The gas enters a T-piece of large diameter, and the air supply, of smaller
volume, enters via a nozzle into the gas stream. With such an arrangement

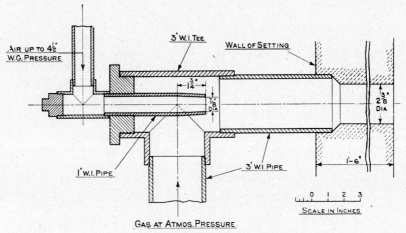

FIG. 83.—Fuel Research Gas Burner.

the air can be varied within wide limits without making the flame smoky.
In addition the CO_2 formed will prevent the formation of smoke when air
is introduced at later points to complete the combustion. This burner
operates equally well on water gas, producer gas or coal gas. With the
latter the important dimension is the distance which the air nozzle projects
beyond the centre line of the air supply. If the amount of projection is
too great the flame becomes smoky; if it is too little, or is negative, the
burner becomes too hot or the flame backfires. In the case of the burner
shown in Figure 83 the optimum conditions for smokeless combustion with
rich gases are shown below:

Gas.		Air volume—cu. ft.		Smoky.	Optimum conditions.
B.Th.U.	Cu. ft. per hr.	Firing back.	Just luminous.		
587	510	1680	1150	832	1480
		ratio 3·30	2·25	1·63	2·90
617	570	2030	1540	850	1790
		ratio 3·57	2·67	1·50	3·14

In both cases smokeless combustion is achieved between fairly wide limits of gas/air ratio. In the above example the ranges are from 73 to 50 and from 74 to 56 per cent. of the theoretical amounts of air required for complete combustion of the gas. As the gas becomes richer, therefore, the range over which smokeless combustion is possible decreases, mainly because the lower limit at which luminosity appears rises.

COMBUSTION CHARACTERISTICS OF GASES AND BURNER DESIGN

Perhaps the first factor in considering the control of combustion of gases is the composition and properties of the gases themselves. This is true even of gases in the same class ; there is, for example, sufficient variation in town gas to affect appreciably the size of jet for a particular form of flame and a desired performance.

The first factor in rich gas mixtures is the concentration of hydrogen. The burning velocity of this gas is much higher than that of any other component and its concentration affects both the rate of burning of the mixture and the stability of any flame. In an aerated burner therefore the amount of primary air possible will decrease with increasing hydrogen content. Flame stability in aerated flames can be defined as the range between the minimum rate of supply of gas—which causes light-back— and the maximum rate—which causes the flame to blow off the end of the burner. In diffusion flames there is no light-back but the blow-off can be related to that of the aerated condition. An intermediate stage of the blow-off is found in flame lift in which the flame may leave the burner tip but occupy a stable position some distance downstream from it. There is more than one theory for the definition of the conditions for stability ; the dead-space theory presumes the existence of a dead space between the burner top and the flame and holds that the determining factor is not the average burning velocity but the velocity at the dead space ; this velocity has been shown to differ with different gas compositions. In the case of blow-off this is held to occur when the gas flow within the flame becomes turbulent. These limits of flame stability control the extent of heat release possible with laminar-flow flames and, in industrial processes where higher rates are required, either flame stabilizers in the form of physical obstructions, or a burner of the turbulent type (below), must be used.

Attempts have been made to define the combustion characteristics of rich gas by the use of certain empirical relationships, and standardized tests. The combustion diagrams of Fuidge and others are prepared by the operation of a simple tubular burner with increasing air/gas ratios and the plotting of the observations against thermal input. A typical set of curves for coal gas and water gas shows the very considerable difference in their behaviour ; these are given in Figure 84.

(1) The disappearance of luminosity is given by the bottom full line.

(2) The blow-off point of the flame is the upper full line.

(3) The back-fire area is to the left of the curved line *ab*.

Anywhere in the area between these three lines the conditions are such that the gas will burn without luminosity, but the height of the inner cone will decrease in the direction of increasing air/gas ratio.

(4) The theoretical air requirement is represented by the central dotted line.

These diagrams, therefore, give a considerable insight into the performance of gas in an aerated burner and can be used to define the limits of

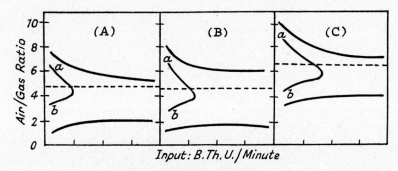

Fig. 84.—Combustion Diagrams of Town Gas.

(*A*) Horizontal-retort gas.
(*B*) Vertical-retort gas.
(*C*) Carburetted water gas.
- - - - - Theoretical air requirement.

conditions of gas input and degree of aeration to give a satisfactory performance and a stable flame.

Arising from the study of these curves a special burner has been designed to give a more rapid appreciation of variations of gas quality. This " Aeration Test Burner " measures the air supply to give a steady well-defined, blue inner cone exactly ¾ in. high when using a gas pressure of 2·5 in. w.g. Since the performance of a burner depends upon the combined resistances of the air-ports and the burner tube as well as upon the flame speed of the aerated mixture, it was necessary to standardize the burner exactly so that it could be duplicated for test work. It is a 12-in. Teclu burner of 0·404 in. internal diameter with a nipple of 0·039 in. diameter. Air enters through a rectangular shutter which is adjustable by a micrometer head, and the A.T.B. number is the extent to which the shutter has to be opened to give an exact cone of 2½ in. height. Since this cone is steady and well-defined it is apparent that the conditions of burning are far removed from the tip of the back-fire area of the combustion diagram.

A considerable number of town gases have been examined by the use of this burner and the following conclusions have emerged.

(1) Calorific value is related to the A.T.B. number fairly directly ; if a given gas is diluted to reduce its calorific value the A.T.B. number decreases to an extent depending upon the specific gravity of the diluent.

C.v.	Diluted with		Waste gas.	C.w.g. alone.
	Water gas.	Producer gas.		
450	30	35	40	22
500	40	45	49	28
525	47	52	55	32

The effect of type of gas is ± 5 units, but the effect of diluent is greater than this. The range with carburetted water gas is quite different.

(2) Specific gravity, at the same calorific value and pressure, determines the thermal input to a burner. Its effect is equivalent to a change of one unit of A.T.B. number for every 0·01 change of specific gravity.

The inference from these results seems to be that, although town supply is governed by strict control of calorific value, this does not constitute a complete safeguard against variation of combustion characteristics. A variation of 5 units in the A.T.B. number can affect quite seriously the performance of an aerated burner in which the primary air is induced. Indeed, for one nipple size, the variation should not normally exceed 1–2 numbers. In order to overcome this difficulty on occasions when, for example, peak-load requirements demand some unusual action, it has been suggested that the gas supply be controlled to a condition of constant thermal input to the burner.

At constant pressure the rate of delivery of gas from an orifice is proportional to $1/d$, where d is the specific gravity, so that the same rate of thermal delivery would be achieved if the calorific value were raised to compensate for increase of specific gravity. This might be important in emergency since the extra cost of the gas of higher calorific value might be less than that of peak-load gas made specially for the purpose. The Wobbe Index (after its proposer) has been suggested as the governing factor and is the factor c.v./$\sqrt{d}$ in the expression :

$$\text{Thermal output} = k \frac{\text{calorific value}}{\sqrt{\text{sp. gr.}}}.$$

The magnitude of the index varies with the units chosen. In British units a normal gas of 500 B.Th.U. per cu. ft. calorific value has an index of 800 at a specific gravity of 0·45. Carburetted water gas at the same calorific value and a specific gravity of 0·65 has an index of 620. It may be calculated that, when operating at a declared calorific value of 500 B.Th.U., an increase of specific gravity of 0·02 would mean that the calorific value would have to be increased by 10 B.Th.U. to maintain the same thermal input from the burner.

These observations relate to gas burners using gas at mains pressure and induced primary air. In industry, where air under pressure may be used, the full measure of control is obtained by adjustment of the air pressure. Neither do they apply to non-aerated jet burners where the degree of

FIG. 85.—British Furnaces Gas/Air Proportioner.

aeration of the flame is determined by the amount of turbulence set up at the tip of the burner. They do indicate, however, that the correct conditions of combustion of a bunsen-type flame is mainly a matter of the correct diameter of gas orifice in relation to the supply of secondary air to give either a short efficient flame, common in domestic applications, or a long soft flame common in industrial heating where large surfaces have to be heated.

Proportions of Gas and Air. In the heating of industrial furnaces the success of the heating may depend upon the control of flame shape to within quite narrow limits. This can be achieved by a number of devices of which the British Furnaces " air/gas proportioner " is one. This device is shown in the sectioned drawing, Figure 85. Air under pressure enters the venturi A and entrains gas through the holes CC in the latter. This causes the piston E to be sucked forward, allowing gas to pass from the inlet D to the space G surrounding the venturi. The movement of the piston also moves the diaphragm H to which it is attached. The latter is mounted vertically, so reducing the pressure to atmospheric and making the amount of gas entering depend wholly on the suction. Final adjustment is on the gas valve. The air inlet can be varied in size and position of gas-entrainment holes and is locked in position by the pin K. Figure 83 shows two sizes. A pressure gauge is attached at L to make certain that the pressure is atmospheric at the diaphragm ; if not, the burner nozzle or the throat of the air intake must be modified.

Thermostatic Control. Gaseous fuel lends itself particularly to the thermostatic control of heat input by the regulation of the temperature of operation. The use of a solid body in the thermostat has many advantages from the point of view of construction and the large majority of gas thermostats are of this type. The action depends upon the difference of thermal expansion of two metal rods of very different coefficient. Materials of low coefficient of expansion are silica, porcelain, invar, Ni-steel, etc., and metals of high coefficient are steel, copper and brass. A good combination up to 260° C. is brass and invar, and for temperature up to 1000° C. steel and silica.

The differential expansion of brass-invar is 1.8×10^{-5} cm./cm./° C. and usually this is magnified by giving the gas valve a wide seating. In this type an invar rod passes down the centre of a brass tube and one end is pressed against the upper half of the valve seating by a spring. On heating the end of the rod and tube the brass tube expands more than the rod and the valve is opened. Since an opening of one millimetre of length means $2\pi r$ mm.² of area it follows that the wider the seating the more sensitive is the control. The setting of the thermostat is adjustable by hand by moving the starting position of the valve, and a bypass prevents the complete shut-off of the gas. When the supply of gas is large the best method of operation is to pass only part of the gas through the thermostat and allow the back-pressure set up to actuate the main valve. In continuous-acting furnaces it is also possible to apply a gas load which is just not quite enough, and to control the additional small amount on the thermostat. This control has a less-abrupt effect and is better, if there is no sudden large demand for gas, than the on-off system which operates when the thermostat closes the main valve.

In selecting a thermostat, several factors must be considered. The outer tube should be thin if quick response to temperature change is

F.—O

necessary ; the depth of immersion of the tube must remain constant, and its position should be that which is subject to the temperatures which matter.

An example of a thermostat is shown in Figure 86. The governor

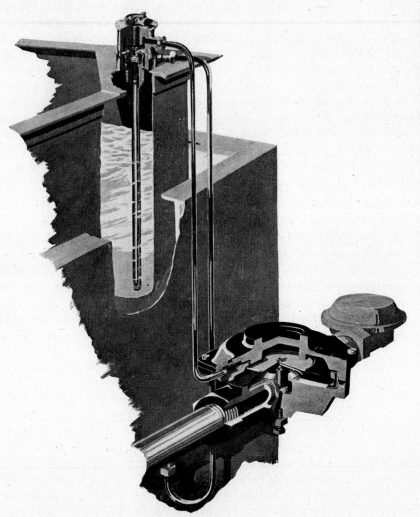

FIG. 86.—Thermostatic Control Equipment for Gas Burners (North Thames Gas Board).

mechanism is shown in section and the expansion tube is immersed in a tank containing liquid. This thermostat is of the direct-acting type in which all the gas is passing through the instrument.

Special Burners. If the bunsen-type burner be accepted as the normal type of gas burner there are several types which should be described

separately. These are the entrainment types, the premixed concentrated
combustion types and the impact type.

The entrainment type is shown in the pinhole jet where entrainment is
wholly by surface convection from the sides, the wide size-range of Bray
jets, and the industrial-size jet or Hypact burner. Such burners are often
termed " non-primary aerated " or " neat-gas jets " since the air for combustion is all introduced at the surface of the flame. The Bray type of
burner is cylindrical with specially-shaped ports made in a porcelain tip
and an inner wire gauze to promote linear flow. In the slotted-port type
a narrow rectangular gas port (length = 2 × width) crosses the top of the
tip. Gas can pass unimpeded through the middle part of this, but the
rounded shape of the inside of the tip causes the
sides of the gas stream to be diverted inwards so
as to impinge on one another. This causes a flat-
tening and spreading of the stream at right angles
to the long side of the slot. The resulting flame
has the familiar batswing shape of thin section
which entrains air with sufficient rapidity to give
complete combustion and a stable flame. The
turn-down range of such flames is very high, from
normal consumption of gas to 1/130 of normal.
At too high a gas pressure the flame becomes unstable, i.e. irregular in shape or tending to blow off,
and burners are normally designed to work in the
range 1·0–2·5 in. w.g. : at 4·5 in. the flame becomes
unstable. Absence of noise is another advantage
over aerated-flame burners. Slotted jets are made
with one central hole or with two ports inclined
towards one another at an angle of 45° to form

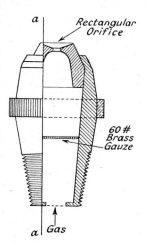

Fig. 87.—Typical Bray Jet
Burner.

impinging flames and can be made to form flames of various shapes.
In output they vary from miniature jets at 0·25 cu. ft. per hour to industrial
jets at over 16 cu. ft. Special jets are made to give luminous flat flames,
perforated tips to give multi-jet flames, and cylindrical jets to give long
flames of the pilot-jet type. A section of a typical Bray jet is shown in
Figure 87.

An industrial entrainment jet has been developed by exchanging the
small apertures of the Bray jet for a wide slot. The gas-side approach to
the slot is shaped in such a way that the two streams of gas impinge on
the flame from opposite sides and give it a characteristic fan shape. In the
Hypact burner practically any gas rate can be achieved by making the
burner of the required size. Figure 88 shows a section of the burner and
a picture. Burners are available in a large number of sizes from the
Aeromatic Co., Ltd. In free air the size of flame varies from 11 in. wide
× 11 in. long and 1·5 in. thick to 48 × 33 × 9 in. ; in use the size varies

with the conditions in the combustion space. The particulars of three sizes are quoted below.

Size.	Gas pressure in. w.g.	Feed in.	Flame size, in.					
			L.	W.	T.	L.	W.	T.
			Vertical.			Horizontal.		
60	1·0	¾	11	11	1·5	7	10	6
	3·0		12	12	2	10	10	7
400	1·0	1¼	19	19	4·5	16	21	16
	3·0		20	23	4·5	18	22	16
1500	1·0	2½	45	26	8	28	30	37

(L, W, T = length, breadth, thickness of flame.)

The flames are noisy and turbulent at high pressures but are remarkably stable. The size 60 burner can be operated with gas at over 20 lb./sq. in.

 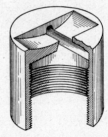

FIG. 88.—Hypact Jet Burner.

and has the remarkable range within these limits of 1–1400 cu. ft. per hour with very little change of flame size.

It is apparent that this ability to burn a large volume of gas in a small space must have valuable industrial applications, e.g. where high rates of heating are required. Other applications are to vessel heating from below, metal melting, air heating, and steam raising in locomotive-type boilers.

Premixing Burners. A rapid rate of local heating in industrial operations can be achieved by burning a premixed stoichiometric mixture of gas and air. In the form known as the " tunnel " burner, rates of heat release of 100×10^6 B.Th.U. per cu. ft. of tube space have been achieved. As shown in Figure 89, a jet of air and gas in stoichiometric proportions is injected into the end of a tube of small diameter, using air at a pressure of 10 lb. per sq. in. or more. Shortly after ignition at the end of the tube

FIG. 89.—Premixing Gas Burner for High Intensity Heating (North Thames Gas Board).

the flame strikes back to the nozzle, a high temperature develops in the tube and a turbulent stream of hot gas issues from the end. The tube or tunnel in which the combustion takes place can vary according to requirements, but the burner illustrated in Figure 89, the "Concentrated Combustion" burner, has a $2\frac{1}{2}$-in. burner tube and a refractory tunnel of 6 in. long × 1 in. diameter, and will burn up to 150 cu. ft. of gas per hour, using air at 1 lb. pressure. Arranged in rows as shown in Figure 89, these burners can give a directional flow of intensely-hot gas over a moving stream of objects so that they are effectively heated to the required temperature in a short time. This type of burner has the disability of being very noisy in operation, but it has been shown that this is due to the fact that the mechanism of combustion consists in a series of explosions of small increments of gas and air of the order of about 8 ml. The frequency of these explosions is of the order of 1000 per second. This is the reason for the extreme turbulence of the issuing stream of hot gas which is the effective principle. It also provides the explanation for the distinctive noise which is the defect of such burners and shows that it cannot be avoided beyond the point of avoiding the harmonic of the tunnel.

Examples of the application of this burner are the hardening of hammer heads to 550 Brinell in $1\frac{1}{2}$–3 minutes, the progressive annealing of $\frac{5}{8}$-in. steel tubing at the rate of 14 ft. per minute with the expenditure of only 2 cu. ft. of gas per lb. of steel, the tube leaving at 700° C. Steel billets can be heated to 1250° C. in the same way at the rate of one per 20 sec. In furnace operation banks of burners would be set opposite one another to give a high-temperature zone through which articles to be heated can be passed. The advantage of rapid heating in a reducing atmosphere is a considerable saving of metal in the avoidance of scale.

Use of Swirl in Burners. In the combustion of low-grade gas, in which the slow velocity of propagation of flame makes it difficult to keep the flame from blowing off the burner, the giving of a strong swirl to the air or gas will keep the flame anchored at a much higher velocity. This technique is also an advantage for rich-gas burners in shortening the flame and giving better control. A burner of the Basequip K or Eddy-Ray types shown in Figures 105 and 106 (Chapter XVI), with air-swirl, is a dual-purpose burner for either rich or lean gas, and serves a useful purpose in circumstances where by-product gas is sometimes, but not always, available.

Burner Efficiency and Flame Temperature. The efficiency of a gas burner can be expressed by the nearness to which the flame temperature developed approaches the theoretical maximum, making due allowance for the gaseous dissociation which must take place at high temperature. In a burner system in which the gas and air approach by parallel flow the speed of combustion which can be attained depends upon the rate of diffusion, and the efficiency is about 70 per cent. only without air preheat. In a premixing or swirl-type burner of the Basequip K or Eddy-Ray type shown in Figures 105 and 106 the rate of combustion may be greatly increased and an efficiency of 100 per cent. approached with cold air. This burner will give a flame temperature of 1750° C. with coal gas when a parallel-flow burner of 70 per cent. efficiency would require an air-preheat of 1100° C. to give the same temperature. I am indebted to Mr. J. W. Reber of the Wellman, Smith Owen Corp. for the following calculations (Table LXI), based on the Rosin It. diagram, which illustrate this point.

TABLE LXI

EFFECT ON FLAME TEMPERATURES OF BURNER EFFICIENCY

Type of fuel gas.	Net cal. value, B.Th.U. per cu. ft.	Excess combustion air. %	Preheat of		Theoretical flame temperatures ° C.		
			Air ° C.	Gas ° C.	100%	90%	70%
					Burner efficiencies.		
Coke-oven gas . . .	470	0	0	0	1945	1750	1360
,, ,, ,, . . .	,,	30	0	0	1700	1330	1190
,, ,, ,, . . .	,,	0	600	—	2160	1940	1510
,, ,, ,, . . .	,,	30	600	—	2000	1800	1400
Blast-furnace gas . .	97	0	0	0	1495	1345	1046
,, ,, ,, . .	,,	0	600	—	1680	1510	1180
,, ,, ,, . .	,,	0	600	400	1825	1640	1280
,, ,, ,, . .	,,	30	0	0	1350	1210	945
,, ,, ,, . .	,,	30	600	0	1585	1430	1200
,, ,, ,, . .	,,	30	600	400	1730	1560	1220
Coke-oven gas . . .	470	0	1100	0	2500	2250	1750

(J. W. Reber, Wellman, Smith Owen Engineering Corporation.)

Domestic Heating by Gas

The burners of domestic gas appliances have until recently all been of the bunsen type and have been fitted with gas orifices and primary air control to suit the particular gas supply and give a flame of the desired length and shape and, of course, with complete combustion. The position is now changed with the return of Bray-type jet burners of the so-called non-primary aerated type. This change began with the instantaneous water heater and is now being applied to the radiant gas fire, with considerable success in the prevention of burner noise.

It is not necessary in this volume to enter into detail regarding the design of gas-burning domestic appliances and it is proposed only to deal briefly with general facts and with recent advances. The high proportion of the gas sold in this market is consumed for cooking, i.e. just over 80 per cent., the remainder is consumed in space heating—gas fires, gas convectors, low-temperature gas radiators—and water-heaters mainly of the instantaneous type. The gas cooker is fitted with bar and ring burners invariably of the aerated type with replaceable nipples to suit the range of gas quality. Thermostatic controls are fitted to the ovens to allow of usage at different levels of temperature. Thermal efficiency of use does not really enter into cooking, but flame length from boiling rings is set to give the optimum rate of heating of cooking vessels. Water-heaters are normally heated by non-bunsen type burners of which the best known is the Bray jet. Jets of a wide range of size and heat output are available to suit all variations of appliance. The thermal efficiency in this case is measurable and is of the order of 75–80 per cent. Ignition of instantaneous heaters is by pilot jet ; although catalyst igniters have been tried they have a short life due to poisoning by certain gas constituents or impurities such as iron carbonyl.

The radiant gas fire, which has been shown to have a radiant efficiency of about 45 per cent., has always suffered from the fact that radiation is unidirectional and a condition of comfort is not necessarily obtained in this way because of radiation from the body to cold walls. This difficulty has been reduced and thermal efficiency increased by making the fire a partial convector as shown in Figure 35 (Chapter VIII). Air for combustion enters below the burners in the usual way and passes out to the flue. Circulation air enters below the burners, is heated by passage between a well-insulated backing and the hot reverse side of the radiant block, and passes through a fret into the room as an upward-flowing stream of warm air which is dry and free from combustion products. This stream creates a circulation which warms the back of the room and increases the feeling of comfort. The heat returned in this way represents some 15–20 per cent. of the gross calorific value of the gas so that the overall efficiency of the appliance is 60–65 per cent.

As a direct radiator, the gas fire gives its maximum efficiency at full load. When " turned down ", the efficiency falls but not appreciably until the consumption is less than half. In one example of a non-convector fire the decrease from full load at 33 cu. ft. of gas per hour was :

Gas, cu. ft. per hour	.	. 33	25	20	15	10
Radiant efficiency per cent.	.	45	43	42	40	34

Until recently, the burners used for the radiant fire have been of the aerated type, but now they are being successfully replaced to a considerable extent by Bray jets set in pairs to aid air entrainment. These jets are silent in operation and cause no sooting below a gas calorific value of about 540 B.Th.U. per cu. ft.

The same principle is now applied to convector air heaters. Formerly these operated under the disability that the products of combustion entered the room and caused trouble by undesirable condensation of water on cool surfaces, corrosion of metal by traces of sulphur compounds, and the risk,

at least theoretically, of the discharge of carbon monoxide. The
latest model of this form of heater
discharges its combustion products
to atmosphere and induces a counter-
current stream of fresh air which
serves for combustion. An appliance of this type is shown diagrammatically in Figure 90. It must, of
course, be fitted to an outside wall,
but the aperture is only one brick in
size, i.e. 9 × 3 in. The outlet is so
designed (" balanced flue ") that all
the air necessary is induced and
is not contaminated by waste gas.
The surface of the appliance is arranged as a low-temperature surface
radiator.

Taking the waste-gas temperature and composition as criteria, the
efficiency of the appliance is of the
order of 75 per cent. The waste-gas
temperature is 350–380° F. and it
contains 5–6 per cent. of carbon dioxide at full load ; the warm air
leaving the surface of the radiator
has a temperature of 240–300° F.

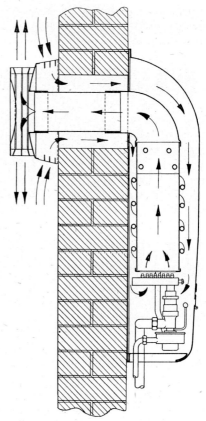

Fig. 90.—Balanced-flue Gas Space-
heater (North Thames Gas Board).

Industrial Gas Heating

The proportion of town gas sold to industry has been steadily increasing
during the last decade. The overall percentage has increased from 21·7
in 1948 to 25·6 per cent. in 1952, but as these are percentages of increasing quantities the actual quantities used in industry have increased by
9–10 per cent. in these four years. These increases have been due to the
increased cost of labour and the obvious advantages of a fuel available in
constant quality and without storage problems. Perhaps more important
has been the high efficiency and high economy of usage which is possible
with a fluid fuel whose combustion can be adjusted to the purpose in view
and controlled within narrow limits by the use of modern equipment.

The widest application in industry is to furnace heating, although
there are very many special cases where the method of use is more concerned with the exact treatment of some material than with combustion.
Baking is one example of this, the fusion of the glass parts of radio valves
on a turntable is another and the high-speed drying of printed paper a

third.   In any application, however, the first principle is efficient combustion
by the use of controlled burners, the second is thermostatic control of
conditions and the third is thermal efficiency of usage.   The first two have

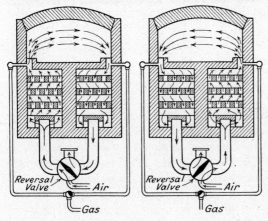

FIG. 91.—Gas-fired Regenerative
Forge Furnace.

been discussed above and the following example of furnace heating is chosen
not only to show a gas-heated furnace but to demonstrate one in which
thermal efficiency is improved, and a high operating temperature is achieved
more readily, by the use of regeneration, to increase the temperature of the

combustion air. In Figure 91 a Revergen oven furnace is shown with the regenerative brickwork and gas cycle in detail. Furnaces of this type are made in a wide variety of sizes from a heating space of 6 cu. ft. up to 200 ft. in length. By using a reversal time of 15–20 minutes a temperature of 1600° C. can be achieved, although normally such furnaces operate at 1400–1500° C. In Figure 91 the furnace doors are closed, the burners and control mechanism are seen on the left ; the regenerators are built into the main structure. On the larger furnaces two fans are provided for the combustion air and for the removal of the waste gases. If a furnace of this type is used for general heat treatment, for which lower temperatures are required, a recuperative system, in which the air is preheated by interchange with the products of combustion, is more convenient and almost as efficient.

Radiant Heating

Many low-temperature heating operations in industry such as drying were at one time all carried out by convective heat transfer. This was in general a slow process and many of them are now replaced by so-called infra-red radiation from heated panels. Since the rate of heat transfer by radiation is proportional to T^4, where T is the absolute temperature, it follows that a high rate of heating should be possible by exposing an object to a relatively high temperature and reducing the time of exposure to the point at which the desired drying or other reaction is accomplished, but damage by overheating is avoided. For maximum rate of radiation it also follows that the radiating surface should be of high emissivity, i.e. a black body, or be a selective emitter emitting radiation in the wavelength suited to the absorptive characteristics of the material under treatment. For low-temperature heating in the range 250–380° C. black surfaces have been invariably used when the heating medium is gas. Electric heating for the same purpose has taken a number of forms and has included batteries of gas-filled tungsten-filament lamps.

Experimental work has shown that high rates of heating are indeed attained in certain suitable applications but that the gas-heated radiant surface at a low temperature has very little selective action and that the rate of heating is almost entirely a function of temperature alone. This is less true of the electric lamp heater which emits radiation largely in the region of $1.2 \, \mu$ wavelength as compared with 4–$5 \, \mu$ from a black panel and which is shown to give higher rates with certain types of plastic which absorb strongly in this emission range. It has also been shown that it is not necessary for the material to be dried to absorb the radiation in the case of paint films on metal ; provided the metal can absorb, the rate of drying is the same.

An example of this form of heating is shown in Figure 92 ; this is a tunnel drier or heater arranged to deal with a moving stream of material or objects and standardized in construction to be of 2, 3, or 4 ft. diameter and

3 ft. in unit length.   The emissive panel which forms the inner cylinder is of 18 S.W.G. sheet steel and is blacked on both sides.   The gas requirement for the 3 sizes to give a surface temperature of 345° C. is 140, 160, and 310 cu. ft. per hour ; heating is by Bray jets and the products of combustion pass up behind the panel and do not come into contact with the materials

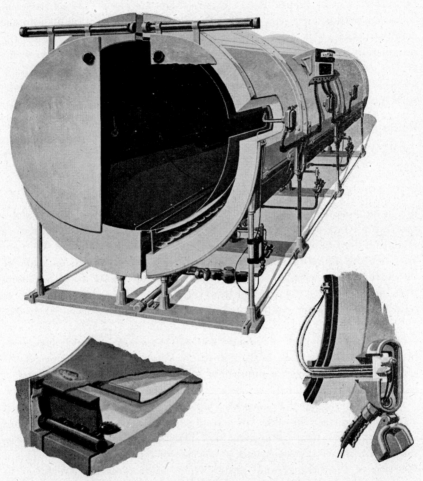

Fig. 92.—Infra-red Radiant-heating Tunnel (North Thames Gas Board).

being heated.   The radiant surfaces for the three diameters are respectively 18, 27 and 36 sq. ft. for each 3-ft. unit.   The temperature of 345° C. is the maximum and lower temperatures can, of course, be used.   The furnace may be made of any desired length by placing 3-ft. units end to end.

The industrial applications of this form of heating are now many and include the drying of paint or enamel films on metal, coated fabrics, posters, synthetic resins, pottery and ceramics, etc.   In some cases the rate of drying can be still further increased by convection in passing a current of air or inert gas through the tunnel.

High-temperature Radiant Heating. The temperature separating the low-temperature from high-temperature heating is quite arbitrary, but the scope of radiant heating has now been increased to about 1000° C. by the use of radiants of the gas-fire type, surface combustors, and heat-resisting steel. In view of the fourth-power law the increase of flux density of heat is 12,000 B.Th.U. per sq. ft. per hour at 500° C. and as much as 95,000 B.Th.U. at 1000° C.; in the low-temperature panel at 345° C. it is 5000 B.Th.U., all assuming an emissivity of 1·0.

Radiating surfaces are built up of modified gas-fire radiants and are heated by low-pressure gas unless it is difficult to supply the secondary air or take away the products of combustion. At this high rate of radiation the temperature of the source must be carefully controlled or the material being treated may be spoiled by overheating. One method of avoiding this is to have the inlet half at a higher temperature than the other. As examples of the special work which a high-temperature radiant can do, the following may be quoted.

(1) Printed letters are fired into spark-plug cores at 700° C. using an emitting surface at 1000° C. heated by insulated portcullis radiants. The arrangement is as shown in Figure 92 and the cores pass through an 18-ft. furnace at the rate of 15,000 per hour at a gas consumption of 7 therms per hour. The core temperature reaches 700° C. in 4 minutes, but does not exceed 759° C. in a further 15 minutes.

(2) Cathode-ray tubes are heated for 10 minutes at 500, 550, 560 and 450° C. in a four-panel oven 60 ft. long. The oven is 21 in. square and is heated by bar radiants, the tubes passing through on a band. Eighty tubes are treated per hour for a gas consumption of 15 therms.

Surface Combustion

The development of means for increasing the rate of combustion of gas at a desired point is founded on the work of Bone, Wilson and McCourt, who followed up the original discovery of Davy that surfaces have the power of accelerating to a varying degree the rate of combustion of gas and air. At low temperatures only certain subjects (e.g. platinum) have the property to a marked degree, but at elevated temperatures all substances are more or less alike.

Industrially the phenomenom is applied by burning a mixture of gas and air at an incandescent surface, thereby ensuring perfect combustion at great rapidity, local application, high temperatures, and enhanced transfer of heat by increase in the rate of radiation. There are several ways in which Surface Combustion may be provided. One of the earliest examples being the " Cox Combustor " which was a commercial development of a porous refractory diaphragm evolved by Bone and McCourt. In this case a gas and air mixture is forced under pressure through a porous but highly refractory material. Upon ignition the mixture burns with a faint blue haze over the face of the combustor, which gradually becomes incandescent. As soon as a state of incandescence is reached the flame recedes into the porous diaphragm which is maintained at a given temperature. The depth of recession is controlled by the thickness of the diaphragm, the speed of the gas and air mixture through the diaphragm, the low thermal conductivity or heat-insulating properties of the material used and its granular structure and the rate of dissipation of radiant heat from the incandescent surface. No flame whatsoever is visible, and that the air already mixed with the gas is sufficient for complete combustion is proved by immersing such a hot diaphragm in carbon dioxide, when no diminution of the action is noted.

Surface-combustion burners are also used for radiant heating (above). A ceramic block of the highest refractoriness may have moulded into it one

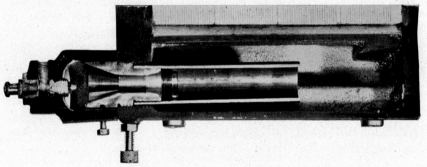

FIG. 93.—Surface-combustion Burner (Radiant Heating Ltd.).

or a multiplicity of circular or rectangular tunnels. A fully-aerated gas and air mixture is fed into the refractory block at one end of the tunnel which after ignition becomes highly incandescent. The incandescent walls of the tunnel promote surface combustion and according to the design and shape of the tunnel, extremely high rates of emission of heat may be obtained with correspondingly high temperatures. Practical applications involving temperatures of up to 1900° C. have been put in use, while experimental work has carried this temperature up to 2300° C. At these very high temperatures the limitation is only governed by the availability of materials having sufficient refractoriness.

In recent years there has been a steady development in gas burners employing some form of surface combustion. The most recent development being a unit operating at about 900° C. on low-pressure gas with inspirated air. The main feature has been to provide a refractory plaque with a multiplicity of fine passages, which may be circular in cross-section, passing from back to front of the plaque. The total port area available for combustion is far greater than that normally provided for a bunsen

SURFACE COMBUSTION 399

type burner, and thus a very low gas-air mixture speed is created. The flames which appear at the head of each passage create local incandescence and commence to recede. Recession is controlled by the cross-sectional area of each hole and the flow resistance which is set up together with a low thermal conductivity in the plaque. A cross-section through a typical burner of this type is illustrated in Figure 93. This type of surface combustion unit is being employed satisfactorily in domestic heating for space heaters and grills as well as in industry.

REFERENCE BOOKS

Gas Distribution Engineering. Le Fevre. Walter King. 1951.
The New Modern Gasworks Practice. Meade. Eyre and Spottiswoode.
Textbook of American Gas Practice. Morgan. J. J. Morgan. 1931–5.
The Manufacture of Water Gas. Hollings and Griffith. E. Benn. 1932.
Fundamentals of Atmospheric Gas Burner Design. American Gas Assoc. Bulletin 10, 1940.
King's Manual of Gas Manufacture. 10 Sections. Walter King Ltd. 1950– .
Combustion, Flames and Explosions of Gases. Lewis and von Elbe. Academic Press, N.Y. 1951.
Flame and Combustion in Gases. Bone and Townend. Longmans Green. 1927.
Gaseous Combustion at High Pressures. Bone, Newitt and Townend. Longmans, Green. 1929.
Industrial Furnaces. Trinks. John Wiley. 1951.
Fuels, Combustion and Furnaces. Griswold. McGraw-Hill. 1946.
Gas Engineers Handbook (U.S.A.). McGraw-Hill. 1934.
Natural Gas and Gasoline. Huntingdon. McGraw-Hill. 1950.
Productivity Report on Gas. British Productivity Council. 1953.
Symposia on Combustion Flame and Explosion Phenomena. Williams and Wilkins Inc., Baltimore. 1948, 1949, 1950.
Science of Flame and Furnaces. Thring. Chapman and Hall. 1954.
Manual of Gas Fitting. le Fevre. Walter King. 1951.
Economics of Fuel from Gas. Foster and Lund. McGraw-Hill. 1950.
Butane-Propane Gases. Denny and Luxon. Jenkins Publ. 1951.
Science and Practice of Gas Supply. Coe. British Commercial Gas Assoc. 1939.

CHAPTER XVI

GASEOUS FUELS OF LOW CALORIFIC VALUE

It is generally understood that the term " gas of low calorific value " refers to gas of the type of producer gas formed by the action of air or steam or both on coal or coke so that the main product of reaction is a mixture of carbon monoxide and hydrogen with the residual nitrogen of the air and a small proportion of carbon dioxide. Blast-furnace gas is a special case of this, complicated by process reactions.

The underlying principle in the production of these gaseous fuels from solid fuels rich in carbon is the conversion of the carbon mainly into carbon monoxide, either by the action of air alone, steam alone, in which case approximately equal volumes of carbon monoxide and hydrogen are obtained, or by a mixture of air and steam. Obviously, the amount of heat available from a given weight of the solid fuel is unaffected whether the fuel is burnt directly on a grate, or is utilized indirectly by first gasifying and then burning the gases. The great advantage gaseous fuel undoubtedly offers in most cases can arise only from the better use, i.e. better efficiency, which can be made of the heat units of the fuel as a whole. Gaseous fuel can be more economical only when the higher efficiency attained in the combustion of the gas more than counterbalances the inevitable losses of sensible heat from the producer brickwork.

In comparison with solid fuel for furnace and general heating purposes the advantages of gaseous fuel depend on several factors. Although the theoretical amount of air for combustion is the same whether solid fuel is burnt directly on a grate to carbon dioxide, or burnt partially in the producer to carbon monoxide, the combustion of this gas being completed finally in the furnace, in practice a considerable excess of air over that demanded by theory is requisite for fuel burnt on a grate, whilst, all told, as gaseous fuel the amount need barely exceed the theoretical. Where high intensity is required the excess air with solid fuel may be so large that efficiency suffers. Excess air means heat loss in the flue gases as sensible heat ; the use of gaseous fuel helps to reduce it.

Further, much of this sensible heat may be recovered in the case of gaseous heating by use of the regenerative system of firing. It is not a very practicable proposition to work on the regenerative system with solid fuel. The combination of the use of gaseous fuel with the regenerative system of firing alone permits of sufficiently high and regular temperatures for many metallurgical operations, as, for example, the production of open-hearth steel.

Again, better control of the temperature is possible, because of the ease of adjustment of the quantity consumed ; more uniform heating effect over a large surface is attained, and at the conclusion of an operation the fuel supply can be shut off immediately.

Turning to power production, the saving in fuel by the direct use of these poorer gaseous fuels was formerly considerable, especially in comparison with steam. Advances in the use of steam, however, by the employment of high pressures and high superheats and the improvement of condensing plant and reheaters have now raised the thermal efficiency of the best steam-power plants to over 27 per cent. Although gas-power plants have also improved in efficiency so that 35 per cent. can be attained, higher maintenance costs have thrown the balance in favour of steam. Similarly, high maintenance costs have operated against the utilization of the still higher thermal efficiency of the Diesel engine in large power stations. Power production from low-grade gaseous fuels has therefore become limited to small plants where some special cause such as isolation has been the deciding factor. The modern producer is now used almost entirely for furnace heating.

It is to be noted that the former belief that low-grade or dirty coals could be utilized to advantage in producers is dying out and that the modern producer calls for selected and closely graded fuel if high efficiency is to be maintained.

Producer Gas

The action of air alone on carbon under producer conditions gives carbon monoxide mainly, diluted by the nitrogen of the air. When the fuel is coal the gas is enriched by coal gas formed and the products of decomposition of the tar vapours. One ton of coal for example will give some 11,000 cu. ft. of coal gas and about 130 lb. of tar.

The action of steam alone, as in one phase of operating a water-gas plant, will give rise to about equal volumes of carbon monoxide and hydrogen, non-bituminous fuel chiefly being employed. The only diluting gases present should be those producer gases of the general composition given above which are left in portions of the plant.

In most cases of producer practice both air and steam are employed in the conversion of the solid into the gaseous fuel. The gases, therefore, partake of the component products of each reaction, the ratio of true producer gas to water gas depending primarily on the ratio of air to steam employed. This is, of course, a simplified explanation since the products of reaction also affect one another as explained below.

Where producer gas from coal is employed in furnaces to which it can be supplied hot, the thermal yield is added to by the heat value of any tar vapour which may be carried in the gas. Where the gas is made centrally and distributed cold this advantage is lost.

To-day the largest applications of producer gas are in the manufacture of iron and steel, glass, refractories and ceramics and in the heating of retorts and ovens in the carbonizing industries.

THEORY OF PRODUCER GAS REACTIONS

The primary reactions which have to be considered are those resulting from the action of an air and steam blast on highly heated carbon. Although bituminous fuels are employed largely, these are still the principal gas-forming reactions, the only difference being that instead of the resulting gas being produced wholly by the air-carbon and steam-carbon reactions, it is composed in part of the destructive distillation gases, accompanied by a residue of ungasified tarry vapours. The gas is in fact a mixture of producer gas and coal gas, where bituminous coal is used, and consequently of higher calorific value than gas made from high carbon fuel such as coke.

Air-carbon Reaction. In ordinary processes of combustion of solid fuel, owing to the comparatively shallow layer of incandescent carbon and a relatively high air velocity, carbon dioxide is formed, and the greatest number of available heat units obtainable from the combustion of the fuel is arrived at. The reaction is

$$(a) \quad C + \overbrace{O_2 + (\text{nitrogen})}^{\text{Air}} = \overbrace{CO_2 + (\text{nitrogen})}^{\text{Flue Gases}} + 169{,}294 \text{ B.Th.U.}$$
$$\text{12 lb. 32 lb.} \qquad \text{44 lb.}$$

This value, and those given below, are based on graphite and are the most accurate available. The carbon in coal is not graphitic, however, and in coke the transition is not complete, so that it is questionable whether graphite data should be used in thermal calculations of these reactions. King and Williams (*Fuel Res. Tech. Paper* 30, 1931) make the value for coke carbon in reaction (*a*) 174,000 B.Th.U. This is actually almost 3 per cent. higher and, of course, affects other reactions in which carbon takes part. The rate of conversion of carbon to graphite is slow in relation to combustion or gasification reactions and it would seem that it is wrong to use graphite values in this context. However, the graphite values are accurate and form a series, whereas no similar series has been proposed for coke carbon. In practice the values should be rounded off to the nearest 100 B.Th.U. The King and Williams values for other reactions are:

$$(b) \ + 103{,}540 \qquad (c) \ - 71{,}240$$

As is well known, too great a depth of fuel may give rise to the formation of carbon monoxide, with corresponding loss of available heat units. With sufficient depth of highly heated carbon in relation to the air velocity, carbon monoxide alone may be the final product, or at least with only certain traces of carbon dioxide, the reaction being :

$$\overbrace{\qquad}^{\text{Air}} \qquad \overbrace{\qquad}^{\text{Producer Gases}}$$

(b) . . $2C + O_2 + \text{(nitrogen)} = 2CO + \text{(nitrogen)} + 95{,}096$ B.Th.U.
      24 lb. 32 lb.   56 lb.

It is now accepted that the action of oxygen on carbon results in the simultaneous formation of carbon dioxide and carbon monoxide, but with a sufficient depth of fuel the carbon dioxide reacts with more carbon, producing carbon monoxide, so that for all practical purposes equation (b) represents the net result in an air-blown producer.

The thermal efficiency as a gas-making machine will be given by
$$\frac{14{,}108 - 3960}{14{,}108} \times 100 = 72 \text{ per cent. approximately.}$$
This is the efficiency with no sensible heat units in the gases produced, and is termed the *cold* gas efficiency. In practice the gases leave the producer at a very high temperature, often 800–900° C. (1470–1650° F.), so that the *hot* gas efficiency equals the cold gas efficiency plus the sensible heat of the gases. This may be 85–90 per cent.

Reactions (a) and (b) above are *exothermic*, and the temperature in a producer blown with air only will continue to rise for a given air blast until counterbalanced by losses of sensible heat in the gases, in the ashes and clinker, by radiation, etc. A limit is reached in practice by the liability to form clinker from the ash of the fuel and/or slag the producer linings. The controlling medium employed almost universally to regulate the temperature is steam.

Steam-carbon Reactions. When steam is blown through a bed of incandescent carbon the following reactions may occur.

(c) $C + H_2O \text{ (liq.)} \longrightarrow CO + H_2$ $- 75{,}423$ B.Th.U.
         12 lb. + 18 lb.

(d) $C + 2H_2O \text{ (liq.)} \longrightarrow CO_2 + 2H_2$ $- 76{,}650$ B.Th.U.
         12 lb. + 36 lb.

(e) $CO + H_2O \text{ (liq.)} \longrightarrow CO_2 + H_2$ $- 1294$ B.Th.U.
         28 lb. + 18 lb.

(f) $C + CO_2 \qquad\qquad \longrightarrow 2CO$ $- 74{,}196$ B.Th.U.
         12 lb. + 44 lb.

(g) $H_2O \text{ (water) at } 25° C. \longrightarrow H_2O \text{ (vapour)} - 18{,}935$ B.Th.U.
     18 lb.   at 25° C.

Normally, reaction (c) predominates, (d) is relatively small and (e) and (f) operate as shown, to the right. Reaction (c) requires a relatively high temperature, over 900° C. (1650° F.), whereas reaction (d) predominates at low temperatures (500° C. or 930° F.).

Clearly, by the simultaneous action of air and steam it will be possible to make such a thermal balance between the air-carbon (exothermic) reaction and the steam-carbon (endothermic) reaction that a constant temperature, dependent on the relative proportions of air and steam, may be maintained and, corresponding with this temperature, a definite composition for the " mixed " gas obtained will be attained, depending on the relative parts played by reactions (b), (c) and (d).

Reversible Reactions in Producer Practice. Further important considerations govern the composition of the resulting gases. In the air-carbon reaction, allowing that all the oxygen already has entered into some form of combination with carbon, there exists simultaneously in the producer hot carbon, carbon dioxide and carbon monoxide.

The proportions are controlled by the reversible reaction

$$(f) \quad . \quad . \quad C + CO_2 \rightleftharpoons 2CO$$

to give what is known as the producer-gas equilibrium. Rhead and Wheeler (*J. Chem. Soc.*, 1910, 2178) showed that at 850° C. equilibrium was attained in this mixture only in 240 hours, whilst at 1000° C. or over it was attained in 48 hours. Further, they showed that at 850° C. the reaction $CO_2 + C = 2CO$ proceeded 166 times more rapidly than the reverse reaction.

The composition of the equilibrium mixture is given by Rhead and by Falke and Fischer as follows :

Temp. ° C.	CO per cent.	Temp. ° C.	CO per cent.
600	31·5	900	97·8
700	63·4	1000	99·4
800	86·2	1100	99·8
		1200	99·9

In practice it is the formation of maximum carbon monoxide that is aimed at. High temperature clearly favours this while pressure (concentration) favours the reverse since the volume of CO is twice the volume of CO_2. The CO, however, is continually being withdrawn from the system and this withdrawal accelerates its formation.

The rate of establishment of the equilibrium under any conditions is clearly important and it is for this reason that fuels of high reactivity are favoured for producer practice. It has been shown that equilibrium is reached at 1300° C. in a few seconds, but that at least one minute is required at 1100° C., and at 1000° C. only two-thirds of the equilibrium concentration is reached in one minute. These equilibrium data are affected by both rate of reaction—the reverse reaction of (f) is very slow in comparison with the forward reaction—and the accessibility of the gases to the surface of the solid.

A general conclusion is that the gas of highest CO content is obtained by increasing the time of contact and the reaction temperature to their practical limits. That this is important is seen in the fact that the time of contact of gases in an air-blown producer is only of the order of one second. The establishment of this equilibrium in relation to time of contact is important in the other direction in the combustion of coal or coke on a grate. The percentage of CO when blowing with air is 34·5 per cent. at equilibrium and it has been shown (Wendt) that this is realized within 10–20 in. above the tuyères.

	Temp. ° C.	CO.	CO_2.	N_2.
At tuyères . . .	—	9·7	15·0	75·3
10 in. above . . .	1400	34·1	0·2	65·7
20 in. above . . .	—	34·3	0·2	65·5
30 in. above . . .	1250	34·5	0·0	65·1

Above 30 in., as the temperature falls, the concentration of CO_2 increases again as the reversal of the reaction comes into play.

More important reversible reactions occur when steam is employed. In this case varying proportions of carbon monoxide, carbon dioxide, hydrogen and steam will be coexistent, and by their interaction at various temperatures a constant composition for a given temperature will tend to be obtained. The reactions may be expressed :

$$(e) \quad . \quad . \quad CO + H_2O \rightleftarrows CO_2 + H_2$$

The composition of the ultimate " mixed " gas clearly will be dependent largely on the relative rate at which change is progressing in either direction, and on whether equilibrium is established for the working temperature. This equilibrium is the *water-gas equilibrium* and is given by the expression $k = CO \times H_2O/CO_2 \times H_2$. The constant k is quoted in *Technical Data on Fuel* as :

Temp. ° C.	k	Temp. ° C.	k
800	0·25	1200	1·44
900	0·45	1300	1·84
1000	0·73	1400	2·27
1100	1·06	1500	2·70

In normal practice, where a temperature of nearly 1100° C. is usual, the constant is about unity. Should the gas be of other composition than that agreeing with this value and attain—either in the producer or regenerator —a temperature of about 1100° C., it will tend to undergo such of the reversible changes referred to as will bring its ultimate composition into agreement with a value of $k = 1$.

Lowering of temperature clearly will result in an increase of carbon dioxide at the expense of carbon monoxide. Again, rise of temperature will result in an increase in the amount of carbon monoxide present in the dry gas, with a corresponding decrease in the hydrogen and carbon dioxide. This is of great importance where the gas passes through regenerators, as is so frequently the case, and the issuing hot gases will be markedly different in composition from the original. Increased concentration of steam, apart from its effect in lowering the temperature and hence the value for k, by increase of concentration alone will bring about a greater proportion of carbon dioxide and hydrogen in the gases.

It is known that the velocity of the forward reaction (e) is much higher than that of the reaction $C + CO_2 = 2CO$ and it is established that equilibrium is established in the bed in the presence of carbon.

The course of the reactions in a gas producer can be followed by withdrawing gas samples from the fuel bed at different levels. As soon as the air passes the ash layer and reaches the fuel bed reaction begins. In

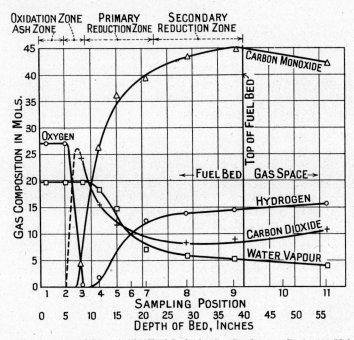

FIG. 94.—Composition of Gases in the Fuel Bed of a Gas Producer. Basis, 100 Mols. of N_2, Anthracite or Coke (Haslam, Entwistle and Gladding).

the next 3 to 4 in. the oxygen is entirely consumed and the CO_2 content of the gases rises proportionately. After this initial rapid increase CO is formed by the reaction $CO_2 + C = 2CO$ and the amount of CO_2 decreases, at first rapidly. These two zones are respectively the oxidation and reduction zones of the producer. After a further 12 in. the CO and CO_2 reach an approximate state of equilibrium depending upon the distribution of temperature.

In the oxidation zone the water or steam remains unchanged and decomposition of H_2O does not begin until the formation of CO has started. The formation of hydrogen increases rapidly over a distance of about 12 in. and then decreases slowly owing to the falling temperature of the bed.

In Figure 94 the proportions of the different gases produced are shown graphically in terms of molecules of each constituent per 100 molecules of nitrogen, this gas remaining unchanged in the process. The volumes of the gas are, of course, in the same proportions. Starting with air containing 79 per cent. of nitrogen the volume of oxygen corresponding to 100 mols. of nitrogen is 26·6 mols. Additional oxygen reacting with the carbon is the difference between 20 and 5 mols. H_2O, i.e. 7·5 mols. O_2.

The reactions taking place, and their zones, are shown diagrammatically in Figure 95. In the *oxidation zone* there would be only one reaction if

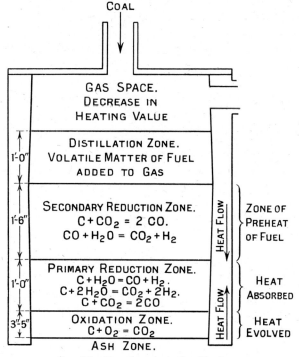

FIG. 95.—Reactions in a Gas Producer.

full contact of the air and steam, and the products of reaction, with solid carbon were assured. Normally this is not so and separate reactions occur (*a*) in contact with carbon and (*b*) in the intervening gas spaces between fuel particles. These may be written :

	At surface of particles.	In gas spaces.
Main bed . .	$C + CO_2 = 2CO$	$CO + H_2O = CO_2 + H_2$
3 dia. . .	$\begin{cases} C + CO_2 = 2CO \\ C + H_2O = CO + H_2 \end{cases}$	$CO + H_2O = CO_2 + H_2$
↑3 dia. . . .	$C + \tfrac{1}{2}O_2 = CO$	$\begin{cases} \\ CO + \tfrac{1}{2}O_2 = CO_2 \end{cases}$
⎸Grate		

In the oxidation zone the reactions are strongly exothermic and this is the hottest part of the bed. In the primary reduction zone the three reactions with carbon are shown but, as suggested above, a further reaction occurs in the gas space between CO and $H_2O \rightarrow CO_2$ and H_2. Above this zone further reduction of the CO_2 continues, but CO_2 is also formed by interaction between CO and steam. The extent of these reactions is comparatively slight. Since steam is not decomposed by carbon in this zone it is termed the *secondary reduction zone.* The main function of the zone is to act as a heat exchanger in which the descending fuel is heated by the rising hot gases ; a deep zone is therefore normally advantageous. In the final zone the fuel is also preheated and, in the case of coal, distilled, the volatile matter enriching the producer gas.

Above the fuel bed loss of calorific value can result if the temperature is too high, owing to the reversal of the reaction $CO_2 + C \rightleftharpoons 2CO$ in the absence of carbon. Working with a deep fuel bed is one means of preventing this loss, which may be as high as 10–15 per cent.

The above is only a schematic arrangement which applies to vertical producers of large size. In practice the fuel bed can be reduced to a matter of a few inches with reactive fuels and suitable blast arrangements, as in the transport producer (p. 42).

Importance of the Use of Steam. The primary advantages in the use of steam are (1) the control of the temperature to the maximum allowable in avoiding fusion of the ash, (2) a reduction of temperature at the top of the bed and therefore a reduction of sensible heat losses, and (3) an increase of the calorific value of the gas.

The first comprehensive experiments on the effect of steam in the gasification of coal were made by Bone and Wheeler in 1907 and still remain a classic (*Engineering*, 1907, **83,** 659 ; 1908, **86,** 837). Their significant conclusions are :

(1) The gas calorific value reaches a maximum with steam at 0·45 to 0·50 lb. per lb. of coal, i.e. a blast saturation temperature of 60–65° C.

(2) At optimum steam the percentage decomposition is 80.

(3) Increase of blast rate reduces the depth of the fuel bed without appreciably affecting gas composition and efficiency. Their greatest decrease was to half-depth.

Operating data for the most efficient conditions are given in Table LXII.

TABLE LXII

BONE AND WHEELER PRODUCER-GAS EXPERIMENTS. COAL

(Gas quantities at 0° C. and 760 mm.)

	Bed depth. 7 ft.	Bed depth. 3·5 ft.
Sat. temp. of blast, ° C.	60	60
Steam per lb. dry coal, lb.	0·45	0·45
Steam decomposed, per cent.	87	76
Air per lb. dry coal, cu. ft.	37·0	37·5
Gas per ton dry coal, cu. ft.	138,250	135,000
Gas calorific value, B.Th.U.	186	179
Efficiency, including blower, per cent.	77·8	72·5

The analyses of the gases were :

	CO$_2$.	CO.	H$_2$.	CH$_4$.	N$_2$.	Sp. gr. (air = 1).
7 ft.	5·2	27·3	16·6	3·4	47·5	1·30
3·5 ft.	5·1	27·3	15·5	3·0	49·1	1·32

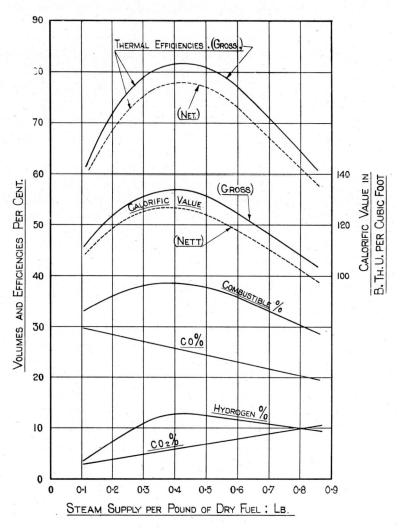

Fig. 96.—Effect of Steaming on Gas Producer Performance.

The addition of too much steam is an obvious disadvantage in its effects on the temperature of the bed and in its influence on the water-gas equilibrium. The effects are best shown graphically as in Figure 96 and can be summarized as follows in respect of the effect of increase of steam in the gasification of coke fuel.

(i) The percentage of CO_2 in the gas increases steadily while that of CO decreases steadily.

(ii) The percentage of hydrogen increases to an optimum at 0·4 lb. water per lb. of fuel, and then decreases.

(iii) The calorific value and thermal efficiency curves show similar optimum points.

Up to the point of optimum hydrogen production the water vapour supplied is completely decomposed, the saturation temperature being 52° C. At higher saturation temperatures the percentage conversion gradually falls off due to decrease of fuel temperature although the weight decomposed increases.

Under theoretical conditions of no loss of heat by radiation, etc., the optimum figure for steam would rise to 0·64 lb. per lb. of carbon gasified as against 0·5 in the above experiment. Similarly, the thermal efficiency would rise from the 78·6 per cent. shown to 95·2 per cent.

Formerly the operation of the gas producer was favoured for the production of by-product ammonia, but with the growth of synthetic ammonia this is no longer of interest. If the producer is operated at a slow rate and the proportion of steam is raised beyond the optimum for thermal efficiency, say, to a saturation temperature of 80° C., as much as 60 per cent. of the nitrogen of the coal can be recovered as ammonia ; this is equivalent to 144 lb. $(NH_4)_2SO_4$ per ton of a coal containing 1·5 per cent. of nitrogen.

The Manufacture of Producer Gas

The building of the first producer is credited to Bischof (Magdeburg) ; this was a simple brick chamber in which air was drawn through coke fed from above. In 1857 the Siemens brothers in Germany evolved the step-grate producer for regenerative furnace work, with water in the ash-pit and blown air. This led to steam/air injection and to the work of Dowson (1880) on steam/air blast and the purification of the gas for use in the gas engine. Dowson also introduced a double-draught principle with the off-take half-way down the fuel bed so that the products of distillation at the top of the bed would be drawn through a hot portion of the bed and the tar vapours from coal more efficiently cracked. The Mond producer for ammonia recovery was introduced about 1883 ; in 1901 the Power Gas Co. was formed to exploit this form for gas production for power purposes coupled with the production of ammonia. The advent of synthetic ammonia and developments in steam engineering soon arrested this development, but the demand for gas producers was maintained in other fields mainly for furnace heating. To-day they conform to two main types, viz. " independent ", from which the gas may be cooled and cleaned for distribution, and " built-in ", where the producer is an integral part of the furnace setting and the gas is passed hot to the combustion chambers or furnace. Of the first type, the static form with hand-operation was formerly the most common, but this is being largely replaced by the mechanical producer which embodies automatic charging and levelling of the fuel bed, rotating grates and automatic ash discharge. This type also has devices for the stirring of the top of the fuel bed when dealing with caking coal so that the formation of masses of coke can be prevented.

During the 1939–45 war small producers were developed for the driving of motor vehicles by producer gas (Chapter III) and for the supply of fuel in war-damaged factories. The latter had a rated output of 5 therms per hour at 125 B.Th.U. per cu. ft. and embodied an air-preheater and a washer-cooler for the gas.

An estimate of the amount of fuel now burned in gas producers is not easy to obtain, but the coal consumption must be of the order of 7 million tons of coal per annum ; in the gas industry alone over 4 million tons of coke are consumed for retort heating.

Fuels for Gas Producers. Since the flow of gas through a bed of fuel is an important factor in the process it is apparent that the type of fuel most suited is that which does not coke or cohere and which allows free passage of the gases. Such fuels are anthracite and coke. The design of the auxiliary plant will be least complicated the purer the gas as it leaves the producer ; the simplest form then will be for plant utilizing anthracite or coke. The advantage of being able to work with bituminous coals of lower cost is obvious, but their use entails greater complication in design, higher first cost and working expenses, where the gas has to be used in engines. The tar vapours may be advantageous in metallurgical operations, by reason of their adding to the calorific value of the gas. In this case the gas passes as directly as possible from the producer to the furnace, and its sensible heat also is utilized. In general, bituminous fuels are best treated in pressure plant, although several forms of suction plant work successfully on certain types of bituminous fuel.

The variety of fuels which have met with successful application in gas-producer practice covers pretty well all carbonaceous materials, ranging from anthracite to colliery refuse containing over 50 per cent. of ash, quite useless for fuel in any other way ; it includes lignites, peat, wood waste, spent tan, coco-nut shells, etc.

In the case of coal the chief limiting factor is caking power since caking coals tend to form crusts which crack and form channels through which the air and steam pass too readily : coals of medium to high caking power can be gasified only in mechanical producers with stirring devices (see p. 419).

The ratio of hydrogen to oxygen in producer coals should normally be less than 0·55. Since high-volatile coals are often non-caking the maximum enrichment of the gas is conveniently obtained by using non-caking coals of 35–40 per cent. volatile matter. Non-caking or weakly caking coals are, however, equally convenient as regards the operation of the producer.

Producer fuels are, therefore, preferentially sized weakly-caking coal or carbonized fuel (coke). The coal may be anthracite or carbonaceous coal of low-volatile matter, but the most common type is high-volatile bituminous coal of types 800 and 900 with caking power represented by the Gray-King index of C–E.

Producer coal should preferably be carefully sized and in particular should contain the minimum of dust. The preferred size grading varies with producer size.

Lb. per hour.	Therms gas per hour.	Size, in. anthracite.	Size, in. carb. fuels.
45	5	$1\frac{1}{2}-\frac{3}{4}$	$1\frac{1}{4}-\frac{1}{2}$
170–850	20–100	$2-\frac{3}{4}$	$2-\frac{3}{4}$
Over 850	over 100	$2-1\frac{1}{4}$	$2-1$

It may be taken that actual size is less important than close grading. A good producer fuel should not cover a wide range of size since this causes inequalities of draught. Owing to their cheapness, non-caking slacks are very frequently used in producer practice although the presence of the fines leads to lower efficiency.

The ash of producer coals should be non-fusible at the working temperature. In the best class of coal a fusion temperature of over 1400° C. ensures absence of clinkering and a high gas output. Too high a moisture content is also unsatisfactory in that this moisture has to be evaporated in the top of the producer, causing a high sensible heat loss, and also in that the steam causes oxidation of the carbon monoxide of the gas with a consequent loss of calorific value and potential heat.

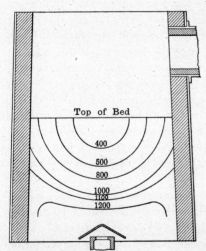

Fig. 97.—Diagram of Temperature Distribution in a Gas Producer.

General Considerations. On theoretical grounds it has been shown that a temperature of about 1000° C. is requisite for the production of gas with low carbon dioxide content. The temperature attainable in practice is limited by the durability of the lining of the producer, but more especially by the liability to form clinker from the ash of the fuel. Also, unless the gas is to be used hot, too high a working temperature may lead to too high a loss of sensible heat in the gases, and a low thermal efficiency.

The distribution of temperature is probably of the type shown in Figure 97, with a maximum of 1300° C. near the tuyères. In this diagram it will be seen that the temperature towards the centre was much lower at a given height than at the sides, and this can be improved by a better design of tuyère. Proper distribution of the blast through the fuel is an important requirement.

The controlling factor with regard to maximum temperature is the steam/air ratio and the final choice of working conditions is obviously a compromise between this, the type of fuel, and the fusibility of the ash. The actual percentage of ash is not important, particularly in producers with a mechanical grate, if the fusion temperature is not low ; colliery wastes up to 50 per cent. ash content can be successfully gasified. Producers for high-ash fuels usually are constructed to work under a higher blast pressure than ordinarily ; in many the water-sealed bottom is replaced by a closed-in bottom, and special mechanical arrangements provided for removal of the ash and clinker.

The rate of gasification is one of the most important factors in producer practice ; for a given consumption it determines the number to be installed. There comes an " ash-fusion " limit to the rate by reason of the very high temperature attained at high blast pressure. The usual rates of gasification vary between 10 and 30 lb. per sq. ft. per hour. In slagging producers, where steam is not used and the ash is removed in a molten state, the rate may be as high as 100 lb. ; in a powdered-fuel slagging producer a rate as high as 160 lb. has been reported.

Ratio of Air to Steam. The graphs shown in Figure 96 show that the calorific value of producer gas reaches an optimum when the air supply contains about 0·4 lb., of steam per lb. of fuel. Since undecomposed steam is an undesirable diluent in producer gas and reduces efficiency both in production and combustion it is normally desirable to inject rather less steam than this, say 0·35 lb. It might, however, be desirable to increase the steam ratio to 0·6 lb. if the ash of the fuel tends to clinker and continuous operation cannot be maintained.

In pressure plants air may be injected by a steam jet but, in large plant, always by fan when the saturation temperature with steam is controlled.

It may be calculated that, with conditions of air and steam supply properly balanced for thermal equilibrium with the production of carbon monoxide and hydrogen only, each pound of carbon gasified requires 42 cu. ft. of air and 0·64 lb. steam, calculating the steam as water. If the steam is supplied as such the air requirement is less, 29 cu. ft. and 0·75 lb. steam. In actual practice heat is lost in other ways than by the endothermicity of the steam-carbon reaction and the practical figure of 0·4 lb. of steam per lb. of fuel (see above) is approached. The proportion of steam to air is calculable from the saturation temperature. The curves given in Figure 98 show the weight of 1 cu. ft. of air at different temperatures, and the weight of steam 1 lb. of air can carry at saturation at various temperatures. The steam should be dry and superheating is clearly an advantage. Since this can be arranged by utilizing sensible heat in the gases produced, this heat is conserved. In many producers further superheating of the air-steam mixture is done by passing it through an annular space around the lower part of the producer. The cooling effect here is advantageous in checking the formation of clinker and reducing radiation losses.

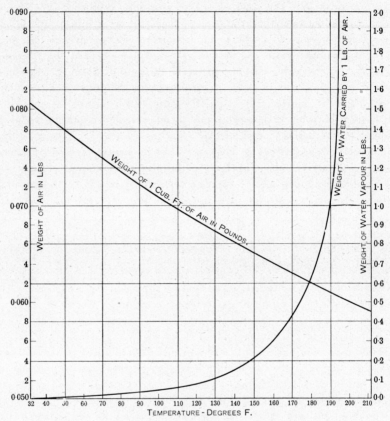

FIG. 98.—Diagram showing Weight of 1 Cubic Foot of Air at Different Temperatures and Steam Saturation of Air.

Rate of Gasification. A producer must be capable of giving a high rate of gasification with good gas quality. The ratio of depth of the incandescent zone to that of the whole fuel bed really determines the upper limit of rate since too shallow a bed could all become incandescent and the gas would be high in CO_2 content. Too deep a bed does effect better preheat of the fuel but offers unnecessary resistance to the flow of gas. The compromise is the highest rate possible with top temperatures not above 400° C., and this requires separate assessment for each fuel; bituminous coal requires 20 per cent. greater depth than carbonized fuels.

The Efficiency of the Gas Producer. The measurement of the efficiency of a gas producer presents some difficulty since it is not always possible to measure the volume of the gas directly, particularly in the case of hot-gas plants, where the producer is directly connected to the furnace and there is no length of main in which to establish uniform rate of flow. The standard method of overcoming this is to prepare a carbon balance from the composition of the gas, and this requires the greatest care in obtaining a representative sample and analysing it accurately. The weight of carbon in the gas is preferably obtained directly by passing a measured volume over copper oxide at 900° C. and absorbing the CO_2 formed in potash solution and weighing it. Calculation from analysis is made from the fact that one lb.-mol. (12 lb.) of monatomic carbon gases occupies a volume at N.T.P. of 359 cu. ft.

The volume of carbon gases V_C per cu. ft. is 1/100 of the sum of the percentages of CO_2, CO, nC_nH_m, and CH_4. The volume of gas made is, therefore, $359C/12V_C$ cu. ft. at N.T.P., where C is the total carbon gasified in lb.

The total carbon gasified is the weight of carbon in the dry fuel as obtained by analysis, less the carbon in the dust, tar, ashes and clinker, all of which must be measured directly. The thermal balance is then computed in the usual way by balancing the total heat in the fuel, steam and air against the potential and sensible heat of the products and any water overflow. The difference represents the heat lost by radiation and convection, unaccountable losses and errors. The thermal efficiency on the basis of cold gas is the potential heat in the gas divided by the heat input. In obtaining the hot-gas efficiency, where the gas is utilized hot, it is necessary to include on the credit side the sensible heat of the gases at the point of utilization (about 540° C.), calculating this from the total volume, temperature and specific heat. Cold and hot gas efficiencies are normally of the order of 80 and 90 per cent. respectively.

Composition of Producer Gases. The composition and properties of gases made under normal conditions from anthracite, carbonized fuels and bituminous coal are given in Table LXIII overleaf.

The appreciably higher calorific value of gas from coal can be important when the gas is used cold.

Suction Producers for Furnace Heating. The simplest form of producer is that used for the heating of furnaces ; the air is drawn through by chimney pull and the steam is either supplied direct as low-pressure steam or obtained by the evaporation of water sprayed on to the hot fuel at the grate. Owing to the low pressure of the draught such producers have a relatively large grate area and are built into the brickwork of the furnace in order to reduce the loss of heat by radiation, etc., and to supply the gas as hot as possible to the combustion flues or chamber.

Figure 99 illustrates such a producer diagrammatically ; a further example is seen in the gas retort setting of Figure 45. The fuel is fed into a vertical shaft A and the bed is supported partly on the step grate B

TABLE LXIII

COMPOSITION AND PROPERTIES OF PRODUCER GAS

	Carbonized fuels.	Anthracite.	Coal of type 900.
Carbon dioxide	4–6	4–6	3 5
Unsaturated hydrocarbons, C_xH_y . .	—	0·4	0·4
Oxygen	0·4	0·4	0·2
Carbon monoxide	28–30	25–27	28–30
Hydrogen	10–12	14–18	11–13
Methane	0·4–0·6	1·2–1·5	2·5
Nitrogen	53–56	51–55	51–53
*Hydrogen sulphide	50	50	50
*Organic S compounds	20	20	20
Specific gravity	0·9	0·9	0·87
Calorific value, B.Th.U.	135	150	165
†Cu. ft. per ton dry fuel	163,000	170,000	160,000
Therms ,, ,, ,, ...	220	255	264
Air for combustion, v/v	1·00	1·20	1·28
CO_2 in waste gases, per cent. . . .	20·5	18·6	19·2

* Grains per 100 cu. ft.   † 8% ash.

and partly on the bottom brickwork. The firebars of the grate are flat castings about 9 in. wide ; they are spaced about 7 in. apart and generally slope inwards at a small angle (8°). The pull of the chimney, acting through

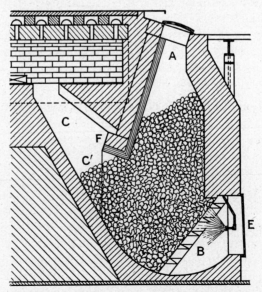

Fig. 99.—Diagram of a Step-grate Gas Producer.

the flue C, draws air through the spaces between the firebars so that the oxidation zone lies between B and C, BC′ being the fuel bed proper and about 4 ft. to 4 ft. 6 in. in thickness. Steam is supplied by projecting a fine spray of water against the grate, from a nozzle placed in a suitable position. The chamber below the grate is normally closed by a door E with air ports in it in order to keep up a reasonable temperature for the vaporization of the water spray, and is opened only when it is necessary to rake out ashes from below the grate. The bottoms of such producers are normally wet owing to the collecting of water which is not evaporated. The work done by a producer of this type is limited by the pull of the chimney ; where this is more than adequate the air supply is limited by moving the louvres in the door. A most important precaution which must be observed is that the level of the fuel bed must not approach the arch F or, when the upper door is opened for charging, air may be drawn into the hot gas flue when an explosion could result.

A producer of the size shown in Figure 99, i.e. shaft 4 ft. × 4 ft., grate area 14 sq. ft. and fuel bed of 4 ft., will gasify coke at the rate of 2 cwt. per hour with a chimney pull of one-fifth of an inch of water. This is equivalent to a rate of gasification of 16 lb. of coke per sq. ft. of grate area per hour.

The control of a producer of this type is simple, the air supply being checked by analysis of the gas and the rate of feed of water to the vaporizing nozzle being controlled in terms of the weight of fuel gasified. The output of the producer is, of course, controlled by the suction or pull of the chimney. In the example above about half of the pull is required to induce the secondary air for combustion so that the pressure difference in the producer is only $\frac{1}{10}$th in. Increase of this pressure difference will, of course, increase output. A producer of this type can be operated as a pressure producer by closing the outer door and supplying the air-stream blast under pressure.

Since the hot producer gas passes directly to the heating flues and the generator may be fed with hot fuel the efficiency of gas production can be very high—over 90 per cent.

An independent producer of suction type for the delivery of clean gas can be exemplified by the Gibbons-Heurtey plant shown in diagram in Figure 100. The generator is steel cased and the lower half forms a steam-jacket boiler. The mechanical grate rotates in a water seal. The saturation of the air-blast is controlled thermostatically and the blast is distributed through the conical grate. The gas is cleaned in a washer-cooler, a plate cooler and a dry filter. The plant is made in capacities up to 200 therms of gas per hour.

Pressure Producers. There are many forms of gas producer in which the air and steam are supplied under pressure, but most of these are variations of only a few types. It will be sufficient to describe in detail one or two typical producers of modern design. Proprietary producers will generally conform to one of these types.

Pressure producers are used principally for the production of gas for furnace heating and are therefore built in close proximity to the furnace so that the sensible heat of the hot gases can be utilized in the furnace.

F.—P

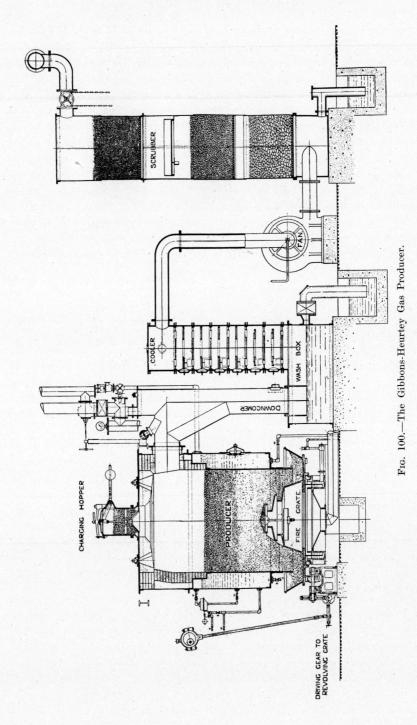

Fig. 100.—The Gibbons-Heurtey Gas Producer.

In addition the tar vapours are allowed to remain in the gas and enhance its calorific value. It is estimated that the increase due to tar vapour may be 15–20 B.Th.U. per cu. ft. Cleaning of the gas is, therefore, not normally attempted although in special cases dust filters (e.g. sand towers) are used which can be maintained at a high temperature.

In pressure producers the pressure is produced either by steam injectors or by steam-driven turbo-blowers. The latter are to be preferred in that they are positive in their action and are susceptible of easy control to meet the requirements of varying load. An injector system is not satisfactory in that the amount of air injected cannot be altered without also changing the air-stream ratio, which is undesirable. Load variations can only be met by altering the steam nozzles, an inconvenience in normal working.

Morgan Producer. The Morgan producer may be taken as an example of the common type of mechanical producer giving a high rate of output of hot raw gas which is used as an adjunct to furnace operations in metallurgical work generally. A producer of 11 ft. diameter will gasify 3 tons of coal per hour. Producers of this type which burn coal, frequently have stirring arms or mechanical pokers and levelling devices with which the surface of the coal is agitated to avoid caking and channelling.

The poker may take the form of a water-cooled oscillating finger (Wellman), water-cooled stirring arms (Wood), rakes with water-cooled prongs (Chapman) or some similar device for controlling the caking of the coal near the surface of the bed. A diagrammatic view of the producer is shown in Figure 101. The body of the producer and the ash pan rotate round a central pillar carrying blast inlets and a spiral scraper bar which pushes the ash towards the outside where it is removed by an intermittently operated plough. The blast inlets are from three hollow radial arms and also from a hollow ring or mantle running round the producer. This arrangement ensures even distribution of the blast over the whole fuel bed. The producer body, 8 ft. high by about 11 ft. diameter, is brick-lined with a water jacket to cool the brickwork sufficiently to prevent slagging with the coal ash. The water jacket accommodates the seal plates of the cover and top casting. The coal is fed continuously by an automatic feed operated by the rotation of the producer. It is claimed that this producer will gasify 3 tons of coal per hour at about 85 lb. per sq. ft. of grate area per hour.

In steel-works producers the emphasis is now on automatic control of the coal feed by a combination of blast-steam pressure and gas-offtake temperature. Variation of the pressure of steam at the jet blower is made to operate a coal-load instrument. The temperature control is also linked with the load instrument in such a manner that the two effects are additive.

Power Gas Producers. Large-scale producers of a rather different type are made by the Power Gas Corporation for either hot gas or clean, cold gas. The arrangement of the latter is shown in Figure 102, as designed for the treatment of bituminous coal.   The coal is fed by gravity and ash removal is by a rotating grate.   The fuel bed in this type is rather deeper than usual to give a tar of sufficient fluidity.   The hot gas contains 1000

Fig. 101.—Morgan Gas Producer.

grains of tar and dust per 100 cu. ft. and is cleaned in six stages of water-washing, dry filtration, and oxide purification from hydrogen sulphide.

The hot-gas producer is similar, in the design and operation of the producer itself, but the treatment of the gas differs.   The hot gas leaving the generator passes through a vortex-type dust extractor before passing

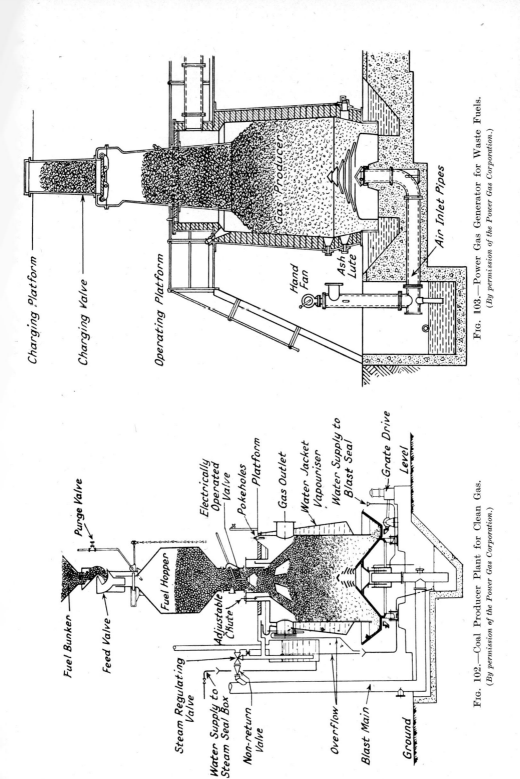

Charging Platform

Charging Valve

Operating Platform

Gas Producer

Hand Fan

Ash Lute

Air Inlet Pipes

FIG. 103.—Power Gas Generator for Waste Fuels.
(By permission of the Power Gas Corporation.)

Purge Valve

Fuel Bunker

Feed Valve

Fuel Hopper

Electrically Operated Valve

Pokeholes

Platform

Gas Outlet

Water Jacket Vapouriser

Water Supply to Blast Seal

Grate Drive

Level

Steam Regulating Valve

Water Supply to Steam Seal Box

Non-return Valve

Adjustable Chute

Overflow

Blast Main

Ground

FIG. 102.—Coal Producer Plant for Clean Gas.
(By permission of the Power Gas Corporation.)

to the furnace. The extractor and the pipe-lines are lined with refractory bricks to avoid undue loss of temperature.

These plants may be built in very large size up to 550 therms of gas per hour from a generator of 12 ft. diameter. A 2 ft. 6 in. diameter generator will deliver about 10 therms of gas per hour.

Waste-fuel Producers. Plants of the Power Gas type with gravity feed can be used for the conversion of waste vegetable matter to gas with suitable modification of the gravity feed arrangements to suit the form of the fuel as indicated in Figure 103.

The G.I. Predistillation Producer. In the usual gas producer consuming coal the tar is only partly cracked and causes difficulty in gas cleaning or by the deposition of soot and pitch in hot-gas applications. The Gas Integral two-stage process overcomes this by the use of a pre-distillation zone. Gas from this zone, Figure 104, leaves by the top offtake.

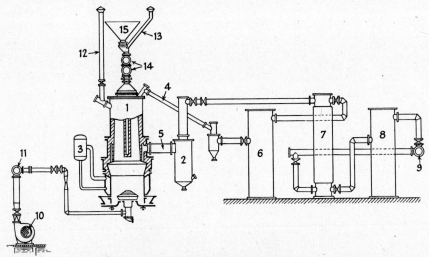

Fig. 104.—The Gas Integral Predistillation Gas Producer.
(*By permission of the International Furnace Equipment Co.*)

1, Producer; 2, Wash column; 3, Steam collector; 4, Distillation gas main; 5, Clean gas main; 6, Electrostatic tar filter; 7, Gas cooler; 8, Electrostatic oil filter; 9, Distribution gas main; 10, Air blower; 11, Air blast main; 12, Producer chimney; 13, Feeder venting chimney; 14, Automatic feeder; 15, Bunker.

Producer gas is made in the lower zone and part of this passes through the distillation zone to provide the sensible heat necessary. The top-offtake temperature is about 130° C. so that the tar vapours are not overheated as in the normal producer where they are at about 500° C. The gas from the top is treated separately by electrostatic precipitation and the tar-free gas from the middle offtake is washed in the usual manner. The process has advantages for the production of either hot or cold gas which overcome higher initial cost. Efficiencies are claimed of 74 to 76 on cold gas and 87 to 90 per cent. on hot gas containing tar vapour.

The use of electrostatic precipitation as a means of cleaning producer gas is tending to increase in other plants also.

Slagging-ash Producers. In order to overcome the difficulties of dealing with fuels which give trouble through clinker formation several types of producer have been evolved in which the temperature of operation is raised to such a height that the ash melts and the molten material can conveniently be tapped from below the grate. In such producers the high temperature is reached by blowing with air only and very high rates of gasification are achieved. The tuyères are water-cooled and the brickwork in their neighbourhood is cooled, by having a water pipe embedded in it, in order to prevent fluxing with the ash. Steam may be introduced above the fluxing zone.

The proposal to operate under slagging conditions is far from new ; the Ebelman producer of 1841 is reported to have been quite successful and the Würth producer of 1913 became quite common for a time. The latter used air preheated to 250° C. and steam was injected through separate tuyères. Later Rambush raised the preheat temperature to 600° C. and produced a slag suitable for the manufacture of slag wool, etc. Despite this early start it is considered that the slagging producer is only at the beginning of its development and that this will take place through the use of oxygen or oxygen-enriched air. Since this would involve operation on a large scale it is also likely that it will be applied more to synthesis gas than to fuel gas. Slagging producers for the production of synthesis gas have been in use in Germany (Leuna) for many years.

The modern slagging producer operates with a deep fuel bed and a high gasification rate of 500 lb. per sq. ft. of grate area which gives a high output in a plant of relatively small size. The B.S.A.F. plant at Ludwigshafen can produce as much as two million cu. ft. of gas per hour. This high load has meant the provision of closely-graded fuel free from fines.

Obstacles to the development of this type of producer have been the relatively low thermal efficiency when making cold gas and the operational difficulty associated with damage to brickwork linings and hearth by the action of the slag and the need to control the temperature of the latter within narrow limits. Control of the temperature of fusion has been achieved by the addition to the fuel of limestone, blast-furnace slag or even iron ore. A new proposal is the gasification of finely-divided brown coal by projection on to the surface of the molten slag by air preheated to 900° C.

The Use of Oxygen in Producer Practice. Attempts have been made to reduce the normal high nitrogen content of producer gas by enriching the air supply with oxygen. Until sufficiently-cheap oxygen becomes available industrially the attempts have only theoretical interest so far as gas for furnace heating is concerned ; to-day its use is limited to the production of synthesis gas. It may be calculated that the use of oxygen can lead theoretically to the production of a gas of 383 B.Th.U. containing 28 per cent. H_2 and 58 per cent. CO. An oxygen producer could be operated either as a slagging producer or as a continuous water-gas plant. The proposal would seem to hold most promise as a process in which the blast is enriched with oxygen, steam being added to keep the temperature under control. By this means the output in terms of cubic feet of gas per square foot of grate area would be considerably increased and the calorific value of the gas would be higher. It can be shown that the following increases of calorific value are possible :

O_2 in air.	H_2 per cent.	CO per cent.	CO_2 per cent.	B.Th.U. per cu. ft.	
				Coke.	Coal.
21	7	30	5–7	118	155
40	14	39	5–7	170	250
60	19	57	5–7	245	320
80	22	63	5–7	270	340

If commercial oxygen should become available at a sufficiently low cost it would seem that development would take place by the use of slagging-ash producers since the temperature in the oxidation zone will certainly be high.

The Power Gas Corporation has erected several plants of this type in Japan to produce gas of 180 B.Th.U. using air enriched to 40–60 per cent. oxygen. The important consideration in successful operation is the intimate mixing of the blast and the steam.

The processes of complete gasification which use oxygen are described in Chapter XVII.

Utilization of Coke Breeze. The difficulties of dealing with slacks or fuels of small size have been referred to. Coke breeze is still best dealt with by burning under boilers on specially-designed mechanical stokers and with a low furnace arch. It can, however, be gasified in standard gas producers provided these are fitted with charging devices to prevent segregation of sizes which would lead to uneven distribution of the blast. The limiting size is probably 50 per cent. passing a $\frac{1}{4}$-in. square-mesh sieve, but the rate of gasification may be only one-fifth to one-tenth of that possible with graded coke of the right size. Also, a high blast-saturation temperature may be necessary to avoid undue formation of clinker and this, with the normal low reactivity of breeze carbon, leads to high losses of carbon in the clinker and ashes. The thermal efficiency is therefore not higher than 65–70 per cent., but the low monetary cost of breeze may justify its use in circumstances where the producer capacity is large enough to accommodate the lower output per square foot of grate area.

Another solution to the use of breeze consists in the application of up-and-down running after the fashion of the water-gas generator. In Fuel Research Station experiments alternate 10-minute up-and-down runs were found to be satisfactory for gas-retort breeze (on $\frac{1}{2}$ in. 24, $\frac{1}{2}$–$\frac{1}{4}$ in. 22 ; $\frac{1}{4}$–$\frac{1}{8}$ in. 24 ; $\frac{1}{8}$–0 in. 30 per cent.). The fuel bed was 4 ft. thick, charging was necessary every two and a half hours and clinkering every twenty-four hours. With fine fuels a thin fuel bed is best since the pressure drop across the bed should not be more than 9 in. (water gauge).

The following are data from the gasification of breeze containing 7·8 per cent. moisture and 11·9 per cent. ash and using 0·77 lb. steam per lb. of breeze.

Coke charged per hour	254 lb.
Consumed per sq. ft. grate area per hour . .	16·0 lb.
Gas made per ton	145,960 cu. ft.
	160·6 therms
Efficiency	62·4 per cent.
Gas calorific value	110 B.Th.U.
C lost in clinker and ash	5 per cent. of coke charged

The analysis of the gas was CO_2, 10 ; CO, 21 ; H_2, 13·0 ; N_2, 56·0 per cent.

The output of gas per square foot of grate area was certainly low, but the amount of unburnt material in the ashes was not high at 5 per cent.

Producer-gas Burners. When producer gas is burned hot, or when it is introduced into a hot combustion chamber, the arrangements are of the simplest in that the gas enters through a port in the brickwork and the air for combustion through an adjacent port. Where cold, clean producer gas is used, however, too high a gas velocity will tend to blow the flame from the port and extinguish it. This can be avoided and a wider range of gas velocity used by imparting a swirl to either gas or air. Theoretically the swirl should be given to the component of greatest volume but, since the air/gas ratio for producer gas is about unity and the air is often under pressure, the swirl is usually given to the air. The Basequip K burner (Wellman, Smith Owen) is designed to give air swirl but also to burn rich gas with a shorter flame. The air enters the gas stream through tangential small holes as shown in Figure 105 to achieve the necessary swirl. The burner will operate down to a gas pressure of $\frac{1}{4}$ in. w.g. and an air pressure of 6 in. w.g., and will stand preheat up to over 300° C. ; capacity ranges from 64 cu. ft. on town gas to one million cu. ft. per hour on blast-furnace gas but, for any one size, decreases in thermal output with increase of calorific value from 100 with blast-furnace gas to 90 with producer gas and 78 with town gas. The tangential velocity of the air entering the gas is about 20 ft. per sec. Using clean producer gas the diameter of the orifice of the burner increases from 1·5 in. at 250 cu. ft. per hour to 31·5 in. at 200,000 cu. ft.   A special type with a tar drainpipe will deal with dirty gas.

The Eddy-Ray burner is a second example as shown in Figure 106 (Thermic Equipment and Engineering Co.).   The air swirl ensures rapid

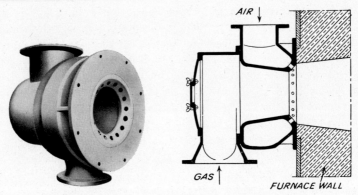

Fig. 105.—The Basequip K Burner for Producer Gas.
(*Wellman, Smith Owen Eng. Corporation*)

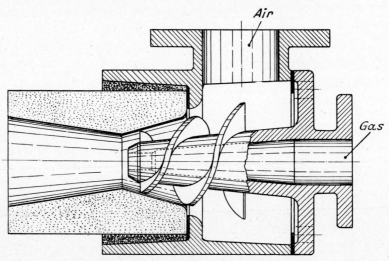

Fig. 106.—The Eddy-Ray Burner for Producer Gas.
(*Thermic Equipment and Eng. Co.*)

mixing and the flame is almost entirely confined to the burner block.   The maximum air pressure required is 8 in. w.g. and a temperature of 1500° C. can be attained, or 1750° C. with coal gas.   The burners are made in standard sizes from 1200 to 10,000 cu. ft. of clean producer gas per hour. The angle of entry of the air to the flame is about 60° to the direction of flow of the gas.

Blast-furnace Gas

In the manufacture of pig-iron in the blast-furnace the low-grade gas which is liberated forms a fuel of considerable importance in the iron and steel and associated industries. The quantity of heat energy represented is considerable ; some 200,000 cu. ft. of gas at 90–105 B.Th.U. per cu. ft. are liberated per ton of pig-iron. In addition, the gas leaves the furnace at a temperature of 250–450° F. and this sensible heat can be utilized.

An average analysis of gas is CO_2 11, CO 27, H_2 2, and N_2 60 per cent., but composition is not so important as the fact that it is available in quantity to the steel industries.

At one time coal was used for the smelting of iron ores but now this is wholly done by coke. In 1920 some 2 million tons of coal were used, but now the consumption consists of 11 million tons of coke. The consumption of coke per ton of pig-iron varies in different districts from 19 to 24 cwt. with an average of 21·4 cwt. The variation is due to variations of type of furnace, nature of ore, and quality of coke.

Average figures for 1952 are given in Table LXIV for coke consumption and pig-iron and gas production, which are taken from the Statistics of the British Iron and Steel Federation. This indicates that the total quantity of gas is about 220×10^7 therms per annum or the equivalent of the coal gas made from 28×10^6 tons of coal in the gas industry.

Utilization of Blast-furnace Gas. About 60 per cent. of the heat of the coke used in the furnace is returned in the gas. In a modern plant, equipped with modern stoves (for preheating the air blast) and blowing engines, about 40 per cent. of this heat is used to meet the heat and power requirements of the blast furnace itself ; 20–25 per cent. being required for heating the stoves, 15–20 per cent. to produce the power required for the blowing engines, and the auxiliary plant. The remainder would be available for heat and power production for the steel-works or plant other than blast-furnaces. In a descending order of importance these are blast-furnace stoves, heating of coke-ovens, soaking pits, general furnaces, and boiler plant. The hot blast reduces fuel consumption and increases output. The stoves are regenerative and 90 per cent. of the heat of the gas used is returned to the blast-furnace.

The use of blast-furnace gas for the firing of coke ovens has already been dealt with in Chapter IX ; it effects a considerable increase of coal gas available for sale. The gas can also be used for the production of power by gas engines or indirectly through steam, for the size of unit likely to be used the gas engine has the higher efficiency. This may not be true when the size of a steam turbine unit reaches 12,000 kW., but normally the gas engine is more applicable to the ordinary uses of running blowers and other small plant.

Despite its lower calorific value the gas is now gradually replacing

TABLE LXIV *

PRODUCTION OF PIG-IRON (including Blast-furnace Ferro-alloys), BLAST-FURNACE GAS AND COKE CONSUMPTION IN GREAT BRITAIN (1952)

Districts.	Pig-iron produced (1000 tons).	Total coke consumption		Blast-furnace gas.
		(1000 tons).	(cwt./ton pig-iron).	
1. Derby., Leics., Notts., Northants., and Essex	2,261·8 mainly foundry and basic	2,432·3	21·5	*Yield per ton of pig-iron:* 150,000–200,000 cu. ft. or 185 therms.
2. Lancs. (other than 10), Denbigh, Flint. and Cheshire	471·9 basic	578·6	24·5	*Calorific value:* 100–112 B.Th.U. per cu. ft.
3. and 9. Yorks. (including Sheffield) other than 5	}			*Average composition:*
4. Lincolnshire	1,505·4 basic	1,842·3	24·4	CO_2 10
5. North-east coast	2,600·8 basic mainly: haematite	2,671·9	20·5	CO 29
6. Scotland	886·3 basic	854·8	19·1	CH_4 1
7. Staffs., Salop, Worcs., and Warwicks.	523·1 basic mainly and foundry	544·4*	20·8	H_2 2
8. South Wales and Monmouth	1,545·1 basic	1,658·1	21·4	N_2 58
10. North-west coast	933·3 haematite	896·1	19·2	
	10,727·7	11,478·9	Average 21·4	

* Includes the coke equivalent of 1,800 tons of coal.

producer gas for soaking pits, preheating furnaces, and, with enrichment, open-hearth furnaces.

Metallurgical Furnaces. In this case the high temperature necessary means that a regenerative system must be used for both gas and air. When this is still not enough, as in the open-hearth process where 1800° C. is required, it is customary to enrich to 240 B.Th.U. by the addition of coke-oven gas. This system has the great advantage that the calorific value of the mixed gas can be adjusted from time to time to suit conditions of furnace operation, e.g. a richer mixture can be used for fast melting down of the scrap. In some cases, tar or liquid fuel is also added in order to give a reducing character to the flame.

For re-heating purposes, however, where temperatures do not exceed 1200° to 1300° C. air and gas regeneration are sufficient.

Heating costs are, as a rule, considerably lower than with alternative fuels. The limitations of metallurgical furnace practice such as the charging and withdrawal of stock, high radiation and external cooling loss, together with high temperatures of the exit gas, make it impossible to attain the high heat-transfer efficiencies that are possible in boiler practice, but even then blast-furnace gas is cheaper than alternative fuels, and with efficient combustion control and operation of the furnace at capacity, good results can be obtained.

In order to utilize the gas to maximum efficiency, it is important that the pressure of the gas should be uniform, that combustion control should be efficient, that the gas should be clean, and that the amount used for each purpose should be carefully measured. Since the blast-furnace operates under rather varying conditions, some method of control of pressure must be adopted. The most effective method is the use of a gasholder, which serves both for storage and distribution. Since the volume of gas produced is very large, storage is possible only with the gas produced during short periods, so that the gasholder acts more as a governor than as a storage vessel.

Failing a gasholder, which is necessarily expensive, many works have adopted a system of automatic pressure control, so that gas is delivered to the various units at a predetermined pressure. If the supply of gas fails, the least important units are cut off automatically, so as to allow the pressure to other units to be maintained ; suitable methods of signalling are adopted to warn the operators of the plants affected.

With gas available at constant pressure, the correct proportioning of gas and air to a consuming unit becomes a comparatively easy matter. This is particularly the case where suitable burners are used, and in a number of burner designs now available theoretical proportioning of gas and air produces a high combustion efficiency. Such burners are particularly useful in boiler and stove practice, where high heat-transfer efficiency can be obtained.

In metallurgical furnaces, where regenerators are used, there are limitations of furnace design and practice which do not allow in all cases of suitable

burners being used.   In such cases the correct proportioning of gas and air
is obtained by suitable port and furnace design, and by chemical control.

There are numerous commercial gas burners available, all with their
own particular assembly detail, but in general they consist of a central gas
port surrounded by a concentric pipe which admits the combustion air
through an annular space.   The combustion air meets the gas stream at or
near the burner nozzle and is frequently given an angular velocity, or
" swirl ", which has some influence on the mixing rate of gas and air, but
primarily stabilizes the flame by causing a recirculation of hot gas to the
burner nozzle.   Without swirl, it is relatively easy to blow a flame off the
burner with a high air velocity.   In some types of burner, the air enters
the central pipe and the gas is admitted through the annulus.

Apart from customary chemical methods to control the composition of
the exit gases, measurement is probably the most effective method of
assessing the control of gas supply to ensure efficiency in use.   Before the
days of efficient gas cleaning, the measurement of volume was a difficult
matter.   These difficulties have now been overcome by cleaning the gas,
and measuring is almost universally carried out in composite works where
the blast-furnace gas is required as a fuel.   Figs. 105 and 106 illustrate
suitable burners.

The gas leaving the blast-furnace has a high dust content, the proportion
of which varies with the operation of the furnace.   Most of the dust is
deposited in flues and dust-catchers ; but further cleaning is necessary if
the gas is to be used efficiently, the final degree of cleanliness being 0·2
grain/cu. ft. for stoves, boilers, or metallurgical furnaces ; and about 0·005
(or less) grain/cu. ft. for gas engines.   The modern trend is in the direction
of complete cleaning of the whole of the gas and both wet and dry methods
are used.   Wet methods depend, in particular, upon the attainment of
intimate contact between dust particles in the gas and water either in
towers or by fan disintegrators of the Thiesen type.   In the wet scrubbing,
the dirt is removed by washing the gas with water sprays, etc.   This is
accomplished in towers fitted with baffles.   Rapidly revolving sprays are
sometimes used to assist in removal of dust partly by centrifugal force.

Dry methods include filtration through bags (Halberg-Beth system) or
electrostatic precipitation.   The basis of the latter is the passage of the
gas through an electrostatic field, during which any dust particle will be
charged and will migrate under the influence of the field to an earthed electrode.   In Lodge-Cottrell precipitators, the earthed electrode consists of a
bundle of tubes.   A high voltage is applied to a series of wires suspended in
the centres of the tubes.   Water washing is used to remove the accumulated
particles.   Choice of method depends on factors such as degree of cleanliness
required, quantity and cost of water available, and the cost of power.
Table LXV gives a summary of performance data given by Jennings (*J. Iron
Steel Inst.*, March 1950) :

TABLE LXV

THE CLEANING OF BLAST-FURNACE GAS

Normal operating conditions : full gas rate

Type of cleaner (names of common makers).	Concentration grains/cu. ft.		Probable size of particle not separated. μ	Energy, consumption/1000 cu. ft. of gas.				Number of installations reported,* and remarks.
	Inlet.	Outlet.		Pressure drop, in w.g.	Water.		Motor power, h.p. per hour.	
					Vol., gal.	Pressure, lb./sq. in.		
Dry cleaners :								
Dust catchers . . .	Max.	0·1-2·0	150	0·5	—	—	—	Used at almost all plants but form of cleaner varies.
Cyclones . . .	Max.	0·5-1·0	100-40, according to size of unit	1·0 and upwards	—	—	—	
Bag filters . . . (Halberg, Dracco)	1·0	0·008	According to pressure drop	6-12	—	—	—	13 : performance varies according to material of filter bags.
Wet cleaners :								
Wet scrubbers . . (McKee, Peabody)	5·0	0·25	25	6-9	7-10	30 about	—	13 : water only has to be pumped to top of tower.
Spray towers . . (Peabody, Whessoe)	5·0	0·125	20	1-2	20-40	100-200	—	Usually classified with scrubbers.
Disintegrators . . (Theissen, Zchocke)	0·5	0·005	10	2-4*	10-15	Small	0·3	20 ; pressure rise of 2-4 in. w.g. through disintegrators.*
Electrical precipitators (Lodge, Elga, R. Corp.)	0·5	0·003	5	1·0	5-10	Small	—	7 ; some dry. Electricity consumption small.

* Survey of Blast-Furnace Practice, Iron Making Division, B.I.S.R.A., 1948.

Gas Burners. When burning a low-grade gas of the type of cold blast-furnace gas an air-swirl burner of the type described for producer gas is an essential to good control and a reasonably short flame. This is not necessary of course, where the gas is preheated as in the case of a regenerative coke oven or when it is burned in an already hot combustion chamber. In these cases the burner is simply a brickwork port.

The Underground Gasification of Coal

The possibility of avoiding the labour associated with the mining of coal by converting the coal in situ to a fluid and pumping it to the surface has attracted interest since the days of Sir W. Siemens in this country (1868) and Mendeleef in Russia (1888), but only recently have experimental attempts been made to find out if there is anything practical in the proposal. Sir William Ramsay actually designed an experiment in the Durham coalfield during 1912, but the experiment was never carried out. The first real step was made in Russia during 1933 when, after some preliminary experiment, no less than five experimental stations were set up under the Podzemgas Trust. By 1938 plans were in hand for large-scale development and it was understood that plans were made to produce as much as 14 million cu. ft. of gas per hour. The war caused a hiatus in progress but interest was stimulated again afterwards. There is no news of how far this has progressed, but the methods used in the early stages are known ; these covered four distinct variations.

(1) A panel of coal was isolated by brickwork and gas shafts made at both sides for inlet air and gas offtake respectively. In the solid coal the result was not successful, the effluent gas showing only 10 per cent. CO. Crushing the coal by explosive gave a gas containing 10–20 per cent. CO and 6–8 per cent. H_2, but crushing was uncertain and gave very variable results.

(2) In the borehole producer method 6-inch boreholes of 100 yards length were drilled through the coal in the seam from one gallery to another. The passage of air after lighting-up gasified the coal until a cigar-shaped section was burned out. The method was considered to be suitable for horizontal or slightly-inclined seams. Using alternate steam and air blows a gas was made of 232 B.Th.U. Reaction ceased when the diameter of the hole became too large for the air velocity to be maintained.

(3) In the stream method, panels of coal are divided lengthwise along the seam by 2 ft. diameter galleries 80 yards apart, which lead to a cross-gallery. Both galleries are connected to the surface by boreholes. A fire is started in one gallery and fed with air which may be enriched with oxygen and the gases are withdrawn from the other. The fire zone advances along the seam and some 10,000 tons of coal can be gasified per panel. Using air enriched to 30 per cent. O_2 a gas was produced of 112–46 B.Th.U., containing 23–7 per cent. CO, 12–15 per cent. H_2 and 2–3 per cent. methane.

Production by this method actually reached 30 million cu. ft. of gas in 20 months.

(4) In the percolation method borings are arranged in concentric circles at 20–40 yards apart, the end of the borehole centring in the seam. The coal at the bottom of one hole is ignited in air supplied by a central pipe and gas withdrawn from the annulus. Later, as cracks develop in the coal it becomes possible to draw the air along the seam to another borehole. In due course all the coal can be gasified from each hole in turn. The method is illustrated in Figure 107.

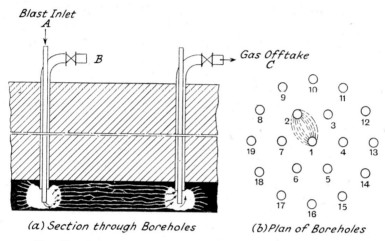

(a) Section through Boreholes   (b) Plan of Boreholes

Fig. 107.—Percolation Method. Underground Gasification of Coal
(Gas Research Board).

It is apparent that it was unlikely that a high proportion of the coal could be gasified by these methods, and indeed only some 20–40 per cent. was realized, but it was intended that the application should be made only to such seams as were unlikely to be worked economically by mining methods.

Since about 1946 experimental work on similar and new lines has been going on in other places ; in Belgium, in French Morocco, in the United States under the auspices of the U.S. Bureau of Mines, and in Britain under the Ministry of Fuel and Power. It is already realized that no one method will be of general application, and that only in certain circumstances will any method be applicable at all.

Bureau of Mines Work. During 1947 preliminary experiments at Gorgas, Alabama, were made by the stream method, which now seems to be regarded as the most promising, by cutting two parallel galleries 150 ft. long and 40 ft. apart, in from the outcrop. A cross-gallery at the end thus isolated a panel of coal. Part of this panel was gasified, about 236 tons of coal, with air blast, and data were obtained for further experiment, also by the stream method, on another site.

In the second site, gasification was promoted along a 300-ft. mined passage 10 ft. wide by 4 ft. high, using an air blast of up to 7200 cu. ft. per minute at 30 lb. pressure. Periodic reversal of flow controlled the position of the fire zone and the width of attack was increased to over 100 ft. Subsidence allowed the velocity of flow to be maintained and it was found that this could be assisted to some extent by filling up with sand. Gas of high calorific value was not made and only occasionally was the value as high as 100 B.Th.U. As a secondary method of attack on the problem attempts were made to burn the coal in the seam completely and utilize the heat as power by the driving of a gas turbine. So far as gasification is concerned, preparation of the site by mining methods and the construction of artificial passages does not lead to a satisfactory reaction zone.

Preparation of a site by mining is evidently not attractive for general reasons and a new method of linking air intake and gas offtake through the coal has restimulated interest in the stream method. This is " *electro-linkage* " and is based on the fact that, while coal is a poor conductor of electricity, coke is a good conductor. Electrodes placed in the coal some distance apart can thus lead to the establishment of a conducting zone which becomes more and more porous and forms a good channel for the passage of gas. It has been found that linkage can be established in this way up to a distance of 150 ft. In one series of experiments using an air flow of 2000 cu. ft. per minute 2280 cu. ft. of gas was made at 93 B.Th.U. having a composition of : CO_2, 9·7 ; CO, 13·1 ; H_2, 9·2 ; CH_4, 1·5, and nitrogen 65·7 per cent. Electro-linkage therefore shows promise of bringing the stream method to a practical solution.

Work in Great Britain. Starting later in this field, the Ministry were able to examine previous work before deciding on a plan. It was realized that the gas at best would be of 160 B.Th.U., including both reaction and distillation gases, that the air must be brought into contact fully with the coal in the area, that the air must not by-pass the reaction zone and cause combustion of the gas, and that the " linkage " of inlet and offtake must be achieved with the minimum of manual underground work.

A start was made with a percolation prospect by boring along the length of a 10-ft. seam from the outcrop and sinking vertical bores to intersect this at an inclined depth of 200 ft. Ignition was started at the bottom of one bore and gas withdrawn from another with air passing at 11,000 cu. ft. per hour. The project was wholly experimental and many variations of conditions were made, but gas was produced of 80–100 B.Th.U. at a thermal efficiency of 65 per cent.

A second series of experiments was undertaken on the understanding that the minimum of boring work would be done and that linkage would be achieved by some forced method. Explosives were not successful but high-pressure air (4000 lb./in.²) passed through a steel-cased inlet gave linkage to a distance of 50 ft. with the very variable expenditure of from

6000 to 130,000 cu. ft. of air or oxygen-enriched air. The gas was again of 70–100 B.Th.U. calorific value. It is considered that the results are promising and that it is possible to visualize a production scheme, and it is proposed to continue experimental work on methods of linkage, including electro-linkage which has achieved 150 ft. in U.S. experiments. The most practical proposal would seem to be radial linkage to a central shaft. A 150-ft. circle over a 3-ft. seam covers 7000 tons of coal and a square mile 3 million tons. It is clear, however, that the method is applicable in this form only to fairly horizontal seams which are not faulted over the area of operations. It could however achieve the working of thin or badly-banded seams or coal of too-high sulphur content which might otherwise be left in the ground.

REFERENCE BOOKS

Modern Gas Producers. N. E. Rambush. Benn Bros. 1923.
American Producer Gas Practice. N. Latta. D. van Nostrand. 1910.
Blast Furnace Practice. Ralph H. Sweetser. McGraw-Hill. 1938.
Manufacture of Iron and Steel. D. J. O. Brandt. British Iron and Steel Federation. 1953.
Gasification. *O.E.E.C.*, March 1953, Feb. 1954.
Gas Producers and Blast Furnaces. Gumz. Wiley. 1950.

CHAPTER XVII

WATER GAS AND COMPLETE GASIFICATION

The term *water gas* has been given to the mixture of hydrogen and carbon monoxide which is produced by the action of steam on carbon at an elevated temperature. In this simple sense the reaction is the basis of one process, the production of " blue " water gas, but there is a large number of other processes in which coal is treated at an elevated temperature with air or oxygen and steam to produce a more complex gas ; these have been termed generally processes of " complete " or " total " gasification, and have been developed mainly for the production of gas intended for the catalytic synthesis of ammonia or hydrocarbons. In addition, water gas is manufactured as a process step in the production of enriched or carburetted water gas, in which the relatively low calorific value of " blue " gas is increased to the level of that of town gas from carbonization plant. In all of these the basic reaction of greatest importance is the same, namely,

$$(1) \quad C + H_2O \text{ (liquid)} = CO + H_2 - 49,902 \text{ calories.}$$

This reaction, involving interaction between solid carbon and liquid water at constant pressure, is strongly endothermic. The reaction takes place normally, however, with steam at a temperature in the region of 1200° to 1400° C. and the thermal quantity involved is affected by the latent heat of formation of steam.

$$(2) \quad H_2O \text{ (vap.)} = H_2O \text{ (liq.)} + 10,520 \text{ cal.}$$

Increase of temperature favours reaction (1) and decrease favours reaction (3),

$$(3) \quad C + 2H_2O \text{ (liq.)} = CO_2 + H_2 - 42,583 \text{ cal.}$$

so that, as the temperature falls, the proportion of carbon dioxide increases. At any given temperature the water-gas equilibrium is established :

$$(4) \quad CO + H_2O \rightleftharpoons CO_2 + H_2.$$

The equilibrium constant, K_p, of this reaction is 1·06 at 1100° C., 1·84 at 1300° C., and 2·27 at 1400° C.

WATER GAS

Water gas is normally manufactured from coke in deep fuel beds in which the requisite high temperature is attained by first blowing the fuel bed with air as explained below. The process is, therefore, a discontinuous

436

one in which the blow gases are separately discharged. Because of this the temperature of the bed fluctuates but is kept as uniform as possible during the " make " part of the cycle by varying the direction of flow of the steam. The finished gas contains a small proportion of methane which comes from a synthesis reaction, and 3 to 5 per cent. of nitrogen through the impossibility of purging the fuel bed completely from blow gas before the make cycle. Industrial water gas has therefore the following approximate composition :

	Per cent.
Hydrogen	48–51
Carbon monoxide	40–42
Methane	0·1–0·5
Carbon dioxide	3–5
Nitrogen	3–6

Its calorific value varies from about 292 to 298 B.Th.U. per cu. ft. (gross) measured at 60° F. and 30 in. pressure.

Since water gas contains only traces of hydrocarbons it burns with a non-luminous flame ; this has, however, a strong bluish colour from which the popular name " blue " water gas was derived. Its early industrial use was fostered by its considerably higher calorific value than producer gas and by the fact that the flame has a high calorific intensity. Because of higher cost, however, it is much less widely applied than producer gas for furnace requirements.

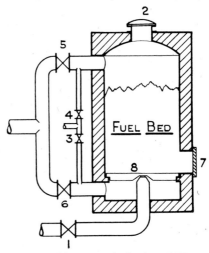

FIG. 108.—Diagrammatic Section of Water-gas Generator.

In its essentials a water-gas generator, Figure 108, is a refractory-lined steel casing containing the fuel bed, supported on a suitable grate, and with air, steam and fuel supplies and a stack for the escape of blow gases. The valves are arranged for central control and the plant is operated on a time cycle as follows, assuming the fuel bed to be approximately at the working temperature :

1. Blow with air (1) with stack valve (2) open for say 60 seconds.
2. Open lower steam valve (3), wait a few seconds for water gas to clear the blow gas through the stack valve. Close stack valve and open gas valve (5) to scrubber.
3. Steam for say one minute.
4. Close lower steam supply (3) and open upper steam supply (4). Close upper gas valve (5) and open lower gas valve (6).

5. Steam for say two minutes downwards.
6. Close the upper steam supply and lower gas valve ; open the lower steam supply and upper gas valve.
7. Steam for say one minute upwards.
8. Close lower steam supply and upper gas valve.
9. Open stack valve and turn on air supply.

This cycle of nine operations, occupying about five minutes, is repeated until it is necessary to recharge the generator with fuel. This is done when the level has fallen by 18 in. during about six complete cycles. During this time the ash and clinker which gravitate towards the bottom of the fuel bed are continuously removed by the rotating grate into a water-sealed trough : this is not shown in the diagram.

A number of precautions are necessary during these operations : these are :

(i) The water gas enters the scrubber through a water seal so that gas from the main, which may be under pressure, cannot return to the hot generator during the blow periods or when charging or clinkering.

(ii) In order that the operations detailed under 4 and 6 above should be done simultaneously, the valves are linked together so that the operator has only one movement to make other than adjustment of the steam to the correct working pressure.

(iii) The main reason for up and down steaming is to maintain the fuel bed at a uniform working temperature and to keep the formation of clinker under control. After charging the generator with fuel, and after clinkering, it is necessary to steam upwards for one cycle in order to bring the new fuel bed to the working temperature. Otherwise the steam used in down running would come into contact with cold coke and a poor gas yield would result.

(iv) Before the top charging door can be opened to admit fresh coke the stack valve must be opened and the air turned on for a few seconds to sweep the space above the fuel bed free from water gas. If this is not done an explosion would result.

(v) For a similar reason an up-run must always precede a blow so that the bottom of the generator shall be full of steam ; if it contained gas, as at the end of a down-run, the introduction of air would again cause an explosion.

As it leaves the generator crude water gas contains surplus water vapour, hydrogen sulphide, fine dust, and traces of iron carbonyl. The first, and some of the H_2S and dust are removed in a water scrubber, but if greater purity is required oxide boxes and an electro-static precipitator are necessary. The total H_2S is about 80 grains per 100 cu. ft.

In full-scale plant there is added to the above a combustion chamber for burning the blow gases and a waste-heat boiler for the recovery, as steam, of the sensible heat of the hot gases and the potential heat of the blow gas.

The arrangement is similar to that described below for carburetted gas. In some types of plant there is also a water-jacket round the generator.

In modern plants of large size the entire programme of operations is now carried out mechanically, the timing being controlled by an electrical timing device which controls all the operations including the charging of the coke at the correct intervals. Clinker discharge is made automatic and continuous by the use of rotating grates which crush the clinker and discharge it continuously through a water-seal or, in some cases, a specially constructed dry seal.

There are a number of factors which affect the yield of water gas, such as depth of fuel bed, rate of blow, working temperature, etc., but before considering these it is desirable first to have a clear idea of the nature

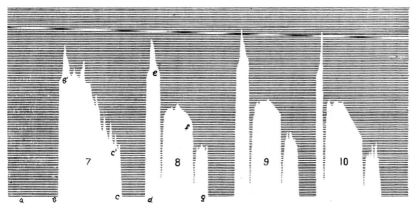

FIG. 109.—Variation of Rate of Gas Making in Water-gas Practice.

of the variations which occur in the different parts of the water-gas cycle. The variations are best illustrated from the work of King and Shaw (*Fuel Res. Tech. Paper* 6, 1923), and King and Williams (*Fuel Res. Tech. Papers* 27 and 30, 1930).

The volume variations appear in a very interesting way when use is made of the photographic recorder of King and Williams (*loc. cit.*). A portion of a chart is shown in Figure 109. This is obtained as a record on a moving chart of the differential pressure on both sides of an orifice plate in the gas stream. The volume of gas is proportional to the square root of this pressure difference, so that after calibration of an instrument the area of the curves can be measured in terms of gas volume. This measurement is facilitated by the use of a square-root planimeter. The horizontal lines are spaced 1 mm. apart on the full-size records.

In Figure 109 the line ab, the base line, represents no gas flow, at b the gas begins to flow in the main and the differential pressure at the orifice is shown by the ordinate bb^1. As the rate of gas production falls off, owing to the endothermic nature of the reactions, the height of the ordinate decreases until, when steam is shut off at cc^1, it is less than half bb^1. During the interval cd, the fire is being blown and no gas is passing in the main. In the second cycle, $defg$, the direction of steaming is altered from upwards to downwards at e and then reversed at f. The momentary pauses caused by the change of direction of flow of gases in the generator are clearly seen. Further cycles repeat the same curves and the zero is continuously checked during the blows. The shape of the curves shows how the rate of gas-making decreases as the temperature of the fuel bed falls. In an extended run a general decrease would also appear in hand-clinkered plants owing to the accumulation of clinker.

The proportions of up- and down-running are variable and depend upon the nature and amount of the ash in the fuel. Generally they are chosen to keep the oxidation zone low and the clinker within reach ; too much down-running would choke the grate with fused clinker. Figure 109, however, indicates that a study of the gas volumes produced in the corresponding parts of each cycle would facilitate an exact balance of conditions in cases where the ash was not of a difficult character.

It will have been realized that the composition and calorific value of water gas must vary, as well as its volume, during the stages described above. The scope of these changes is illustrated in Table LXVI. During the first one minute up-run gas is made at the rate of 571 cu. ft. per minute, during the down-run at 450 cu. ft., and during the last up-run at only 370 cu. ft. From beginning to end of a gas-making cycle the decrease in rate may be as much as 50 per cent.

TABLE LXVI

RATE OF PRODUCTION AND COMPOSITION OF WATER GAS AT DIFFERENT STAGES
(In a Small Generator producing 500,000 cu. ft. per day)

	During first up-run.	During down-run.	During final up-run.	Average.
Gas volume, cu. ft. per min. . .	571	450	370	436
Gas composition :				
CO_2	2·2	2·3	9·0	4·5
CO	45·8	43·6	39·4	41·6
H_2	47·0	52·5	51·0	50·5
CH_4	0·3	0·4	0·1	0·2
N_2	4·7	1·2	0·5	3·2
Gas calorific value, B.Th.U . . .	298	310	290	296
Maximum temperature of gases leaving generator—deg. C. . .	670	440	600	Blow gas 780

Blow gas	CO_2	CO	H_2	CH_4	N_2
	14·6	9·3	3·7	0·8	71·6
Calorific value . . .	49 B.Th.U. per cu. ft.				

The thermal balance of operations in a water-gas plant is best illustrated in a system which shows the considerable amount of heat available in the hot gases. Such a balance is shown in Table LXVII.

TABLE LXVII

THERMAL BALANCE OF WATER-GAS PROCESS

Percentages of Heat to Generator

Coke	92·52	Water gas, potential	57·81
Steam	7·35	,, ,, sensible	3·23
Air	0·13	Blow gas, potential	18·95
		,, ,, sensible	9·33
		Clinker and ashes, potential .	2·28
		Unburnt coke, potential . . .	2·26
		Dust, potential	0·33
		Sensible heat of last three . .	0·33
		Water vapour	2·13
		Difference, including radiation,	0·07
		etc., losses	3·28
	100·00		100·00

The conclusions to be drawn from this table are :

(1) The heat available in the finished water gas is not more than 60 per cent. of that in the coke and steam used.

(2) The proportion of heat carried by the hot gases is as high as 30 per cent. and recovery is imperative.

(3) The loss of unburned fuel in the ashes is about 3·5 per cent. and the losses by radiation and convection are low at about less than 3 per cent.

In modern plants, size has increased until a unit generator may produce as much as 10 million cu. ft. per day. Such plants are built with jacket and waste-heat recovery boilers and are thermally well-balanced units in which all the process steam and the power required for operation are obtained with a probable surplus of steam of 4 per cent. of the thermal value of the coke gasified. The total of steam recovered is about 80 lb. (at 90 lb. pressure) per 1000 cu. ft. of gas made and represents an efficiency of recovery from the heat in the hot gases of about 45 per cent.

In practice it is usual to consider performance in relation to coke at 85 per cent. free carbon and averaging 2 in. in size. It is also useful to compare yields on a basis of dry, ash-free fuel. Comparative figures on this basis are, for example :

Water gas per lb. of dry, ash-free coke	. . .	30·1 cu. ft.
Water gas per lb. of steam .	. . . .	30·3 cu. ft.
Coke per 1000 cu. ft. of gas	. . . .	33·2 lb.
Steam used per 1000 cu. ft. of gas	. . .	33·0 lb.

Important Factors in Water-gas Practice. It will be realized from the above that the important factors in the obtaining of a good thermal yield in water-gas manufacture are (i) the storage of heat in the fuel bed in the minimum time and with the minimum loss, and (ii) the efficient utilization of the heat thus stored.   Provision (i) can be attained by increasing the efficiency of the blow, assuming that the final temperature cannot be raised beyond a certain point determined by the fusibility of the ash. This can be done by blowing as completely as possible to CO_2, either (a) by using a shallow fuel bed, as in the old Dellwik-Fleischer process, or (b) increasing the rate of blowing.   The first alternative reduces the output of a given plant, and the second seems more desirable, the time of blowing being reduced correspondingly with increase of rate so that the mean temperature of the fuel bed remains the same.   The limits imposed on this alternative are the practical ones of cost of high-pressure fans and disturbance of the fuel bed.

King and Shaw have reported experiments with a shallow fuel bed in a Humphreys and Glasgow generator rated at 500,000 cu. ft. per day.

Fuel bed—ft.	3·0	3·5	4·0	7·0
Thermal efficiency, per cent.	54·7	57·8	59·9	57·8
CO_2 in blow gas, per cent.	19·5	19·0	19·1	14·5
Gas made per day, cu. ft.	237,000	230,000	219,000	378,000
Heat lost by radiation, etc., per cent.	11·8	10·6	11·2	3·3

The above results show that a higher thermal efficiency is obtainable in this way despite the higher proportional losses due to radiation, etc., which are the result of lower output.

Modern practice is more in favour of the deep fuel bed with some 12 to 14 per cent. of carbon dioxide in the blow gas, and about 10 per cent. of carbon monoxide.   Under these conditions the carbon consumed during the blow is approximately equal to that consumed in making the water gas. Since the blow period is a loss to gas production it is apparent that an increase of efficiency is possible by increasing the rate of blowing :

	1.	2.	3.
Rate, cu. ft. air per minute	4,780	2,300	1,400
Volume of air per blow	802	997	1,167
Efficiency of blow	86	84	61
Efficiency of process	76·8	72·4	68·7
(therms water gas per 100 therms coke)			

Small increases in efficiency can be assured by finding the optimum conditions for the rate of passage of steam through the fuel bed.   In British practice the normal efficiency in steam decomposition is about 70 per cent.

During the blow period the CO content of the blow gas increases.   The air used for its combustion should also be gradually increased in proportion so as to avoid passing an undue amount of cold air through the system. This can be achieved by using a special " creeper " valve which opens on an arranged time cycle.

Careful regulation of the duration of the purge period for sweeping the blow gas from the fuel bed is also important for striking a balance between a high gas yield and a high gas calorific value.   Normally it would take about 30 sec. to remove the blow gas completely—it is never quite complete because of air leakage past the valves—but so long a period is not allowable since it could mean a loss of thermal output of as much as 15 per cent. (King, *Gas Eng.*, 1933, p. 207). A compromise is therefore necessary and experiment has shown this to be of the order of a thermal loss of gas of 4 per cent. and a 5 per cent. decrease of calorific value below that of nitrogen-free gas.

Temperature of Operation. The higher the temperature range over which the fuel bed fluctuates, the higher will be the thermal efficiency of the process and the better the water gas produced. The normal range is about 250° C., i.e. 1400° C., at the end of the blow and 1150° C. at the end of the run. King and Williams (*Fuel Res. Tech. Paper* 30, 1931) have shown that, by reducing the output of a generator until the temperature range is such that clinker troubles are prevented an increase of efficiency of as much as 20 per cent. over normal conditions is possible.

Preheating of the Blast. The reactions in the generator could be influenced in the direction of higher efficiency if the steam and air to the generator could be preheated. This has been explored by the Gas Research Board (G.R.B. 60, 1950) in connection with a system of methane-enrichment (see below) and it has been shown that preheating to about 400° C. increases the gas yield by some 6 therms per 100 therms of coke and also gives an increased output of 12 per cent. This improvement is not yet in common practice.

Industrial Applications of Water Gas. It is necessary to remember in the usage of water gas that the composition of the gas varies during the cycle of operations. Where uniformity of composition is of importance it is therefore necessary to discharge the gas into a mixing holder unless a number of generators are on stream to equalize the flow.

The chief industrial use of water gas is now in its carburetted form (see p. 444) as an ingredient of town gas. " Blue " water gas is, however, of special service in many heating operations. Its calorific value is about 295 B.Th.U. gross, and 270 B.Th.U. net per cu. ft. The gas is capable of giving a very high flame temperature. With preheated air a temperature well above the melting-point of platinum (1780° C. ; 3236° F.) can be attained ; under ordinary conditions of combustion the hottest part of the flame is from 1530° to 1645° C.

For furnace heating, where the work is intermittent and quick heating is desired, water gas has the advantage over ordinary producer (mixed) gas. It has been used to a limited extent in steel furnaces, but here producer gas—used hot and with its tar vapours—with its simpler production, continuous make, and less costly plant is more generally advantageous. For furnaces for heating drop forgings and stampings and such class of work, it is employed, and to a limited extent for metal melting. Plant is, however, unlikely to be installed specially for these uses.

An important, if not extensive, use of water gas is in the production of hydrogen for industrial use as such, or for the production of synthetic ammonia. In the former, the water gas is used for the reduction of granular spathic iron ore to ferrous oxide ; the hydrogen is then obtained by the reoxidation of the oxide with steam. The process is a discontinuous one but is of value in that the hydrogen can have a purity in advance of 99·5 per cent. The process is used industrially for the production of hydrogen for the hydrogenation of fats. It was also used widely for the making of hydrogen for balloon barrages during the last war. The need for high purity (high ascensive power) combined with a high output gave rise to marked improvements of technique. It was found possible to produce, under full-scale conditions, one volume of hydrogen from not more than 1·8 volumes of water gas.

In the production of synthetic ammonia the water gas is converted to carbon dioxide and hydrogen by passage over an Fe/Cr catalyst at 500° C., the CO_2 washed out with water under pressure, any residual CO removed by washing with ammoniacal cuprous chloride solution. With some adjustment of the water-gas cycle the final gas has H_2 and N_2 in the correct proportions for ammonia synthesis.

Carburetted Water Gas. The most extensive usage of carburetted water gas is as a component of town gas. In this context it is of special importance for the following reasons :

(1) The plant is flexible in operation and can be brought into use from cold in a matter of a few hours to meet emergencies and peak loads of gas demand.

(2) Since it consumes coke as its fuel its use serves as a balancing factor in the variation of public demand for town gas for seasonal or other reasons.

(3) In some countries, and to a less extent, it reduces the demand for caking coals where these are less available and gas oil is more available.

For the first two reasons the production of this gas tends to fluctuate quite widely in Great Britain, but for many years it has represented from 10 to 20 per cent. of the total town gas sold. The rates of consumption of coke and gas oil are of the order of 44 lb. and 2·0 gal. per 1000 cu. ft. of finished gas at a calorific value of 500 B.Th.U. per cu. ft., using coke containing 85 per cent. of fixed carbon and averaging 2 in. in size.

The generator and its system of valves are the same in a carburetted water-gas system as for simple or " blue " water gas. The additional plant necessary are the carburettor for vaporizing the enriching oil and the superheater for cracking the vapour to permanent gas.

The general arrangement of a modern plant embodying the requirements for minimum labour is shown in Figure 110. The generator has a jacket-boiler, mechanical grate, and automatic controls on valve-operation and coke feed. The latter is situated on a suitable platform with an instrument

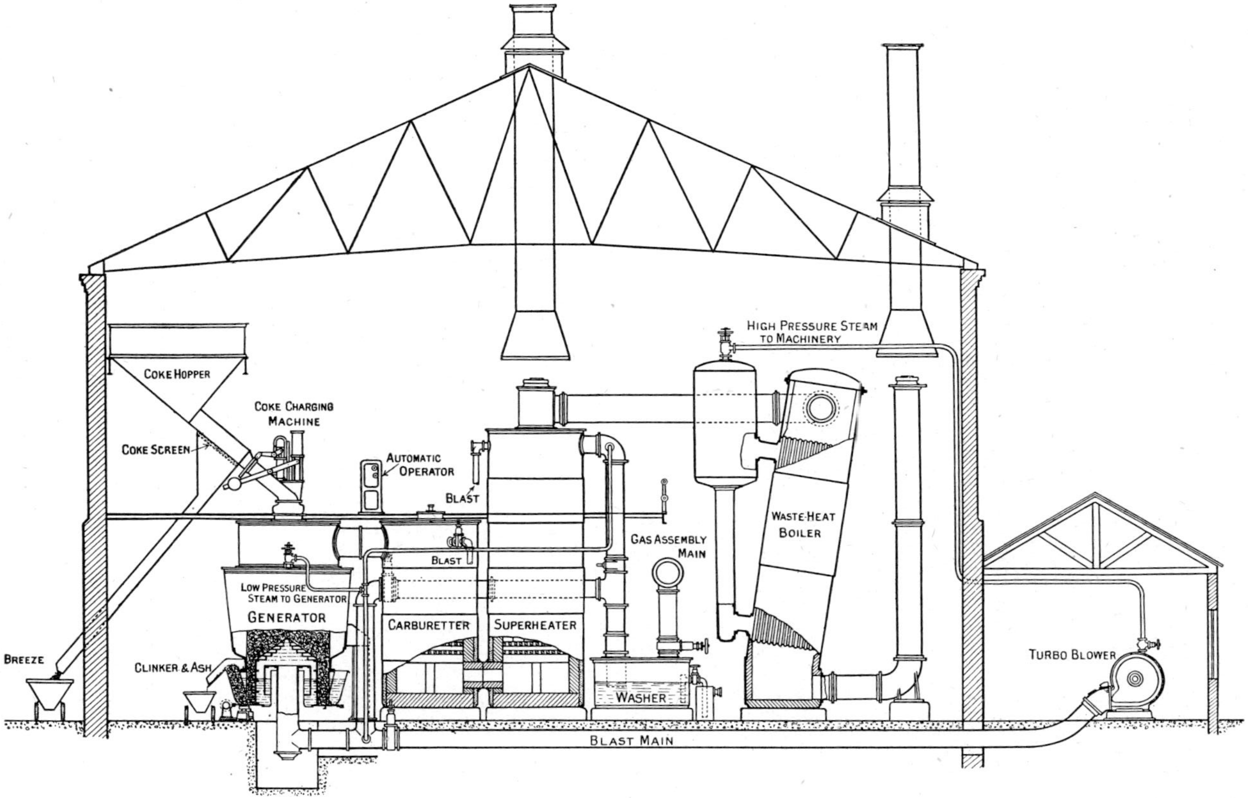
COKE HOPPER
COKE CHARGING MACHINE
COKE SCREEN
AUTOMATIC OPERATOR
BLAST
BLAST
HIGH PRESSURE STEAM TO MACHINERY
WASTE-HEAT BOILER
GAS ASSEMBLY MAIN
LOW PRESSURE STEAM TO GENERATOR
GENERATOR
CARBURETTER
SUPERHEATER
BREEZE
CLINKER & ASH
WASHER
TURBO BLOWER
BLAST MAIN

FIG. 110.—Carburetted Water-gas Plant. Humphreys and Glasgow System.

board. The handling plant comprises wagon tippler, skip-hoist, conveyor-belts and bunker for coke, and an ash-disposal belt. A similar plant but with a different type of carburettor is shown in Figure 111. Typical dimensions for a plant producing about three million cu. ft. of gas per day are : generator 18 ft. high and $8\frac{1}{2}$ ft. internal diameter, carburettor (Figure 110) 18 ft. high and 6 ft. i.d., superheater 27 ft. high and 6 ft. i.d.

In Figure 110 the carburettor is a cylindrical brick-lined chamber filled with brick chequer work over which the oil is sprayed. In Figure 111 the carburettor does not contain chequer brickwork and the oil is injected upwards through a water-cooled injector against the descending stream of hot water gas. A system of baffles in the dome distributes the products uniformly to the superheater. This latter arrangement is claimed to give improved decomposition of the oil but its main purpose was to allow heavier (and cheaper) oils to be used, the empty carburettor being easier to clean from deposited carbon. A further improvement has been the use of a reverse-flow system in which the hot water gas enters the bottom of the carburettor and the top of the superheater, while steam flow during the back-run is in the reverse direction. The improvement of gasification is claimed to be due to the progressively higher temperature to which the oil vapour is subjected during flow. The superheater is normally filled with chequer brickwork ; its function is to complete the cracking of the oil vapour to permanent gas.

The plant is operated as for water gas. During the blow the carbon monoxide in the gases is burned with air in the carburettor and super-heater, raising these chambers to the working temperature. When water gas is being made oil is admitted to the carburettor immediately after opening the steam valve. The oil is vaporized, leaving some coke in the chequer work. The oil supply is checked before the end of the run so as to make sure that all of it is vaporized before the next blow. During the blow the residual carbon is partly burned off.

The correct temperature for cracking the oil is from 730° to 760° C. in the superheater. The temperature in the carburettor tends to vary widely (1000–600° C.), but this is less important. The time of contact of the gases with the hot surfaces may vary from one to ten seconds without much change in efficiency of cracking. The oil normally used is petroleum " gas oil " (boiling-range 200–300°). The amount of oil used depends upon the degree of enrichment required. In good practice the cracking of one gallon of gas oil will yield 70 cu. ft. of gas having a calorific value of about 1550 B.Th.U. per cu. ft. In order to raise the calorific value of water gas from 295 to 500 B.Th.U. it would therefore be necessary to crack over 2 gal. of oil per 1000 cu. ft. of carburetted gas made. This represents an efficiency of cracking of about 75 per cent., the remaining 25 per cent. being accounted for as carbon deposited and as heavy unvaporized residue which is collected from the system as water-gas tar. This tar may amount to about 15 gal.

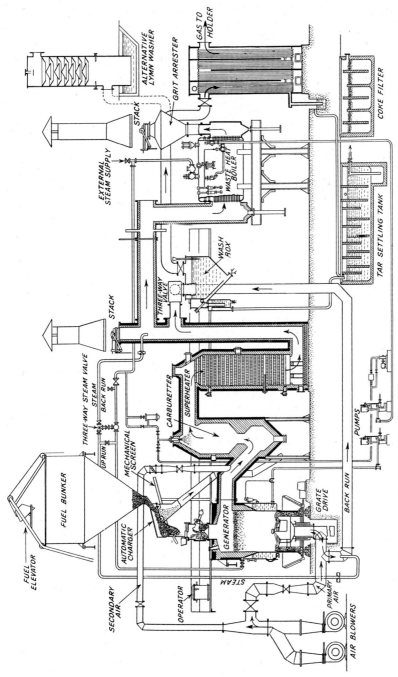

FUEL ELEVATOR

FUEL BUNKER

SECONDARY AIR

AUTOMATIC CHARGER

OPERATOR

STEAM

GENERATOR

GRATE DRIVE

BACK RUN

PRIMARY AIR

AIR BLOWERS

PUMPS

UP RUN

BACK RUN

THREE-WAY STEAM VALVE

STEAM

MECHANICAL SCREEN

CARBURETTER

SUPERHEATER

STACK

THREE-WAY VALVE

WASH BOX

WASTE HEAT BOILER

EXTERNAL STEAM SUPPLY

STACK

GRIT ARRESTER

ALTERNATIVE LYMN WASHER

GAS TO HOLDER

TAR SETTLING TANK

COKE FILTER

FIG. 111.—Section through C.W.G. Plant with Reverse-flow Carburettor and Superheater and Opposed Oil Injection (Power Gas Corporation).

per 100 gal. of oil cracked.   A portion of the oil vaporized is present in the gas as condensable, rather than gaseous, hydrocarbons.   This may amount to 10 per cent. of the oil gasified.

Coke	53·4	Gas		62·0
Oil	40·0	Tar		6·0
Air	0·1	Steam recovered		10·0
Steam	6·5	Undecomposed steam		3·2
		Sensible heat of gas		3·8
		„ „ tar		0·3
		Waste gas at 270° C.		4·3
		Clinker and ash		3·2
		Radiation, etc.		3·2
				—— 18·0
	100·0			96·0

In this example the calorific value of the gas is 500 B.Th.U. per cu. ft. and the amount of oil sprayed is 2·0 gal. per 1000 cu. ft. of c.w.g. made. It is noteworthy that the amount of steam recovered is more than sufficient for the process.   Of the total heat available for recovery as steam (18·4) 10·0 is recovered at an efficiency of about 55 per cent.   This is a satisfactory result in view of the fact that the sensible heat of the hot c.w.g. is not recovered because, owing to its high tar content, this gas cannot be passed through the waste-heat boiler.   Further recovery of low-grade heat is possible from the waste gases from the boiler, which have a temperature of 270° C., for example, for heating boiler feed water, but this is not normally done.

The loss of sensible heat in the carburetted gas is reduced to a minimum by the adoption of the back-run modification (q.v.) in which the steam for down-running enters the top of the superheater and cools the chequer work at this point, thereby reducing the exit gas temperature.   The proportion of back-run steam is about 50 per cent. of the whole, and in the above example the total heat carried away is about 6 per cent.

The Cleaning of Water Gas.   The gases leaving the generator of a water-gas plant contain water vapour, sulphur compounds and dust.   The dust in particular must be carefully removed to avoid trouble with valves and mains.   This is done by means of baffled dust traps followed by counterflow water washers and finally, if very efficient cleaning is desired, by centrifugal cleaners.   Such treatment removes only a small proportion of the hydrogen sulphide, and this must be removed by the usual iron oxide method.   Normal amounts are 70–80 grains per 100 cu. ft. of gas.

In the manufacture of carburetted water gas the position is complicated by the presence of tar from imperfectly cracked oil, and tar extractors and separating tanks are added to the system.

Since the rate of production of the gas is not uniform it is customary to interpose a " balance " gasholder between the condensers and the exhauster having a capacity equal to about one hour's production so as to allow the exhauster to be run at a uniform speed.

Variations in Carburetted Water-gas Practice. Generally speaking, the variations which are possible in making carburetted water gas are less than in making simple water gas. It is essential that the temperature of the cracking surface be maintained at the right level so that other conditions must be arranged to suit. The higher the calorific value aimed at, the greater is the volume of oil to be cracked and the generator must have a higher temperature in order that the blow gases will contain more carbon monoxide and provide more heat on combustion.

Two variations of the water-gas process, the back-run and the down-run, are employed to increase the efficiency of operation. In the Crisman down-run process the relatively cool down-run gases are by-passed so that they do not cool down the carburettor and superheater. The necessary oil-cracking is, in this process, all done on the up-run gas which leaves the generator at a higher temperature. It has been estimated that this simple change reduced the fuel consumption by 2 to 3 lb. per 1000 cu. ft. of water gas made. It will be apparent that the generator efficiency is not increased by this modification.

The Back-run Process. In this process the steam for the down-run is introduced at the top of the superheater, thereby cooling the brickwork so that the blow gases which follow do more work and leave the system at a lower temperature. The down-run gas, as in the Crisman back-run, is not carburetted and all the enriching is done on the up-run gas. This modification is stated to reduce fuel consumption by about 3 lb. per 1000 cu. ft. of gas made. Most of the saving is effected by the return of heat from the superheater to the generator and a lower rate of cooling of the fuel bed. One disadvantage is the loss of steam when the superheater is swept by the up-run which follows the down-run.

The most precise evaluation of down-run and back-run procedure is contained in the 31st Report of the Research Committee of the Institute of Gas Engineers, 1932. The plant was a commercial one by Humphreys and Glasgow, having a rated capacity of 1·75 million cu. ft. of gas per day at a calorific value of 490 B.Th.U. The following data from the Report give a picture of comparative performance and show the appreciable saving in oil-consumption made possible by the back-run modification.

To complete the picture there are added to the table gas compositions and calorific values for several c.w. gases at several different levels of calorific value.

It is noteworthy that the specific gravity of c.w. gas is appreciably higher than that of coal gas of the same calorific value. This difference constitutes a difficulty in the utilization of c.w.g. in town gas since it affects the rate of flow of the gas through burner orifices and may require a different burner

F.—Q

setting for efficient usage. In practice efficient mixing and limitation of the proportion of c.w.g. avoids much of the difficulty.

	Back-run.	Down-run.
Coke consumption, lb. per 1000 cu. ft. . . .	41·9	41·3
Steam to generator ,, ,, ,, ,, ,, . . .	41·2	40·4
,, ,, plant ,, ,, ,, ,, ,, . . .	41·3	42·2
Total ,, ,, ,, ,, ,, . . .	82·5	8·26
,, raised in annular boiler	36·4	38·3
,, raised in waste-heat boiler	86·5	87·3
Oil . . . . gals.	2·44	2·24
Efficiency per cent. of production of water gas .	48·0	49·1
,, ,, ,, ,, ,, ,, carburetted gas	68·8	68·5

COMPOSITION OF CARBURETTED WATER GASES

	CO_2.	C_xH_y.	O_2.	H_2.	CO.	CH_4.	C_2H_6.	N_2.	B.Th.U. per cu. ft.	Sp. gr.
(1)	5·3	12·4	0·5	34·6	28·6	10·2	2·0	6·4	520	0·649
(2)	3·7	7·5	0·5	36·5	35·5	8·6	1·6	6·1	491	0·630
(3)	4·3	5·9	0·1	38·0	36·0	7·6	1·3	6·3	450	0·610
(4)	2·5	4·0	0·3	40·6	40·1	4·5	1·2	6·8	400	0·611
(5)	3·8	2·7	0·2	44·2	38·6	3·6	1·0	5·6	350	0·580

The Use of Oxygen. If industrial oxygen were available at a sufficiently low cost the manufacture of water gas could be facilitated by the elimination of the blow period and its conversion to a continuous process. Tonnage oxygen can now be made on a large scale at such a cost that at least one large water-gas plant is using it. On this scale, 360 tons of oxygen per day, the cost is 17 to 21 cents per 1000 cu. ft.

Although the rate of gasification is limited by the necessity to avoid undue fusion of the ash it is reported that the output of the generators is increased by some 40 per cent. Under these conditions the composition of the gas differs from that of normal water gas by having a higher proportion of CO_2. A suitable blast ratio is of the order of oxygen/steam = 7/3, which gives a gas of the following composition.

CO_2	O_2	C_nH_m	CO	H_2	CH_4	N_2	B.Th.U.	Sp. gr.
13·2	1·1	2·3	32·9	42·8	1·1	6·6	292	0·67

It is unlikely, however, that there will be any real expansion on these lines except for very special applications.

The Use of Oils Heavier than Gas Oil. For reasons associated mainly with costs, attempts have been made to use fuel oils in the carburetting of water gas. This is just being applied in Great Britain but had a measure of success in the United States, even with oils as heavy as Bunker " C " showing a Conradson coke residue as high as 11 per cent.

In order to handle heavy oil the carburettor is constructed without chequerwork and that of the superheater is set in flue style, not in staggered courses. The oil is injected, using a fine spray of which the cone comes inside the walls of the carburettor. The heat there is not sufficient and a portion is sprayed into the fire top of the generator, usually less than 50 per cent. This oil need not be sprayed but must be evenly distributed over the fuel bed. With these modifications, the admission of secondary air to the top of the generator, and a back-run cycle, the set will carburet with either gas oil or heavy oil. Dashiel reports that, working with an 11-ft. generator and making 9 to 10 million cu. ft. of c.w.g. per day, the carburettor must be cleaned once per day when using oil of carbon residue 10 per cent., and every third day when using oil of 5 per cent. residue.

Recently a much more satisfactory method has been demonstrated on a Humphreys and Glasgow plant using a chequer-work carburettor. It is indicated that successful gasification of heavy fuel oil can be achieved by doubling the size of the carburettor and using the upper half as a preheater for secondary air to burn off, in part of the normal cycle, all deposited carbon. It has been shown that oil up to 8 per cent. carbon (Conradson) can be wholly gasified in the carburettor when allowing 10 per cent. of the cycle for carbon burning. This means a reduction of plant output of the same amount and an oil consumption of 8 per cent. more than gas oil for the same gas calorific value. The treatment of this heavy fuel oil is therefore technically assured, and whether it is used depends upon relative costs. At the time of writing the difference in cost is from $13\frac{3}{8}$ to $9\frac{5}{8}$ pence per gallon, which would be reduced to 3·4 pence to allow for greater consumption. This should more than cover the reduced output. The scheme has the immense advantage over the U.S. work of no loss of time and no labour charge for cleaning carbon out of the carburettor.

Still heavier oil can be used by pumping a proportion of it to the top of the generator and without increasing the allowance of 10 per cent. of cycle for combustion. In experiments, oil of 11 per cent. carbon value has been gasified in the ratio of 50/50 to require 40 per cent. more oil than gas oil, but further experiment is required to indicate how much more can be treated in the carburettor ; the experimental carburettor had only half the intended surface area.

OIL GAS

Oil gas is made by the cracking or thermal decomposition of oil as in the enrichment of water gas. In the United States, in certain districts where oil is cheap, the oil gas is distributed as a town gas, while in Great Britain it was formerly used quite widely in isolated districts. Extensions of the natural gas pipe-lines in the U.S.A., however, and the use of bottled gas in Great Britain, have now made the process practically obsolete.

Several processes are available which give good yields of permanent gas and one recent process which gives a town gas of high calorific value. Of the first the best known was the Dayton process, in which a cracking chamber is heated externally by oil burners and a mixture of gas and air atomized into the chamber. It is possible to vary the calorific value of the gas from 300 to 560 B.Th.U. per cu. ft. conveniently. The consumption of oil is about 4 gal. per 1000 cu. ft. of gas of 450 B.Th.U., and its cost in the U.S.A. is stated to be about 35 cents. The thermal efficiency of the process is about 75 per cent. to gas, while about 8 gal. of tar are produced per 100 gal. of oil cracked. Careful control of the conditions of cracking is necessary in order to avoid the accumulation of carbon in the retort.

The most recent process is the Hall " high-B.Th.U." process, which was developed for the gasification of heavy oils at a time when the high cost of gas oil for carburetting was giving some concern to manufacturers of carburetted water gas. Since then, however, the extension of the natural gas pipe-lines in the U.S.A. has almost completely done away with the manufacture of town gas by any process.

The Hall process consists essentially in the operation of two pairs of combustion and gasification chambers in a special cycle. Oil and steam are reacted on the hot chequerwork of one chamber and the gas stabilized on the other. The necessary heat is provided by the combustion of deposited carbon in the blow part of the cycle. The system is balanced by combined operation of the two pairs of chambers. The chambers are about the size of the carburettor of a normal c.w.g. plant and an output is attained of about 6 million cu. ft. per day. Oil consumption is of the order of 12 to 14 gal. per million cu. ft. of gas from heavy oil even up to a Conradson figure of 10 per cent.

The gas has a high calorific of 1050 B.Th.U. per cu. ft., but suffers from the drawback of a high specific gravity (0·855) which makes it less easy to mix with natural gas except in limited proportion. Its composition is approx. CO_2 5, C_nH_m 26, CO 3, H_2 18, C_nH_{2+2} 33, N_2 15 per cent.

Conversion of the heavy oil to gas is efficient, the production of tar being not greater than the 15 per cent. normal to c.w.g. plants. If the gas is washed the recovery of light oil is only 0·35 gal. per million cu. ft., and the reduction of calorific value 50 B.Th.U. Efficiency of cracking depends upon the temperature level in the superheater; this is normally 650° C. at the top and 900° C. at the bottom. The thermal efficiency of the whole system is about 80 per cent.

THE COMPLETE GASIFICATION OF COAL

Processes for the complete gasification of coal were originally the direct result of attempts to manufacture water gas with coal as the fuel instead of coke and some success resulted, particularly in the United States. The process was not developed to any large extent and was superseded by the use of coke even before the latter was replaced by the extensions of natural gas.

In the meantime a number of new proposals have been made which embody plant specially designed for the purpose, mainly with the objective of making at low cost and in high yield, synthesis gas for the production of synthetic ammonia or fuels. In every case excepting that of Lurgi the resultant is of low calorific value.

In a water-gas generator the obvious difficulties which the use of coal gives rise to are those caused by the caking of the coal, swelling and sticking in the generator, resistance to the passage of the gases, etc. The tar carried by the gas is another source of trouble in the operation of valves, especially as the tar fog is present in the blow gas as well as in the water gas. When using coal the blast pressure is generally lower, the output of the generator less by perhaps 30 per cent., and amount of fuel used for a given output of gas greater by about 10 per cent. Sometimes the gas made in the last portion of the blow is passed to the wash-box since it is rich enough not to dilute the water gas too much. A modification of the generator is due to Murdock, Evans and Lungren (Amer. Gas Assoc., 1925), who introduce a brick pier into the coal bed so that the rate of heat transfer is increased by disturbing the central plastic zone. Output and yield are both increased as a result.

	With pier.	Without pier.
Fuel, lb. per 1000 cu. ft.	37·2	41·2
Output	144	100

The use of coal in this way is obviously wasteful since too high a proportion of the coal gas is lost in the blow gas. The idea of using the sensible heat of the water-gas process to carbonize coal has, however, given rise to complete gasification proper where the coal is treated in two zones, the blow gas leaving the system at the top of the gasification zone. Since the sensible heat of the water gas is insufficient alone to carbonize the coal in the carbonization zone, heat must be supplied either externally or by superheating the water gas or by using the potential heat of the blow gases to heat the carbonization zone.

The advantage to be gained by gasifying coal in a single process rather than by combining coal carbonization with a water-gas plant can be illustrated by the following yields per ton of coal :

	Therms.
Coal gas, 13,400 cu. ft. at 560 B.Th.U. . . .	75·0
Water gas, 30,000 cu. ft. at 296 B.Th.U. . . .	88·8
	163·8
Complete gasification (Humphreys and Glasgow) : 53,720 cu. ft. at 340 B.Th.U.	182·8

In making the comparison it is assumed that 3 cwt. of coke per ton of coal are required for carbonization purposes, that 10 cwt. remain for treatment in the water-gas generator, and that the latter recovers from waste heat all the steam necessary for running it.

Against this gain of 12 per cent. there is the loss of tar since the coal is not completely carbonized when it reaches the gasification zone. The complete gasification plant should take up less space, involve less capital expenditure and use less labour. Its most important implication is the complete consumption of coke, and from this point of view the partial utilization of the process in gas manufacture should be of importance as a means of balancing coke demand and supply in outside markets.

Specialized Processes for Town Gas

Most of the plants of this type consisted of a carbonization chamber situated above a water-gas generator; gases from the blow period are burned in chequer-brick chambers round the carbonization chamber and provide the heat necessary. The water gas passes upwards through the carbonization zone, providing more heat for this purpose, and mixes with the coal gas formed. The best known of these processes were the Tully, Mond, Strache, and Kraemar and Aarts; in this country Tully plants were in operation in 30 to 40 gasworks at one time.

The Travers-Clark system (*J. Soc. Chem. Ind.*, 1928, **47** 203) is rather different in principle. The blow gases pass from the gasification zone to a separate regenerator where they are burned with air. During the run part of the gas made is drawn back through the heated regenerator and carries its heat through the coal charge, thereby effecting carbonization. Griffith (*Manufacture of Water-Gas*, Ernest Benn, Ltd.) quotes the results of test work on a Travers-Clark plant (quantities per ton of coal):

Uncarburetted gas, cu. ft.	41,900
„ „ therms	150·7
Oil for carburetting, gal.	58·8
Carburetted gas, cu. ft.	45,900
„ „ therms	204·5

The efficiency of the process is quoted at 55·3 per cent., including steam for the auxiliary plant or 65·2 therms of gas per 100 therms of coal gasified.

In the Humphreys and Glasgow plant, the regenerator is replaced by the carburettor and superheater of a normal carburetted water-gas plant. The plant (Figure 112) consists of a water-gas generator with a superimposed carbonizing chamber. The blow gases leave the generator via an annular chamber surrounding it and are burnt in the carburettor with secondary air, storing heat therein and in the superheater. During part of the run the coal in the carbonizing chamber is carbonized by the sensible heat of the water gas resulting from a modified back-run produced by admitting steam to the superheater top and leading the superheated steam to the generator base. In another part of the run the coal is carbonized by the sensible heat of the up-run gases made from steam not superheated in this way. Since this sensible heat is not sufficient for the purpose additional heat is returned from the superheater and carburettor by circulating some of the gas made during the back-run along with the usual back-run steam. Simple adjustment of the amount of recirculation gives complete control of the carbonizing zone and ensures a properly carbonized coke for the water-gas zone. During the time the fixing vessels are not being used to superheat steam they are used, as in normal carburetted-gas practice, for cracking the oil necessary for enrichment to a desired calorific value. A certain proportion of down-running is used; the minimum necessary to bring the clinker down to the grate.

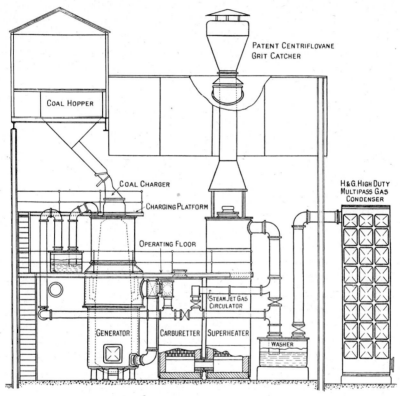

Fig. 112.—Humphreys & Glasgow Complete Gasification System. Coal-carburetted Water-gas Plant.

The plant can deal with caking coals as well as weakly-caking graded coals, and give a gas thermal yield of 180 therms per ton without the addition of oil. The calorific value of the gas is about 340 B.Th.U. and its composition CO_2 6, C_nH_m 28, CO 1, H_2 48, CH_4 7, N_2 10 per cent.

Further carburetting of the gas to the desired calorific value is, of course, achieved at the normal efficiency of this process. The plant as a whole is a flexible addition to gasworks equipment, being able to operate as desired on coal or on coke, to take peak loads, or render more coke available for sale.

An example of the combined system with a carbonization chamber above a gasification chamber is found in the plant made by the Power Gas Corporation. Coal is distilled in the upper section by the sensible heat of hot water gas rising from the chamber below, and also by the heat of the blow gases which pass through heating flues surrounding the coal zone. All the coke is not necessary for carbonizing the coal and part of it is discharged as such. The mixed gas produced has a calorific value of about 400 B.Th.U. per cu. ft.

In Germany, and later in the U.S.A., the development of processes of complete gasification has received much more attention ; in the former because of the desire to utilize indigenous brown coal and of their more advanced use of industrial oxygen, and in both countries because of interest in the manufacture of synthesis gas for the production of synthetic oils from coal. Those processes which have reached the stage of industrial application in Germany form three classes, as follows : (a) Heating of the gasification zone by the recirculation of hot gases, e.g. Pintsch-Hillebrand. (b) Those involving an externally-heated reaction chamber, e.g. Heller, Ahrens, Strache, Didier-Bubiag. (c) Those using oxygen, e.g. Winkler, Lurgi-Drawe, Thyssen-Galoczy, Koppers. The advances most important to our immediate problem have been brought about in Germany by the use of industrial oxygen.

The first two classes are applicable only to brown coal and it is only in the third class that the techniques developed promised adaptability to the complete gasification of bituminous coal. For this reason certain of them have been the subject of research and development in the United States with the objective of synthesis gas, and the subject of research in this country with the main objective of town gas. Since, in Great Britain, the objective at present is town gas of a calorific value of 450 to 500 B.Th.U. per cu. ft., special interest attached at first to the technique of the only process capable of achieving this level of calorific value which had reached the stage of full-scale development, i.e. the Lurgi-Drawe process.

An important factor in considering complete gasification as a future method of making town gas is that the final gas would consist essentially of the three components hydrogen, carbon monoxide and methane, and that the utilization of such a gas would be much less subject to those variations of combustion characteristics which now tend to upset the efficient operation of gas-burning appliances.

Underlying all the projects employing oxygen is the problem of the manufacture of industrial oxygen on a large scale (tonnage oxygen) at an economic price, or alternatively the production of hydrogen-rich gas by a method not involving the use of oxygen.

As a result of this work the field is extended so that systems of complete gasification fall into three groups : (1) fixed fuel bed, of which the simple gas producer and the water-gas machine are the first example ; (2) fluidized fuel bed and (3) entrainment in the gasification medium.

One quite distinct system is available but has not been applied in practice, namely, the enrichment of water gas by the conversion of part of it to methane (see p. 466).

Fixed Fuel Bed. The most important of the new processes is the Lurgi-Drawe process for brown coal, using oxygen and steam at a pressure of 20 atm.

The Texaco Development Corporation is operating a modified generator with separate carbonization and gasification zones and including ash slagging. It is claimed that the type of coal is not critical and that gas of 450 B.Th.U. calorific value can be made. The Gas Research Board (Britain) has done a considerable amount of research work in the development of a similar process.

The Lurgi process embodies a generator as shown in Figure 113, which is essentially a pressurized gas producer with closed coal-charging and ash-discharging vessels and operated by a steam/oxygen blast. In Germany the process has been developed to the stage of a generator of 9 ft. diameter and 25 ft. high, and one installation of 10 generators at Bohlen supplies Leipzig and Magdeburg with town gas at a calorific value of about 450 B.Th.U. Efficient operation requires the careful preparation of the brown coal to a grain size of 2 to 10 mm. and to a moisture content of not greater than 20 per cent. With such fuel (4·4 tons per hour) and an operating pressure of 20 atm., $2\frac{1}{2}$ million cu. ft. of gas or 11,000 therms can be obtained per generator per day.

So far it has been necessary to use a steam/oxygen ratio which avoids slagging the ash, and this represents the only limitation of choice of fuel of the brown-coal type ; it is also the main limitation of gas output. The fuel bed is about 6 ft. deep plus 1 to 2 ft. of ash. The reaction which provides the gas-enriching agent (methane) was supposed to be the direct combination of hydrogen and carbon monoxide, but, as will be shown below, is more probably mainly the hydrogenation of most of the volatile matter during liberation from the coal in the upper part of the bed, the necessary hydrogen being formed by the $O_2/H_2O/C$ reactions of the lower part. This hydrogenation is favoured by increase of pressure, but, since brown coal is a highly-reactive material, sufficient methane formation is achieved at a pressure of 20 atm. to give town gas in one operation, despite the fact that the concentration of hydrogen in the hydrogenating zone is below 40 per cent. As produced, the final gas contains over 30 per cent. CO_2, but is washed with water under pressure to a CO_2 content of less than 5 per cent. before distribution. This washing also removes the H_2S and a small proportion (4 per cent. by volume) of the fuel gases ; on liberation from the water these and the H_2S are burnt under the boilers to utilize their heat value (90 B.Th.U. per cu. ft. ; 9 therms per ton of coal), and this serves as a convenient method of disposing of them.

The thermal efficiency of the process and its yields are given overleaf.

The heat and power requirements for the process are indicated as equivalent therms of coal. The actual yields of gas could be increased from 110 therms to 117 therms if the gases evolved from the coal-charging pocket were recovered ; this would have the effect of reducing the average calorific value from 456 to 450 B.Th.U. per cu. ft. The combustible gases from the scrubber are not recoverable as such.

THE EFFICIENCY OF THE LURGI PROCESS ON BROWN COAL *

	Therms per ton of coal gasified.
Coal gasified	193
Steam to generator	25
Oxygen, power	42
Purified gas	110 (456 B.Th.U.)
Gas from charging pockets	7 (330 B.Th.U.)
Gas from CO_2 scrubber	9 (90 B.Th.U.)
Tar	28
Benzole	12
Ammonium sulphate	27 lb.
Thermal efficiency—Gas/coal gasified . . .	0·57
Gas/total coal . . .	0·43

* Ash 10 per cent. ; moisture 20 per cent. ; 8,600 B.Th.U. per lb. ; steam 7·5 lb. oxygen 15 cu. ft. per 100 cu. ft. of purified gas.

The percentage compositions of the gases made are as follows :

	O_2	CO_2	C_nH_m	CO	H_2	CH_4	H_2S	N_2	B.Th.U. per cu. ft.	Therms ton.
Crude gas .	—	32	0·9	14	35	15·5	1·6	1·0	356	120
Washed gas	—	7	0·8	19	50	22	—	1·2	456	110
Coal hopper gas . .	1·5	30	0·9	13	32	14·1	1·5	7	330	5
CO_2-washer gas . .	—	85	0·5	2·2	4·5	3·1	4·0	0·7	90	9

The latest development in Germany is the construction of a new plant to be operated on German bituminous coal by Ruhrgas A. G., but information is not yet available regarding the performance. The plant is constructed to allow of operation up to 50 atm. pressure, but otherwise there is no important alteration from the design of the brown-coal generator (Figure 113) ; arrangements have been made to recover the gas liberated when the coal hopper is periodically charged.

The work of the Gas Research Board started with a study of the reactions in the upper part of the generator with the special objective of discovering whether the process would operate with weakly-caking bituminous coals and be suitable for the making of town gas in Great Britain. It was established that the reactions were essentially those of hydrogenation of the coal by hydrogen-rich gases formed by the action of steam on reactive coke in the lower part of the generator, the main product of the reaction being methane. A Nottinghamshire coal of type 802 gave 110 therms of methane per ton under conditions which gasified 45 per cent. of the coal. The activity of the coke residue with steam was extremely high. Assuming the gasification of this residue to produce a hydrogenating gas it was possible to visualize a combined process in which the coal would be completely gasified and the gas would have a calorific value high enough for use as town gas.

A visualization of the process is shown in Figure 114. The pressure of operation in this is 50 atm., the steam/oxygen volume ratio 7/1 and the calculated yield of gas 64,000 cu. ft. per ton at a calorific value of 490 B.Th.U. or 245 therms per ton. With full integration of waste heat with power requirements the additional fuel required for all purposes would not exceed 20 per cent. so that the overall thermal efficiency could be about

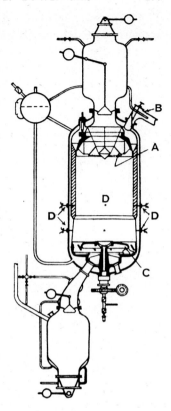

Gas made/process coal = 0·86
Gas made/total coal   = 0·72

It would be interesting to see such a process developed.

Fig. 113.—Lurgi Producer.

A, Deflector plates for coal feed.   B, Gas offtake.
C, Revolving grate.   D, Temperature-control points.

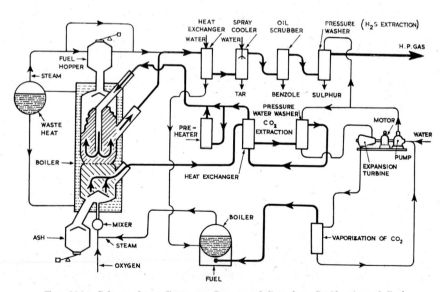

Fig. 114.—Scheme for a Generator Process of Complete Gasification of Coal.

Fluidized Fuel Bed.   An alternative system to the above is to use the boiling-bed or " fluidized " technique in which fuel is gasified in a tall vertical chamber in an oxygen/steam blast supplied at such a velocity as to maintain the bed in a turbulent condition.   The first application of this technique was made in the Winkler process for brown coal.   In Germany the Winkler generator reached a throughput of 40 tons per hour on a grate of 18 ft. dia., the depth of bed being 5 ft. and the output of gas being 2·5 million cu. ft. per hour.   The fuel was closely sized (0·2 to 0·4 mm.).   The temperature is controlled not to exceed the ash-fusion temperature which means a steam/oxygen volume ratio of about 5/1.   Some of the fine dust is carried over, about 20 per cent., and is extracted and used for power generation.

Considerable advances in the handling of finely-divided solids in this way have arisen in the fluidized system of catalytic cracking of petroleum (p. 255) and could be applied in the Winkler process, with the addition of pressure, to make it suitable for the treatment of bituminous coal.   This has been done on a small scale by the Gas Research Board, which has demonstrated that the hydrogenating reactions can be controlled with finely-divided weakly-caking coal to give high yields of the methane for enrichment.

A complete system operating on this technique is visualized in Figure 115 with two reaction zones.   In the lower zone coke residue is gasified with steam and oxygen to provide the hydrogenating gas for the upper zone on which coal is hydrogenated largely to methane.   In order to raise the hydrogen content of the gas from the lower zone the removal of carbon dioxide and unconverted steam is postulated.   A cyclone burner is included to burn out residual carbon from the solid reject from the bottom of the lower zone.

In the U.S.A. experiment on these lines has been on quite a large scale but has been less successful than entrainment methods and its development has consequently been delayed.   The U.S. Bureau of Mines has however developed a special method of feeding pulverized coal into a vessel under pressure which will be of particular value in any process of this type. Termed the Morgantown Feeder, this plant has reached a scale of 600 lb. per hour.   Since mechanical feeders for pulverized coal are not uniformly steady in delivery and tend to compact pulverized coal, and since an airborne system is unsatisfactory when making gas because of the appreciable amount of air necessary for entrainment, the method adopted has consisted in a modification of the fluidized technique.   Two similar 10-in. cylindrical vessels are used ; in the first the coal is maintained in a fluid bed and delivers to the second bed, which in turn delivers at a uniform rate to the gasification plant.   A delivery rate of 600 lb. per hr. is achieved from a tube of 0·33 in. diameter.   The first vessel is operated batchwise and the second continuously under steady conditions.   The feeder has been found satisfactory in use up to a pressure of 450 lb. per sq. in. ; it also allows of the control of caking power to prevent agglomeration, by arranging for preheating and/or oxidation of the coal in either or both vessels. A uniform rate of feed varying only by ±1 per cent. is claimed for coals sized to 90 per cent. passing a 200-mesh sieve, and 100 per cent. passing a 10-mesh

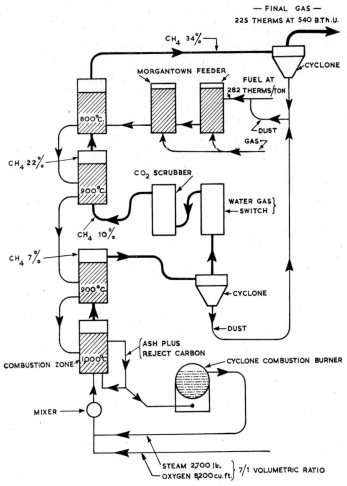

Fig. 115.—Scheme for a Fluidized Process of Complete Gasification of Coal.

sieve. The concentration of solid in the flow stream is 20 per cent. and is independent of pressure between 1 and 10 atm.

In this country a novel application of the non-static fuel bed which differs from that of the fluidized bed is the " moving burden process " of Imperial Chemical Industries, Ltd., for making gas for ammonia synthesis or for the hydrogenation of oils. Powdered fuel is carbonized at 800° C.

in a fluid bed in a current of hot coal gas, of which the temperature is raised (and maintained) by partial combustion with a controlled small amount of air.   The char is then carried into an air-blow vessel from which it travels in suspension during combustion.   The top of this vessel is enlarged to deposit the incandescent coke from the gas stream and it then feeds by gravity to a steaming vessel similar to the carbonizing vessel, where water gas is generated.   Any residue of coke which is cooled below reaction temperature by the steam/carbon reaction can be returned to the air-blow vessel and recirculated.   This process has been operated on a high-ash pulverized coal, but it does not seem that the technique can be modified to make it applicable to the production of town gas.

Entrainment in a Gasification Medium.   This method has been developed mainly to manufacture gas for the synthesis of ammonia or of hydrocarbons for motor fuel or the chemical industry.   Only one, a pressure vortex, has shown promise of being applicable to the making of town gas. Other developments are for power production via the gas turbine.   The most important developments are :

(1) The Koppers process for gasification of pulverized coal in highly-superheated steam and oxygen.

(2) The U.S. Bureau of Mines modifications of this.

(3) The U.S. Institute of Gas Technology gasification of crushed coal by expansion from 50 lb. to atmospheric pressure to disrupt the coal, followed by a cyclonizer to complete the gas/solid reactions.

(4) Gasification in an induced vortex to make hot gas for the gas-turbine (Fuel Research Station) or, under pressure, town gas.

Entrained gasification processes in general must suffer from some of the disadvantages of fluidized systems ; for example, the gas must leave the system at a high temperature, necessitating the careful design of heat-exchange arrangements, while the purification of the finished gas from entrained dust is not easy.   Further, since the carbon surface available for reaction per unit volume of combustion space is low, the rate of gasification of carbon is controlled by diffusion rather than by the rate of chemical reaction.   In order to overcome this fully it is necessary to work at a high temperature, probably above the fusion temperature of the ash, but to keep the time of residence of particles in the hot zone down to a few seconds in order to avoid actual slagging of the ash.   Further, owing to the high speed of the combustion reactions, the oxygen disappears in the early stages of combustion of volatile matter, and the greater part of the reaction space or time is devoted to reactions between carbon, oxides of carbon, and steam. The water-gas shift reaction probably reaches equilibrium at the exit gas temperature.

On the other hand, an important advantage of an entrained gas system is that it is independent of the type of coal, and the preparation of a suitable size of coal is easy.

One process of this type, Koppers (Germany), reached the stage of full-scale trial during the 1939–45 war for the production of synthesis gas.   In this process powdered coal is introduced about one-third of the way up a vertical shaft while an oxygen/steam blast is introduced at the bottom.

A second Koppers (Germany) process was not developed to this extent, but has been advanced to plant scale by the American Koppers Co. on behalf of the U.S. Bureau of Mines (Morgantown) for the manufacture of synthesis gas.   In this design, turbulence is created in a single chamber by introducing steam and oxygen blast, and coal dust, in opposing jets. This plant (at Louisiana, Missouri) is designed to gasify 28 tons of coal per day.   Earlier results from a pilot plant on these lines have been published ; in this plant the generator was a vertical cylinder of 37 in. diameter, 20 ft. high, and achieved continuous operation satisfactorily at a coal consumption of 450 lb. per hr.   Steam was introduced at two tangential inlets

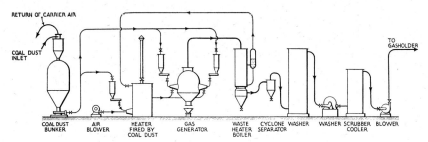

Fig. 116.—Complete Gasification of Powdered Coal (Koppers).

near the bottom of a vertical shaft, and pulverized fuel at one-third of the height of the shaft.   The steam was strongly preheated up to 3000° F. or higher to reduce oxygen consumption.   This reduction is achieved at the expense of higher steam consumption and higher steam preheat, the quantities per 1000 cu. ft. of synthesis gas being as follows :

	Steam.	Coal.	Oxygen.
2,904° F.	81·2 lb.	33·4 lb.	167 cu. ft.
238° F.	29·0 lb.	42·3 lb.	394 cu. ft.

The value of this saving in oxygen depends upon the relative monetary costs of oxygen and superheated steam and is probably in favour of reduced oxygen consumption.   The composition of the synthesis gas was : CO_2, 20 per cent. ; CO, 28 per cent. ; H_2, 45 per cent. ; N_2 7 per cent.   It is apparent that the problem of ash removal still remains to be solved in the first plant, since in this pilot unit some 30 to 40 per cent. was retained as slag on the walls of the generator.

As a result of this work a full-scale plant has been designed by the German Koppers Co. for ammonia synthesis in Finland ; it consists of three generators each capable of gasifying 50 tons of coal dust per day and arranged as shown in Figure 116.

In an entrained gas system the chief limiting factor is the low relative velocity between carbon and gas ; turbulence cannot remedy this since the coal particles tend to move freely in the gas stream and follow its direction of movement. If some means could be found, however, to achieve a relative velocity of some magnitude, chemical rates of reaction rather than diffusion rates would become the controlling factor. Mayers has shown that at 900° C. the reaction $C + CO_2 = 2CO$ is controlled by diffusion below a relative velocity of 0·7 ft./sec. and above this velocity by the rate of chemical reaction.

A novel system of entrainment is proposed by the Texas Co., in which the coal is pumped under pressure in a preheated coal/water slurry. Gasification is achieved with oxygen under pressure. No details are available, but the process is regarded in America as holding special promise.

An entrainment system which does offer relative velocity of some magnitude is the induced vortex ; this was first used for gas/solid reactions by Lander (Brit. Pat. 338108, 1929) in the form of a pulverized-fuel burner. When solid particles are introduced into a spiral vortex they rapidly acquire the same velocity as the fluid. The forces operating on them are (a) the centrifugal force, tending to move the particle outwards, and (b) the radial component of fluid velocity resulting in inward movement of the particle. It is theoretically possible to equate these forces so that each particle rotates in stable equilibrium at a radius determined by its size and density, and by the velocity, temperature, and viscosity of the fluid. If the size of particles should decrease, e.g. if a gasification reaction were proceeding, the particle would move towards the centre and in doing so would be continually scrubbed by the fluid as this passes more rapidly from circumference (or inlet) to the centre. There is therefore a relative velocity of some magnitude between gas and solid which it is not possible to attain by indiscriminate turbulence, and a higher rate of reaction should be reached.

High gasification rates are theoretically possible and have been achieved in the course of combustion experiments, e.g. producer gas has been made containing up to 26 per cent. of carbon monoxide and at an output equivalent to 500,000 B.Th.U. per cu. ft. of reaction space per hour.

In its simplest form an induced vortex operates as shown in Fig. 117 and may be illustrated by means of a water vortex. In the former, air, or the gas-phase of any gas/solid reaction, is introduced tangentially through a number of specially-shaped ports in order that the volume required may be introduced as smoothly as possible and without creating secondary eddies which may disturb any desired pattern of flow. The pulverized coal is introduced with the minimum of carrier gas or air, also through ports so that disturbance is minimized. Where no reaction occurs, a suitable system can be produced in which each group of particles of similar mass revolves at its equilibrium radius. Where reaction occurs between the gas and the solid this condition is not maintained, owing to the steadily diminishing mass of the particles. With coal it is reasonable to assume that some fusion of particles may occur during devolatilization, but the rate of reaction is so great and the spacing of the particles such that agglomeration is avoided. As each particle decreases in mass it moves inwards towards the gas outlet but at a slower rate than the gas. As the gas/solid reaction supervenes, e.g. $C + O_2 = CO_2$, the particle will diminish in size

by reaction and by fragmentation, and the inward velocity will show acceleration. If the temperature is kept below the fusion temperature of the ash and the combustion reaction completed, the gases leaving the outlet should contain all the ash in the form of fine particles. If the temperature rises above the fusion temperature the ash particles will tend to agglomerate, at least in part, and the agglomerates will acquire sufficient mass to be projected towards the walls. In such circumstances the only continuous system would be one in which complete fusion is achieved and fluid molten ash removed so effectively as to avoid building up. It is difficult to visualize the complete removal of fused coal ash in this way and the necessity of operating below the fusion temperature would seem to merit primary consideration.

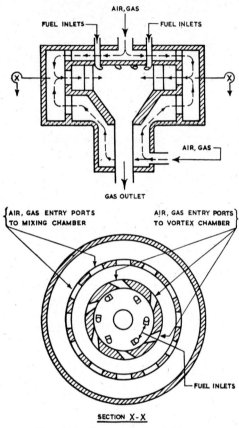

Fig. 117.—Typical Induced Vortex.

Not being entirely satisfied with the Koppers process, the U.S.B.M. have developed a vertical-shaft gasifier to work at either atmospheric pressure or up to 300 lb./sq. in. The former, as a demonstration unit, has indicated that it is ready for operation on the full plant scale. The unit gasified 2000 lb. of coal per hour with 0·9 lb. steam and 9·5 cu. ft. oxygen per lb. of coal to give a synthesis gas containing CO_2 18, CO 40 and H_2 40 per cent. The latter, on a pilot scale of 1280 lb. per hour, and with the oxygen consumption of 9·3 cu. ft. and the lower steam consumption of 0·33 lb. per lb. of coal, has given a synthesis gas of the composition CO_2 10,

CO 53 and H_2 33 per cent.   In both plants the extent of conversion of the carbon of the coal to gas was about 88 per cent.

The Influence of the Cost of Oxygen.   The cost of tonnage oxygen is an important factor in the economics of the above gas-making processes. The systems now available are based on the Frankl cold accumulator which is satisfactory for the production of oxygen of a purity of 98 per cent. or less.   Heat exchange is mostly by regeneration in reversible heat-exchangers with simultaneous removal of water vapour and carbon dioxide ; refrigeration for liquefaction is by means of a turbo-expansion engine.   By duplication of certain parts, mainly heat-exchangers, continuity of operation for more than 300 days per annum is assured.

Power consumption is within the range of 320 to 380 kWh. per metric ton at a rate of 150 tons per day.   This is the main cost and, taking power at 0·75 penny per unit in Great Britain, the total cost would be about £2 15s. per metric ton of 95 per cent. oxygen or 20 pence per 1000 cu. ft. This low cost is assured only on a " tonnage " basis and postulates gas production on a very large scale only, about 1000 tons of coal per day.

The Catalytic Synthesis of Methane.   The catalytic synthesis of methane has been taken to the stage of semi-scale success by the Gas Research Board and data are available for development to a full scale. Synthesis is achieved over a nickel catalyst at 350° C. and a space velocity of 2000 at either atmospheric pressure or 20 atm. using either plain water gas or a hydrogen-enriched water gas.

$$\text{(i)} \quad 2H_2 + 2CO = CH_4 + CO_2 + 59{,}080 \text{ cal.}$$
$$\text{(ii)} \quad 3H_2 + CO = CH_4 + H_2O \text{ (vap.)} + 49{,}300 \text{ cal.}$$

There are two difficulties in the process.   The gas must be freed from sulphur compounds to the level of 2×10^{-5} gr. per cu. ft. and the exothermic heat of reaction must be controlled and utilized.   A satisfactory method of purification has been established which has given a catalyst life of over 6 months.   Several methods of controlling reaction temperature have been established and one is the recirculation of finished gas in the ratio of 4/1. Heat of reaction is recovered by suitable heat interchange and by the inclusion of a waste-heat boiler in the circuit.   The steam produced would cover both process and compression steam and the overall efficiency would be 52–55 per cent.

The high output of the plant is attractive, a catalyst vessel of 4 ft. diameter by 6 ft. high would enrich 5 million cu. ft. of water gas to 2·5 million cu. ft. per day of gas of 450 B.Th.U. calorific value.   Full-scale application has not yet been attempted but it is interesting to realize that this would consume all the spare coke from a 100 ton per day carbonizing bench and leave no coke available for sale.

Methane-enriched gas at a calorific value of 500 B.Th.U. per cu. ft. has the composition :

CO_2	CO	H_2	CH_4	N_2	Sp. gr.
3	11	39	34	13	0·46

It does not have the disability which oil-carburetted gas has of high specific gravity.

REFERENCE BOOKS

Gas Engineer's Handbook.   Pacific Coast Gas Assoc.   McGraw-Hill.   1948.
Manufacture of Water Gas.   Griffith.   Ernest Benn.   1932.

GENERAL BIBLIOGRAPHY :
  J. G. King, *J. Inst. Fuel*, 1951, **24**, 147.
  F. J. Dent, Gas Council Res. Comm., I, 1952.

ENTRAINMENT GASIFICATION :
  A. D. Singh, *Power, Plant Eng.*, 1947, **51**, 112.
  G. L. Newman, *Ind. Eng. Chem.*, 1948, **40**, 559.
  G. R. Strimbeck, Amer. Gas Assoc. Conf., May, 1950.
  J. J. Sebastian, U.S. Bur. Mines Rept. 4742, 1951.

FLUIDIZATION :
  J. G. King, Inst. Gas Eng. Publ. 315, 1948.
  Gas Res. Board, Ann. Repts., 1944 to 1950.
  J. H. Holden and C. W. Albright, Amer. Gas Assoc. Conf., 1950.

METHANE SYNTHESIS :
  F. J. Dent and D. Hebden, *G.R.B.*, **51**, 1949.

OXYGEN :
  C. C. Wright, Amer. Gas Assoc. Conf., 1950.
  J. Wucherer, *J. Iron and Coal Trades Rev.*, 1949, **159**, 723.

CHAPTER XVIII

FUEL ANALYSIS

During recent years, methods of fuel analysis have become closely standardized. Following the lead of the Fuel Research Board in 1923, methods for solid fuels have been published by the British Standards Institution, and for petroleum products, by the Institute of Petroleum. Methods for gaseous fuels have not yet been dealt with. These standards have passed through a number of stages of development, of which the latest are :

Analysis and Testing of Coal and Coke.	B.S. 1016, 1942
Sampling of Coal and Coke.	B.S. 1017, 1942
Institute of Petroleum.	Standard Methods

The reader is recommended to refer to these standards, or to revised editions of them, for matters of detail since only questions of principle are dealt with in this volume. B.S. 1016 and 1017 are now (1954) under revision.

An approach to international agreement on the methods of analysis of solid fuels is now being attempted under the aegis of International Standards Organization (I.S.O./T.C. 27) of which the secretariat is vested in the British Standards Institution, London.

SAMPLING OF FUELS

It is obvious that the results of analysis of any fuel will be representative of the fuel used only when the sample received in the laboratory is truly representative. For this reason methods have also been under close examination, particularly for solid fuels, which are not homogeneous in character. In the case of oil and gas fuels, which are, or can be made homogeneous, sampling presents no real problem, but special procedures are followed to ensure a true sample. With crude oils, which contain water or sediment, the technique is more specialized.

The theoretical basis of the standardized methods for solid fuels has changed several times owing to uncertainty regarding the validity of the theory of selection of the sample. The present British standard is based upon the theory put forward by Grumell and King of " characteristic variability " as a function of average ash content. But this is now being re-examined in the belief that duplicate sampling is necessary with unknown coals to determine probable accuracy and a new specification is being prepared.

In the meantime the operative specification is B.S. 1017 (1942). The specifications for oil sampling are contained in the *I.P. Handbook*. There are no standard specifications for gas sampling but the common methods are all based upon the withdrawal of a small portion or " increment " at a uniform rate for a stream flowing at a uniform velocity.

Coal. Accuracy in the sampling of coal is usually referred to its " ash " content, although moisture is an impurity of equal importance. Strictly speaking, this procedure is not altogether correct since the ash-forming constituents are not uniformly distributed and concordance in ash percentage does not necessarily mean that the coal substance is accurately represented. For this reason some authorities have discussed the accuracy of sampling in terms of calorific value or volatile matter, but this basis is subject to the same errors and has not been pursued. Since complete accuracy in sampling is not possible and is approached only with considerable trouble, it is apparent that the degree of accuracy required may vary with the purpose for which the coal is being handled. It may be sufficient, for example, that separate samples should agree for export purposes within ± 8 per cent. of the ash content while for industrial purposes ± 5 per cent., and for power station and experimental purposes ± 3 per cent., may be required.

In dealing with coal the sampler has to contend with widely varying conditions in the size and nature and position of the coal, all of which demand different methods of taking the initial or gross sample. The limitation of the size of the gross sample in terms of the accuracy required is therefore an important consideration.

The first approach to a scientific basis for sampling a heterogeneous material was not made until 1909 when E. G. Bailey (*J. Ind. Eng. Chem.*, 1909, **1**, 160) developed an empirical relationship between the maximum error in sample reduction and the ratio of the largest particles of impurity (mineral matter) to the weight of the sample. It is now realized that this is consistent with the theoretical relation between the variance of single pieces and the number of particles in the sample.

It was not until after 1930 that a theory was advanced to cover the distribution and number of the small portions or " increments " of coal which together would give a bulk sample whose ash content would not differ from the true ash content of the consignment by more than a certain amount.

These theoretical questions are fully discussed in papers by Grumell and Dunningham, and Grumell and King (*J. Inst. Fuel*, 1933, **6**, 143, and S.T.M. Conf. Zurich, Sept., 1933 ; Eng. Stand. Assoc., 1930, 403). Experience over a number of years had shown these experimenters that each coal had a characteristic variability which could be expressed as the " average error " of ash content of a large number of samples from the true ash content. This average error was found to be the same whether calculated from the increments of one truck, or a number of trucks. Further, the average error was found to increase regularly with increasing ash content for any one coal, though not necessarily for mixed coals.

Each coal has been found to have a characteristic variability which can be expressed as the " average error " of ash content of a large number of samples from the true ash content, and for a given coal the " average error " varies with the ash content approximately as follows :

Average error	.	< 1·0	1·0 to 1·5	1·5 to 2·0	2·0 to 2·5
Per cent. ash	. .	Up to 7	7–10	10–15	Over 15

With mixed coal the " average error " may be as high as 2·5 to 3·0, irrespective of the ash content.

The practical issues are that the total weight of the gross sample taken will :

1. Increase with the ash content of the coal owing to the greater number of increments necessary.

2. Increase with the size of the coal owing to the increase in weight of the increment.

The greatest weight of gross sample is demanded when the coal is large and of high ash content, the smallest for low ash coal of small size.

The British Standards Specifications were based on these proposals and detailed instructions for sampling coal and coke are to be found in B.S. 1017, 1942. The minimum weight of sample is given for several degrees of accuracy for groups of coals of different ranges of size and ash content. The following are important points in procedure.

In taking the increments of coal from a consignment even spacing is the first consideration. When the coal is in motion as in conveyors, or flowing from chutes or hoppers at a uniform rate, a time basis is correct; with irregular rates the sampler must assess his increments in terms of tonnage passing the sampling point. The main precaution necessary is to cover with the sampling scoop all parts of the flowing stream since coal tends to segregate into sizes.

Sampling from wagons or heaps is not to be recommended since it is extremely difficult to obtain an average sample. Sometimes it is essential that wagon trains of coal should be sampled ; in this case the best procedure is to take the increments from the bottom of holes (1 ft. deep) spaced evenly over the consignments. In doing so it must be borne in mind that the small coal and large coal must be suitably represented in the gross sample since their ash contents may differ widely. In order to do so lumps must sometimes be broken and suitable quantities taken. It is apparent that this method leaves considerable room for error, but it is an interesting fact that an experienced sampler can attain a considerable measure of success when sampling from trucks.

The reduction of the initial or gross sample to one of laboratory size should follow immediately the whole sample is available. Since moisture content is frequently an important factor a coal sample should always be collected by placing the increments in a covered bin so that loss of moisture by either drainage or evaporation is prevented. The bulk sample should be spread on a clean hard floor and mixed, and reduced in weight by crushing, mixing and subdivision. The latter may be done by " coning and quartering " by hand, but preferably with the aid of some mechanical device, such as a " riffle " (see Brit. Stand. Sampling of Coal for Boiler Trials ; King and MacDougall, *Fuel*, 1933, **12,** 93). For most of the determinations the air-dried material reduced to pass a 72-mesh British Standard Test sieve is employed.

The underlying principles of sample reduction have been made clear by E. G. Bailey (*loc. cit.*), who first recognized that an important factor was the ratio of the weight of the largest pieces of dirt or shale in the coal to the weight of the sample. This ratio he called the " size : weight percentage ", i.e. $100x/w$ where x is the weight of the dirt particle and w the weight of the sample. After exhaustive experiment Bailey drew curves for one coal containing 11·5 per cent. of ash (of which 5·0 was dirt, slate, etc.), connecting the size-weight percentage and the probable and possible errors of ash percentage. In drawing the curves Bailey omitted certain apparently discrepant points and drew what is essentially a curve of mean values. Also, although his papers quote " the size of the largest particle " he actually used the mean of a number of the largest particles.

It must be pointed out that Bailey's findings refer to coal of 11·5 per cent. ash content, i.e. 5 per cent. free ash and 6·5 per cent. inherent ash. It has been accepted that British coals have only about 4 per cent. inherent ash so that a British coal corresponding to Bailey's would contain only 9 per cent. of total ash. Bailey's found errors can therefore be applied directly to British coal of 9 per cent. ash. From this base-line the errors for other coals can be calculated from the finding that the error is proportional to the square root of the free ash content.

It is possible to draft tables connecting weight of sample with each size of coal for a series of S.W.R. or maximum errors. Such tables are of great value in the reduction of samples, but their use is subject to two reservations :

(i) The errors in each stage of reduction may be additive in one direction ; reduction in one stage to very small size is therefore a safer method if practicable.

(ii) If the dirt in the sample is hard the largest particles after crushing may be entirely dirt and not coal, so that the mean weight taken for this size in the graph is too small.

Coke. The sampling of coke conforms to the same rules as that of coal. From the point of view of ash content metallurgical coke is less variable than coal since it is normally made from coal crushed to pass a $\frac{1}{8}$-in. screen and well mixed. Gas coke made from larger coal is more similar to coal. Experiment has shown that the moisture content of metallurgical coke is a more variable factor than ash content and the sample necessary for a given accuracy has been deduced from a consideration of the variation of moisture content in the same way as described above for ash in coal. Variation in moisture content increases with the percentage up to 9 and remains constant between 9 and 15. Variation in ash content is less than this except when the moisture content is about 2 per cent. It has been found by experiment that the size of increment must not be less than $2\frac{1}{2}$ lb. The specification recognizes two classes of coke, (1) containing less than 5 per cent. moisture and $7\frac{1}{2}$ per cent. below one inch in size, and (2) other cokes. The number of increments necessary for these two classes in order to give an accuracy within ± 1 per cent. 99 times out of 100 is as follows:

Moisture per cent.	No. of increments.		Weight of sample.	
	(1)	(2)	(1)	(2)
Up to 2	20	35	50	88
4 to 5	95	170	238	425
7 to 8	126	300	315	750

Statistical Methods. Following the adoption of the B.S.I. standards a number of attempts have been made to find an exact mathematical basis for coal sampling on the assumption that coal was a system in which there was random distribution of coal particles of different sizes, and random distribution of mineral matter. The first attempt was by A. B. Manning (*J. Inst. Fuel*, 1935, **9**, 132), but was not followed up. In 1944 B. A. Landry was the first to point out that it could not be assumed that the ash in coal was ever distributed in a random manner; that coal was a " patchy " material in which there was considerable segregation of both size and mineral matter varying from coal to coal. He suggested the inclusion of a factor in theoretical treatment to cover this, and claimed that the variance of the ash figure decreased with increasing size of increment. J. Visman (*Trans. Fuel Econ. Conf., Hague*, 1947, **2**, 430) later held that variance reached a limiting value at some size of increment.

However, experimental work carried out by the Sampling Committee of the B.S.I. has established that there is no clear relation between weight of increment and variance, and it has concluded that the irregular distribution of ash in coal (patchiness) makes the establishment of a sound theory a practical impossibility. The Committee are therefore working on the lines of establishing a practice of sampling which, by giving a measure of the accuracy obtained, will give a guide to the number of increments, and their size, likely to be satisfactory with unknown coals. The method of assessing accuracy during sampling is based on duplicate sampling as suggested by R. L. Brown (*B.C.U.R.A. Info. Circ.* 39, 1950). This consists in two samples from each unit, or selected units (trucks, etc.), of the bulk, and analysing both samples of each unit. The standard deviation of each pair will be the mean difference divided by 1·13. The S.D. of the overall mean (M) of P pairs will be M/2P, from which the limits of accuracy can be calculated for the desired tolerance of, say, 95 times in a 100.

For example, in a consignment of 50 units, 7 are selected which show differences between duplicates varying from 2·5 to 0·2, and an overall mean of 1·21, the S.D. is 0·29. At a tolerance of 95 per cent. the variance is ±0·6, much less than that of the unit samples.

The application of statistical methods to data collected in this way is expected in time to give a really reliable guide to the sampling of solid fuels. The actual size of increment necessary for a given accuracy can be arrived at only by experience but is considered to be quite close to that calculable from B.S. 1017.

Oil. The sampling of oils or liquid fuels is not by any means as com-plicated as in the case of solid fuels, for in general the liquid is of much more uniform composition. Sampling has normally to be carried out either from tanks, barrels, etc., in which the oil is stored or when the oil is in course of transfer from storage to some other position. Nevertheless, certain general principles must be adhered to so that properly representa-tive samples may be obtained, and full directions for sampling of petroleum and petroleum products will be found in the Standard Methods of the Institute of Petroleum (London) and the American S.T.M. The main material is, of course, oil, but products may be semi-solid, liquefied gases, or gases. Methods and containers are specified for each. In the case of oil in flow, arrangements may be made for the collection at intervals of samples which will then be mixed, and an appropriate final sample drawn, or a continuous sample may be taken from the pipe-line. In the latter case, in order that it may be average, it is recommended that the sample pipe be inserted into the delivery pipe to a distance of one-third of its diameter and bent to face the oil stream. If possible, the pipe should be installed in a rising section on the delivery side of the pump.

Where the material is in vessels which permit of it being thoroughly mixed, this should be done before sampling, but it is obviously impossible with large tanks or receptacles which are nearly filled.

From tanks, drums, etc., samples are best obtained by means of a " thief "—usually a metal cylindrical tube of about $1\frac{1}{4}$ in. diameter fitted with a valve operable by a rod leading to a lever at the other end. By plunging this into the oil, allowing it to fill and closing the top opening with the thumb, the sample can be withdrawn.

From tanks an all-levels sample is taken by sinking a weighted bottle in the tank, the bottle being provided with a cork which is easily removed by means of a line, and raising the bottle to the surface at such a rate that a fair sample is withdrawn throughout the depth of oil. In the case of deep tanks, drums, etc., samples are drawn at the bottom, about the middle, and near the top in a similar manner, but the proportion of each quantity taken to make the bulk sample will depend upon the cross-section of the tank. In the case of a vertical cylindrical or a square tank of uniform cross-section, one volume of the upper dip, one of the lower and three of the middle are taken as an average when mixed, whilst from a full horizontal cylindrical tank eight parts of the middle sample are taken to one each of the upper and lower samples.

Semi-solids are sampled by an auger which will allow a core to be extracted, or by a scoop.

Liquefied gases are sampled either from gauge-glass connections or from sample lines.

For the sampling of a heterogeneous liquid such as tar the main stream and the sample stream are arranged to discharge through orifices having the same relation between pressure and rate of discharge whatever the rate. The pressures at the orifices are kept equal and time lag is prevented. If solid matter is likely to cause clogging of the orifices a filter of the " auto-clean " type is used.

For closing receptacles containing oil samples, sound wood stoppers should be employed, rubber is inadmissible and no sealing by wax or paraffin poured over the corks is permissible.

Certain petroleum samples stored in glass bottles require protection from light.

Gases. The obtaining of a gas sample from a flowing stream of gas of uniform quality or of uniform speed is a relatively simple matter. Special gas-sampling tubes are used which are cylindrical glass vessels drawn out at each end to take glass stopcocks, preferably of the 2-way type. In taking the sample, the tube is filled with a containing liquid and attached to the sampling cock with rubber tubing. If the gas is under pressure it is allowed to blow out of the side tube of the upper stopcock in order to displace air from the connections. Both stopcocks are then opened and the containing fluid allowed to run out of the sampling tube. If the gas is not under pressure, it is necessary to use a suction ball to clear the connection. In some cases where it is inconvenient to use a containing liquid, a suction ball may be attached to the lower stopcock of the sampling tube and the sample drawn through by suction. In this case sufficient time must be allowed to elapse to clear out the air completely.

If the gas stream is not uniform in rate or composition, the gas-sample can be taken at a uniform rate by a sample-tube with a containing liquid, clamping it in a vertical position with the top connection made to a sample pipe-line along which the gas to be sampled is blown or sucked at a suitable rate. The bottom connection is then made to a reservoir which can be lowered at a uniform rate so as to fill the tube with gas over any desired period. This may be done by clockwork, the weight of the clock being attached to the lower stopcock, or it may be done by water displacement, the levelling tube being connected to a float in a water tank in which the level of the water is made to rise at a uniform rate by the flow of water from a calibrated jet. Such an apparatus is illustrated in B.S. 1756, Figure 6, for the sampling of flue gases.

The capillary bore of the stop-cocks prevent loss or change of sample sufficiently over normal periods of sampling.

When the main gas stream is being passed through a gas meter, a uniform sample may be collected by gearing a small meter to the drive of the large meter and by-passing through the small meter an aliquot portion of the main stream. In such cases the gas sample is usually measured and is collected in a small gasholder.

The only really satisfactory containing liquid for gas sampling is mercury. Even this is affected by gases which contain hydrogen sulphide. Water and aqueous solutions introduce difficulties, since they dissolve carbon dioxide readily. Saturated solutions of magnesium chloride and 50/50 solutions of glycerine in water have low solubilities for carbon dioxide, and can be used for periods of several hours without causing appreciable error.

ANALYSIS OF COAL

For details of the methods of analysis of coal the reader is referred to text-books.

Frequently, requirements in the way of analysis of fuel are only the " proximate " analysis, the percentage of sulphur, and calorific value. For special applications, however, the examination of coal embraces also " ultimate " analysis, assay, washability, nature of ash and its fusion temperature, proportion of banded constituents, caking index, softening temperature and certain specialized tests. It would be impossible to describe these fully in this volume, and it has been decided to take the methods themselves as read and to describe instead certain important facts which are the essential bases of the methods adopted, but which do not appear in the bare details of manipulation.

Coal used for analytical purposes should be ground to pass a 72 B.S. sieve, air-dried and thoroughly mixed. The bottle in which it is stored should be air-tight and quite full. If it is subjected to much handling before analysis the contents should be re-mixed before any portion is withdrawn.

Moisture Content. The moisture content of coal at the moment of sampling is of special importance since it is the base-line for any calculations on the composition of the coal as used or as purchased. For this reason a special moisture sample is called for in the sampling specifications and special precautions need not be taken in the handling of the analysis sample to avoid loss of moisture in preparation for the laboratory.

Proximate Analysis. This consists of the determination of moisture, volatile matter, fixed carbon, and ash and sometimes also sulphur content.

The proximate and other analyses should always be made on coal which has been air-dried in the laboratory so that its moisture content is in approximate equilibrium with the atmosphere. Changes in moisture content during weighing, etc., are in this case less likely to introduce errors. The precaution is only partial, since atmospheric humidity shows sometimes large changes, and when the analysis is spread over several days the moisture content should be checked more than once per day. The most common method of determination of moisture is that of loss of weight on drying in an oven at 105° to 110° C. The average oven is badly designed since it contains too large a free space and efficient sweeping out of the moisture-laden atmosphere is difficult. Similarly, when oxidation must be prevented by using an atmosphere of nitrogen, it is practically impossible to achieve this. The only oven which will allow of this method giving the true result is one in which the free space is reduced to a minimum and the coal is heated in a current of nitrogen. Such ovens are only just coming in, and it will not be long before drying in nitrogen will entirely replace drying in air. When coal is heated in air at 105–110° C. it will first lose moisture and then begin to gain in weight owing to oxidation. Some coals show this phenomenon within the time specified in moisture determinations ; the observed loss in weight is then less than the true moisture.

The true moisture in coal is obtained by using a nitrogen oven and also when the coal is distilled with toluene in an apparatus similar to that in Figure 122. Both methods in careful hands give results which agree with that obtained by the direct method of weighing the moisture liberated by passing a stream of dry nitrogen over coal heated to 105–110° C., the moisture being collected in a tared tube containing a drying agent.

Volatile Matter, Coke, Fixed Carbon. Since the determination of volatile matter in coal is an empirical test it is of the greatest importance that the stipulations of the standard method should be carefully followed. The important factors are rate of heating and temperature used. The coal (1 gm.) is heated to 925° C. $\pm15°$ C. out of contact with air in a crucible of standard size. Formerly platinum crucibles only and gas heating were used, but it has now been found possible to obtain the same results by using silica crucibles in a muffle furnace. The platinum crucible was the ultimate standard, however, and any muffle used must have sufficient reserve of heat so that the introduction of a batch of crucibles does not reduce its temperature so much that it does not recover the full temperature within the coking time. Otherwise, the figure obtained for volatile matter will be low.

Carbonaceous coals and anthracites do not give satifactory results by the crucible method and should be treated by the method used for coke (see p. 485). Coking in a current of hydrogen by Rose's method will give fairly concordant results.

Some coals tend to decrepitate when heated rapidly and give high results. These must be heated more slowly at first and then at the full temperature. This expedient affects the result to a variable extent, generally in the direction of giving low values.

At one time in the preparation of the B.S. specifications the temperature was 965° C. This increase of temperature of 40° C. caused a relatively small decrease in the figure obtained ; in coal containing 35 per cent. of volatile matter the difference is only about 0·3.

The residue from the determination of volatile matter is referred to as the ": crucible " coke or coke button and its appearance gives an indication of the caking power of the coal. In quoting a proximate analysis the analyst should always describe the coke. Unfortunately, the appearance of the coke differs sometimes, depending upon whether a gas-heated platinum crucible or a muffle-heated silica crucible is used : the method of making the coke should therefore be quoted also.

The coke comprises " fixed carbon " and ash, the former being an empirical figure obtained by deducting from the coke percentage obtained in the volatile matter test the ash percentage obtained by the standard method of ash determination.

Alternative methods for the determination of volatile matter are the high-temperatured distillation methods of Bone and Silver and of Lessing. These methods, embodying great control of the rate of heating and the temperature, offer some advantages over the crucible method, particularly as regards the definition of the nature of the coke and the correlation of the volatile matter (gas and tar) to carbonization processes. It has been shown that the Lessing method gives figures for volatile matter which are closely related to those of the crucible method. The details of these methods are given in the British Standard specifications but are not included here.

Ash. A most important factor in the determination of ash content in coal is that there should be free circulation of air over the coal during its combustion. A second is that initial combustion should be slow in rate since some coals tend to spit or decrepitate. The reason for free circulation of air is to make certain that the inorganic constituents should be fully oxidized. Ash dishes should not be covered during burning off since this increases the amount of sulphur fixed in the ash when the latter contains much calcium oxide.

It is apparent that the ash weighed differs from the original inorganic constituents present in the coal by (i) the CO_2 evolved from carbonates, (ii) the water of hydration of clays, (iii) the change in state from pyrites FeS_2, to iron oxide Fe_2O_3, (iv) the fixation of organic sulphur in the ash as sulphate, and (v) the evolution of chlorine. Some small loss of alkalis may also occur, but not to any large extent if the temperature does not exceed 800° C. Ashes should not contain sulphides if the coal is burned in the proper way with free access of air. The proportion of inorganic constituents (M) in the coal may be calculated from the ash content by the formula.

$$M = 1{\cdot}09\ \text{ash} + 0{\cdot}5\ S_{pyr.} + 0{\cdot}9\ CO_2 - 1{\cdot}1\ SO_{3\ ash} + SO_{3\ coal} + 0{\cdot}5\ Cl$$

This formula assumes that the water of hydration of clays is 8 per cent., that 3 parts FeS_2 form 2 parts Fe_2O_3 and that half the chlorine is inorganically combined.

A convention such as this is useful in calculations of the true composition of the coal substance, free from inorganic matter, since the inorganic matter may differ from the ash by several per cent. and the use of the ash figure would involve large errors in, say, the true carbon content of " pure " coal.

The large amount of analytical work involved is, however, rather against the wide adoption of the formula, and a simplified version has been suggested by F. Fereday and D. Flint (*Fuel*, 1953, **32**, 115), which is :

$$M' = 1{\cdot}060\ A + 0{\cdot}53\ S + 0{\cdot}74\ CO_2 - 0{\cdot}33$$

The K.M.C. formula, however, remains the standard of reference in the meantime. It does require close examination in relation to other coals and some modification for local application.

The formula commonly used in the United States (S. W. Parr and W. F. Wheeler, *Univ. Ill.*, *Bull.* No. 37, 1909) is not regarded as satisfactory in Britain since it includes all the sulphur with the mineral matter, although the greater proportion of the sulphur of most coals is organic in type and must be part of the coal substance. The Parr formula is :

$$\text{Mineral matter} = 1{\cdot}08\ \text{ash} + 0{\cdot}55\ S$$

Ash Analysis and Fusion Temperature. Fusion temperature was first determined by comparing the behaviour of a cone made of the ash when heated in a furnace alongside Segar cones of known melting-points (Cobb, *J. Soc. Chem. Ind.*, 1904, 11). The present more precise method consists in moulding a small quantity of coal ash into a pyramid and heating it to the fusion-point under controlled conditions of atmosphere and rate of heating. The method was first evolved by Fieldner, Hall and Feild (*U.S. Bur. Mines, Bull.* 129, 1918) and later modified by Blackie, King and Millott (*Fuel Res. Paper* 23, 1929) and the latter is the basis of the standard method included in B.S. 1016.

Two temperatures are observed : (i) the initial softening of the test piece and (ii) the final settling of the fused cone to a blob. In the case of ashes which contain iron oxide the nature of the atmosphere over the ash affects the result. An atmosphere which is sufficiently reducing to reduce the iron oxides to the ferrous state gives the lowest fusion temperature obtained. Stronger reduction to free iron gives a higher fusion temperature as does also oxidation to ferric oxide. The atmosphere which gives the minimum fusion temperature varies with the type of ash but may vary between such wide limits as 80 and 20 per cent. of oxidizing gases. Oxidizing gases are oxygen, carbon dioxide and water vapour, while reducing gases are methane, carbon monoxide and hydrogen. A suitable reducing atmosphere can therefore be arranged in several ways; two convenient ways are (1) by introducing cooled flue gas and (2) by burning over the ash, hydrogen saturated with water at 80° C., i.e. a 50/50 hydrogen-steam mixture. The difference in temperature of fusion caused by the atmosphere may be very considerable.

In reporting ash-fusion temperatures it is customary to describe the successive stages of deformation of the cone. The " cone " used is a three-sided pyramid about 1 in. high, and with one side vertical, and weighing about 0·7 gm. The temperatures are observed by means of a hot-filament pyrometer, the filament being focused on the tip of the cone.

The methods of analysis used for the examination of the composition of coal ash are those of silicate rock only slightly modified. The methods were originally described by King and Crossley (*Fuel Res. Tech. Paper* 23, 1928) but the present standard is the modified version of this (*Tech. Paper* 50, 1952.)

Other methods are in common use on the Continent which make precise optical measurement of the rate of settling of the pyramid or cone. Most of these stem from the original work of Bunte and Baum (*Gas. Eng.*, 1932, **49**, 639).

Although the fusion temperature of a test piece of ash can be fairly accurately determined in this way, there still remains the difficulty of interpreting them in terms of the actual conditions under which the coal is used, when the components of the ash are not uniformly mixed and are even of large size. The observations therefore can be of only very general use and must be very carefully interpreted in terms of the conditions of usage of the coal.

Ultimate Analysis. By this is meant the determination of the percentages of the chemical elements which form the coal substance. The methods adopted are therefore very similar to those used in normal organic analysis.

The determination of carbon and hydrogen is done on a very small quantity of coal (200 mgm.) and it is therefore necessary to observe certain precautions other than those used with a pure substance. The chief are that the coal sample should be carefully mixed before taking the quantity for analysis and that a moisture sample should be taken at the same time so that a correct allowance may be made for this in calculating the results. The figures obtained directly for carbon and hydrogen contain the carbon of any carbonates in the coal and the hydrogen of the water of hydration of clays. The true carbon figure is obtained by deduction, but the hydrogen figure is not usually corrected. It is known that some coals contain an appreciable amount of chlorine so that the use of a silver spiral is theoretically necessary. It will usually be found, however, that the lead chromate used to catch sulphur compounds will trap all but negligible amounts of chlorine also.

King and MacDougall (*Fuel*, 1926, **5,** 33) have shown the carbon-hydrogen determinations can be conducted with uniform accuracy if the oxidation zone is maintained at a uniform temperature of 800° C. and a period of about eighty minutes is taken over the combustion of the coal, i.e. two hours for a complete determination.

If the combustion temperature is raised to 1350° C. the time taken for multiple work may be 24 per tube per day as against only 3 by the Liebig method. In order to achieve this it is necessary to use a modified apparatus including a molybdenum-wound furnace and burn 0·5 g. of coal in a rapid stream of oxygen. The coal is burned to CO_2, oxides of sulphur and chlorine: a roll of silver gauze at 800° C. retains the two latter and the water and CO_2 are absorbed on solid reagents. The method (Belcher and Spooner) will be included in the revised edition of B.S. 1016.

Nitrogen is determined by the well-known Kjeldahl method for the determination of nitrogen in foodstuffs. One g. of coal is heated with 10 g. of K_2SO_4, 0·2 g. powdered Se and 30 ml. of concentrated sulphuric acid. Heating should continue for 2 hours beyond the time when the solution becomes clear.

Sulphur is determined by the Eschka method or by the combustion of the coal in a closed vessel or bomb with oxygen. Both methods are reliable but certain precautions are necessary in the latter (see King and Crossley, *Fuel*, 1929, **8,** 544). In the Eschka method the flux should not contain more than a trace of sulphur since there is danger that this may not be uniformly distributed.

The sulphur determined in this way is the total sulphur and the figure quoted in the ultimate analysis (combustible sulphur) should be less by the amount of sulphur which is fixed as sulphate in the ash. This latter amount is determined directly in ash prepared under the same conditions as those obtaining during the determination of the percentage of ash.

The proportion of oxygen in coal cannot be determined directly by any reliable method and it is customary to obtain this as the difference from 100 per cent. of the sum of the other determined constituents. To do this as accurately as possible it is necessary to calculate, as shown above, the analysis to a mineral-matter-free basis. This is not always done at present, but should eventually become common practice.

Elements not normally present in appreciable quantity do not appear in the " ultimate " analysis, but their proportion is stated separately. These are chlorine, phosphorus and arsenic. Chlorine is determined by a variation of the Eschka method. Phosphorus is determined in the ash by a modification of the phosphomolybdate method and arsenic by the Gutzeit method.

The results of a coal analysis should always be reported in such a manner as to include both the actual analytical figures and the analysis of the coal as it was used or, failing this, as it was delivered to the laboratory. Calculations to dry coal or to dry ash-free coal should be made only if specially required. The misleading nature of the latter is now recognized. An example of a completely corrected analysis is given below :

	Per cent. as analysed.		Per cent. as corrected.
Moisture	5·1	Moisture	5·1
Ash	6·2	Inorganic matter [1]	7·1
Carbon	75·4	Carbon [2]	75·3
Hydrogen	5·2	Hydrogen	5·2
Sulphur (combustible) . . .	1·5	Sulphur (combustible) [3] . . .	1·5
Nitrogen	1·5	Nitrogen	1·5
Difference	5·1	Chlorine [4] (organic)	0·1
		Oxygen [5]	4·2
	100·0		100·0

Carbon dioxide	0·3	Total sulphur	1·7
Sulphur in ash	0·2	Carbon dioxide	0·3
Chlorine	0·2	Total chlorine	0·2
S yr.	0·6		
Sulphate	0·2		

[1] Calculated as shown under ash on page 477, K.M.G. formula.
[2] Total carbon less carbon in carbon dioxide.
[3] Total sulphur less sulphur in ash.
[4] The true correction is as yet uncertain, but there are indications that about half of the chlorine is organically combined.
[5] This is still a difference figure but is more nearly the true oxygen content than the difference figure shown in the " as analysed " column.

In order to make the calculation from ash to inorganic matter it is necessary to determine in the coal the amount of pyrites and sulphate present. The methods adopted in modern standards, without fundamental change, are due to Powell and Parr (*Univ. Ill. Bull.* 111, 44, 1919) and are based upon the solubility of sulphates and not pyrites in dilute hydrochloric acid. The sulphate and pyritic sulphur are determined together by digestion of the coal with nitric acid. Organic sulphur is determined by difference.

In industrial practice it is now considered correct to show the data in separate columns (1) as analysed on the air-dried coal, (2) calculated to the moisture content of the moisture sample and representing the coal as used or purchased, (3) calculated to dry coal for test purposes, (4) calculated to dry, ash-free, coal for purposes of comparison and (5) calculated to mineral-matter-free coal. (4) is not recommended except for coal of low ash content.

F.—R

Special Tests Supplementary to Coal Analysis. Bituminous coals are put to so many diverse uses that their characterization by proximate and ultimate analysis is not always sufficiently accurate. For this reason a number of special tests have been devised for coal to be used for specific purposes. Most of these tests are empirical and depend for their success upon the close application of standardized conditions.

Three methods have been standardized in Great Britain for the evaluation of the caking power of coal; these are the Crucible Swelling Index, the Gray-King Assay (coke-type), and the Agglutinating Index. In international discussion the Roga and Audibert-Arnu methods are also included. These tests measure different factors in the caking of coal and can be correlated only broadly.

The Crucible Swelling Number is obtained by heating 1 g. of coal in a special crucible to 820° C. under standardized conditions and comparing the profile of the coke produced against a series of standards.

The Agglutinating Index is determined by a standardized form of the original Campredon method of mixing coal with an inert material such as graded sand and stating the proportion which fails to give a coherent mass. The B.S. inert material is a pure silica sand graded by elutriation between 52 and 72 B.S. sieves; it is obtainable from the Fuel Research Station.

The Gray-King Assay was developed for the examination of coals for carbonization purposes to provide information not given by analysis. It consists in the controlled distillation of 20 g. of coal and examination of the products (*Fuel Res. Tech. Papers* 1, 21 and 24) in the apparatus shown in Figure 118. The results have been correlated with coal-gas production (J. G. King, *J. Inst. Fuel*, 1939, **12,** 350) at one level of temperature (900° C.) and at the other level (600° C.) have been used in recording the properties of coals for survey purposes, and in defining one index of caking properties. This consists in comparing the appearance of the coke residue with a series of standards. Using powdered coal, absence of caking power gives a pulverulent coke; medium caking power (about 16 Campredon) gives a " standard " coke about the same volume as the original coal and strong and hard; greater caking power is assessed numerically by the proportion of electrode carbon which must be added to give the " standard " coke.

The Gray-King assay coke-type (Chapter V and Figure 17) is now adopted as one of the standards of caking power used in the International Standards Organization's work on a scheme of coal classification, and all three methods will be included in the new British standards (B.S. 1016 revised).

Other assay methods of a similar type have been developed from time to time and are applied to a less extent. These are Lessing (*Fuel*, 1923, **2,** 152), Fischer (*Gas Abhandl. z. Kentniss, der Kohle*), used in survey work by the U.S. Bureau of Mines, and Bauer (*Fuel*, 1926, **5,** 347). All such methods are related to the well-known one-thousandth-ton assay of the gas industry which is directly correlated to plant performance.

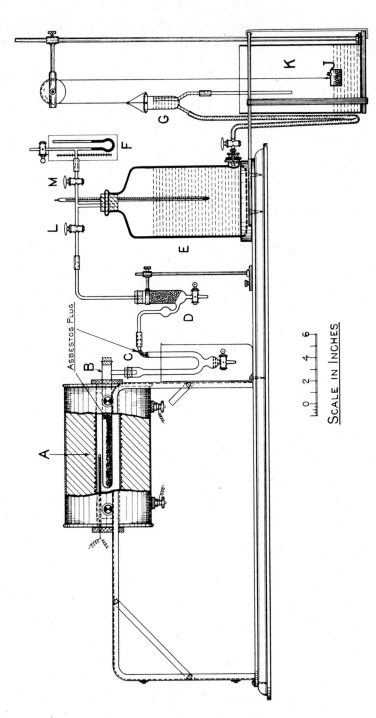

ASBESTOS PLUG

SCALE IN INCHES

Fig. 118.—Gray-King Low-temperature Assay Apparatus.

The behaviour of coal on heating has been the basis of a further group of laboratory methods for the evaluation of coking coals. These have measured the melting-point of coal or its softening temperature or swelling power, all of which are significant in coke manufacture. The most important of these are the melting-point method of Audibert (*Fuel*, 1927, **6**, 131), the penetrometer methods of Greger, Dame and Agda and Von Lyncker (*Brenn. Chem.*, 1929, **10**, 86) and the swelling pressure method of Jenker (*Fuel*, 1931, **10**, 232).

Accuracy of Coal Analysis. Finally, it is desirable that the reader should have some idea of the accuracy of the results obtained in coal analysis. This subject has been examined by the Fuel Research Division (Survey Paper 29, 1933), who have defined the probable error of the determinations and the amounts by which the means of two determinations may differ from the true result. Certain of their findings are quoted below. The probable error of a determination is a measure of its precision ; a given value A has a probable error of " e " when it is a 50/50 chance that the true value lies within $A + e$ and $A - e$.

	Probable error.	Accuracy of mean of duplicates.	
		Odds 10 : 1.	Odds 100 : 1.
Moisture	0·044	± 0·08	± 0·12
Volatile matter	0·072	0·13	0·19
Ash	0·035	0·06	0·10
Carbon	0·138	± 0·25	± 0·37
Hydrogen	0·042	0·08	0·11
Nitrogen	0·020	0·04	0·05
Sulphur	0·014	0·03	0·04
Difference	0·152	0·27	0·42
B.Th.U. per lb. . . .	24·9	44	67

The probable error is, of course, smaller than the possible error which may occur in the usual laboratory practice of averaging two results. The accuracy of such means is assessed in the second column at odds of 10 : 1 and in the third at odds of 100 : 1. These odds are in favour of the true value being within range of mean result ± the amounts shown. The figures are in some cases disappointing, but in others indicate that the standard methods in use are satisfactory. The probable error of calorific value determination is, for example, rather high as stated and should be more nearly 10–15 B.Th.U.

Recent work on the accuracy of analytical data does not indicate any higher degree of accuracy.

ANALYSIS OF COKE

The methods of proximate and ultimate analysis of coal are also those used for coke with the exception of volatile matter, and certain small variations for which reference should be made to the British Standard

(B.S. 1016, revised).   The proportion of volatile matter in coke is so small that, in order to avoid oxidation, the coke must be heated in a stream of nitrogen or in the presence of 2 to 4 drops of benzene to displace the air.

There are, in addition, a number of tests which are special to coke.   These are mainly physical in character relating to the properties of the coke for metallurgical purposes and combustion.   They are true specific gravity, bulk density, reactivity index, thermal value of residual volatile matter, and, for evaluation of strength, shatter index, and abrasion index.   Details of the methods are to be found in B.S. 1016 (revised) and only one or two special points are considered here.

The reactivity index is known as the C.A.B. value (Bladen, Noble and Riley, *J. Inst. Fuel*, 1934, **7,** 139) and consists in measuring the minimum rate of air which will just maintain combustion in a closely-graded fuel contained in a quartz tube of specified dimensions.   The more reactive the fuel the lower is its C.A.B. value.   The value for wood-charcoal is about 0·005, for low-temperature coke about 0·015, and for high-temperature cokes from 0·055 for gas-coke to 0·065 for metallurgical coke.

The thermal value of the residual volatile matter is determined by distillation at a high temperature and is important in providing a measure of the ease of ignition of coke in domestic appliances.

The shatter index is a measure of breakdown of size of graded coke when it is subjected to a standard series of shocks by dropping it on a steel floor. This, and the abrasion index, is a measure of the resistance of the coke to breakdown in industrial usage.

EXAMINATION OF LIQUID FUELS

Standard methods for the examination of petroleum products are drawn up in Britain by the Institute of Petroleum and in the United States by the American Society for Testing Materials, and are under constant review in annual publications.   The British publication *Standard Methods for Testing Petroleum and its Products*, 12th ed. 1952, contains some 120 methods.   The following are some notes on certain of the methods, but the above book should be referred to for details.   Certain tests, like the determination of the octane number of motor spirit, are specific to the purpose for which the oil is to be used ;   these are dealt with in the appropriate chapters of this volume.

Specific Gravity.   This is determined by the usual methods for liquids, i.e. by hydrometer, pyknometer, specific gravity bottle or balance.   The standard temperature is 15° C.   The American *A.P.I.* convention is computed as

$$\text{Deg. A.P.I.} = \frac{141\cdot5}{\text{Sp. gr. } 60° \text{ F./}60° \text{ F.}} - 131\cdot5$$

In many cases, with heavy fuel oils, the weight delivered is computed from the volume and a temperature correction must be applied ; an average figure is 0·0006 per degree C., but other coefficients of expansion are given on page 289.

Flash-point.   This is defined as the lowest temperature at which vapour is given off from the oil in sufficient quantities to be ignited by a flame.

The *Fire Test* or *ignition-point* is defined as that temperature at which sufficient vapour is given off not only to be ignited, but with sufficient rapidity for the oil to continue burning.

This must not be confused with the Spontaneous Ignition Temperature (S.I.T.) which is the temperature at which ignition occurs when an inflammable liquid is allowed to fall in drops into a hot metal crucible.

Clearly the flash-point will be dependent upon, first, the vapour pressure of the oil, which to a minor degree will be dependent on the barometric pressure ; secondly, the proportion of oil vapour in air requisite to form an ignitable mixture.   This proportion will vary little for the different petroleum distillates, but several factors will determine when the requisite quantity is reached.   If the apparatus is open to the air it will be reached only at a higher temperature than in an enclosed apparatus.   In the latter the ratio of the air space to the surface of oil exposed will influence the result, so that standard sizes for closed testers must be adhered to rigidly if results are to be comparable.   Again, in a closed apparatus, when the test flame is lowered through the testing port, the air and vapour inside are replaced by fresh air drawn down through the other open ports provided, and if testing is performed at regular temperature increments, but at different rates of heating, the time given for sufficient vapour to diffuse into the air will vary and hence also the result.

These points are mentioned in order to emphasize the necessity for adopting standardized apparatus and procedure, if discrepancies are to be avoided.

The *open flash test* is clearly liable to considerable variation and is only an approximate test, though often of value for lubricating oils, some crude oils, and residues.   The I.P.T. standard method is to use the cup of the Pensky-Marten tester, the cover being replaced by a clip around the rim arranged to carry the thermometer and test flame.   The thermometer is fixed at the centre of the cup, and the centre of the bulb must be $\frac{1}{2}$ in. below the filling line.   The apparatus must be carefully screened from draughts, the oil must not be stirred, and the rate of heating must be approximately 10° F. ($\pm1°$) per minute.

The United States (A.S.T.M.) open test is carried out in a special shallow brass cup—Cleveland open cup, $2\frac{1}{2}$ in. internal diameter and $1\frac{5}{16}$ in. internal depth, the filling mark being $\frac{3}{8}$ in. below the rim.

Closed Tests.   The *Abel apparatus* is the legally standardized tester in Britain and the Commonwealth and is used for burning oils.   The apparatus, together with dimensions for the principal parts, is shown in diagrammatic section in Figure 119.   In the latest form of apparatus the thermometer is entered at an angle from one side so that the bulb is central and a hand-stirrer enters at a similar angle from the other side.   This arrangement is suitable for viscous materials.

The cup A is insulated from direct contact with the heating vessel B by a vulcanite ring v, on which the flange rests.   There is an air space C $\frac{1}{2}$ in. across between the sides and bottom of the cup and the wall of the heater, so that with water always at one temperature in the latter when commencing

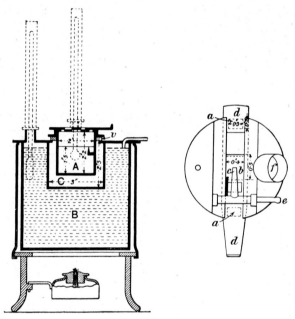

Fig. 119.—Abel Flash-point Apparatus.

the rise of temperature of the oil is always regular, though not uniform for equal increments of time.

The procedure for legal testing is laid down strictly, but need not be detailed here.   For ordinary purposes the following directions will suffice :

The heater is filled with water at a temperature of 130° F.   The oil cup is placed on a level surface and filled to the proper level, care being taken that none is splashed on the sides.

The cover is placed on the oil cup, the thermometer inserted, and the test flame adjusted to the size of the bed provided and mounted on the cup.

The cup is placed carefully into position in the heater, the whole apparatus being in a situation free from draughts.   Testing is commenced at 66° F., the slide being drawn open *slowly* and closed *quickly*.   This is repeated at every degree rise of temperature until a flash is obtained.

If a flash occurs between 66° and 73° F. (the lower legal limit) a fresh portion of the oil is cooled to 55° F. before putting in the cup, and testing is commenced at 60° F.

If no flash is given at 90° F. the bath is emptied and refilled with water at 90° F., also the air space to a depth of 1½ in ; fresh oil is taken, and the whole warmed up by the burner, testing being carried out at degree intervals.

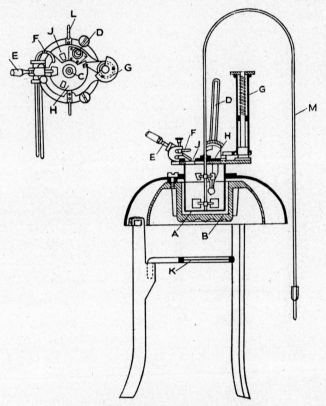

FIG. 120.—Pensky-Marten Flash-point Apparatus.

A, Oil cup ;   *B*, Heating vessel ;   *C*, Stirrer ;   *D*, Thermometer ;   *E*, Ignition burner ; *F*, Pilot burner ;   *G*, Spring handle ;   *H*, Revolving shutter ;   *J*, Orifice ;   *K*, Gauze disk ; *L*, Lifting hooks ;   *M*, Optional form of stirrer operating device.

With very low flashing oils the sample may be cooled to 32° F. in melting ice, also the oil cup itself, before filling. The cup may be mounted conveniently through a sheet of asbestos card, so that it extends into a beaker containing water (with ice) at 32° F. If there is no flash under these conditions the temperature is raised slowly until the proper flash-point is reached. A special thermometer will require to be fitted by means of a cork, as the one supplied with the apparatus does not record these low temperatures.

Where special accuracy is demanded, the flash-point is corrected for barometric pressure, 1·6° F. being added or subtracted for each inch above or below 30 in.

The *Pensky-Marten* apparatus is the most suitable for all oils flashing above 120° F. The construction, dimensions and method of use of these instruments have been agreed between the I.P.T. and the A.S.T.M. With these oils it is necessary to provide a stirrer in the oil, and also one to mix the heavy vapours with the air. A mass of metal is employed instead of water for the heaters. The apparatus is illustrated in Figure 120. The stirrer is operated by means of a flexible wire, and the cup ports opened, the test flame inserted and the ports closed by turning the milled head on the upright pillar.

The rate of heating should not be less than 9° F., or more than 11° F. per minute, and the stirrer should be turned approximately one revolution per second. The test flame should be applied at every 2° F. for oils with a flash-point below 220° F. and above this temperature at every 5°. Suitable " low " and " high " reading thermometers are specified. In applying the flame, one half-second is allowed for opening the port, the flame must remain in the testing position for one second, then the port is quickly closed. Stirring must be discontinued during the application of the test flame (I.P.T. standard method).

It is most important with all these testers to see that oil does not remain between the sliding and fixed plates forming the cover. These should be separated and thoroughly cleaned if necessary.

Viscosity. The absolute viscosity of fluid oils is determined by the classical method of measuring the rate of flow of the oil through a capillary tube kept at a uniform temperature. Several patterns of tube have been standardized of the Ostwald type for different ranges of viscosity. Values are expressed for kinematic viscosity in centistokes and for dynamic viscosity in centipoises.

The tubes, which have a capacity of only a few millilitres, are calibrated with water, but suitable oils can be used as secondary standards. The kinematic viscosity in centistokes is calculated from the formula :

$$V = Ct - \frac{B}{t}$$

where C is the calibration constant of the instrument, B an experimental constant of design, and t is the time of flow in seconds.

The Viscosity Index is an empirical number indicating the change of viscosity with temperature and is of importance with particular regard to lubricating oils. A low index indicates a large change of viscosity. It is measured by taking the viscosity at 100° and 210° F. and calculating from the formula :

$$\text{V.I.} = \frac{L - U}{L - H} \times 100$$

where U is the viscosity at 100° F., L is the viscosity at 100° F. of an oil of zero V.I. having the same value at 210° F. as the sample, and H is the viscosity at 100° F. of an oil of 100 V.I. having the same viscosity at 210° F. as the sample.

For ordinary purposes, where the accuracy of the Ostwald method is not necessary, two empirical viscometers have been standardized for two ranges of viscosity. These are the Redwood Viscometers I and II, of which I is

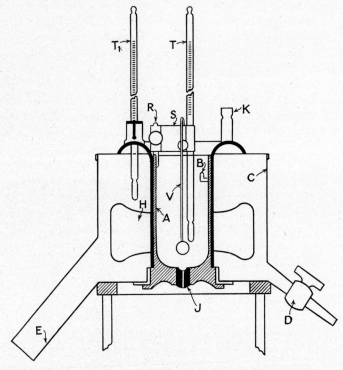

Fig. 121.—Redwood Viscometer I.

A, Oil cup ; *B*, Levelling wire ; *C*, Copper bath ; *D*, Tap ; *E*, Heating tube ; *H*, Stirrer ; *J*, Agate jet ; *K*, Stirrer handle ; *R*, Standard ; *S*, Thermometer clip ; *T* and *T*$_1$, Thermometers ; *V*, Ball valve.

illustrated in Figure 121. The oil to be examined is contained in a central cup, having an orifice at the bottom drilled through a piece of agate. This is kept closed by a simple ball valve until the experimental conditions are realized. The water in the jacket is brought to any desired temperature by a burner placed under the extension limb, and paddles for stirring the water are provided, these centring round the oil cup.

Owing to the bad heat conduction and sluggish convection currents in most oils, it is always advisable to bring the oil to within a degree or so of the required temperature before filling the oil cup. This is done best by using a flask of about twice the volume of oil required for the test, a little more than half filling with the sample, and immersing in a large beaker of water at the proper temperature. The oil then can be shaken about and brought quickly to the bath temperature.

Having filled the cup to the top of the gauge point and obtained the correct temperature, the ball valve is opened, and 50 ml. of oil run into a graduated flask placed below, the time being taken by a stop-watch. The flask should not be insulated in any way. Viscosity determinations are usually made at one or more of the following temperatures : 70°, 100°, 140°, 200°, 250° F. In the latter case oil is used in the heating bath.

The *Redwood No. I* is employed for all oils with an efflux time of less than 2000 seconds at the temperature of test. The outflow tube is 1·62 mm. dia. and 10 mm. long.

For oils of greater viscosity the *Redwood No. II* (or Admiralty pattern) is employed. This instrument is designed to give ten times the rate of flow of the Redwood I, and is therefore suitable only for oils of high viscosity.

It is similar in design to the above, but the oil flows through an agate tube 5 cm. long and about 3·8 mm. internal diameter. The oil cylinder is raised on legs so that it and the full length of the agate tube are surrounded by the heating medium contained in the outer vessel. Each instrument has to be standardized by experiment.

In technical work the viscosity is usually expressed as the number of seconds for 50 ml. of oil to flow through the instrument at the stated temperature (° F.). It should also be stated whether in Redwood No. I or Redwood No. II.

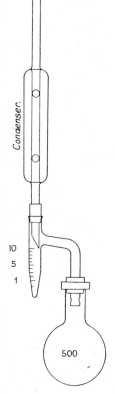

Fig. 122.—Apparatus for Determination of Water in Oils.

Water in Oils. Distillate fuel oils should be free from water and solid suspended matter, but residue fuel oils often contain these impurities, and their estimation is of importance. Water and sediment may be determined together by dilution of the oil with an equal volume of 90 per cent. benzole and allowing the mixture to stand several hours in a suitably graduated measure, or by centrifuging the mixture at 120° F. Special measures with a narrow graduated lower portion are standardized.

Water is most accurately determined by distillation from a mixture of 100 ml. of the sample with 100 ml. of petroleum distillate boiling in the range 90–160° C. but with 20 per cent. distilling below 100° C. The apparatus is closely standardized, but is set up as shown empirically in the diagram Figure 122. The flask is of 500 ml. capacity and the rate of distillation is 2–5 drops per second. The water separates in the receiver and the spirit flows back into the flask.

Distillation Tests. With the exception of fuels of high vapour tension (petrol, benzole, etc.) distillation tests are not required. For petrol the standard method of the I.P.T. and A.S.T.M. is adopted.

An Engler flask is used, the side lead being connected to a brass seamless condenser tube, 22 in. long, $\frac{9}{16}$ in. outside diameter. This is cooled in an ice/water mixture contained in a rectangular bath, 15 in. long. The lower 3 in. of the tube is curved downwards, the end being cut off at an angle. The flask is mounted vertically on a sheet of asbestos, and rests in a hole $1\frac{1}{4}$ in. diameter. The flask, support, and source of heat must be effectively screened from draughts.

One hundred ml. of the sample are measured into the flask, and the same measuring cylinder is used to collect the distillate. The bulb of the thermometer is adjusted so that the bottom of the capillary is level with the side tube. The flame is adjusted to give a rate of distillation of 4–5 ml. per minute, being suitably increased as distillation proceeds. The initial boiling-point (I.B.P.) is the temperature when the first drop falls from the end of the condenser, and the final boiling-point (F.B.P.) is the maximum temperature the thermometer reaches which is usually when the bottom of the flask is just dry. Distillation tests should record the I.B.P., the temperature at which each 10 per cent. is collected, and the F.B.P., also the total volume of distillate, the volume of residue in the flask, the loss, and the barometric pressure.

The Standard Method for Testing Tar Products (lower-boiling fractions) is very similar, except that a glass condenser tube 60 cm. long and 1·5 cm. bore is employed, with a water-jacket 45 cm. in length. Cooling in this case does not require to be below water-supply temperatures. With petrols, however, especially when casing-head spirit is a component, these temperatures would not ensure efficient condensation.

Sulphur. The determination may be required in any of the liquid fuels, ranging from petrols to the heavy fuel oils.

For petrols and kerosines the I.P.T. lamp method is employed and this consists in burning 3–5 g. in a special small glass lamp of about 25 ml. capacity at the rate of 2 g. per hour.

The products of combustion are gently aspirated through a double-bulb U-tube containing 10 ml. of a standard solution of sodium carbonate, diluted with an equal volume of water. This absorbs the oxides of sulphur resulting from the combustion. The sodium carbonate solution contains 3·306 grams per litre. A corresponding strength hydrochloric acid solution contains 2·275 grams per litre.

After some 4–5 grams of the sample have been burnt, the apparatus is washed out thoroughly, and the sodium carbonate solution titrated with the

HCl (using methyl orange as indicator).   Each ml. of acid used corresponds to 1 mg. of sulphur.

The Tar Products method differs in many respects—the form of apparatus, the absorbent, which is neutralized hydrogen peroxide, and the estimation of the sulphur, which is volumetric, N/10 sodium carbonate being used. The fuel is mixed with five times its volume of rectified spirit of wine before introduction into the lamp.

For heavy oils the bomb method (see Calorimetry, p. 503) is the standard. The determination of sulphur is necessary in all cases where the correction of the calorific value for the formation of sulphuric acid during the combustion has to be made.

Paraffins and Naphthenes in Benzole Mixtures.   A method devised in the laboratories of the National Benzole Company, and which yields reasonably accurate results, depends upon the solution of the aromatic hydrocarbons in 98 per cent. sulphuric acid   The method has the merit of simplicity, compared with the many other methods which have been proposed.

A special mixing and measuring tube is employed, having a cylindrical portion of such diameter and length that it will hold rather more than 20 ml., for which volume the tube is graduated.   At each end there is a bulb, the lower one provided with a stopcock, the upper with a stopper.

Eighty ml. of 98 per cent. sulphuric acid are poured into the tube, up to the lower mark on the graduated scale, and 20 ml. of the sample added. The tube is stoppered, inverted and gently shaken, the pressure being released by opening the tap cautiously.   Cooling is necessary if the action is too violent.   After eight minutes' good agitation the mixture is allowed to stand and the volume of residual spirit read.   Shaking is repeated until no further diminution of the volume is noted.   After cooling, the volume of " paraffins and naphthenes " is then read.

With mixtures containing unsaturated hydrocarbons, for example, with mixtures containing cracked spirit, treatment with 80 per cent. sulphuric acid, followed by distillation to separate high-boiling polymers, must precede the estimation of paraffins and naphthenes.

Carbon Residue.   For fuel oils for internal combustion engines, and also for lubricating oils for similar engines, the amount of carbon (coke) left by heating the oil to a high temperature in the absence of air is important. Results are liable to great variation unless special attention is given to procedure and a standard apparatus is used.   For the standard method (Conradson Coking Test) a silica or porcelain crucible, 30 ml. capacity, is placed in an iron crucible 65–82 ml. capacity.   This is provided with an iron cover having an opening 6·5 mm. diam.   This again is placed inside a large iron crucible (with a lid) 200 ml. capacity.   Enough sand is placed in this outer crucible to bring the cover of the inner iron crucible nearly to the top of the outer one. The three crucibles are carried on a triangle and surrounded by a hollow heating block with a short chimney.

Two glass beads about 0·1 mm. diam. are placed in the porcelain crucible and included in its first weight and such a quantity of oil is taken that the coke residue does not exceed 0·4 gram. The apparatus is set up, and heated till vapours ignite, then the heating is moderated to give a flame less than 2 in. high from the top of the short chimney. When vapour ceases to come off, the heat is increased and the lower part of the large crucible is kept red-hot for five minutes. The apparatus is allowed to cool and the porcelain crucible removed, placed in a desiccator and weighed.

An alternative method is that of Ramsbottom, which was included in the Royal Air Force specifications for lubricating oils. It is applicable to distillate fuel oils but is not suitable for asphaltic fuel oils, owing chiefly to excessive frothing. Moreover, results by this method are not strictly comparable with those by the Conradson method.

Approximately 4 grams of the sample are introduced into a glass bulb, which is approximately 38 mm. from the base to the shoulder, where it is terminated in a capillary 9·5 mm. long and 1·5 mm. diam. This bulb fits closely into a tube 80 mm. long and 25 mm. diam., and when the charged bulb is inserted, the sheath is lowered into a bath of molten lead, so that not more than $\frac{1}{8}$ in. is above the surface of the lead. The lead bath is maintained at 550° C., and the bulb is allowed to remain at this temperature for 20 minutes. It is then cooled, cleaned outside if necessary and weighed.

Asphaltenes. Asphaltic bodies are those bodies of an indeterminate character, probably polymers, and are undesirable constituents of distillate oils, particularly if required for the internal combustion engine. They are defined as material which is wax-free, insoluble in I.P. petroleum spirit, but soluble in hot benzene. A measured quantity of the oil is treated with I.P. spirit, filtered on a filter paper, the paper extracted with hot spirit to remove wax, and the asphaltenes removed by hot benzene, evaporated to dryness and weighed.

" Hard " asphalt determined in this way is an undesirable constituent of fuel oils for internal combustion engines, and its determination is required in most specifications.

The petroleum spirit must be free from benzene and other aromatic hydrocarbons. The I.P.T. specification requires not more than 0·5 per cent. of aromatic hydrocarbons and that at least 90 per cent. distils between 60° and 80° C. It should have a specific gravity not above 0·690 (60° F.). To prepare it the spirit having a boiling range of 60–80° C. (by the standard method, p. 492) must be thoroughly shaken with three volumes of strong sulphuric acid (98–100 per cent. H_2SO_4).

Such a weight of oil is taken (not, however, over 10 grams) that the precipitated asphalt does not exceed 0·25 gram, and dissolved in warm petroleum spirit, the quantity used (in ml.) being ten times the weight of oil (in grams) taken. The mixture is allowed to stand twenty-four hours. The solution is filtered through an 11-cm. folded filter and the filter and material washed with the spirit until the washings are colourless. The asphaltic material is then dissolved in benzene, the solution being collected in a weighed conical flask. The benzene is distilled off and the asphalt dried in a steam oven for one hour.

In cases where the asphalt content is high a smaller amount of the sample must be used, for it is undesirable to have more than 0·25 gram of the insoluble asphalt to filter, wash, etc.

Ash. This estimation is important for fuel oils for internal combustion engines. Even more important perhaps than the actual quantity is the character of the ash, a harsh gritty ash being very abrasive in the cylinder.

The usual method of determination in distillate oils involves evaporating down some considerable quantity (250 grams or over), transferring to a platinum dish and continuing the evaporation, and finally igniting until all carbon has been burnt.

Heavy residue oils can generally be evaporated directly in the platinum dish, and this is necessary if they contain much asphalt. In such cases 30–50 grams is usually sufficient for the estimation.

Special Tests. Other tests which are more closely concerned with the usage of the oil, such as the knock-rating of petrol, are dealt with in the appropriate chapters.

Reference Books

Standard Methods for Testing of Petroleum and its Products. Inst. Petroleum (London).
British Standards Institution. Specifications of standard methods and apparatus.
Fuel Testing. G. W. Himus. Leonard Hill. 1953.
Gas Analysis. Altieri. Amer. Gas Assoc., New York. 1945.
Technical Gas Analysis. Lunge and Ambler. Gurney and Jackson. 1934.
Viscometry. Barr. Oxford Univ. Press. 1931.
Methods of Analysis of Coal and Coke. Fuel Research Survey Paper 44, 1940.
Methods of Analysis of Coal and Coke Ash. Fuel Research Survey Paper 50, 1949.
The Science of Petroleum. Dunstan. Oxford Univ. Press. 1938.
Methods of Analysis of Fuels and Oils. Gibb. Constable. 1951.

CHAPTER XIX

DETERMINATION OF CALORIFIC VALUE

Definitions of the units employed and a discussion on gross and net calorific values have been given in Chapter II. Here it is proposed only to consider the methods by which calorific value is measured. These may be divided into those based upon calculations from the known individual values of the constituents, and those obtained by direct determination in some suitable calorimeter.

Calculated Calorific Values. For coals the calorific value may be calculated on a basis of the elementary constituents, or on the proximate constituents. For oils it is based on the elementary constituents and for gases on the values of the individual combustible gaseous constituents.

In calculations based on the ultimate composition of the coal it is assumed that the elements have the same heating value as they have in the free uncombined state, and that oxygen is present in combination with its equivalent of hydrogen in the form of water, an assumption justified only by experience. It involves likewise the assumption that heat is neither expended nor evolved in rendering the atoms of the constituent elements free to enter into fresh combinations with oxygen on combustion. Since coals low in oxygen have been shown to be only slightly endothermic in formation, it so happens that this is very nearly true, which explains the otherwise anomalous fact that calculated results in the majority of cases do agree fairly well with the determined values.

The original formula is that of Dulong, but numerous modifications have been proposed. Its original form was :

$$\text{Gross C.V.} = \tfrac{1}{100}[8080 \text{ C} + 34{,}400 \text{ (H} - \text{O/8)}] \text{ cal. per g.}$$

where C, H and O are the percentages by weight of these elements.

If it be assumed that the oxygen is wholly in combination with hydrogen the surplus of hydrogen available for combustion is H − O/8. Also, the nitrogen content of coal is never far away from one per cent. and this can be assumed in the formula. These amendments give :

$$\text{Gross C.V.} = \tfrac{1}{100}[8080 \text{ C} + 34{,}500 \text{ (H} - \text{(O} + \text{N} - 1)/8) + 2220 \text{ S]} \text{ cal. per g.}$$

Other expressions have also been suggested. Grumell and Davies (*Fuel*, 1933, **12**, 199) have obtained quite close agreement with a large number of coals using a formula based on the Berthier theory that the heat evolved by a fuel is proportional to the volume of air required for combustion, i.e. $Q_s = kV_c$, where Q_s is the quantity of heat, V_c the volume of air and k an empirical constant. Their formula is :

$$Q = (3\cdot635\ H + 235\cdot9)(C/3 + H - (O - S)/8)$$

In his system of classification of coal Seyler derives the following formula based on " pure coal " as calculated by the Parr convention. Unfortunately the Parr convention assumes that all the sulphur in coal is not part of the coal substance and the calculation is in error.

$$Q = 123\cdot9\ C + 388\cdot12\ H - 4269\ \text{cal. per g.}$$

If the oxygen is over 10 per cent. and carbon less than 83 per cent add $\delta Q = O^2/4$ to Q.

The assumptions behind these formulæ are not correct, but it is true that the results compare quite closely with those of determinations in the case of coals of low oxygen content, say below 7 per cent. In this case the agreement is within one per cent. With oil fuels in which the ash complication is avoided the agreement is appreciably closer. The calculation of calorific value has, however, some application in comparing the compositions of similar coals and in providing a useful check on the accuracy of analytical data. It should not, however, be allowed to take the place of actual determination.

In the case of coal the nearest approach to accuracy is obtained by using the oxygen figure from an ultimate analysis corrected to a mineral-matter-free basis. This is not always available, but its wider use would probably make calculated values of greater service until such time as the direct method of determination of oxygen is made more exact.

Calculation from Proximate Analysis. Goutal claims that a relationship between the amount of fixed carbon and volatile matter and the calorific value may be traced in coals. This he deduced for a large number of French coals by comparison with the calorific value determined in a bomb calorimeter, constants for varying amounts of volatile matter being determined. These constants must necessarily be calculated on the dry and ash-free coal, i.e. on the pure combustible. Goutal's formula is $82C + aV$, where C represents the fixed carbon, a the constant, and V the volatile matter found on the whole coal.

The values for the constant a, for different values of V^1, the volatile matter in the pure coal substance, which equals $\left(\dfrac{V \times 100}{C + V}\right)$, are :

V^1	5	10	15	20	25	30	35	38	40
a	145	130	117	109	103	98	94	85	80

Taylor and Patterson (*J. Soc. Chem. Ind.*, 1929, **48**, 1051) report values varying from $-15\cdot3$ to $+5\cdot4$ per cent. for a variety of coals, divergence which really rules the formula out of court.

The lack of agreement shows that the heating value of the volatile constituents of coal varies with different types of coal or perhaps with different proportions of volatile matter. This suggests that a modified formula with a factor for the magnitude of the latter would meet the case.

Calculation for Gaseous Fuels. In the case of gaseous fuels, which are mechanical mixtures, the constituent gases preserve their heating value and the calculated results are accurate. Where the gaseous mixtures contain hydrocarbons more elaborate calculations are necessary. In the cases of the saturated hydrocarbons C_nH_{2n+2} the value of " n " is usually determinable in accurate gas analyses and represents the mean molecular weight of the hydrocarbons present. The calorific value of the mixed hydrocarbons is then usually determined by B.Th.U. per cu. ft. $= 995 + (0 \cdot ab \times 735)$ where $0 \cdot ab$ is the decimal part of the " n " value and 995 is the calorific value of methane saturated at 60° F. and 30 in. The value for ethane is $995 + 735$, i.e. 1730 B.Th.U. This assumes that the gases are methane and ethane only and is satisfactory for gases in which the " n " value is less than 1·20. In other cases the formula should be

$$C.V. = \frac{100(3n + 1)}{4} \text{ B.Th.U. per cu. ft. saturated at 60° F. and 30 in.}$$

In this formula all members of the saturated hydrocarbon series may be present ; the calculation involving the fact that the calorific value of oxygen burning in a saturated hydrocarbon gas is constant at 500 B.Th.U. per cu. ft.

Unsaturated hydrocarbons present greater difficulty since their composition is difficult to measure by ordinary gas analysis and a mean value must be assumed for each type of gas. Manning, King and Sinnatt (*Fuel Res. Tech. Paper* 19, 1928) have suggested mean values (1) for high-temperature coal gas and (2) for low-temperature gas as follows :

(1) C_2H_4 two-thirds   of 1560 ⎱
    C_6H_6 one-sixth   of 3740 ⎰ 2050 B.Th.U. per cu. ft. satd. at 60° F. and
    C_3H_5 one-sixth   of 2300 ⎰ 30 in.

(2) C_6H_6 one-quarter   of 3740 ⎱
    C_2H_4 three-eighths   of 1560 ⎰ 2520 B.Th.U per cu. ft. satd. at 60° F. and
    C_3H_6 three-sixteenths of 2300 ⎰ 30 in.
    C_4H_8 three-sixteenths of 3040 ⎰

In other types of gas the proportions would certainly differ and, as the calorific values of these gases are high, lack of knowledge may introduce a large error into calculated calorific values.

Where *accurate* gas analyses are not available direct determination is necessary ; in any case it should always be adopted where possible as the direct method. When the gas sample is available only in small amount and a flow calorimeter cannot be used an explosion calorimeter of the Union type is recommended.

CALORIMETRY OF SOLID FUELS AND OILS

The general principle of all calorimeters is the transference of the total heat of the combustion of a known weight of the fuel to a known weight of water ; from the rise of temperature of the latter the calorific value is deduced. Not only is the water raised in temperature, but the whole of the instrument in contact with it, and it is necessary to know the heat utilized in doing this, measured in terms of water. This is known as the *water equivalent* of the instrument, and must be determined accurately and checked at intervals.

For the direct determination of the heating value of fuel certain essential conditions must be fulfilled for accurate results. Combustion must be complete ; hence there must be no smoke, no carbon monoxide formed, and no invisible unburnt hydrocarbon gases escaping. There should also be no unburned carbon and any determination in which traces of carbon are seen should be rejected. Even if this carbon appears in the crucible it is unsound to determine the quantity and make a correction from the known value for carbon, since the appearance of carbon may imply invisible incomplete combustion.

The heat must be transferred completely to the water, losses by cooling during the determination must be corrected for, and finally the rise of the temperature of the water must be determined with great accuracy, since the mass of fuel used is very small as compared with the mass of water heated.

Calorimeters may be classified as follows :

1. Where combustion is achieved by admixture of the fuel with a solid oxidizing agent.
    (*a*) A mixture of nitrate and chlorate of potassium (Lewis Thompson).
    (*b*) With sodium peroxide (Na_2O_2) (Parr and Wild).
2. By combustion with oxygen at atmospheric pressure.
    (*a*) Where the temperature of the escaping products can be ascertained (Favre and Silbermann, Fischer, etc.).
    (*b*) Where the products escape through water, and are assumed to be cooled to its temperature (William Thomson and innumerable modifications).
3. By combustion with oxygen at high pressures (Berthelot-Mahler bomb calorimeter and all modifications).

Comparison of the results obtained with solid fuels in different types of calorimeters against those given in the Berthelot bomb type have shown liability to such errors that in modern specifications and methods the bomb type is now alone recognized for solid and liquid fuels (B.S. 1016, 1942).

A solid-fuel calorimeter which uses air or oxygen at atmospheric pressure seldom achieves complete combustion, and heavy oil is even worse. For this reason practically all national standards are based on (3) and employ a standardized calorimeter of the type first employed by Berthelot and Mahler. Experience has shown that even in their time an accuracy was achieved which it is possible to improve upon only by the very greatest care and with the use of accurately-standardized thermometers.

The accuracy which can now be achieved with coal is such that the difference between duplicates in one laboratory should not exceed 25 cal. per gram ; with oil, and in the absence of the sampling difficulty, this is reducible to 10 cal. Recent comparison in a number of coal laboratories has given 28 cal. for determinations made in one laboratory and 56 cal. for determinations made in different laboratories on the same coals.

The Bomb Calorimeter. The modern bomb calorimeter is a development of the original calorimeter of Berthelot. It includes a number of improvements in design and construction but in principle remains unchanged.

The original bomb was made of steel and protected from corrosion by a lining of platinum (or enamel). The modern bomb is made of corrosion-resisting steel and, since the tensile strength of this is less than mild steel, is considerably heavier, about 3250 g. as against about 2500 g. The effect of this has been to lengthen the main period of observation of rise of temperature and to make more essential the accuracy of the cooling correction. The metal now specified is the type resistant to intergranular corrosion, e.g. austenitic steel containing nickel, chromium and molybdenum (B.S. 1503).

The top joint was formerly made by screwing a sharp-edged ring on the lid down on to a lead washer inset in the body of the main vessel. This is now replaced by a rubber ring which not only can be tightened by hand but is not subject to corrosion troubles. The gas escape valve is now of the Schroeder type and is also corrosion-resisting.

Other important features of the bomb and its ancillary apparatus are :

(1) The capacity of the bomb shall be such that, when closed and filled with oxygen, it shall contain at least two-and-a-half times the amount of oxygen required for the complete combustion of the fuel. The action volume should be from 250 to 350 ml.

(2) The water capacity of the water-jacket shall contain at least as much water as is equivalent to five times the water equivalent of the bomb plus the amount of water necessary to cover this in the calorimeter vessel. Alternatively the jacket may be of the isothermal or adiabatic type.

(3) The stirrer shall be efficient, giving a straight-line temperature curve, and the thermometer shall be graduated to $0 \cdot 01°$ C. and have certified corrections to $0 \cdot 002°$ C.

(4) The oxygen shall be free from combustible matter (electrolytic oxygen contains some hydrogen) and the firing wire shall be of platinum or nickel-chromium of 36 S.W.G. (0·19 mm. dia.).

(5) The crucible used for holding the sample of fuel should be of platinum or nickel-chromium alloy. Porcelain or refractory crucibles have a tendency to cause incomplete combustion, particularly in the case of coke. They may be used with bombs of 350 ml. capacity.

A modern calorimeter assembled for use is shown in Figure 123 (*a*), and a section of it in Figure 123 (*b*).

The calorific value as determined is the gross calorific value, expressed in 15° calories, under conditions of constant volume. The 15° calorie is the amount of heat required to raise the temperature of one gram of water from 14·5° C. to 15·5° C. and is equal to 4·1855 joules. The actual value is the number of heat units liberated when unit weight of fuel is burned in oxygen saturated with water vapour, the products being carbon dioxide, sulphur dioxide, and water. Water not in the vapour state is taken as liquid water.

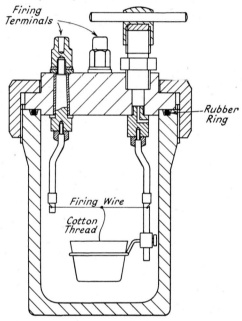

FIG. 123 (*a*).—Diagram of Calorimetric Bomb (Baird & Tatlock (London) Ltd.).

The difference between this value and the higher value taken at constant pressure is, for bituminous coal, of the order of one part in 1000. Since this is within the accuracy of the determination, the difference may be regarded as not having significance. The calorific value of a solid fuel decreases with increase of temperature from 0·1 to 0·3 cal. per g. per ° C., the lower change being for anthracite.

Procedure. About one gram of the air-dried coal or coke is weighed into the crucible ; in the case of oil one gram is added by means of a pipette and weighed. For solid fuels a moisture determination must be made at the same time so that any correction of the result to a basis of dry fuel shall be accurate. Coal may be previously compressed into the form of a cylindrical pellet.

A piece of the firing wire is stretched across the inner terminals and a piece of sewing cotton is attached to it with the other end in contact with

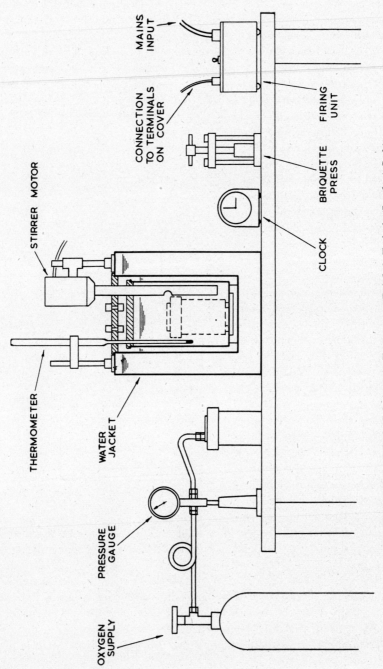

MAINS INPUT

CONNECTION TO TERMINALS ON COVER

FIRING UNIT

STIRRER MOTOR

BRIQUETTE PRESS

CLOCK

THERMOMETER

WATER JACKET

PRESSURE GAUGE

OXYGEN SUPPLY

Fig. 123 (b).—Bomb Calorimetric Equipment (Baird & Tatlock (London) Ltd.).

the fuel or tied to it.   2 ml. of water are placed in the bottom of the bomb and the cover assembled.   The bomb is charged with oxygen to a pressure of 25 atm.

The calorimeter vessel is then charged with a weighed quantity of water sufficient to cover the lid and the whole apparatus assembled as illustrated and the stirrer started.   The water should be at room temperature in order that the "cooling" correction shall be as small as possible.

After an interval of not less than 5 minutes read the temperature to $0\cdot001°$ and continue the readings at intervals of one minute, tapping the thermometer gently at the level of the mercury for 10 seconds prior to taking the reading.   If after 5 minutes the rate of change is constant, close the electrical circuit momentarily to fire the charge and continue the readings of temperature for 5 minutes after a maximum has been reached and the fall of temperature has assumed a steady rate.

The bomb is then removed from the calorimeter, allowed to stand for 30 minutes to allow the acid mist to settle, and the pressure released through the valve.   On opening, the crucible is inspected for signs of carbon; if these are found the result is rejected; the bomb and crucible are rinsed with a small quantity of distilled water and the washings used if desired for the determination of sulphur.   The figure obtained is the combustible sulphur.

In the case of anthracite or coke a tendency to incomplete combustion can be avoided by placing a thin layer of pure silica or granular fused alumina ($0\cdot75$ g. 120–240 B.S.) on the bottom of the crucible.   This is also helpful with coals of high ash content or having a fusible ash.

Corrections.   The observed data must be corrected for cooling during the determination, for the heat of combustion of the cotton thread, and for the heats of formation of sulphuric and nitric acids.

The acid correction is made by the titration of the bomb washings with standard alkali.   To the washings 50 ml. of $0\cdot1N$ Na_2CO_3 solution are added, the solution boiled down to 10 ml., diluted, filtered (from the ash and any lead sulphate which may have been formed) and washed.   When cold the filtrate is titrated with $\dfrac{N}{10}$ HCl using methyl orange.   The difference between these two titrations gives the total acidity (50 − T), and from this that due to H_2SO_4 (measured by direct precipitation as barium sulphate) must be subtracted to give the HNO_3 acidity $\left(\text{in terms of } \dfrac{N}{10} HNO_3\right)$.

Since 1 ml. $\dfrac{N}{10}$ H_2SO_4 is equivalent to $0\cdot0016$ gram of sulphur, this becomes

$$(50 - T) - \frac{\text{sulphur in wt. of coal}}{0\cdot0016} = n \text{ ml. } N/10 \text{ nitric acid.}$$

The deductions in terms of calories to be made are then :

HNO_3 correction $n \times 1.43$

H_2SO_4 S (per cent.) $\times$ 22.5

An alternative and simple method for routine work is based on the close agreement between the heat of formation of nitric acid per gram (227 calories) and the molecular weight of barium sulphate (233).

A solution of sodium carbonate containing 3.706 grams per litre is equivalent to 0.0044 gram of HNO_3 per ml., which means a correction of 1 calorie. Direct titration of the washings with such a solution, followed by filtration, washing, acidification with hydrochloric acid and precipitation of the sulphur as $BaSO_4$, will give the data for applying the following formulæ :

HNO_3 correction = ml. of standard Na_2CO_3 − 100 (wt. of $BaSO_4$)

H_2SO_4 ,,   = percentage sulphur $\times$ 22.5

The magnitude of these corrections, and hence the importance of taking them into account, is shown by the following averages : nitric acid 15 calories, sulphuric acid 30 calories, a total of 0.6 per cent. on a coal of 7000 calories.

Cooling Correction. Elaborate systems of correction have been proposed, but for normal purposes one of these has been reduced to a form in which it can be applied conveniently by using a tabulated form. This is the Regnault-Pfaundler, the formula of which has the form (see B.S. 1016, 1942) :

$$\text{Correction} = nv + \frac{v' - v}{t' - t}\{\Sigma_1^{n-1}(t) + \tfrac{1}{2}(t_0 - t_n) - nt\}$$

$$= nv + kT$$

where n = number of minutes in chief period, usually 5

        v = rate of fall of temperature per minute in the preliminary period

        v' = rate in after period

    t, t' = average temperatures in preliminary and after periods

  $\Sigma_1^{n-1}(t)$ = sum of readings during chief period

$\tfrac{1}{2}(t_0 + tn)$ = mean of firing temp. t_0 and first temp. after which the rate of change is constant, t_n

and $k = \dfrac{v' - v}{t' - t}$ and is the " cooling constant " of the calorimeter and should be less than 0.0025

Although the formula looks formidable, the use of a blank form with spaces for the various readings makes its use as convenient and almost as rapid as that of the shorter methods. One shorter method is as given below in the form of an example. In this case the calorimeter had attained a constant temperature when the fuel was ignited.

Initial temperature (t_1), 15·52°

Time after firing.	Thermometer reading.	Mean temperature of minute.	Mean difference from initial t.
1 minute	17·37	16·445	0·925
2 minutes	17·94	17·655	2·135
2½ ,,	17·95	17·945	2·425
3 ,,	17·95 (t_2)	17·945	2·425
4 ,,	17·945	—	—
5 ,,	17·935	—	—
10 ,,	17·860	—	—

$$\text{Rise} = 17·95 - 15·52 = 2·43$$

$$\text{Loss per minute} = \frac{17·935\,* - 17·860}{5} = 0·015$$

$$
\begin{aligned}
\text{Loss in 1st minute} &= 2·43 : 0·015 : : 0·925 = 0·006 \\
,, \quad 2\text{nd} \quad ,, &= 2·43 : 0·015 : : 2·135 = 0·013 \\
,, \quad 3\text{rd} \quad ,, &= 2·43 : 0·015 : : 2·425 = 0·015
\end{aligned}
$$

Total correction . 0·034

Corrected rise of temperature $= 2·43 + 0·034 = 2·464°$

* At the minute when the maximum temperature is reached and for the succeeding minute or two heat is still passing out from the bomb, more or less balancing the loss by radiation. To ascertain the true loss per minute by radiation alone, the temperature at which the rate becomes uniform must be taken.

The calorific value of the fuel is then calculated from the formula :

$$\text{calories} = \frac{(T + t) \times (W + w) - (HNO_3 \text{ correction} + S \text{ correction})}{\text{weight of coal in grams}}$$

T = observed rise W = weight of water
t = radiation correction w = water equivalent

Determination of the Water Equivalent. The above expression contains a factor for the water equivalent which must be the subject of accurate determination. Several methods are possible. Calculation could be made from the weights and specific heats of the parts, but this could not be more than approximately accurate. The direct determination of specific heat by the measurement of rise of temperature during the input of a known amount of heat by electrical means is the most accurate. It is satisfactory, however, in the case of fuels to make the determination by burning a suitable quantity of a pure organic substance of known calorific value. Benzoic acid is recommended by the International Union of Pure and Applied Chemistry and the Commission on Chemical Thermodynamics, and a pure material, with a guaranteed calorific value, is obtainable from the U.S. Bureau of Standards ; the calorific value of this material is 6324 15° calories per gram. A similar standard is now available from the British Drug Houses Ltd. with an N.P.L. certificate ; the calorific value of this is 26,435 ± 2·1 joules per gram.

In making a determination of water equivalent 1·2 g. should be taken, fused lightly in the crucible to remove traces of moisture, and a normal determination carried out. It should be remembered that, in this case, the heat of combustion of the cotton and of fusion of the fuse-wire (3·5 cal.

for 10 mg. wire), and the heat of formation of nitric acid from the air must be added to the heat of combustion of the benzoic acid taken. In order to obtain a sufficiently exact figure for the water equivalent a fair number of determinations must be made, say ten, and the average taken.

CALORIMETRY OF LIQUID FUELS

The calorific value of the heavier liquid fuels—all which do not give rise to an explosive mixture with oxygen—may be determined in a bomb calorimeter, and the general details are similar to those given above, with small variations in procedure to suit individual liquids.

Most liquid fuels may be directly weighed out into the fuel crucible and ignition effected by a cotton thread attached to the platinum ignition wire and dipping in the sample. The weight of the thread used must be ascertained and the heat resulting from its combustion deducted. The calorific value of thread is 4140 calories per gram.

If it is found that the fuel does not ignite and burn completely it may be absorbed in three or four paper discs or special cellulose blocks (weight being ascertained), but usually the absorption of the oil by a non-combustible material, kieselguhr, is preferable. With paper considerably less than the usual one gram of oil must be taken. The tray is half filled with kieselguhr (previously ignited, as it always contains organic matter), the surface corrugated, the whole weighed, and the oil distributed over the kieselguhr and reweighed. More dry kieselguhr is then spread over the surface and an almost "dry" oil-impregnated mass obtained. Some kieselguhrs are very fusible and are unsuitable for this use, for a considerable proportion of carbon may remain in the fused mass, which should be examined carefully at the conclusion of the experiment.

With very volatile liquids, such as motor spirit, the bomb calorimeter, as defined above, is used, but their high volatility calls for special care, first to avoid accidents, and secondly to prevent loss by evaporation *after* weighing. Several expedients have been adopted in order to overcome both difficulties. These are (1) the covering of the crucible with a piece of thin rubber sheet, (2) the enclosing of the spirit in a glass bulb, and (3) the use of celluloid capsules.

The first is not too easy to achieve as the spirit vapour tends to dissolve the rubber and break the seal. The second is successful if the tip is broken only at the last moment, but the bulb tends to eject its contents violently sometimes and part of the charge may escape combustion. The celluloid capsule is the most successful.

An alternative method is to burn the fuel after vaporization in a gas calorimeter as shown in Figure 124. A volumetric method of measuring the fuel has been devised at the Fuel Research Station (Report of the Director, 1929, p. 67). In this apparatus a number of glass vessels in series, and arranged vertically, are connected to a burner. The bulb nearest the burner is filled with the fuel and the others with water. Mercury is delivered to the lowest bulb at a constant rate, displacing water and therefore spirit. The burner is constructed so that the fuel is vaporized

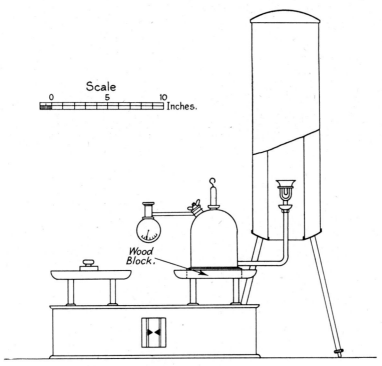

FIG. 124.—Gas Calorimeter adapted for Liquid Fuels.

as it passes the jet. The rates are so arranged that a Boys gas calorimeter can be used. The time over which combustion is measured is that during which the level of spirit passes two marks above and below the topmost bulb. The results are accurate to within ±0·5 per cent., a small correction being necessary for CO in the products of combustion.

CALORIMETRY OF GASES

The calorific value of a gas may be determined in a bomb, but the most suitable form of calorimeter is one with a constant flow of water, and from the volume of gas burnt, the rise of temperature and weight of water heated, the calorific value is calculated.

The original pattern is the *Junkers calorimeter*, which is employed almost exclusively on the Continent and in America, and quite largely in Britain. A bunsen burner burns the gas in a central flue of sufficient diameter to ensure no impingement of the flame against the walls, the hot products of combustion pass to the top of the flue and then descend through small metal tubes arranged in a double circle around the central flue, finally making their exit near the bottom of the instrument. The water is supplied from a constant level tank and flows through the calorimeter in a reverse direction to the gas flow, consequently the exit gas should be cooled to the temperature of the inlet water.

The sectional diagram (Figure 125), although of an older pattern, is

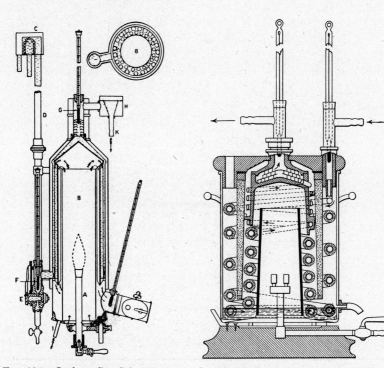

FIG. 125.—Junkers Gas Calorimeter.   FIG. 126.—Boys Gas Calorimeter.

most suitable to illustrate the construction and operation of this calorimeter. The hot gases rise to the top of the chamber, B, descend through the surrounding tubes, escaping at the lower flue, where a thermometer checks the temperature. The water is supplied to the constant level device, C, flows down D and passes through the quadrant control tap, E, past the inlet water thermometer, F. It escapes past the outlet thermometer, G, into the small tank, H, from which it flows through K to the measuring vessel, while a determination is being made, or alternatively to waste.

Water which is condensed from the products of combustion drains to the lower part of the instrument and escapes by the tube, I, under which a graduated receiver is placed. The water collected from a suitable volume of gas burnt furnishes data for the deduction from the gross calorific value when the net calorific is required also.

The *Boys calorimeter* was designed by Prof. C. V. Boys, one of the Gas Referees, at the time when official tests of the calorific power of the gas supply were introduced. Its essential features are that a very small volume of water is actually in the instrument at any one moment, the heat from the gases being abstracted by this water flowing through two spiral copper pipes in series, these being wound with wires, to increase their heat absorption.

A section of the apparatus is shown in Figure 126. The inlet water passes first through the outer coils downwards, then returns upwards through the interior coils, which are heat-insulated by a partition from the exterior coils, finally it flows around suitable channels on the exterior of the metal casting immediately above the chimney, and passes into a mixer with a labyrinth formed of coiled brass strips. Into the top of this chamber the outlet thermometer is fixed.

Two luminous flames from suitable jets are employed. The central chimney is always too hot for condensation of water to take place in it. At the commencement water is poured into the bottom of the vessel until it overflows at the spout provided. Proportionately condensation water flows from this spout during a run, and is collected and measured for the net calorific value determination.

An accurate gas meter is necessary, recording 0·1 cu. ft. per revolution, and with a pressure regulator on each side. The temperature and pressure must be noted and the volume corrected to 60° F. and 30 in. pressure. With coal gas a rate of 6 cu. ft. per hour is suitable (weaker gases in proportion) and the water supply regulated to a temperature of 10° to 12° C. The water flow should be regulated so that the products of combustion should leave the instrument at as nearly as possible air temperature. In the Junkers calorimeter considerable control of this is possible by alteration of the damper in the exit flue. For the Boys calorimeter a correction of $\frac{1}{6}$ calorie for each deg. C. difference in temperature between the exit gases and the air temperature must be added or subtracted from the results.

A convenient quantity of coal gas to employ in a test is 0·3 cu. ft. The temperature of the inlet water thermometer should be read just before the test, as nearly as possible at the completion of the first and second revolutions of the meter, and immediately after the test. The exit water temperature should be noted at every quarter revolution; in each case the mean temperature from the observations is employed.

The main water supply must be adjusted so that a small quantity is always flowing to waste over the weir in the constant pressure device, and the calorimeter should always be run for from twenty to thirty minutes before taking a test, in order that conditions may become settled. When fresh water has been added to the meter or new rubber tubing employed, gas should be run through for some time in order to saturate them thoroughly.

Some small error is introduced by measuring the water instead of weighing it ; in Britain measuring is usual, in America the water is weighed. The simplest plan is to calibrate the measure for the weight of water around the average temperature at which it will be collected in practice. The thermal efficiency of a flow type calorimeter is about 99·5 per cent.

The calorific value is obtained from the equation :

$$\text{Gm.-calories per cu. ft.} = \frac{\text{Weight of water in kilos} \times \text{difference of temp.} \,^{\circ}\text{C.}}{\text{Cu. ft. of gas at } 60^{\circ}\text{ F. and 30 in.}}$$

In an actual example—Temp. of gas 68° F. ; barometer 29·7 ; water collected 3·945 kilos (litres) ; gas burnt 0·3 cu. ft. (= 0·297 at 60° F. and 30 in.) ; difference of temperature 11·6° C.

$$\textit{Gross} \text{ calories per cu. ft.} = \frac{3945 \times 11·6}{0·297} = 154·0 \text{ (610 B.Th.U.)}$$

For the *net* calorific value it is necessary to burn at least 1 cu. ft. of gas and measure the quantity of condensed water (in ml.) collected from the drip pipe ; calculate this to the amount obtainable per cubic foot of gas. The amount of heat to be deducted from the *gross* value per cubic foot will be obtained with sufficient accuracy by multiplying the number of ml. of condensed water per cubic foot of gas by 0·6 calorie.

Example. In experiment above, water collected from 2 cu. ft. of gas = 42 ml.

$$\text{Net value} = 154 - \left(\frac{42}{2} \times 0·6\right) = 141·4 \text{ cal. (563 B.Th.U.)}$$

Still-water Calorimeters. Where a regular supply of water is not available there are a number of calorimeters which can be operated with a fixed quantity of water. The first was that of Thomsen in which the gas is burned in a combustion chamber surrounded by water, the combustion gases passing through a spiral in the water. The water is stirred mechanically and the rise of temperature noted after a certain volume of gas is burned. Several modifications have been made to Thomsen's model by other investigators, but to-day none of them are used to any extent.

The Simmance-Abady portable calorimeter gives results which are correct only to about 3 per cent. A measured quantity of gas is burned in a calorimeter containing water such that its total heat capacity is equivalent to one litre. The temperature is read before and after the calorific value calculated using an instrument factor.

Instruments of a different type are explosion calorimeters, which are suitable for the examination of small quantities of gas. The best known are the Strache, Union and Löffler. In the Strache the heat produced by explosion is given to the air in a jacket round the explosion vessel. The

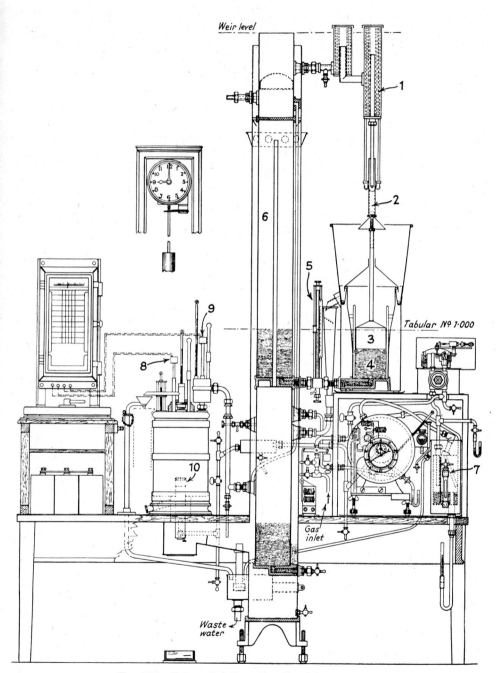

Weir level

Tabular Nº 1·000

Gas
inlet

Waste
water

Fig. 127.—Fairweather Recording Gas Calorimeter.

511

increase of pressure of this air is taken as a measure of its calorific value. The Union is similar in principle, the air being replaced by an oil having a high coefficient of expansion. Blackie and Moss (*J. Sci. Inst.*, 1930, **7**, 84 ; 1935, **12**, 188), after indicating certain necessary precautions, have shown that up to 750 B.Th.U. an accuracy of 0·5 per cent. is possible. This calorimeter has considerable value in laboratory work where only 100–200 ml. of gas are available. The Löffler calorimeter is really an improvement of the original Strache. A few ml. of gas are exploded in a small pipette with a vacuum jacket and the rise of temperature observed. The results obtained do not seem so reliable as those of a calorimeter of the Union type.

RECORDING GAS CALORIMETERS

With the introduction of the Gas Regulation Acts of 1921 the sale of gas on a " therm " value necessitated the introduction in Great Britain of continuous recording calorimeters, the intermittent tests made with the usual type of gas calorimeter not fulfilling altogether what is required. Only one calorimeter of this type is recognized by the Gas Division of the Ministry of Fuel and Power, namely, the Fairweather, but there are other types which will give satisfactory results in good hands. The Sigma type is widely used in the gas industry for general control. In some cases the recording instrument is set to show zero at the declared calorific of the undertaking so that only the variations from this value are recorded. A frequent check by direct determination is necessary.

The Fairweather Calorimeter (Figure 127). This employs a Boys calorimeter which has been slightly modified to permit of its functioning as part of a recording instrument, yet allowing of its being used in the customary manner for individual check tests of the actual calorific values of the gas. The modifications include the use of differential thermometers which translate the temperature rise of the water flow into a record of calorific value or c.v. variations from a standard level.

The water supply should be from a tank at room temperature and is at a pressure head equal to the height between the water levels in *1*, and at the rim of cup *2*. The latter cup is supported in float *3* which, in oil-chamber *4*, forms part of the tabular control. The oil-level, shown on gauge *5*, is graduated from 0·9 to 1·1 so that the amount of water in millilitres at 15° C. which flows during 4 minutes is 2000 G., where G. is the gauge reading. The correction to 15° C. is necessary because the outflow water is warm. The rate of flow of the water is compensated for the variation of gas temperature and pressure by the action of the air contained in air-vessel *6* (at water temperature) on the oil level in *4*.

The gas is metered at the inlet-water temperature after passage through a saturator *7* and metered in a wet meter at a rate of 5 cu. ft. per hour

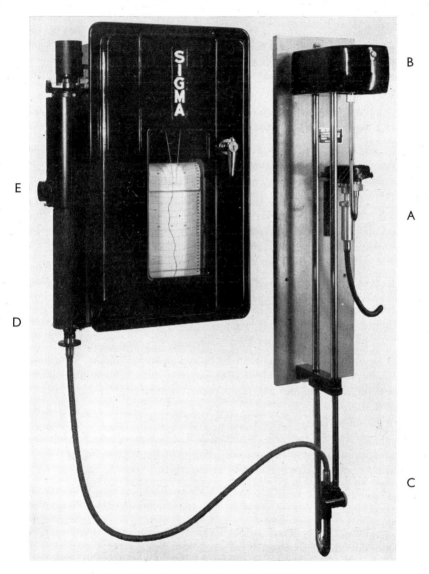

E

D

B

A

C

FIG. 128.—Sigma Recording Gas Calorimeter.

controlled by a clock with an electrically-operated escapement. The gas pressure is from 3 to 4 tenths of an inch of water.

The calorimeter is a modified Boys with the inlet and exit temperatures thermometers *8* and *9* connected to a differential electrical recording thermometer. The burner is of a special low-pressure type (*10*) giving an annular flame, and will deal with gas up to 550 B.Th.U. in calorific value. The temperature difference is recorded in B.Th.U. at 50 B.Th.U. per inch of chart. The record should be checked periodically by making determinations on the calorimeter in the usual way.

The apparatus can be set up to work on a closed cycle with distilled water by providing a storage tank and fitting cooling tanks in the stream.

The Sigma Calorimeter. This instrument is based in principle on the relative expansion of one of two long steel tubes, the inner one heated by the combustion of the gas, whilst the outer one is cooled by the incoming air. By a system of levers the differential movement is imparted to the pen of the chart.

The tubes are concentric, and are 17 in. long, firmly fixed together at the lower ends. Outside these there is a larger tube and the incoming air passes from the open top downwards to the flame, thus acting as a protection from loss of heat from the pair of inner tubes, and warming the air for combustion.

The assembled apparatus is shown in Figure 128 with the new gas-flow regulator, Mk. 2. This regulator assures a constant rate of flow of gas at 60° F. and 30 in. Hg using two governors in series followed by an oil-sealed bell *B* placed at a height of 36 in. above an orifice *C*. With the gas pressure at the orifice equal to atmospheric, automatic compensation is achieved for changes of specific gravity, barometric pressure, and gas temperature.

The gas flows from the orifice *C* through a flexible pipe to the burner *D*, which heats the expansion tubes in *E*. The air-supply to *C* and also to *E* can be the subject of control for change of barometric pressure.

It is claimed that the instrument is suitable for all gases from 90 to 2000 B.Th.U. An independent calorimeter is necessary for independent checking.

REFERENCE BOOKS

Methods of Analysis of Coal and Coke. B.S. 1016 (revised 1954).
Microcalorimetry. Swientoslawski. Rheinhold Publ. Corp. 1946.
The Modern Calorimeter. White. Chem. Catalog. Co. 1928.
Gas Calorimetry. Hyde and Mills. Ernest Benn. 1946.

CHAPTER XX

THE CHOICE OF FUEL AND ITS EFFICIENT UTILIZATION

In the preceding chapters the nature and properties of alternative fuels have been discussed, and some indication given of the methods best suited to their utilization. In some instances the development of the fuel and the appliance have marched together as, for example, high-octane motor spirit and high-compression ratio in the internal combustion engine, and the user is not in doubt regarding the right choice for the most efficient result.

In the case of solid fuel particularly there are, however, many variations of quality which impose on the user the need for such choice if he is to achieve either high thermal efficiency, or low cost, or both. In the case of fluid fuels ease of control makes high thermal efficiency more readily attainable. Since the calorific value of oil fuels varies only within small limits, the user's choice is limited to that of fitting his appliance to the type of fuel, or *vice versa*, and conserving heat by exchange with the combustion air. Fuel gases may vary considerably in calorific value and properties but, given the right conditions of combustion, they also are usable with absolute control and high efficiency.

In the production of power the aim is to convert the heat units in the fuel to a usable form with minimum loss, and here the object is, strictly, high thermal efficiency. Where the process is the conversion of the fuel to a different form, as in the carbonization of coal to coke and gas, heat is consumed in making the change, and the plan is to apply that heat with the minimum loss from the system. High thermal efficiency is therefore implied here also, although rather less directly. Where the fuel is applied to carry out some reaction which demands both time and heat, as in many metallurgical processes, the deciding factor may be the time of treatment at a specific temperature, and thermal efficiency cannot be expressed directly but only in terms of the least amount of fuel possible to complete the desired reactions in a stated mass of material.

The efficient use of fluid fuel is, therefore, largely met by a suitable choice of combustion equipment allied with heat interchange, whereas solid fuel, mainly coal, has a fuel value dependent in part on properties other than thermal, which must be first assessed and then allowed for in terms of efficiency. Before the war and the present era of national coal the prices ruling were largely a matter of supply and demand and had no technical significance although it was realized, of course, that properties such as caking power, granular size, etc., affected actual choice.

Coal Specification. Many times in the past decades has it been suggested that coal should be sold on a basis of calorific value, on the understanding that its value as a fuel was directly proportional to calorific value, but only in isolated cases has this been carried out. The failure was probably due to the fact that coal is a natural product, subject to considerable variation of properties even in the same source of supply, and methods of sampling and analysis were not adequate to deal with the difficulty. The standardization of methods have largely resolved these difficulties now and present-day methods are probably adequate for the exact specification of coal and for the control of deliveries. Granted that this may be so, it follows that the only factors necessary for success in coal distribution are :

(1) An agreed price scale depending on purity and size distribution.

(2) High repeatability in deliveries.

(2) applies without qualification although it might be considered that penalty clauses should apply against failure.

(1) is subject to secondary factors. In the first place the coal must have the right basic properties, such as high caking power for coal to be carbonized, low sulphur content for coal to be converted to metallurgical coke, free-burning properties for house coal, and high combustion rates for furnace firing on grates. It might be that these could be part of the price scale, but it would seem unfair to penalize one market more than another since all of them have preferred coals and all for different reasons. The position is also complicated by considerations of transport cost ; it might be more economic to make use of a local coal of less suitability but low freight cost, and modify the appliance to overcome the discrepancy as far as possible. The residual difference in efficiency might then be more than compensated for by lower monetary cost. This procedure could not apply to all coals but only to those within a certain range of properties for the purpose in view. As an example, the gas industry may prefer a highly-caking coal to give good coke and a high thermal yield of gas, but the continuous-vertical retort will operate perfectly well on coal of much lower caking power if its size is right. Freight charge alone would seem to decide this choice.

It is evident that free moisture and mineral matter (ash) should be the first factors in a price specification. Both may be regarded as impurities but they do not operate in the same way.

Moisture as an ingredient of a fuel is unsatisfactory in that its latent heat of evaporation is lost in the waste gases in addition to the *pro rata* decrease of thermal value which it represents. The latent heat is calculable as :

(*a*) Heat raising water from air temperature to 212° ($212 - t_1$).

(*b*) Heat to convert to steam from and at 212° (967 B.Th.U. per lb.).

(*c*) Heat to raise steam from 212° to flue gas temperature (t_2). ($t_2 - 212$) × specific heat steam (0·48).

Then :

Weight of water per lb. of coal $\times$ $[(212 - t_1) + 967 + 0.48(t_2 - 212)]$.

The magnitude of the values will be appreciated best by taking an actual example.

With coal : Ash 7·5 per cent. Calorific value of dry coal 13,000 ; on combustible, 14,050 : Air temperature, 60° F. ; Flue gases at 500° F.

Moisture per cent.	Calorific value of wet coal.	Additional B.Th.U. expended on evaporating moisture.	Percentage loss of calorific value.
5·0	12,350	62·5	0·50
10·0	11,700	125·0	1·06
15·0	11,050	187·5	1·70

In this example the loss of heat in the evaporation of moisture is equivalent to a percentage reduction of calorific value of one-tenth of the percentage of moisture. The serious loss is the *pro rata* loss and it would seem that can only be met on the basis of an agreed normal moisture content to average out over a period of time.

Mineral matter or ash is less easy of assessment. In high-ash coals the ash content as determined by analysis may be quite appreciably different (lower) from the percentage of mineral matter. The latter is still too difficult to assess in commerce, however, and it must be accepted at present that the loss of calorific value is *pro rata* to the ash content in the first place. Above a certain percentage of ash, however, its presence is detrimental in far greater ratio than the actual percentage will show, and a *pro rata* deduction does not compensate the consumer properly when the ash is much above the standard.

There is additional trouble in the handling and disposal of ashes ; if of a clinkering character it will be very troublesome ; it leads to deposition of much dust in tubes and flues ; it interferes with proper combustion on grates, may cause slagging and heavy loss of carbon in the clinker and may be entrained in the gases and cause extensive shut-down periods for flue cleaning. The magnitude of these effects can be assessed from experience and it would seem fully justified that they should form a factor in the assessment of price.

Size grading is, or can be, another factor in coal quality which can have a considerable effect in determining the efficiency of utilization. Where it is necessary to have a sized coal the important consideration is the proportion of fines (say smaller than $\frac{3}{8}$ in.) which are contained in it. Even in the case of coal which is admittedly " smalls " the proportion of very small material should be subject to limitation if efficiency is not to be impaired. In the case of house coal the limitation of fines, and even of material below one inch in size, is important and in this, and in similar uses, the achievement of close grading might also form a price factor qualifying the basic price.

The factor could not apply to other than graded sizes ; for example, coke-oven coal—less than $\frac{3}{8}$ in. in size—would not be subject to it, nor would slack intended for power production via pulverized fuel.

The Price Structure Scheme of the National Coal Board. The National Coal Board have made proposals for a scheme along these lines.

Since coal is utilized primarily for its heat content the basic factor is calorific value. Since the full calorific value cannot always be utilized the Board propose to adjust the observed calorific value for efficiency of use and certain technical factors in its usage.

Where the coal is used for the production of heat or power it is assumed that the adjusted heat content bears a direct relationship to the ash content since it is known that ash content above a certain level affects heat losses through handling, in increasing unburnt carbon in the ashes and clinker, in causing boiler fouling on the furnace side, increasing time-off for cleaning, and in loss of combustion efficiency on the grate through clinker formation, etc. The adjustments are based on established data which indicate that thermal efficiency decreases with increase of ash content and must be allowed for by adjustment of price. The deductions from the determined calorific value to give what might be termed the " effective " value are shown below for the range 10 to 30 per cent. ash content in a coal containing 7 per cent. of moisture and having a dry, ash-free calorific value of 15,000 B.Th.U. per lb., or 13,950 B.Th.U. at 7 per cent. moisture.

Ash per cent.	B.Th.U./lb. as received.	adjusted.	Relative evaluation.	Per cent. loss.	Deducted.
10	12,450	12,140	1·00	2·1	260
20	10,590	9,920	0·815	9·4	1,030
30	9,450	7,010	0·58	25·8	2,440

Coal at 10 per cent. ash is presumed to have a loss of efficiency of 2·1 per cent. due to the effects of the ash. Above this value the effects increase to 9·4 per cent. at 20 per cent. ash, and to 25·8 per cent. at 30 per cent. ash. Between 10 and 20 per cent. ash the loss represents 0·73 per cent. per one per cent. of ash; between 20 and 30, 1·62 ; and between 10 and 30, 1·18 per cent.

Taking as a standard a small industrial coal of type 602 with a maximum size between $\frac{3}{4}$ and 1 in. as having an adjusted calorific value of 11,250 B.Th.U. per lb. and a monetary value of 43s. per ton, it can be said that $\frac{1}{100}$ lb. or 112·5 B.Th.U. represents one " evaluation point ", and 43s. divided by 112·5 gives 4·59 pence per point. Any industrial coal can then be valued by calculating its adjusted calorific value and multiplying the number of points by 4·59. To this must then be added certain agreed flat-rate additions to cover size grading and freight.

For coals with pronounced caking power, and therefore presumably earmarked for carbonization, the Board have decided to introduce an additional factor to make the cost higher to the consumer. It is an open question whether this is justified since such coal could well be unsuitable, or at least less suitable, for other purposes, but it is understandable in view of the increasing scarcity of caking coals. In this case the coal is presumed to be converted to solid and gaseous products and the thermal values of these calculated separately on the same points system of C.V./100.

The calculations are as follows, where FC is fixed carbon, CF is coking factor and P the per cent. correction for ash in the coke.

	Solid B.Th.U.	Gaseous B.Th.U.
Taken	$(FC \times 14,400)/100 = A_s$	Actual C.V. $- A_s = A_g$
Adjusted	$A_s \times CF \times (100 + P)/100 = A_{s_1}$	$10/7\ A_g = A_{g_1}$

$$\text{Total points} = (A_{s_1} + A_{g_1})/100.$$

The above 602 coal with moderate caking power, 10 per cent. ash and 7 per cent moisture would have 133·3 points by this calculation. The gaseous heat unit is assessed at 10/7 times the monetary value of the solid heat unit. A separate adjustment is made for the content of the coke since it is known that the value of coke decreases with increasing ash content at the rate of about one per cent. for each one per cent. of additional ash.

If the value of the same coal at different ash content is calculated by the two formulæ and graphed against ash content the curves are not parallel. A strongly-caking coal becomes cheaper on this basis than on the industrial basis if its ash content exceeds 12 per cent. Similarly a weakly-caking coal becomes cheaper on the carbonization basis above 5 per cent. of ash. Since it is not intended that any coal can have two prices depending upon the use to which it is put it is felt by the Board that this scientific approach to coal evaluation will give the intelligent user ample scope for the selection of the most suitable coal for his purpose.

Choice of Fuel and Equipment. The correct choice must depend upon the range of fuel available and the installation of the most suitable plant or, alternatively, upon the best choice of fuel both technically and as to price to suit existing plant.

It has already been explained in preceding chapters how the type of fuel can alter the efficiency of an appliance, and how equipment has been developed to achieve the best result from an inferior fuel, but it is proposed to summarize the most important points here in order to obtain a composite picture.

In the case of fluid fuels we have the outstanding virtue of greater ease of control of the supply of the fuel and of the conditions of its combustion. It is possible, therefore, to develop more easily the right conditions of heat release, the flame temperature required, and the flexibility necessary to meet changes of load. Beyond this point equipment modifications are only such as are necessary to meet variations of properties which are much less in range than the difference between fluid and solid fuels.

In the case of oil fuels preheat is necessary for viscous fuels to achieve efficient atomization, distillate fuels are necessary for small appliances with automatic control, burners of many types are necessary to suit the viscosity of the fuel and to produce the length and shape of flame required for different appliances. If these factors are met the problem of achieving high efficiency is then limited to (1) the exact proportioning of oil and combustion air, (2) the recovery of heat from the waste gases, and (3) the adequate thermal insulation of the furnace. The choice between oil fuel and solid fuel must be determined by consideration of handling and storage problems and monetary cost.

With gaseous fuels the secondary problems are limited to those associated with the calorific value of the fuel. Fuels of low calorific value require special burners and preheated air if high flame temperatures are to be achieved in the furnace. This may mean a higher equipment cost but no loss of thermal efficiency. The high flexibility of use of gas has promoted its use above solid and even oil fuel, even in circumstances where cost was higher. In the case of by-product fuels such as blast-furnace gas the problem is not affected by cost and the aim has been to improve appliances to the maximum in the interests of fuel economy. With gaseous fuels the same needs arise for combustion control, heat recovery and adequate thermal insulation.

In the case of oil fuels for the internal combustion engine the improvement of fuel properties and engine design have marched together and cannot be separated within each type. For example, the knock-rating of gasoline has improved to a level which is almost beyond that required by the present compression ratio of the road-vehicle engine. The pursuit of high efficiency, however, is causing a movement in favour of the replacement of the petrol engine, with an efficiency of the order of 25 per cent., by the Diesel engine with an efficiency of 35 per cent. The implications of such a trend upon petroleum refining could be considerable. In aviation also, the use of jet propulsion can change the demand for really high-octane gasoline to distillates of higher boiling-range.

Coal, and to a lesser extent coke, present more difficult problems in every utilization. It is basically variable in composition, in ash and moisture content, in size, and in caking power, and all of these must be allowed for in the choice of the fuel and the appliance in which it must be consumed. Its use is also complicated by problems of handling and storage and by the greater difficulty of achieving automatic control of rate of flow to an appliance and rate of combustion in it. For the domestic market coal requirements must vary with the nature of the appliance. The open fire prefers weakly-caking coal of fairly large size with a small proportion of fines and a reasonably low content of ash, which is not white and cloaking on the fire. Efficiency of use has been improved by the introduction of better-insulated grates and by adding the effect of convected warm air from the fire back, but regrettably the open fire can never be efficient except under bright-fire conditions, and these normally represent only a small proportion of the working life of the fire. For stoves, which offer more scope for steady operation and better control, the preferred fuel is coal of low volatile matter, or anthracite, or coke. With convective heating of air the efficiency level for space heating may be as high as 65 per cent. in comparison with the non-convector open-fire average level of about 15 per cent. In Great Britain, the desired high-comfort level of background heating, with supplementary radiation when required, would seem to be still in the future despite the fact that the amount of fuel burned in this way is a high proportion of the country's fuel consumption and economy in this field could make a real saving in national fuel consumption.

The combustion of coal in industry carries many problems of which not the least is the effect of the scale of the using plant or furnace. In small plant the means of application are normally manual and the refinements of control which can be used in large-scale plant are uneconomic or even unpractical. Under such conditions it is necessary to treat each plant or application separately and balance cost against gain of efficiency. The only way to achieve this successfully is through the study of fuels, their properties, and the methods available for their efficient combustion.

CONTROL OF COMBUSTION THROUGH COMPOSITION OF FLUE GASES

The method of calculating the amount of air required theoretically for the combustion of fuel of given composition and the theoretical composition of the flue gases have been given in Chapter I, and data for such calculations in Table LXXIII, Appendix.

When the combustion of a fuel is complete the whole of the carbon should appear in the flue gases as carbon dioxide, accompanied by the nitrogen previously associated with the oxygen in the air. If this were attainable without excess air, carbon dioxide, water and nitrogen alone would constitute the flue gases. With excess air, as must be the case always with a solid or liquid fuel, free oxygen will be present in addition. On the other hand, when combustion is not complete carbon will be found in the flue gases partly as carbon monoxide and partly as hydrocarbons ; theoretically there should be no free oxygen under these conditions.

The efficiency of the combustion process is dependent upon two main factors :

1. Complete development of the maximum number of heat units of the fuel, attainable only by complete combustion.

2. Maximum utilization of these units, attainable only by avoiding all preventable waste.

F.—S*

The first condition is very important. All carbon appearing as the monoxide leads to serious loss, for 1 lb. of coke carbon then develops only 4,420 B.Th.U. per lb., instead of 14,650, as it does when burnt to carbon dioxide. Further, incomplete combustion of the volatile constituents (or products resulting from their decomposition by heat) leads to escape of hydrocarbon gases of high calorific value.

In general these losses through incomplete combustion can be avoided only by admission of a certain excess of air over that demanded theoretically, and necessarily this entails losses through sensible heat units carried by the flue gases, which up to a certain limit are unavoidable. For maximum practical efficiency a course must be steered clear on the one hand of the losses through incomplete combustion, without on the other hand running the risk of still bigger losses through unnecessary excess of air. Heat units must be sacrificed; the important point is to adjust conditions of air supply so that this sacrifice is reduced to the minimum.

Assuming combustion were perfect with the theoretical air, heat would still be lost through the hot flue gases, the actual loss depending on the weight of the gases, their specific heat and temperature, or :—

$$m \times \text{Sp. ht. } (t_1 - t_2) = \text{B.Th.U.}$$

where m is the weight of gases per lb. of fuel, t_1 the temperature of the flue gases, t_2 the temperature of the air supply. Excess of air which must be allowed, as shown already, increases m, and the losses become proportionately large as $(t_1 - t_2)$ becomes greater. In addition to losses in the flue gases excess air causes direct cooling in the furnace, and reduces the efficiency of the heat transmission to the burden.

It is clear then that the control of the amount of air actually employed in the combustion process is essential to high thermal efficiency, and consequently the means by which a proper judgment of the actual air supply can be ascertained must be considered carefully.

The determination of the proportion of carbon dioxide alone can be a sufficiently good guide with known fuels. Pure carbon on combustion with the theoretical air yields a volume of carbon dioxide equal to the volume of oxygen with which it combines; hence, as air contains approximately 20·9 per cent. of oxygen, the gaseous products consist of 20·9 per cent. of carbon dioxide and 79·1 per cent. of nitrogen. If more air than the theoretical amount is used so that the CO_2 content of the gas is lower the percentage of excess air is given by $100\ [20·9/\text{observed } CO_2 - 1]$ per cent. If the theoretical CO_2 content of the waste gas is, say, 18·5 per cent., the proportion of excess air is calculable in the same way as a rough guide.

Fuels, however, contain also hydrogen and small amounts of sulphur which combine with oxygen and the exact calculation of excess air is more complicated and requires an exact analysis of the fuel being burned. It is assumed that the carbon burns to CO_2, the hydrogen to water, and the sulphur to sulphur dioxide. From stoichiometric relationships the CO_2 content of the waste gas is then calculable, assuming the lb. mol. of a gas to occupy a volume of 359 cu. ft. at 32° F. and 30 in. Hg pressure. The same calculation will also give the amount of oxygen consumed and therefore the volume of air used. If we assume that the dry gas composition is CO_2 18·3, SO_2 0·1, and N 81·6 per cent., and that the theoretical air required is 131·4 cu. ft., the amount of excess air used when showing a CO_2 content of 14·1 per cent. is given by the above calculation as 30 per cent.

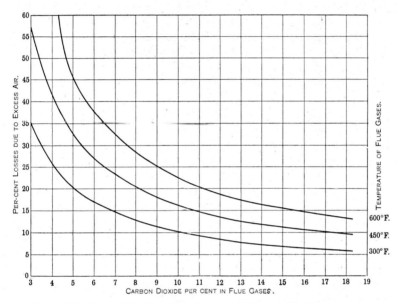

FIG. 129.—Loss of Heat in Flue Gases at Different CO_2 Percentages.

Calculated for a steam coal, 87·0 per cent. carbon ; 4·5 per cent. hydrogen ; assuming a mean specific heat for the flue gases of 0·24 ; 18·3 per cent. CO_2 in flue gases corresponds with 11·6 lb. of air theoretically required.

The effect of undue excess air on loss of heat as sensible heat in the waste gases can be expressed graphically and the combustion engineer is well advised to have such charts prepared to cover the range of fuels he normally burns. Their use will provide a warning of undue changes which will not only indicate when the excess air is too high but whether uneven distribution of the air has led to incomplete combustion, as indicated by the appearance of unburnt hydrocarbons despite an apparently reasonable amount of excess air. Graphs of this type for all the usual fuels are to be found in *Technical Data on Fuel* (1950, pp. 420–6). An illustration of the effect of sensible heat loss for one coal at different flue-gas temperatures is given in Figure 129 ; the normal 20–25 per cent. of excess air corresponds in this figure to 15 per cent. carbon dioxide.

The degree of incompleteness of combustion is usually measured by the amount of carbon monoxide present in the flue gas. The amount of excess air necessary to prevent incomplete combustion depends upon the fuel burned and the type of furnace. Almost complete combustion with little more than theoretical air can be obtained with gas and oil firing and with pulverized coal. With grate firing of coal or coke this is not possible, and even 100 per cent. excess air does not eliminate CO from the flue gases. It is generally conceded that a compromise between heat losses by incomplete combustion and as sensible heat in the flue gas is obtainable with about 25 per cent. of excess air. This is illustrated in Figure 130, where

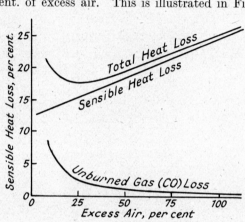

FIG. 130.—Variation of Total Heat Loss with Increasing Excess Air in a Coal-fired Furnace.

the steadily-increasing flue-gas loss is shown to give a minimum total heat loss when the undeveloped heat in carbon monoxide is still over 2 per cent. of the heat of the fuel burned.

The position is rather different in the case of oil or pulverized fuel firing. In the latter, substantially complete combustion is achieved with 15–20 per cent. of excess air and incomplete combustion is first evidenced by the appearance of carbon smoke rather than by the escape of carbon monoxide and hydrogen. In the case of oil firing 25–30 per cent. of excess air may be necessary for complete combustion, but this may be reduced to about 10 per cent. by the use of a high air-preheat temperature.

Combustion Recorders and Instrumentation. In order to control combustion efficiency by waste-gas composition and temperature it is apparent that sound methods of gas sampling and analysis must be used and that, in addition, continuously-recording instruments should be available to indicate short-period changes or detect the start of any adverse change of conditions. Space is not available to describe the correct methods of sampling of waste gases and reference should be made to B.S. 1756, 1952, for details. The analysis of the sample may be made by hand, but in large-scale practice it should be made by recording instruments. In test work where high accuracy is desired sampling must be done over mercury and the analysis must be made by an apparatus of sufficiently high inherent accuracy.

Combustion recorders may be either chemical or physical. The former depend upon the taking of a gas sample at intervals of several minutes, absorbing the carbon dioxide in a solution of caustic potash, and recording the diminution of volume. In more elaborate but less common forms the oxygen may also be determined by sorption in alkaline pyrogallol solution, but the time interval between samples is then twice as long. In another form each alternate sample of gas is passed over heated copper oxide where any carbon monoxide or hydrogen is oxidized to CO_2 and H_2O before washing with alkali. If these gases are present each alternate line on the chart will be longer, and the difference will represent $CO + H_2$ and be a visible reminder of potential-heat losses.

Several types of recorder use a physical property as the means of measurement. Diffusivity is used in one : the gas is aspirated through a metal cylinder containing a porous pot which contains a cartridge filled with a solid absorbent for carbon dioxide. The CO_2 is absorbed and creates a pressure difference across the wall of the pot. This is recorded and is proportional to the concentration of the CO_2.

A second type makes use of differences of density. Average waste gas is some 8 per cent. more dense than air and this difference can be magnified to give a sensitive indication. In the Ranarex instrument this is done by impelling air and waste gas, with a powerful swirl, by fans attached to the shafts of two independent electric motors against two other fans with flat vanes. The air and gases being impelled with opposite rotary motions, the difference of torque of the two shafts enables a system of levers to be coupled to the respective ends of the shafts of the energy-absorbing vanes and so operate an indicating pointer and trace a record on a wax paper chart. The impelling motors have a speed of 3000 r.p.m. If there is a slight difference of speed this is readily compensated for by a small adjustment of the zero.

Since water vapour will affect the density, it is necessary to bring both the air and flue gases to the same state of humidity-saturation. This is arranged for by humidifiers through which the gases pass.

It is found that small differences of density of two gases can be determined with a considerable degree of accuracy. Its rapidity of action enables it to be used for this purpose where rapid changes have to be studied and other apparatus is inadmissible.

Electrical Recorders. A third type is based upon differences of thermal conductivity of gases. If a wire of non-oxidizable metal such as platinum be heated by an electric current in a stream of gas, the temperature which it attains is determined by the thermal conductivity of the gas. Since the conductivity of carbon dioxide is 0·59 when air is taken as 1·00 it is apparent that the temperature attained by two wires in exactly similar cells containing saturated air and saturated waste gas respectively can be calibrated to read in terms of CO_2. The only difficulty is that the conductivity of hydrogen on the same scale is 7 and even a small amount of this gas can make a large error in the reading. Fortunately the proportion of hydrogen likely to be in waste gases is very small and its presence should be recognized in other ways.

An instrument based on these principles was designed by Siemens as early as 1908, and G. A. Shakespear is responsible for the instrument described below, now made by the Cambridge Instrument Co.

This comprises (a) the soot filter (necessary with all recorders), (b) the CO_2 metering unit, (c) indicating and/or recording instruments, connected to (b) by suitable lengths of insulating leads.

The arrangement of the metering unit is illustrated by the diagram

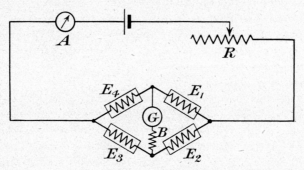

Fɪɢ. 131.—Electrical Arrangement of Cambridge CO_2 Recorder.

(Fig. 131). Four identical spirals of platinum wire are enclosed in separate cells, E_1–E_4, in a metal block, each forming an arm of a Wheatstone bridge. When two gases of different thermal conductivity are introduced, one into the pair of cells E_1, E_3, and the other gas into E_2, E_4, the respective wires in these will cool at a different rate and maintain a different temperature. The difference of resistance will throw the Wheatstone bridge out of balance and the galvanometer, G, will be deflected to a degree which depends primarily on the difference of conductivity of the two gases. It is arranged that changes in temperature of the gases affect both sides of the bridge equally. If the cells E_2, E_4, contain air, and the cells E_1, E_3, flue gas, the extent of deflection will indicate the amount of CO_2 present, the galvanometer being calibrated to show the percentage. Carbon monoxide, nitrogen and oxygen have so nearly the thermal conductivity of air that small variations in these accompanying gases have no appreciable influence on the results. Hydrogen, however, as already mentioned, may have an influence.

The current in the Wheatstone bridge circuit, as shown by the ammeter, A, is adjusted to a constant amount by the rheostat, R, whilst the resistance,

B, in the galvanometer circuit enables the electrical zero of the CO_2 meter to be adjusted.

The method can be extended to indicate the amount of carbon monoxide in waste gas by using a second pair of cells and burning the CO to CO_2 before passing the waste gas through the gas cell. The difference between the CO_2 content as then measured and the value obtained in the other pair of cells is a measure of the CO content.

Use of Combustion Recorders. The recording of carbon dioxide alone is the easiest and most applicable method of estimating excess air, but carbon dioxide is only a measure of the heat losses due to this *when it is not accompanied by carbon monoxide*. A further small error is introduced by sulphur dioxide, produced from combustible sulphur in the fuel. This gas is absorbed also by the reagents which absorb carbon dioxide.

The saving of fuel when recorders are installed can be very considerable. In many cases they have revealed that not more than 5 per cent. of carbon dioxide had been obtained in ordinary working before this check was introduced. With the instruments fitted in a suitable position, the record is at all times visible to the stokers, who are found usually to take a proper interest in maintaining the standard of the flue gases, and as a check to excessive firing at infrequent intervals during the night shifts they have proved of great value. In power stations with widely varying load it is difficult to obtain proper adjustment of conditions for the best results without the employment of some such system, and as a means of detecting irregularity in the working of automatic stokers they are valuable.

A word of caution is necessary in reference to air leaks through boiler settings, etc. This would lead to low carbon dioxide, and the cause would be detected by failure of reduction of the air supply to the furnace to raise the carbon dioxide. There is, however, the risk that in attempting to do this, in the absence of knowledge as to an air intake, losses through incomplete combustion might be incurred.

In the operation of producer gas plants the automatic carbon dioxide recorders are of value in controlling the working conditions, as the carbon dioxide is a most useful indication of the reactions taking place.

Automatic recorders, especially those of the chemical type, require regular attention if they are to be kept operating satisfactorily, but this attention, if regular, need occupy but little time. Particular attention must be directed to the cleansing of the gases by a suitable soot filter, which should be readily accessible for cleaning and renewal of material, and to arranging the gas pipes so that water does not condense and collect in bends : drain cocks should be provided at such points. The pipe system should be blown through at frequent intervals with compressed air or steam. With attention to the recorders as part of the daily routine of the boiler-house the instruments are capable of invaluable service, but with neglect for some days so much requires doing that it is never attempted.

Measurement of Temperature. In all fuel utilization the measurement of temperature is an important factor. In the first place it is necessary to know whether the temperature required in the process is being attained and in the second place to know the temperatures which determine the heat losses from the system ; these are those of the waste gases, the air if it is preheated, the external surface of the furnace, and the product of heating.

The mercury-in-glass thermometer can be used (if filled with nitrogen) up to 550° C. Mercury in steel will cover only the same range but is robust. Thermocouples can be used to 1100° C. for base-metal junctions and to 1370° C. for the platinum metals. Thermocouples must always be protected by sheaths of refractory material since the gases affect the metal and slowly alter the e.m.f. given by the junction. The use of a cold junction is always to be recommended. In using thermocouples it is necessary to make sure that the junction is sufficiently immersed and, if it is the temperature of a gas stream which is being measured, that it is screened from direct radiation from the furnace wall. An alternative method of screening is to draw the gas at a high rate past the end of the couple so that the high rate of heat transfer masks radiation effectively.

Furnace temperatures may be measured by an optical pyrometer, which is focused on a surface at the temperature to be measured. The temperature in the field is compared with the temperature of a standardized lamp filament or the total radiation is focused on a black body which operates as a thermopile.

The surface temperature of brickwork or metal can be measured by either a thermometer or a thermocouple specially designed for the purpose. In both cases the element is protected from heat loss by a screen and has a time factor depending upon the temperature to be measured. Thermocouple wires may also be embedded in the surface by cutting suitable grooves, or by inserting several couples at different depths and integrating the results to zero depth. Paints which change colour at different temperature are useful for observation but not for measurement ; they have also a very short life. Heat-flow gauges are available for the measurement of total heat flow from a hot surface. The Blackie gauge collects the heat on the blackened surface of an air capsule and measures the pressure at which the rate of rise of temperature of the air is just balanced by the rate of leakage through a capillary leak. It is found that this pressure is constant for an appreciable length of time. The instrument is calibrated to read in terms of B.Th.U. per sq. ft. per hour.

Smoke, Water, Steam, etc. Instruments for the measurement of these quantities are beyond the scope of this volume, but it is apparent that they play an important part in the instrumentation of any fuel-using plant and are essential for adequate plant control and for the preparation of heat-balance tests.

Heat Transfer. In considering the efficient use of fuel it is not enough to achieve good conditions of combustion; it is also necessary to bring about the combustion under conditions which achieve the highest rate of heat transfer to the object to be heated. Heat transfer may be by conduction, convection or radiation and an excellent example of the effects of these in the utilization of fuel is provided by the apparently simple case of steam.

In Figure 132 it is seen that radiation from the furnace side falls directly upon the film of soot or scale which normally coats the surface of the boiler tube while convection can operate only by thinning the gas layer which is stagnant on the surface and is increased in thickness by the roughness of any deposit. A clean surface therefore increases heat transfer in two ways, (a) by allowing the radiation to fall directly on the metal and (b) by ensuring a thinner gas layer. The conductance of such gas layers has been measured and is of the order of 6 B.Th.U. per sq. ft. per ° F. per hour. In the layer of scale or carbon, heat transfer is by conduction, but the rate is proportional to the conductivity of the scale ($k = 0.6$) which is much lower than that of the metal plate or tube ($k = 30$ in British units). On the other (water) side there is also scale of low conductivity and a water/steam film to overcome, but the conductance of this film is much higher than that on the gas side and is of the order of 1000 units.

Taking these factors into consideration, and assuming flame radiation at 2500° F. and hot gases at 2500–1500° F., it is calculable that the resistance to heat flow in a boiler furnace is nearly all in the gas film: it is shown by the very high temperature drop through this film, the temperature of the "dry" surface being only about 500° F. and that of the metal about 430° F.

Resistance to Heat Flow

	Per cent.
Furnace gas film	87
Furnace scale	5
Metal	1
Water scale	6
Steam-water film	1

It follows from this that the desiderata for a high rate of heat transfer are:

Direct radiation to a clean surface.
A high rate of gas flow to reduce the thickness of the gas layer.
A minimum of scale of low conductivity on the water side.
An efficient circulation of water over the heated surfaces.

A further consideration bears on the importance of high flame temperature since radiation is proportional in rate to the fourth power of the absolute temperature.

The same considerations determine the modern trend in steam raising towards "radiant" boilers in which the wall of the furnace is lined with boiler tubes which receive high-temperature radiation from the flame. In metallurgical furnaces also, where high rates of heat transfer are aimed at, arrangements are made for short flames and high temperatures as near as possible to the theoretical. There are, however, many industrial applications where too high a temperature would do damage to the materials

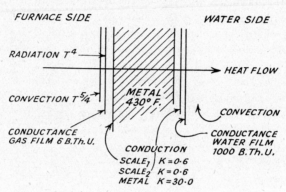

FIG. 132.—Transfer of Heat in Steam Boiler.

Conductance in B.Th.U./sq. ft./° F./hour.
Conductivity in B.Th.U./sq. ft./° F./hour/foot thickness.

under treatment : in such cases adequate rates of heat transfer are attained by increase of the time of contact at a moderate temperature or by a much shorter time of contact under radiant conditions. Each process, therefore, poses a separate problem and should be solved by the study of the principles of heat transfer in relation to the heat requirements of the process. Only in this way can the maximum thermal efficiency be realized.

Conservation of Heat. Granted that the right conditions of combustion and heat transfer have been established for any industrial process the next problem is to conserve the waste heat which inevitably flows from any process which employs fuel. This heat may be in the form of sensible heat of combustion gases, or radiated heat from the heated surfaces of the plant, sensible heat in the treated product, or potential heat in by-product or other gases.

Sensible heat in combustion gases is recoverable normally by heat interchange with the combustion air but is sometimes recoverable by preheating the material under treatment provided no damage is thereby incurred. In the case of steam raising it may also be recovered by superheating the steam and by preheating the feed water.

Heat-exchangers are usually divided into two groups :

Recuperation : in which heat is transferred from one material to another through a solid wall, e.g. recuperators, condensers, air-heaters, economizers.

Regeneration : in which the waste heat raises the temperature of a refractory mass for a period of time and the heat is withdrawn by the counterflow of cold fuel gases or air.

In recuperation the gases may flow parallel to one another (parallel flow) or in opposite directions (counter flow) or at right angles (cross flow), but in each case the rate of transfer depends upon the thickness and conductivity of the partition wall and the area of surface exposed. An example of counter flow is seen in Figure 43, where the waste gases from a retort setting are passing countercurrent to the inward flow of combustion air. In this case the efficiency of interchange is about 37 per cent. and the waste gases are cooled to 600° C. In any such system the surface required for a given air-preheat is calculable from the relative volumes of gas and air, their specific heats, and the conductivity of the partition. The actual choice of conditions depends on the process involved but, under steady conditions of flow, the highest efficiency is obtainable from counter flow in which the heated gas is last in contact with the heating gas at its highest temperature. In the above example the area could be increased to give a lower waste-gas temperature, but recovery as steam is preferred (see below).

In regeneration there is implied a number of chambers to serve as heat-storage vessels. These may be brickwork chambers filled with chequer-work through which the gases may flow with minimum loss of pressure head. The hot waste gas passes through one chamber and raises its temperature to the same level ; a valve is then operated to make the gases flow through a second chamber while the air to be heated passes through the first one until the temperature is reduced to a predetermined level. The valve is then operated again to reverse the flow. In practice, conditions are chosen to give a required air-preheat temperature and to reduce that of the waste gases to the minimum temperature which will create adequate chimney draught. An example of this system is shown in Figure 40 ; with a time cycle of 20–30 minutes the air is preheated to 1050° C., the waste gases cooled to 260° C., and an efficiency of interchange achieved of 78 per cent. In view of the intermittent character of the process, design calculations are difficult and the student is referred to text-books on the subject of heat transfer.

Either of these systems, but more usually recuperation, can be associated with heat recovery by the raising of steam in a " waste-heat " boiler. In the horizontal-retort example quoted above (Figure 43) the recuperator is followed by a boiler in which the temperature of the waste gases is reduced to 240° C. from 600° C. If the heat in the steam raised is added to the heat given to the air the total recovery represents 61 per cent. of the heat in the waste gases, which is appreciably less than can be achieved by regeneration as, for example, in the coke oven exemplified. The plant is, however, more manageable in applications of this type and the steam is an asset in a process which has a high demand for steam.

Heat losses from any system by other means than in the waste gases occur mainly by radiation, etc., from the outer walls of the plant, and the competent engineer will not only reduce them by suitable insulation but will observe the actual losses which occur in order to guard against breakdown of insulation by cracks or other causes. In the first place the loss of heat is the result of flow by conduction through the walls and is a function of the thermal conductivity of the material and its thickness. Since the thermal conductivity of firebrick is about 0·003 at 1000° C. in C.G.S. units or about 0·7 B.Th.U. per sq. ft. per hr. per ° F. per ft. of thickness, while the corresponding values for insulating brick are about one-tenth of this, it is apparent that outer layers of insulating brick are of considerable value in reducing the outer temperature of a furnace and therefore the heat losses from it.

In intermittently-operated furnaces the rate of flow of heat is not steady, but the material of the walls is raised in temperature each time the furnace is operated. In this case it is the thermal diffusivity of the material which is proportional to the rate of heat loss. If the thermal conductivity is k, diffusivity $d = k/cs$, where c is the specific heat and s the apparent specific gravity. It is, therefore, the rise of temperature in unit volume produced by one heat unit in unit time through unit area one unit thick. The value for firebrick is about 0·004 in C.G.S. units.

Having reduced heat losses through the brickwork to the practical minimum, it is still necessary to observe the surface losses by measurement in order to keep check on structural breakdown or to construct thermal balances in order to obtain a picture of thermal efficiency. This can be done on plane surfaces by an instrument such as the Blackie heat-flow gauge (p. 528) or by measuring the area of the outer surface of the plant, taking a series of surface temperatures, and calculating radiation and convection losses separately. In the case of radiation the receiving surface t_0 may be the wall of an adjacent building but is usually taken as the temperature of the air; radiation is then calculated by the fourth power law. Convection losses are more difficult since they are affected by geometry. In still air the convective heat loss from an exposed surface is given by :

$$H = C \times 0\cdot3(t_1 - t_0)^{5/4} \text{ B.Th.U. per sq. ft. per hour}$$

where t_1 is the temperature of the surface, t_0 that of the surrounding air, and C varies with the position of the surface. For large bodies of irregular shape C may be taken as 1·0, but it can vary quite appreciably as follows :

Surface.	Plane vertical.	Plane horizontal up.	down.	Hor. wire or cylinder. 1·0 mm. dia.	10 mm. dia.
C	1·0	1·3	0·65	6·5	2·0

The Thermal Balance. When all the above factors have been considered and an apparently sound compromise reached between heat requirements and thermal efficiency, it is still a sound policy to construct a complete thermal balance of the process or plant and to study the details of it to determine whether or not there is some loss of heat from the system which can be avoided. In order to be complete, the balance must not only record the heat units entering and leaving the system but should show each integral part separately and include the heat of reaction of all internal reactions. For example, in studying the performance of a steam boiler it is necessary to know the performance of the furnace, the superheater, the economizer, and the air heater, separately. This means a large number of observations must be made and samples taken. The "Test Codes" of the British Standards Institution provide exact instructions for most of the

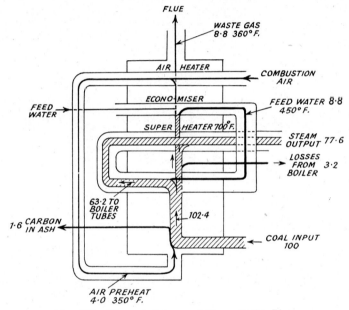

FIG. 133.—Thermal Balance of Steam Boiler Plant.

common industrial fuel-consuming processes and the reader is referred to these for instructions and methods of calculation.

In order to present a picture of the heat flow in any process the data can be presented graphically. To show how this is done two examples are given in Figures 133 and 134, for steam-raising plant and carbonizing plant, while the data from which they were constructed are tabulated in Tables LXVIII and LXIX. It is clear that the diagram is more immediately comprehensible than the tabulated figures.

These balances represent good, if not the best practice, with the waste gases leaving at about 360° F., a level which is necessary to ensure good chimney draught. In the latest power-station practice the overall efficiency may approach 89 per cent. with a carbon loss of 0·9, a radiation loss of 0·6, and a stack loss of 9·5 per cent.

TABLE LXVIII

THERMAL BALANCE OF STEAM BOILER PLANT

Heat in coal . . . . . . 100·0	To saturated steam . . 63·2	
Heat in air . . . . 4·0	To waste gas . . . . 36·0	
	To radiation, etc. . . . 3·2	}104·0
	To carbon in ashes . . 1·6	

To superheat . . . . 14·4	
To feed water . . . . 8·8	
To air . . . . . 4·0	} Waste gas 36·0
To flues . . . . . 8·8	

Superheater . . . 14·4/36·0 = 40 per cent.	
Economizer . . . 8·8/21·6 = 41 ,,	Overall E. = 77·6 per cent.
Air heater . . . 4·0/12·8 = 31 ,,	

The second example of a complete thermal balance is taken from a coal carbonization plant. The diagram is shown in Figure 134 and the data balance in Table LXIX. In this case the heat in the waste gases is recovered as steam in a waste-heat boiler. An important aspect of this balance is

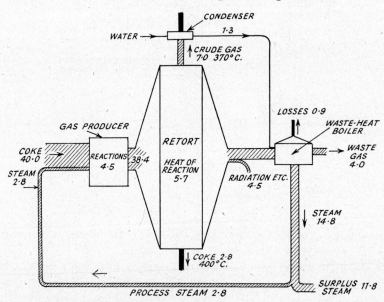

FIG. 134.—Thermal Balance of Continuous-vertical Gas Retort.
(Quantities in therms per ton of coal.)

that it discloses a weakness in carbonizing plant of this type in that the main products of gas and coke both carry off a high percentage of the heat used for carbonization and this is not recovered. It could be recovered from the gases by using the boiler feed-water to a greater extent for condensation, and from the coke by cooling it with inert gas and using the hot gases for the raising of more steam. Both of these have been attempted and the fact that they are not common practice is due to practical reasons which outweigh those of fuel economy. The example does explain how such balances are valuable in indicating the occurrence and magnitude of losses in any thermal system.

TABLE LXIX

Thermal Balance of a Continuous-vertical Gas Retort

(Therms per ton of coal)

Coke to producer	40·0	Gas producer reactions 4·4 E. = 80%
Steam to retort	2·8	Radiation, etc., losses 4·5
	———	Crude gas at 370° C. . 7·0*
	42·8	Coke at 400° C. . . 2·8
		Reactions in the retort 5·7
		Waste gases at 1100° C. 18·4
		42·8

* Used to heat boiler feed water 1·3.

Waste gases	18·4	Steam to retort	2·8
Feed water	1·3	Steam to fan	0·2
		Steam surplus	11·8
		Final waste gases	4·0
		Radiation, etc.	0·9
	19·7		19·7

Recovery of heat from crude gas . . 1·3/7·0 = 19 per cent.
Recovery from waste gases . . . 13·5/18·4 = 73 per cent.

Fuel Consumption for Power. A large proportion of the fuel consumed in the world is converted into power either directly as in the case of engine fuels, or indirectly as in the case of solid fuels by conversion of heat into power.

It is not possible to convert all the heat energy of fuel by either method into power and, even under the optimum conditions for each consuming plant, the proportion which modern technique can convert varies over quite a wide range. This proportion is termed the thermal efficiency of the plant, engine or cycle, and it is of the greatest importance that the fuel technologist should realize just what efficiencies are possible in general power production in order that he may adequately evaluate the plant under his control. He must further be in a position to (a) decide where changes or improvements can be made and (b) realize when certain losses of efficiency are unavoidable.

In fuel utilization for heat or power the process may occur in a cycle of several stages; each stage requires separate consideration by thermal balance or otherwise if the final or overall efficiency of utilization of the heat energy of the fuel is to be adequately high. For example, coal may be burned to raise steam, the steam used to drive a turbine to produce electricity from a dynamo, the electricity may be distributed, and finally used for (*a*) heat or (*b*) power via an electric motor. It is clear that the overall efficiency is a compound factor of boiler efficiency, electrical generation with (i) efficiency of conversion to heat or (ii) motor efficiency to power. It is also clear that inefficiency in any part of the cycle can destroy the effect of high efficiency in any or all of the others.

When the final usage is heat the efficiency may be measured in terms of effective heat utilization, i.e. either as a percentage of the heat of the fuel or simply as the amount of fuel consumed per unit of goods produced. When it is power the efficiency of conversion of heat energy to power is also involved. The common measure of power is the horse-power (H.P.) which is equivalent to 33,000 ft.-lb. of work done per minute. One H.P. hour is therefore 33,000 × 60 or 1,980,000 ft.-lb. Since the B.Th.U. is equivalent to 778 ft.-lb. a perfect heat engine with no loss of energy would require : 1,980,000/778 or 2545 B.Th.U. per H.P. hour.

In any practical engine the number of heat units required per unit of power is higher than this by the reverse factor of engine efficiency. The Diesel engine at 40 per cent. efficiency therefore requires 6362 B.Th.U. per H.P.Hr., while at the other end of the scale the small, non-condensing steam engine may require, at 5–6 per cent. efficiency, as much as 50,000 B.Th.U. The present normal levels of efficiency of a number of power units at full load are :

Diesel engine . .	0·35 to 0·40
Petrol engine . .	0·22 to 0·26
Gas engine . .	0·25 to 0·30
Large steam turbine .	0·26 to 0·29 including steam generation at E. = 0·88.

These factors refer to operation of the engine at full load and are not realized if the engine is run at less than full load. The effect of running at low load is considerable as shown in Table LXX, and it is clear that it is more efficient, when a number of engines are available, to shut down altogether enough of them to allow the others to run at full load. Efficiency may increase further at overload, but there are mechanical reasons why no engine should be run for other than short periods on appreciable overload.

TABLE LXX

VARIATION OF ENGINE EFFICIENCY WITH LOAD

	Fuel B.Th.U./lb.	Efficiency at load (per cent.) 0·25.	0·5.	1·0.
Gasoline engine . . .	20,800	18	21	24
Diesel engine	19,800	30	34	40
Gas * engine	2,500	15	23	28

* Producer gas.

With the internal combustion engine, the efficiency does not increase very much with increase of size, but with steam there is a considerable increase, not only in the engine or turbine, but in the generation of the steam, so that the overall result is markedly affected by size. In the case of large power stations to-day (500,000 kW.) the boiler efficiency has reached practically 90 per cent. and the generation of the electricity 31 per cent. In industry, fuel consumption per H.P.Hr. is much higher than this owing to the smaller scale of operation, to intermittent demand, and to other reasons. Variation of load is very difficult to define, but it is possible to make comparisons of fuel consumptions at full load, and this is done in Table LXXI for the common fuels.

TABLE LXXI

COMPARISONS OF OVERALL CONSUMPTIONS OF FUEL AT FULL LOAD PER B.H.P. HOUR

	Overall E. per cent.	Lb. of Fuel. Coal.	Oil.
Steam generation with turbo-generator :			
Large scale	26·0	0·9	0·5
Small scale	18–22	1·2	0·65
Multiple expansion condensing	8–12	2·4	1·3
Non-condensing	5–10	3·2	1·9

Gas Plants, Town Gas, Blast-furnace Gas

	E. per cent.	Lb. of fuel in generator.	Cu. ft. of gas.
Pressure producers	20	0·9–1·1	80–90
Suction producers	22	0·8–1·0	80–90
Town gas	25–27	—	16–18
Coke oven gas	25–27	—	20–21
Blast furnace gas	25–27	—	100–110

Oil Engines

	E. per cent.	Fuel and specific gravity.		Lb.	Pints.
Gasoline motor	22–26	Gasoline	0·722	0·52	0·57
Oil engine	22–28	Kerosine	0·825	0·51	0·50
Semi-diesel engine	30–33	Diesel oil	0·870	0·42	0·37
Diesel engine	36–40	Diesel oil	0·870	0·34	0·31

The figure of 26 per cent. for electricity generation shown in Table LXXI is the present day (1953) average of the larger power stations in Britain. The average of all stations is 22·7 and only 20 per cent. of the production is obtained at the higher figure ; no doubt the general average will rise from year to year.

Of the amount generated not all reaches the consumer ; some 15 per cent. is consumed, or lost in distribution, so that the available energy from the best stations is only 0·26 × 0·85, or 22·1 per cent. of the heat energy of the original fuel, which in this case is coal. If this available energy is fully utilized, as for example in the use of the domestic electric radiator, the basic efficiency of use of the fuel is indeed 22·1 per cent. In industry, however, where a high proportion is used (over 60 per cent.) the picture is very different, mainly because of the low load factor, but partly because of consumption in machinery, etc. It has been estimated by Sir Oliver Lyle and others that in British industry the efficiency of utilization is not higher than 20 per cent. although it should be quite possible by better planning to achieve twice this figure. If this is true the basic efficiency of the use of power station electricity in industry lies on the average between $0.227 \times 0.85 \times 0.2$ and 0.4 or only 4 to 8 per cent. It is easy to realize the cause of this when plant operates at low load or in a plant using a high proportion of belt-driven machinery ; in the latter case the useful work done may be only 10–15 per cent. of the actual load.

This low level may be increased if the electric power is generated in the industry itself provided the factory can usefully absorb for its processes heat energy equal to about 10 times the heat energy of the power required. In this case the steam may leave the turbine at a sufficient temperature for

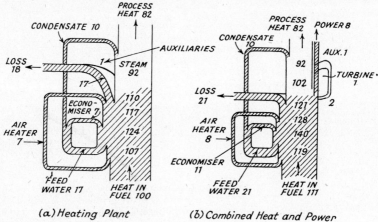

(a) Heating Plant   (b) Combined Heat and Power

FIG. 135.—Thermal Balances of Industrial Heating and Combined Heating and Power.

the process and the residual heat may be utilized at the much higher level of about 80 per cent., and give an overall efficiency of utilization of, say, 60 per cent. This is brought about by the fact that the energy of low-pressure steam at, say, 20 lb. pressure is as much as 80 per cent. of the energy of high-pressure steam at, say, 900 lb. superheated to 900° F. The combination is not of course possible in more than a proportion of factories. Thermal balances of these two sets of conditions are shown in Figure 135 (a) and (b).

Figure 135 (a) suggests that it should be possible to achieve in industrial heating as high a level as 82 per cent. Figure 135 (b) shows that if the same amount of heat is supplied but combined with the production of power, the addition of eleven more heat units will also provide 8 units in the form of power. This power is, further, obtained at an efficiency corresponding to 0.4 lb. of coal per electrical unit as against one lb. per unit in a " power only " plant.

In actual fact, however, the utilization of heat in industry is not so efficient as 80 per cent. The value must vary quite widely, but Lyle places the average as only 23 per cent. as against 40 in non-industrial applications and 15 per cent. in the domestic open fire.

Altogether, therefore, the problem of fuel utilization has many facets from the nature of the fuel itself to its final conversion into useful work or heat at the point of usage.

All the above factors combine to emphasize the need for the proper consideration of all the factors which can lead through a wide variety of stages to the efficient use of fuels. These can include :

The careful choice of fuel in relation to the purpose or process for which it is to be used.

The variation of the process or plant to utilize the fuel to the best advantage.

The application of scientific methods of achieving high temperatures or high rates of heat transfer or other considerations basic to the process, with full efficiency of combustion.

The full conservation of waste heat and its return to the process or the factory.

The avoidance of preventable heat loss by radiation, convection, or conduction.

The recovery of heat from any product of heat treatment which may leave the system at a high temperature.

If this volume has given a sound introduction to fuel variation and choice, to the general principles of the primary applications of fuels, and has stimulated the student of fuel to read more deeply into the literature of the subject than it is possible to give in one small volume, it will have realized its purpose.

REFERENCE BOOKS

The Efficient Use of Fuel. Ministry of Fuel and Power. H.M.S.O. (Under revision.)
The Efficient Use of Steam. Oliver Lyle. H.M.S.O. 1947.
Technical Data on Fuel. World Power Conference. 1950.
National Policy for Fuel and Power. The Ridley Report. H.M.S.O. 1951.
Post War Building Studies. The Egerton Report. H.M.S.O. 1946.
Domestic Fuel Policy. The Simon Report. H.M.S.O. 1946.
Plan for Coal. National Coal Board. 1950.
Introduction to Heat Transfer. Fishenden and Saunders. Clarendon Press. 1950.
Industrial Heat Transfer. Schack. Chapman and Hall. 1933.
Calculation of Heat Transmission. Fishenden and Saunders. H.M.S.O. 1932.
Heat Transmission. McAdams. McGraw-Hill. 1942.
Methods of Measuring Temperature. Griffiths. Griffin. 1947.
Kempe's Engineering Handbook. Morgan Bros. Yearly.
Fuel and the Future. Min. of Fuel and Power. 3 vols. 1948.

APPENDIX

TABLE LXXII

Composition, Cubic Feet per Lb., Weight of 1 Cubic Foot and Calorific Value of Dry Gases burnt at Constant Volume

Gas.		Molecular wt.	Weight per cu. ft. (dry) lb.		Cu. ft. per lb.		Calorific value in B.Th.U. per cu. ft. (dry).	
			At 0° C. and 760 mm.	At 60° F. and 760 mm.	At 0° C. and 30 in.	At 60° F. and 30 in.	At 0° C. and 760 mm. Gross.	At 60° F. and 30 in. Gross.
Oxygen	O_2	32·00	0·0892	0·0846	11·22	11·82	—	—
Nitrogen [1]	N_2	28·17	0·0785	0·0745	12·74	13·42	—	—
Air		(29·0)	0·0807	0·0766	12·39	13·05	—	—
Carbon dioxide	CO_2	44·00	0·1226	0·1163	8·15	8·60	—	—
Hydrogen	H_2	2·02	0·0056	0·0053	178·50	188·70	343·2	325·6
Carbon monoxide	CO	28·0	0·0780	0·0740	12·82	13·52	341·1	323·6
Methane	CH_4	16·03	0·0447	0·0424	22·38	23·58	1067·0	1012·0
Ethane	C_2H_6	30·05	0·0837	0·0794	11·95	12·59	1856·0	1761·0
Ethylene	C_2H_4	28·03	0·0781	0·0741	12·80	13·49	1673·0	1587·0
Propylene	C_3H_6	42·05	0·1171	0·1111	8·54	9·00	2467·0	2340·0
Benzene	C_6H_6	78·05	0·2174	0·2063	4·60	4·85	4011·5	3805·0
Hydrogen sulphide	H_2S	34·08	0·0950	0·0901	10·50	11·10	675·7	640·7

[1] Atmospheric.

Oxygen in air taken at 21·0 v. per cent.

TABLE LXXIII

WEIGHT AND VOLUME OF DRY OXYGEN AND AIR FOR COMBUSTION, INCLUDING WEIGHT OF PRODUCTS AND COMPOSITION OF FLUE GASES

Fuel (dry).	Weight in lb. Per lb. fuel.		Volume in cu. ft. per lb. At 0° C. and 760 mm.		At 60° F. and 30 in.		Volume in cu. ft. per cu. ft.		Products of combustion. Lb. per lb. of fuel.					Composition by vol. (water condensed).	
	Oxygen.	Air.	Oxygen.	Air.	Oxygen.	Air.	Oxygen.	Air.	Total.	CO_2.	H_2O.	N_2.		CO_2.	N_2.
Hydrogen . . .	7·94	34·24	89·1	424·3	93·9	447·3	0·5	2·38	35·24	—	8·96	26·28		—	100·0
Carbon (to CO_2) .	2·67	11·50	29·9	142·5	31·4	150·2	—	—	12·50	3·67	—	8·83		21·0	79·0
,, (to CO) .	1·33	5·73	14·9	71·0	15·7	74·9	—	—	6·73	2·33	—	4·40		34·7(CO)	65·3
Carbon monoxide	0·57	2·46	6·4	30·5	6·7	32·1	0·5	2·38	3·46	1·57	—	1·89		34·7	65·3
Methane . . .	3·99	17·21	44·8	213·4	47·2	224·9	2·0	9·52	18·21	2·75	2·25	13·21		11·7	88·3
Ethylene . . .	3·43	14·78	38·5	183·4	40·6	193·3	3·0	14·28	15·78	3·14	1·29	11·35		15·0	85·0
Acetylene . . .	3·07	13·26	34·4	163·8	36·3	172·6	2·5	11·90	14·26	3·38	0·69	10·19		17·5	82·5
Benzene . . .	3·08	13·28	34·6	164·8	36·5	173·8	7·5	35·70	14·26	3·38	0·69	10·19		17·5	82·5

TABLE LXXIV

Composition and Properties of Gaseous Fuels

Gas.	CO_2.	O_2.	C_nH_m[1]	CO.	H_2.	C_nH_{2m+2}.	N_2.	S.G. air = 1.	B.Th.U. per cu. ft. at 60° F. Gross.	B.Th.U. per cu. ft. at 60° F. Net.	Air for combustion. Theory.	Air for combustion. Practice.	Approx. vol. in cu. ft. per lb. at 60° F. and 30 in. Hg (dry).	Theor. CO_2 of dry waste gases.
Coal gas:														
Horizontal ret.	2·0	0·4	3·6	8·0	52·0	30·0 [2]	4·0	0·40	560	500	4·9	8·0	32·5	11·1
Continuous ret.	4·0	0·4	2·0	18·0	49·4	20·0 [3]	6·2	0·48	475	426	4·06	7·0	27·3	13·3
Water gas	4·7	—	—	41·0	49·0	0·8 [4]	4·5	0·54	295	270	2·22	4·0	24·3	20·6
Carburetted	5·6	0·4	7·0	30·8	37·0	14·0 [5]	5·5 [1]	0·63	500	458	4·27	7·5	19·2	16·8
Producer gas:														
Coal	4·0	—	0·4	29·0	12·0	2·6	52·0	0·37	163	154	1·28	1·4	15·0	19·2
Coke	5·0	—	—	29·0	11·0	0·5	54·5	0·30	132	126	1·00	1·2	14·6	20·5
Air only	1·0	—	—	33·5	1·5	—	64·0	0·98	110	109	0·83	1·0	13·4	—
Blast-furnace gas	11·0	—	—	27·0	2·0	—	60·0	1·02	92	91	0·69	1·0	12·7	24·9

Assumed [1] $C_{2·5}H_5$. [2] $C_{1·07}H_{4·14}$. [3] $C_{1·05}H_{4·10}$. [4] CH_4. [5] $C_{1·1}H_{4·2}$.

543

SUBJECT INDEX